THE BACTERIAL LIPIDS

CHEMISTRY OF NATURAL PRODUCTS

Edited by

EDGAR LEDERER

FACULTÉ DES SCIENCES DE PARIS-ORSAY
AND INSTITUT DE CHIMIE DES SUBSTANCES NATURELLES, GIF-SUR-YVETTE

English Series

French Series

JEAN ASSELINEAU

Professor of biological chemistry, University of Toulouse, France

The Bacterial Lipids

HERMANN

Éditeurs des sciences et des arts, Paris, France

HOLDEN-DAY INC., PUBLISHERS

728, Montgomery Street, San Francisco, California, U.S.A.

Library of Congress Catalog Card Number: 66-26033

This is a revised edition of the original French book "Les lipides bactériens" published by Hermann, Paris, 1962.

Printed in France.

CONTENTS

SECOND PART

Simple specific constituents

THIRD PART

Lipid groups occurring in bacterial lipids

FOURTH PART

Composition of the lipids of various bacterial species

FIFTH PART

Biological properties of bacterial lipids

INTRODUCTION

It may be useful to recall the importance of the role which bacteria play in life on the Earth since, in the introduction to their book "The Microbe's Contribution to Biology", published in 1956, Kluyver & van Niel wrote: "Nowadays, most scientists are vaguely aware that something would go wrong if somebody were to succeed in exterminating the microbe world. Few people, however, realize how quickly terrestrial surroundings would deteriorate, transforming our greenest pastures and our tropical forests into barren areas"[1].

Too often, the word "bacteria" only evokes thoughts of infectious agents which cause disease. Rahn ([2], p. 134) has tried to give some idea of the relative proportion of inoffensive, useful, or actually indispensable bacteria to those which are pathogenic to plants or animals: he arrives at an approximate ratio of fifty thousand to one.

Bacteria are indispensable to the functioning of the carbon and nitrogen cycles. Not only is their qualitative importance very great, but they constitute an enormous mass of living matter. "Ignoring the microbe would obviously mean that a very considerable part — perhaps one half — of the living protoplasm on earth is left out of consideration"[1]. In one gram of cultivated soil, for example, there are approximately five billion bacteria[3], which represent one to two milligrams of living material.

Whereas the constituents of higher forms of life have been the subject of far-reaching studies over many years, the nature of bacterial constituents is only just beginning to be investigated systematically. This situation is particularly well illustrated by the case of the lipids. Only the lipids of a few bacterial species have been intensively examined. For example, the lipids of the tubercle bacillus have been the subject of a great deal of research because it was recognized quite early that they have an influence on the pathogenicity of this bacillus. The lipids of certain other bacterial species have been more or less thoroughly investigated because they happened to crop up in research on antibiotic factors (in the case of *Pseudomonas* strains) and on substances which lower the requirement for biotin (in Lactobacillae) and, in still another instance, in research on plant tumour formation (*Agrobacterium tumefaciens*). In proportion to the number of species of bacteria actually catalogued (see, e.g.[5]), those which have had their lipids examined, even summarily, are very few indeed. However, during the last five years, a great many papers on the chemistry and the biochemistry of bacterial lipids have been published, showing that more and more interest is being devoted to this field of research.

Reviews on the chemistry of bacterial lipids have been published by Anderson[60], by Asselineau and Lederer[4,63], by O'Leary[5b] and by Kates[5a].

On the occasion of the publication of this book, I wish to express my gratitude to Professor E. Lederer, Director of the "Institut de Chimie des Substances naturelles du C. N. R. S. ", who guided my first steps in the field of bacterial lipids about eighteen years ago.

I should also like to thank the "Centre National de la Recherche Scientifique ", which has enabled me, by its grants. to devote myself to research for fourteen years, and the Rockefeller Foundation for allowing me to work in the laboratories of Professor E. Stenhagen and Professor S. Ställberg-Stenhagen at Gothenburg.

Professor K. Hofmann (University of Pittsburgh) has kindly permitted the reproduction of the distillation curve of the fatty acid esters of lactobacilli : I am glad to thank him, as well as the editors of the *Journal of Biological Chemistry* for authorizing this reproduction.

My thanks are also due to Mrs. D. Milhet who had the hard work to make neat typescript from an untidy manuscript.

Methods

I. PRODUCTION OF BACTERIA

In order to study the synthetic capacities of a bacterial species, it is preferable to cultivate it in a medium, the chemical composition of which is as well defined as possible. This condition is best fulfilled by the so-called synthetic media. Table 1 shows the composition of a few common media, synthetic and otherwise.

TABLE 1. EXAMPLES OF CULTURE MEDIA USED FOR MYCOBACTERIA
AND CORYNEBACTERIUM DIPHTHERIAE

	Media of :				
	Sauton	Long	Lockemann	Dubos and Middlebrook	Loiseau and Phillipe
Reference	21	22	23	24	25
Monosodium phosphate	—	—	0.3	—	
Disodium phosphate ($12H_2O$) . . .	—	—	—	6.3	1/3 meat infusion
Monopotassium phosphate	0.05	0.3	0.4	1.0	2/3 pepsin hydrolysate of hog belly
Magnesium sulphate	0.05	0.1	0.25	0.01	
Sodium chloride .	—	0.2	—	—	then addition of :
Sodium carbonate .	—	0.3	—	—	
Calcium chloride .	—	—	—	0.0005	glucose : 1.5 g/1
Zinc sulphate . . .	—	—	—	0.0001	sodium acetate :
Copper sulphate . .	—	—	—	0.0001	10 g/1
Iron ammonium citrate	0.005	0.005	0.001	0.05	
Citric acid	0.2	0.5 (NH$_4$salt)	0.25 (Na salt)	—	
Asparagine	0.4	0.5	0.5	2.0	
Glycerol	6.0	5.0	2.5	—	
Various components	neutralized with NH_3 to pH 7.2			enzymic hydrolysate of casein Na oleate Tween 80*	

All contents are expressed in grams per 100 ml.
*Sorbitol mono-oleate.

Bacterial chemistry often leads to a comparison of the chemical composition of strains that differ in certain biological characteristics. For the conclusions to be valid, the various strains must be grown under absolutely identical conditions.

The temperature of the culture can qualitatively influence the synthesis of lipids. Thus, Terroine & Bonnet[6] observed that the liquid fatty acids of *Mycobacterium phlei* have an iodine number that varies inversely with the temperature of cultivation. Similar results have been obtained by Marr & Ingraham[7] on the fatty acids of *Escherichia coli*: there is a progressive increase in the saturated fatty acids and a corresponding decrease in the unsaturated fatty acids as the temperature of growth is increased. At a given value of the temperature of growth, important variations in the fatty acid composition may occur, according to the composition of the growth medium. Bishop & Still[8] have found that the content of unsaturated (and *cyclo*propane-ring) fatty acids in *Serratia marcescens* remains almost unchanged when the temperature is 30° instead of 37°. However, cells grown at 37° have a content of three β-hydroxy-acids much lower than that of the cells grown at 30°: an increase in the temperature of growth seems to cause the hydroxy-acids to be retained in bound form[8]. Growth of *Serratia marcescens* at 10° results in a decrease in the amounts of cyclopropane and palmitic acids, relative to those at 30°, and in an increase in the amounts of hexadecenoic and octadecenoic acids[8a]; in the case of *E. coli*, see also[8b,c]. Gaughran[9] differentiates between mesophilic and stenothermophilic species of bacteria: in mesophilic species, the total cellular lipids and their degree of unsaturation decrease as the temperature of cultivation is increased; while in stenothermophilic species the total amount of lipids and their degree of unsaturation are strikingly constant.

The chemical composition of the medium greatly influences the lipid content. For example, Frouin[10] observed that the lipids in tubercle bacilli vary from 8.5-13 % when grown on a medium devoid of glycerol to 23-45.5 % when grown on a medium containing glycerol. On the other hand, Frouin & Guillaumie[11] noticed that the addition of iron salts to the culture medium lowers the lipid content of the tubercle bacillus; see also Long & Finner[12] and Chargaff ([13, 14]). As glycerol provokes a high lipid content in Mycobacteria, many authors have studied the effect of replacing glycerol with glucose. Terroine & Lobstein[15] observed an important decrease in the percentage of lipids (up to 60 %). Creighton *et al.*[16] were unable to find any phosphatides in tubercle bacilli (strain H_{37}) grown on a modified Long's medium in which the glycerol had been replaced by glucose; furthermore, the same authors were unable to isolate high-melting waxes (wax D, see page 181) — a result that was not confirmed by Lederer[17]. In the case of the B.C.G., Portelance & Panisset[18] found that the progressive substitution of glucose for glycerol in Sauton's medium tended to lower the percentage of total free lipids (at the same time increasing slightly the percentage of chloroform-extractable lipids).

Since acetate is the precursor of numerous constituents (particularly fatty acids) of living beings, it has been tempting to study the effect of its addition to culture media. The first observations, made by Stephenson & Whetham[19] in the case of saprophytic Mycobacteria were enlarged by Barbier & Lederer[20]: the addition of 1.4 % sodium acetate to Sauton's medium led, in the case of human strains of tubercle bacilli, to an increase in the yield of bacteria (up to 180 %, compared with the controls), but the content of lipids was lower than that of the controls. Bovine strains do not grow on acetate-containing media, however small the amount of acetate. Saprophytic Mycobacteria (*M. phlei, M. smegmatis*) show an increase in the yield of bacteria and in the content lipid. Therefore, the influence of sodium acetate can vary greatly among the various strains of Mycobacteria, and even within the heterogeneous group of non-pathogenic acid-fast bacteria, since Goodwin & Jamikorn [26] did not observe any stimulation of growth of another strain of *M. phlei* after adding acetate to the culture medium.

The effect of acetate and mevalonic acid on growth and lipid content of Lactobacilli was thoroughly investigated by Thorne & Kodicek [27-29]. *Acetobacter suboxydans*, grown on a pantothenate-deficient medium, exhibits a lipid content lower than that of cells grown on usual media [30] (see biosynthesis of fatty acids, page 143). The effect of diphenylamine on the fatty acid composition of *M. lysodeikticus, Sarcina lutea* and *Chromobacterium violaceum* was studied by Cho et al. [30a].

The influence of the composition of the culture medium on the lipid content was also studied in the case of *Corynebacterium diphtheriae* [31], [32], of *Agrobacterium tumefaciens* [33], of *Bacillus mucosus* and *B. megaterium* [34], and of *Escherichia coli* [35]. It should be noted that Tween 40 "does not seem to be so inert metabolically as has been generally supposed" and that it stimulates the synthesis of fatty acids by *Lactobacillus delbrückii* [35a]. The influence of the salt concentration in the growth medium on the lipid composition of *Micrococcus halodenitrificans* has been studied by Kates et al. [36]: the content of unsaponifiable matter increases with the salt concentration.

The age of cultures constitutes another factor capable of causing large variations in the lipid content of a bacterial species. In the case of tubercle and diphtheria bacilli, the percentage of lipids increases with the age of the culture [37-39]. However, very old cultures cannot be used because they contain a significant proportion of dead bacilli, and autolysis is likely to modify the lipid composition in a way difficult to determine. It is therefore best to limit the growth of the tubercle bacillus to four weeks: "It is certain that aging of the culture brings about profound alterations in its various chemical constituents" [40]. On the other hand, it is necessary to note, as stated by Andrejew [41], that "l'âge réel d'un bacille tuberculeux n'a pas de rapport précis avec le nombre de jours passés à l'étuve" (the real age of a given tubercle bacillus does not bear any exact relationship to the number of days spent in the incubator). According to the medium employed, the culture growth can be more or less rapid, and bacilli with the same time of incubation may then have different physiological ages.

The age of cultures may affect the various lipid fractions very differently, as observed by Lemoigne et al. [42] in the case of *B. megaterium*, by Čmelik [43] in the case of *Salmonella typhi* (see table 2), and by Asselineau [38] for *M. tuberculosis* (see page 245). It should be noted that the content of total free lipids in *B. megaterium* decreases with age.

The relative proportions of lactobacillic acid to vaccenic acid [44, 45], on the one hand, and of tuberculostearic acid to oleic acid [46], on the other hand, vary with the age of cultures: young cultures have a higher content of the C_{18}-unsaturated acid (vaccenic and oleic acids),

TABLE 2. INFLUENCE OF THE AGE OF CULTURES ON THE LIPID COMPOSITION

Species	Bacillus megaterium			Salmonella typhi			
References	42			43			
	Total lipids %	Poly-β-hydroxybutyric acid %	Soluble lipids %	Total lipids %	Phospha-tides %	N/P ratio	Neutral lipids %
Age of the culture							
1 day	24.08	22.7	1.38	6.67	4.25	1.56	2.42
2 days	20.97	19.1	1.97	6.05	2.73	1.85	3.32
3 days.	16.30	12.6	3.7	—	—	—	—
4 days.	11.90	9.2	2.70	—	—	—	—
5 days.	—	—	—	6.75	2.79	2.33	3.96
7 days.	11.2	7.9	3.3	—	—	—	—

which is a precursor of the branched chain C_{19}-acid (lactobacillic and tuberculostearic acids), whereas the situation is reversed in older cultures.

The influence of light on the lipid composition of bacterial cells seems to have been generally neglected (except as far as the production of pigments is concerned).

In the case of pathogenic bacteria there is the problem of the relations that exist between the composition of bacilli cultivated in vitro (usually from strains stabilized by numerous subculturings on rather simple media) and that of bacilli as present in their host's tissues. Studies of bacilli grown in vitro under varying experimental conditions (see above) show the important variations that may be observed in their chemical composition and, particularly, in their lipids. It is therefore probable that the lipids obtained either from bacilli grown in vitro or from bacilli isolated directly from animal tissues will show considerable differences among themselves (at least quantitatively).

No detailed analysis of bacilli isolated from lesions has been obtained as yet, because of the difficulty of isolating from infected tissues the quantity of bacilli required for a chemical analysis. However, a few observations have already been made which confirm the existence of clear-cut differences.

Fethke (47, p. 20) mentioned, without comment, that a strain of tubercle bacillus isolated from an animal organism contained a reduced proportion of lipid substance. Anderson et al. [48], working with 2,225 kg of pulmonary tuberculous lesions, were not able to isolate any lipid constituents characteristic of bacilli cultivated in synthetic media (phthiocol, tuberculostearic and phthioic acids). However, these authors were able to isolate these same compounds from healthy pulmonary tissue to which they had been added in very small amounts. After remarking that this negative result could come from too few bacilli (whole cells or debris) present in the lesions studied, Anderson et al. speculated that "our negative results might indicate that tubercle bacilli growing in living tissue do not produce the same characteristic chemical compounds that are found in bacilli that have been cultivated on an artificial medium" [48]. On the other hand, the lipophilic dye Black Sudan B colours the bacilli present in animal tissues much more strongly than it does those cultivated in vitro [49].

Raffel et al. [50] observed that tubercle bacilli isolated from human sputum are more completely agglutinated by an immune serum than those from cultures: "One might infer from this that an antigen is present in bacilli of infection which is not formed (or produced only in small amount) by organisms growing in vitro" [50].

More recently, Segal & Bloch [51, 52], using a differential centrifuging technique to isolate tubercle bacilli from the lungs of infected mice, observed differences in metabolic activity between bacteria so isolated and those of the parent strain ($H_{37}Rv$) grown in Dubos' medium. Furthermore, these authors note that the bacilli obtained in vivo contained fewer chloroform-extractable lipids than bacilli of the infectious strain grown in vitro. Noll (unpublished results, quoted in [53]) even mentions the presence of cholesterol in the lipids of these bacilli obtained in vivo whereas no sterol was ever isolated from Mycobacteria grown *in vitro*.

The lipids of *Mycobacterium lepraemurium* were isolated from bacilli obtained from subcutaneous tumours of rats [54], but in this case the relative data for bacteria cultivated *in vitro* are missing.

Although not concerned with lipids, we would also like to mention in this regard he work of Smith & Keppie [55], who discovered a lethal factor in *Bacillus anthracis* but only in organisms grown *in vivo*.

II. ISOLATION OF THE BACTERIAL LIPIDS

The bacterial cells, obtained with attention to the factors just mentioned, should first of all be separated from their culture medium. This operation is usually carried out by filtering or centrifuging. Special precautions, belonging to the field of bacteriology, must be taken in manipulating masses of bacilli, sometimes pathogens, the more so since it is desirable to avoid killing them by autoclaving because of the risks of altering their chemical composition.

In this manner, "moist bacilli", which can be manipulated with a lessened danger of infection (because they do not have a tendency to become dispersed in the surrounding air), are obtained, the dry weights of which can be determined by classical techniques. Drying the bacilli, even non-pathogens (except by lyophilization) is proscribed because important enzymic reactions can take place during such drying; phospholipid breakdown was observed during drying of baker's yeast [55a]. The simplest and one of the best procedures consists of immersing the living bacteria in a solvent which will dry the bacterial cells and begin the extraction of the lipids. Acetone or alcohol serves these functions very well.

Use of apparatus such as those of Soxhlet or Kumagawa is convenient for certain analytical determinations. But in order to study the composition of the lipids, it is better to avoid the more or less prolonged heating in a boiling solvent which these methods require. Modifications of the composition of lipid fractions (in particular, phospholipid fractions) were observed by Hanahan[56] on extracting yeast lipids at 55-60°, instead of room temperature, even when working under nitrogen. A possible solution is provided by the apparatus described by Macheboeuf & Fethke[57], which performs the extraction under reduced pressure and avoids any increase in the temperature of the solvent. The complication introduced by the use of such an apparatus, especially when large batches of bacteria must be handled, is unnecessary: the extraction can be effected very simply by allowing the bacilli to stand in a large volume of solvent, with occasional stirring. A high ratio of solvent to bacterial mass must be employed, especially during the first extraction. Pathogenic bacteria (tubercle bacilli, for example) are usually allowed to stand for four weeks without changing the solvent; too much dilution of this first solvent with water (contained in the moist bacteria) increases the risks of enzymic alterations (see below).

The tubercle bacillus is very resistant to the action of many chemical agents. K. Bloch[58] reported that these bacilli still gave a strong positive culture test after 14 days standing in acetone with occasional stirring. Experiments made by Dr. J. Bretey[1244] at the Pasteur Institute, Paris, showed that after four weeks of immersion in a mixture of alcohol and ether (1:1 v/v) no living bacilli were present. The tubercle bacillus can resist treatment with 30-40% sulfuric acid for a short time and with 10% sulfuric acid for quite a long time; on the other hand, they are killed in less than 30 minutes by 5% acetic acid[59]. This behaviour is probably related to the wetting properties of the bacterial cell.

The solvents utilized to extract bacterial lipids, and the succession in which they are used, vary greatly depending on the worker. Anderson[60] employed an extraction procedure for Mycobacteria, which is applicable in many diverse cases; it is shown diagrammatically in fig. 1. Each extraction solvent (alcohol-ether, then chloroform) is frequently changed and renewed until the quantity of lipids extracted becomes negligible. Neutral solvents are incapable of completely extracting all the lipids from bacterial cells. After all the "free lipids" have been extracted, the bacterial residue is treated with hot dilute acid or alkali (in an organic solvent). New lipid fractions are thus liberated, the so-called "bound lipids". The existence of "bound lipids", which was recognized early on in the case of bacteria (see e.g. [61]), is a common phenomenon, also observable in the case of higher organisms.

The lipid fractions thus obtained are contaminated with more or less important amounts of bacterial cells or cell fragments. These debris, of relatively slight importance in chemical studies, can upset the results of biological experiments. It is therefore necessary to remove them. The major part of these impurities is retained by classical bacteriological filters (Chamberland candles, Seitz filters, etc). It should be pointed out that since the vehicle used in these filtrations is an organic solvent, the results obtained are definitely less satisfactory than is the case with the aqueous suspensions usually employed in bacteriology. A more complete elimination of bacterial debris can be achieved either by centrifuging at great speed in a solvent of the lowest possible density or by passing a solution through a column of very fine powder (e.g. talc [62]). In this latter procedure, some loss of lipids by adsorption on the column may occur.

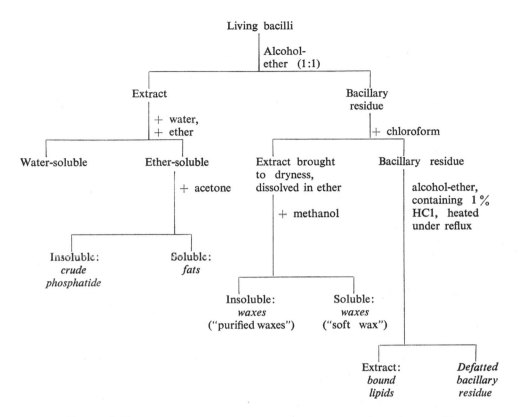

FIGURE 1. EXTRACTION OF BACTERIAL LIPIDS BY ANDERSON'S PROCEDURE [60]

Very little is known about the bacterial cell's supply of enzymes that act on lipids (for a review, see [63]). However, in some cases, the presence of lipases and phospholipases has been demonstrated. Consequently, it may be wondered whether the bacterial extracts, obtained by the methods just briefly described, contain the intact constituents originally present in the bacterial cell, or whether they are contaminated to a more or less important degree with products of enzymic degradation. This is a question which it is very difficult to answer.

In certain special cases, lipolytic phenomena have been observed (ref. 64, p. 57; ref. 65, p. 677), but in general very few criteria are available to determine whether enzymic changes have taken place or not. The long immersion in the same mixture of alcohol and ether required in handling pathogenic strains of tubercle bacillus is sure to cause alterations. It is probable that all preparations of bacterial lipids contain enzymic degradation products (even if only those originating from the dead bacteria present in the cultures). This is all the more probable since some enzymes, such as phospholipases, can act in a moist solvent (ether)[66] and even have their activity accelerated by the ether or mixtures of alcohol and ether [67]. One can only seek to reduce these alterations to a minimum by multiplying the precautions during the cultivation of the cells and above all during the first stages of lipid extraction. It would seem advantageous from this point of view to apply to the bacteria a treatment currently used in plant chemistry, i.e. to submit the mass of bacteria to a brief treatment with a boiling solvent such as alcohol before the actual extraction (see, e.g. ref. 68).

III. FRACTIONATION OF THE LIPIDS

No special method has been elaborated for the fractionation of bacterial lipids. The principal methods used for the fractionation of lipids in general have been applied in this particular field. It may be useful to give here a brief account of these methods, including, as far as possible, the most recent ones.

1. SEPARATION BY MEANS OF DIFFERENTIAL SOLUBILITY

This method, which may appear old-fashioned, continues nevertheless to have great practical utility. Its principal advantages reside in the facility with which it can be set up, equally well on a small or a large scale, and in the fact that no special apparatus is required. Its principal drawback, which is very serious, is that it only gives rough separations. It is well known in lipid chemistry that a substance which is insoluble in a pure solvent, can dissolve in it to a great extent when the solvent contains other substances.

On the other hand, Lovern[69] stresses the fact that, in the course of such separations, the insoluble fractions are generally enriched in saturated fatty acids (with straight chains), while the soluble fractions contain more unsaturated acids (or possibly acids with branched chains). The fatty acid composition of the fractions obtained by precipitation may, in consequence, not be representative of the fatty acid composition of a given lipid group.

The solvents which are most usually employed in this type of separation are, in the first place, acetone, followed by methanol and ethanol. Crude lipids are usually submitted to a preliminary fractionation, e.g. by precipitation from their ether solution by the addition of acetone (at a temperature which can vary from —50 to +56°), and the fractions obtained are then separated by finer methods. In particular, this first separation reduces the amount of material to be manipulated during the second phase of fractionation and enriches the mixtures with a limited number of constituents. It should be noted that some phosphatides have a rather high solubility in acetone[70].

Separation by means of differential solubility in solvents is applied in various forms to solve one of the major problems of lipid chemistry — the separation of the fatty acids. First of all, the separation of the acids from the unsaponifiable material in a mixture of the saponification products of a lipid fraction is based on the different solubilities when an ether solution is washed with sodium hydroxide. To diminish the formation of emulsions, the products can be partitioned between light petroleum and an alkaline water-alcohol mixture (see, e.g. [71]).

The saturated fatty acids can be separated from the unsaturated ones by means of their lead salts: the lead salts of "solid"acids (saturated straight-chain acids) are only slightly soluble in ether or alcohol, while the lead salts of "liquid" acids (unsaturated acids) are soluble[72-75]. The lead salts of branched-chain acids are soluble in ether and insoluble in alcohol[60], and sometimes even insoluble in boiling alcohol[76]. Cason & Sumrell[77] studied the solubilities of the lead salts of branched-chain acids in ether and ethanol (see table 3): on the whole, these lead salts are soluble in ether and only slightly soluble in alcohol; however, some exceptions were observed.

TABLE 3. SOLUBILITY (G/100 ML) OF THE LEAD SALTS OF SOME BRANCHED-CHAIN ACIDS (AFTER CASON & SUMRELL [77])

Solvent	Ether	95 % Ethanol
Hendecanoic acid	0.004	0.018
2-n-Butyl-2-ethylnonanoic acid	> 36	> 36
4-Methyloctadecanoic acid	> 15	0,09
8-Methyloctadecanoic acid	> 17	0.34
11-Methyloctadecanoic acid	> 25	0.30
14-Methyloctadecanoic acid	0.40	0.02
16-Methyloctadecanoic acid	0.10	—
15-Ethylheptadecanoic acid	> 28	0.12
3,3-Dimethyloctadecanoic acid	> 19	0.20
12-n-Hexyloctadecanoic acid	> 20	0.16
6-Methyltetracosanoic acid.	0.34	0.04
10-Methyltetracosanoic acid.	> 22	0.09

Within the group of unsaturated acids, a separation can be made with the help of their lithium salts[78, 79] or their barium or magnesium salts.

Crystallizations from cold acetone, as devised by Brown[80, 81], can be used to separate unsaturated acids. This method is relatively simple and avoids all danger of alterations; nevertheless, it is hampered by the necessity of operating at low temperatures, by the long time required to obtain equilibrium between the crystals and the mother-liquors, and by co-crystallization phenomena.

2. SEPARATION BY COUNTER-CURRENT DISTRIBUTION

This method is based on the differences in the partition coefficients of the constituents of a mixture between two immiscible solvents[82]. Dutton[83], in a review on its application in the field of lipids, wrote in 1954: "(one) may be surprised that greater use has not been made of this method in the lipid field". A more succinct review was published by Ahrens in 1956[84]. This method has been very rarely applied to the fractionation of bacterial lipids.

The separation of mixtures of homologous fatty acids requires a high number of transfers:

400 transfers to obtain the separation of the C_{12}, C_{14}, C_{16} and C_{18} straight chain acids with the solvent system *n*-heptane/acetic acid/formamide/methanol (3:1:1:1)[85]. Separation of hydroxy-acids from simple ones can be achieved in the solvent system *n*-heptane/85 % ethanol[86] with only 70 transfers. Acetonitrile/pentane is a useful solvent system because of its selectivity toward unsaturation; the low boiling point of these solvents facilitates the recovery of fatty acid esters (see, e.g. ref.[87, 88]).

This method appears to be helpful in separating complex mixtures of lipids on a relatively large scale (see, e.g. ref.[89—92]); however, difficulties may be encountered with complex phospholipids[92a].

3. Separation by formation of inclusion compounds

Some substances are able to form inclusion compounds, that is to say to crystallize and incorporate molecules of other substances in their crystal lattice (see Cramer's review, ref. 93).

Urea is a widely used substance able to form inclusion compounds (*); several reviews give information about its use in the lipid field[93-98, 98a].

Although pure urea crystallizes with tetragonal symmetry, its inclusion compounds crystallize with hexagonal symmetry. The hexagonal prisms possess an internal canal of approximately 5.5Å diameter; the section of a stretched hydrocarbon chain is about 4.5 Å. Therefore the urea crystal can "include" a straight-chain aliphatic compound, but the presence of a branch, even though only a simple methyl group, makes the inclusion difficult because of steric hindrance. This explanation is in good agreement with all the observations that have been made up to now on the properties of urea inclusion compounds. In particular, it explains why there is no simple relation between the number of molecules of urea and the number of "included" molecules (see table 4.)

TABLE 4. COMPOSITION OF INCLUSION COMPOUNDS OF SATURATED FATTY ACIDS
(AFTER KNIGHT *et al.*[99])

Acid	Number of urea molecules per molecule of acid	Acid	Number of urea molecules per molecule of acid
Decanoic	8.0	Hexadecanoic	12.0
Undecanoic.	8.9	Octadecanoic	14.7
Dodecanoic.	9.7	Oleic	13.6
Tridecanoic	11.8	Elaidic	13.6
Tetradecanoic	10.6		

(*) In agreement with Schlenk[97], we prefer the term *inclusion compound*, avoiding particularly the term "complex", usually employed in a precise and different meaning.

The formation of inclusion compounds with urea, therefore, furnishes an easy means of separating aliphatic compounds (in particular fatty acids), according to whether their carbon chain is straight or branched. In practice, the phenomenon is not quite so simple.

Entrainment phenomena can, in fact, occur : 3-methylheptane alone does not form an inclusion compound, but it can be included in the presence of *n*-decane. On the other hand, a methyl group located in the middle of a hydrocarbon chain generally prevents the formation of an inclusion compound.

$$CH_3—(CH_2)_5—\underset{\underset{CH_3}{|}}{CH}—O—CO—(CH_2)_2—CH_3 \qquad [1]$$

$$CH_3—(CH_2)_2—\underset{\underset{\underset{\underset{CH_3}{|}}{CH_2}}{|}}{CH}—CH_2—O—CO—(CH_2)_6—CH_3 \qquad [2]$$

However, such substances as 1-methylheptyl butyrate [1] or 2-ethylhexyl octanoate [2] give adducts with urea [100], showing that two short chains can be as effective as one long chain. Acids (or esters) having a methyl group near the end of the hydrocarbon chain (acids of the *iso* or *ante-iso* series) form inclusion compounds, while their esters with branched chain alcohols (isopropyl, isobutyl alcohols), which possess a branch at each extremity of the carbon chain, give no adduct [101]. Table 5 gives some examples of substances with various substituents which are able or not to give rise to urea inclusion compounds.

Unsaturated aliphatic substances form inclusion compounds with urea; however, the more unsaturated they are, the less easily they form adducts. It is therefore possible to obtain fractions that are enriched with saturated or unsaturated acids, by fractional crystallization of inclusion compounds from a mixture of these acids (see, e.g. refs. 106-109).

Separation by means of inclusion compounds does not give pure fractions, but leads to the enrichment of certain groups of compounds, enrichment which can attain values as high as 90 %. Another cause of the imperfect separations lies in the difficulty of washing the crystals of inclusion compounds: "no washing agent has been found which may be relied upon to remove the adherent mother-liquor without decomposing the complex to an appreciable extent" [110].

The formation of inclusion compounds, which is based on steric phenomena, can furnish information about the stereochemistry of a compound. Since this aspect of the method is outside the field of the present discussion, we will only cite its application to the stereochemistry of the 9,10-dihydroxyoctadecanoic acids [111] and to the determination of the cis-trans isomerism of ethylenic compounds [112]. In one case (DL-2-chlorooctane), separation of the enantiomorphs has even been achieved [113].

From the analytical point of view, the dissociation temperatures of inclusion compounds,

TABLE 5. BEHAVIOUR OF VARIOUS ALIPHATIC COMPOUNDS TOWARDS UREA

| Formation of inclusion compounds | | Ref. |
With ease	With difficulty or not at all	
n-Heptane 1-Tridecene 1-Cyclohexyleicosane 1-Phenyleicosane	n-Pentane n-Hexane 7-Methyltridecane 3-Ethyltetracosane 5-n-Butyldocosane	102
1-Methylheptyl butyrate 2-Methylbutyl decanoate 3-Methylbutyl hexanoate	1-Methylheptyl acetate 2-Methylbutyl octanoate 3-Methylbutyl propionate	100
9-(or-10)-Bromooctadecanoic acid	Tetrabromooctadecanoic acid 9,10- Dibromooctadecanoic acid Octadecanoic acid oxime	104
Methyl 12-methylmyristate Isopropyl oleate 12-Docosenoic acid 12-Methyltetradecyl acetate 1-Bromohexane	Isopropyl 12-methylmyristate 2-Bromooctane	103
Mono-and diglycerides	Triglycerides	105
12-Hydroxyoctadecanoic acid	12-Hydroxyoctadecanoic acid formate, acetate, tosylate	104

easily observable under the microscope, have been suggested for characterization [99]. The fatty acids contained in inclusion compounds can be directly titrated and furthermore unsaturated compounds are preserved from the action of atmospheric oxygen.

The principal application of this method to the fractionation of bacterial lipids concerns the isolation of tuberculostearic acid (10-methyloctadecanoic acid, see page 87) from the fatty acids of *M. tuberculosis* [114]. This isolation was achieved by passing a mixture of esters through a column of powdered urea (300 moles per mole fatty acid). By using Truter's technique [100], it was possible to isolate tuberculostearic acid from the fatty acids of *M. phlei* [115] and 9,10-methylenehexadecanoic acid from the acids of *E. coli* [549].

4. SEPARATION BY FRACTIONAL DISTILLATION

Fractional distillation does not have the widespread application that methods based on solubility have. Here, the limiting factor is the thermal stability of the compounds at the temperature at which they distill. Therefore, fractional distillation is limited in the lipid field to the separation of simple compounds such as fatty acids (principally as methyl esters), alcohols, and hydrocarbons.

TABLE 6. TABLE OF EQUIVALENCE FOR CALCULATING THE BOILING POINT OF A SUBSTANCE
(after ref. 116)

Element to convert	Equivalent number of CH_2 groups	Element to convert	Eauivalent number of CH_2 groups
Cl	2	O (ether)	— 1
Br	3	O (ester, anhydride, acid chloride)	1
I	4	O (aldehyde, ketone)	2
S (sulphur)	3	O (alcohol)	3
S (thiol)	3	N (amine)	2
		N (nitrile)	3

It is often convenient to know, even approximately, the boiling point of a substance. For this purpose, Pearson[116] related the substance to a hydrocarbon, using the equivalents mentioned in table 6. The boiling point of the hydrocarbon is calculated according to table 7. In addition, Pearson[116] gave some general indications, applicable to fatty acid esters, which were later formulated by Cason et al.[117] as follows:

(i)   A methyl group lowers the boiling point about 5° compared with that of the straight-chain isomer; the effect is a little more pronounced when the methyl group is located at the middle of the chain rather than near either end.

(ii)   Lengthening of the side-chain introduces little difference compared with a simple methyl group (a n-hexyl group lowers the boiling point by 7° instead of 5° for a methyl group).

(iii)   Three methyl groups lower the boiling point by a value corresponding to twice that attributed to a single methyl group (whether the methyls are grouped near the carboxyl or dispersed along the chain).

(iv)   A tetrasubstituted carbon atom leads to a decrease in the boiling point of 22—23°.

(v)   A double or triple bond causes little change in the boiling point.

(vi)   The presence of a six-membered carbocyclic ring (aromatic or saturated) brings about an elevation in the boiling point of about 10°.

Since the simple compounds present in lipids generally contain more than 10 carbon atoms, fractional distillation should be carried out under reduced pressure. The (approximate) boiling point of a substance, under a given pressure, can be calculated from graphs based on its boiling point at atmospheric pressure. Very roughly, it can be said that the boiling temperature is lowered by 100° when the pressure is reduced from 760 to 20 mm. Table 8 gives some boiling point values of pure fatty acid esters under reduced pressure. Below 10 mm, reduction of the pressure by half results in a lowering of the boiling point by approximately 13°.

TABLE 7. APPROXIMATE BOILING POINTS OF STRAIGHT-CHAIN HYDROCARBONS
(at atmospheric pressure)

Number of carbon atoms	Boiling point °C	Number of carbon atoms	Boiling point °C
4	0	10	175
5	35	11	195
6	70	12	215
7	100	13	235
8	125	14	250
9	150		

Above C_{14}, add about 20° for each supplementary CH_2 group.

The equipment utilized for fractional distillation under reduced pressure has been considerably improved during the last few years. The two types of columns most widely employed are spinning band columns (which have the great advantage of causing only a

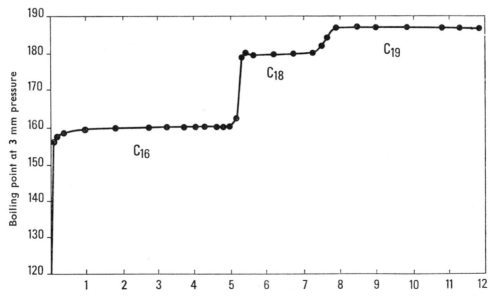

FIGURE 2. Distillation curve of the methyl esters isolated from the bound lipids of *Lactobacillus arabinosus* (after Hofmann *et al.*, ref. 122).

small drop in pressure), and Heligrid-filled columns (of the Podbielniak type), which consist of a helix made of metal ribbon in a closely-spaced winding around a central axis. The results which can be obtained with these columns are particularly well illustrated by the isolation of 12 constituents from a preparation of methyl "phthioate" from tubercle bacillus (121, see page 96) and by the separation as esters of the fatty acids isolated from the lipids of *Lactobacillus arabinosus* [122] .The course of this latter distillation is shown in fig. 2; the very clear separation of the esters of the C_{18} and C_{19} acids should be noted. Murray's excellent review [123] gives many details concerning the application of reduced-pressure fractional distillation to the separation of fatty acid esters.

Weitkamp [124] elaborated "amplified distillation" as a means of isolating the constituents from a mixture of which only a small sample is available or of isolating a constituent present only in a very small amount. A mixture of substances which distil in the same temperature interval as the constituents of the mixture to be separated is added to the original mixture and, in the course of the distillation, it eliminates the unresolved "intermediary fractions". These added substances should have properties which permit their easy elimination from the constituents of the mixture to be separated, once the distillation has been achieved. Mixtures of petroleum hydrocarbons are well suited to the separation of the methyl esters of fatty acids. However, this amplifying mixture cannot be used for the separation of free fatty acids, because of the formation of azeotropes [125]. According to Murray [123], the deceptive results obtained by Cason & Sumrell [77] in the course of their work on the isolation of the fatty acids of the tubercle bacillus by amplified distillation, were probably due to their use of an insufficiently efficacious column.

TABLE 8. BOILING POINTS OF THE METHYL ESTERS OF FATTY ACIDS UNDER REDUCED PRESSURE
(after refs. 118, 119, 120)

Number of carbon atoms in the acid	Pressure in millimetres of mercury					
	20	10	6	5	2	1
10		106.6°	96.2°		77.0°	66.0°
12		134.0	121.6		103.7	92.3
14	172.5°	160.8	148.8	143.5°	127.0	114.8
16	196.5	183.8	172.0	166.5	148.9	137.0
18	222.0	206.0	194.3	189.5	171.4	158.0
Oleate	218.5	.	190.8	186.0	167.4	154.4
Linoleate	215.0		190.2	182.5	167.1	154.0
Linolenate			191.1		168.0	155.0
20					189.0	176.0
22					206.0	194.0
24					223.0	211.0
26					238.0	226.0
28					253.0	241.0
30						255.0

The fractional distillation of esters of higher fatty acids, even under reduced pressure, requires the prolonged heating of the esters at a high temperature. For example, Table 8 shows that methyl n-hexacosanoate distills at 238° under 2 mm, and it must be remembered that some strains of bacteria synthesize fatty acids containing more than 30 atoms of carbon. In the course of the distillation, the mixture of esters is heated to 250—300° in the distilling flask; such temperatures may induce pyrolytic reactions. β-Hydroxy-acids (and their esters) bearing a long branch in the α-position (such as mycolic and corynomycolic acids) undergo thermal cleavage at these temperatures (see page 127, [126]); while the acetates of tertiary alcohols can be decomposed at these temperatures into acetic acid and olefin (see, e.g. 127). This latter reaction can occur at very much lower temperatures if a free fatty acid (such as palmitic acid) is present in the distillation mixture: first, a trans-esterification occurs, giving rise to an alkyl palmitate, which then readily pyrolyses to palmitic acid and olefin [128]. The pyrolysis of esters of alcohols (even primary) with long-chain acids constitutes a convenient method of preparing 1-alkenes [129]. The higher the molecular weight, the lower is the temperature at which pyrolysis takes place [130]. The pyrolysis of ethyl esters has been proposed for the preparation of free acids, without saponification; in this case, a temperature of 560° is employed [131]. However, Hatt [132] observed that at 300° the methyl esters of saturated acids undergo decomposition to a significant extent. Under the influence of heat, highly unsaturated esters can be isomerized (conjugation) or polymerized [133]. Furthermore, at high temperatures, the distillation must be carried out in an atmosphere of nitrogen, even in the case of saturated esters, because oxidation of the hydrocarbon chains by air bubbles may occur (123, p. 266).

5. SEPARATION BY CHROMATOGRAPHY

Chromatography is the most efficacious and most general method that can be used for the fractionation and analysis of mixtures. This is in part due to the fact that included under the term chromatography are methods of extremely different principle and, consequently, with very varied fields of application. One of the principal disadvantages of chromatography lies in the practical difficulty of working on large quantities of substances.

Detailed reviews on the chromatography of lipids have been recently published [134, 135]. Excellent papers dealing with the chromatography of phosphatides have been written by Marinetti [136], by Wren [137] and by Ansell and Hawthorne [137a]. We shall give here only some data about the applications of these methods to bacterial lipid fractionation.

a) Adsorption chromatography

This type of chromatography has the greatest variety of applications. It permits the separation of compounds according to the functional groups they contain. Generally, the technique consists of differentially eluting the adsorbed compounds with a series of solvents of gradually increasing strength. The adsorbents most commonly employed are alumina, magnesium silicate (which has adsorbent properties very close to those of alumina, but with less risk of secondary reactions such as saponification), silicic acid, and silica gels.

Silicic acid (Mallinckrodt or Bakers) is one of the best adsorbents for phospholipids (see [137]). Separation of lipid classes by chromatography on Florisil (a magnesium silicate) has been studied by Carroll [138].

The glycerides in the fats of Mycobacteria have been fractionated by chromatography on alumina or magnesium silicate [139] or silicic acid [140]. A separation of saturated and unsaturated glycerides (present in the waxes of *M. marianum*) has been accomplished by chromatography on alumina after permanganate oxidation of the mixture: the saturated glycerides are rapidly eluted, whereas the acid glycerides (arising from the oxidative fission of the unsaturated glycerides) are strongly adsorbed [141]. Silicic acid has been used for the fractionation of phosphatides from Mycobacteria [142], for the purification of a peptido-glycolipid [143] and for the separation of glucosyl-diglycerides from phosphatides [143a]. Breakdown of lecithins on alumina columns has been observed [144].

Free fatty acids present in a lipid fraction can be separated by adsorption chromatography; it is also the method to choose when the acids have a molecular weight high enough to render their alkaline salts soluble in ether (e.g. mycolic acids from the Mycobacteria, [126]).

Fatty acids are best fractionated in the form of their esters (methyl, for example). Adsorption chromatography permits the separation of saturated, unsaturated, and hydroxylated esters (see, e.g. [76]). Stereoisomers can be separated: during the course of the synthesis of racemic C_{27}-phthienoic acid, the methyl cis-and trans-erythro-2,4, 6-trimethyltetracos-2-enoates were separated by chromatography on alumina, the cis ester being the less strongly adsorbed [128] (see page 99). In another case, methyl 2D,4D, 6D-trimethylnonacosanoate was isolated by chromatography on magnesium silicate of a mixture with the 2L,4D,6D-isomer [145].

The separation of mixtures of homologous acids is best realized by partition chromatography; nevertheless, palmitic and stearic acids have been partially separated by chromatography on charcoal [146]. Use of silica columns impregnated with silver nitrate has been proposed by De Vries [147] for the separation of unsaturated compounds; see also 165a, 165b.

b) *Partition chromatography*

—On columns

Column partition chromatography has had little application in the field of bacterial lipids. This is partially explained by the complexity of the mixtures of acids which are frequently encountered and by the small amounts of material that one can conveniently chromatograph by this method. However, the method of Ramsey & Patterson [148], based on partition between a stationary phase of 2-aminopyridine and furfuryl alcohol (1:1 w/w) on silicic acid and a mobile phase of hexane, has been employed to separate the C_{17} and C_{25} acids obtained by degradation of a mycolic acid [149], to isolate *n*-tetracosanoic acid from the lipids of *M. phlei* and *M. smegmatis* [150], and to analyse the saturated fatty acids of a *M. tuberculosis* strain [76]. Nojima [151] utilized the method of Silk & Hahn [152] to separate the acids of a phospholipid isolated from B.C.G. Hofmann *et al.* [153] studied the fatty acid composition of strains of Lactobacilli by chromatography on a column of powdered rubber: octadecanoic acid and lactobacillic acid (11,12-methyleneoctadecanoic acid) were not separated.

— On paper

In the case of complex lipids, paper chromatography has been employed especially in the examination of the water-soluble constituents they contain (sugars, glycerol, nitrogenous bases, amino-acids, etc.) (see, e.g. ref. [64, 139, 154,]).

Chromatography on paper, usually with "reversed phases", has been applied to the analysis of fatty acids present in the lipids of *Salmonella ballerup* [155], of Mycobacteria [156], and of *Corynebacterium diphtheriae* [157]. During a study of the paper chromatography of saturated and unsaturated fatty acids, Ballance & Crombie [158] included tuberculostearic acid among the acids studied. A simple and rapid procedure of circular chromatography (on paper impregnated with vaseline oil) has been used by Nowotny *et al.* [159] to demonstrate the presence of C_{10}—C_{24} saturated and unsaturated acids in the lipo-polysaccharides of gram-negative bacteria.

Reversed phase chromatography on paper allows the separation of acids differing by two CH_2 groups up to C_{24}. More recently, Fiker & Hajek [160, 160a] have separated acids from C_{12} to C_{20}, working at 55°, and from C_{20} to C_{34} at 85°.

c) *Thin-layer chromatography*

The first applications of this method to the lipid field were described in 1956; this technique is now very widely used, particularly to test the homogeneity of column chromatographic fractions (see, e.g. ref. [161, 161a, 162]).

Three points have to be noted:

(i) The amount of product required for an analysis is very small (about 30—60 µg).

(ii) The development of a plate is usually very rapid.

(iii) An inorganic binder (such as plaster of Paris) can be used to fix the adsorbent on the glass plate; it is then possible to detect any organic compounds by the charring produced after spraying with a corrosive reagent and heating on a hot plate — a procedure particularly useful in the case of triglycerides.

Excellent reviews, on the application of thin-layer chromatography to the lipid field, giving practical data, have been written by Mangold [163]. The separation of unsaturated compounds can be improved by using silica impregnated with silver nitrate [164, 165].

d) *Gas chromatography*

In the field of bacterial lipids, gas chromatography is essentially used for the separation of fatty acid esters[166, 166a] (Fig. 3).

This technique is continually being improved, mainly in regard to the following points:

(i) Extension of the range of application to the higher fatty acids. Separations of acids having more than 30 carbon atoms have been described [145, 167]; temperature programming is particularly useful in this respect.

(ii) Setting up apparatus for collecting the eluted fractions on their exit from the column. The samples obtained are then analysed by I.R. or mass spectrometry (see below). Columns for preparative gas chromatography have been devised.

(iii) Use of the "capillary column", invented by Golay[168], which, because of the low resistance offered to the passage of the gas, can have a very great length and therefore

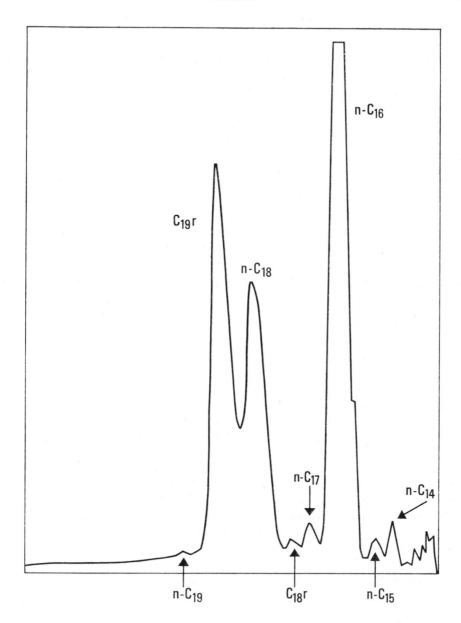

FIGURE 3. Gas chromatogram of a mixture of the methyl esters of the lower fatty acids up to C_{20}, obtained from the lipids of the human strain *Canetti* of *Mycobacterium tuberculosis* (Griffin and George instrument; stationary phase containing 5% silicone; temperature 220°). (J. Labarrère and J. Asselineau, unpublished results). r = branched.

a very high efficiency. The separation on the microgram scale of a mixture of esters ranging from C_8 to C_{20} has been described[169]. A fine application of this technique to the analysis of a complex mixture of fatty acids (containing branched chain isomers) has been described by Odham[169a].

(iv) Successive use of non-polar and polar stationary phases (such as silicone and glycol polysuccinate), which allows the complete analysis of saturated and unsaturated fatty acid esters with straight and branched chains (see, e.g. ref.[170]); or use of the same polar column operated at two different temperatures[171] but with the loss of the advantage conferred by temperature programming. β-Cyclodextrin valerate appears to be a promising stationary phase for the separation of branched and straight-chain esters[172].

By plotting the retention time of saturated straight-chain esters against chain length on semilogarithmic paper, straight lines are obtained. When unknown esters are observed on a chromatogram, use of this graph gives a "carbon number", corresponding to the length of the hypothetical saturated straight chain ester having the same retention time. This "carbon number" may be helpful in identifying unknown peaks[173]. Series of esters having the same type of characteristic groupings (esters of dicarboxylic acids, of 2-methyl-substituted acids, etc.) give parallel straight lines on such a graph (see, e.g. ref.[145, 166]).

On ethyleneglycol polyadipate, an iso ester has a shorter retention time than the ante-iso isomer, which itself has a shorter retention time than the straight-chain isomer[174]. On Reoplex 400 (a polyester stationary phase), an α-methyl ester has a retention time identical with that of the straight-chain ester having one less carbon atom; methyl branches in other positions cause the retention times to fall near the point midway between the normal isomer and the next lower homologue[175]. The logarithm of the retention time on a silicone phase[145] of methyl 2,4,6-trimethylhexacosanoate (ester of a C_{29} acid) is the same as that of methyl 2,4,6,8-tetramethylhexacosanoate (ester of a C_{30} acid). The carbon number of methyl 3,7,11,15-tetramethylhexadecanoate, chromatographed on ethyleneglycol polyadipate, is 17.1[176]. On a silicone phase (DC 550), methyl 9,10-methylenehexadecanoate has the same retention time as methyl n-heptadecanoate[177].

No other method (chromatographic or otherwise) can achieve performances like those obtained by gas chromatography, and it is being applied more and more often to the analysis of bacterial fatty acids. Besides the very fine pioneering studies of James & Martin[178] on the acids of *Pseudomonas aeruginosa*, we will only mention its use in the course of the structural studies on C_{27}-phthienoic acid[179], mycocerosic acids[145], and phthiocerol[180]. Vapour phase chromatograms of the whole fatty acids isolated from a bacterial batch mays be very useful in chemical taxonomy[177, 181]. For quantitative aspects, see e.g. 181a, and for radioactive applications, 181b.

e) *Ion-exchange chromatography*

Ion-exchange chromatography has been used to separate certain degradation products of lipid fractions, such as phosphoric esters of polymanno-inositides on Dowex-2[151] or ninhydrine-positive compounds from phospholipids. As regards true lipid compounds, the application of ion-exchange chromatography appears to have been limited to the purification of C_{27}-phthianoic acid [182].

6. SEPARATION BY DIALYSIS

Although dialysis had been used to separate some lipid fractions (e.g. [183]), a convenient procedure, which allows the separation of neutral lipids from phospholipids [184], was devised only recently. In a non-polar solvent (light petroleum), polar lipid molecules are aggregated into micells which cannot penetrate through the pores of a membrane (rubber fingerstall) while non-polar lipids (glycerides) readily pass to the outside.

This method has been applied to a preliminary fractionation of the lipids from *Staphylococcus aureus* and *Salmonella typhimurium* [185].

7. SEPARATION BY CHEMICAL METHODS

The preceding methods permit the separation of mixtures of constituents, without any preliminary chemical transformation being required (with the exception of the esterification of acids). This section affords a brief insight into those methods based on selective chemical transformations of certain groups of compounds, so that their properties are modified sufficiently to make their isolation from the initial mixture easier. The chemical methods of isolating alcohols, carbonyl compounds, and acids are discussed in succession.

a) *Alcohols*

In 1896 Haller [186] suggested the separation of alcohols by the formation of acid phthalates, which are soluble in aqueous sodium carbonate. However, the acid phthalates of higher aliphatic primary alcohols give rise to sodium salts insoluble in water and ether, whereas the sodium salts of acid phthalates of secondary alcohols are very soluble in alcohol and ether and insoluble in water. Chibnall *et al.* [187] made use of these properties in the separation of the primary and secondary alcohols of plant waxes (isolation of (+)-10-nonacosanol, hexacosanol, octacosanol, and triacontanol).

Sandulesco & Girard [188] suggested the combination of the alcohol monochloroacetates with a tertiary base: betaine esters of alcohols, soluble in water, are thus formed. This method needs considerable care, which limits its use. The possibility of using malonic monoesters, prepared with the monochloride of malonic acid [189], may also be noted. Neither of these two latter procedures appears to have been applied to the isolation of higher aliphatic alcohols.

b) *Carbonyl compounds*

With C_{16} and C_{18} saturated aldehydes, *p*-carboxyphenylhydrazine gives hydrazones soluble in aqueous sodium hydrogen carbonate [190] — a property which is used in their isolation. The same reagent can be employed to separate aliphatic carbonyl compounds with much longer chains (12- or 15-nonacosanone, 16-hentriacontanone); in this case, the sodium (or potassium) salts are insoluble in water and the separation relies on the insolubility of the barium salts in boiling methanol (or acetone) [191].

The T and P reagents of Girard& Sandulesco [192] are very widely utilized for the isolation of carbonyl compounds from complex mixtures (for recent reviews, see ref. [193] and [194]). Their employment in the lipid field is limited by the difficulty of making long paraffin chains water-soluble. However, Seher [195], with the aid of reagent T, isolated methyl octadec-14-ene-10, 12-diyn-8-onoate and Polgar [196], with reagent P, purified 4-methyl docosan-2-one. Using this procedure Berschandy [197] and Brini [198] separated long chain ketones from hydrocarbons; the solubilization of the T hydrazone required the addition of a large proportion of alcohol to the aqueous solution, so that the insoluble impurity (hydrocarbon) could be eliminated by filtration.

With reagent T, Demarteau-Ginsburg et al. [199] were able to isolate the ketonic compounds phthiodiolone $C_{35}H_{70}O_3$ and phthiocerolone $C_{36}H_{72}O_3$ from the crude phthiocerol of M. tuberculosis (see page 73).

c) Acids

Partial saponification of lipids can furnish an initial separation of acid constituents: Chanley & Polgar [200] separated in this manner the phthienoic acids (easily liberated from glycerides) from the mycocerosic acids (present in the form of waxes and difficult to saponify).

Partial esterification was utilized by Cason et al. [175, 201, 202] to fractionate the higher fatty acids of the tubercle bacillus: the α,β-unsaturated acids and the acids with a side-chain longer than methyl in the α-or β-position remained in the free state under conditions that led to the esterification of the other acids (0.26 N hydrochloric acid in methanol, $2\frac{1}{2}$ hrs. at 32-33°).

Sodium salts of fatty acids react with monochloroacetone to give acetol-esters, whose semicarbazones are usually crystalline. Polgar [203] observed that the semicarbazones of acetol-esters of normal saturated fatty acids are very slightly soluble in cold alcohol, whereas derivatives of branched-chain saturated acids are relatively soluble. It is, therefore, possible to separate the straight-chain acids from those with branched chains by this procedure. Polgar [203] applied this method to the isolation of branched-chain acids from the lipids of the tubercle bacillus.

Unsaturated acids can be isolated by converting them into dihydroxy-acids (e.g. by hydroxylation with performic acid), which are easily separable either by means of chromatography (ref. [153]) or by making use of their low solubility in light petroleum [203]. Mercuric acetate in methanol reacts at room temperature with unsaturated compounds to give adducts that may be easily separated from the saturated compounds; good separations are obtained (e.g. refs. 163, 204, 205). Poly-unsaturated acids can also be transformed into polybromide derivatives by addition of bromine to the double bonds (e.g. ref. 206). Many other procedures could also be cited.

IV. ANALYTICAL METHODS

The classical methods for the analysis of lipids, including among others the determination of various numbers (e.g. ref. 207), are sufficiently well described in the standard literature and need not be reviewed further here. Instead, in this chapter, attention will be concentrated on those methods whose use is becoming more and more widespread and which, because they are generally applied to very small quantities of materials, are particularly useful in the study of bacterial lipids.

1. ULTRAVIOLET SPECTROGRAPHY

Among the most recent reviews in this field, those of O'Connor[208] and of Pitt & Morton (ref. 209; see also ref. 210 and 210a) may be cited.

Ultraviolet spectrography permits the rapid detection of the presence of conjugated groups in a compound and, furthermore, the determination of the number of substituents constituting the chromophore. To compare the values of absorption maxima, the same solvent must, as far as possible, be used. It is well known that the position of the absorption maximum can, in fact, vary to a considerable degree with the nature of the solvent. By way of example, the positions of the absorption maximum (λ_{max}) of pseudo-ionone in various solvents[211] are as follows:

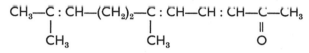

Hexane : 284.5 mμ	Ethanol : 292 mμ
Ether : 285.5 mμ	Methanol : 293 mμ
Dioxan : 287 mμ	Chloroform : 296 mμ

The two solvents most commonly used are hexane (or cyclohexane, isooctane, etc.) and 96 % ethanol.

The interest in ultraviolet spectrography is particularly well illustrated by the study of phthioic acid (see page 96) : this acid was isolated from the lipids of the tubercle bacillus in 1929, but it was not until 1950, thanks to the use of ultraviolet spectrography, that the presence of α,β-unsaturation was detected.

Table 9 gives some examples (limited to the aliphatic series, since it concerns lipids) of the principal types of conjugation that may be found in bacterial lipids. Particular mention ought to be made of the important rôle played by ultraviolet spectrography in detecting and determining the proportion of poly-unsaturated acids (after alkaline isomerization): the position of the absorption maximum is an indication of the number of double bonds. Since this type of acid is apparently very rare in bacterial lipids, the reader is referred to the reviews already cited[208, 209, 212]. It has to be remembered that steric hindrance caused by the presence of alkyl substituents in the conjugated system may greatly alter the position of the absorption maximum[213] (see page 142).

Woodward[214] showed that the position of the absorption maximum of conjugated dienes (or of unsaturated ketones) can be calculated by adding to the wavelength of the absorption maximum of the simplest diene (1,3-butadiene) as many times 5mμ as there are substituents in the compound studied in comparison with the molecule of butadiene. Since 214 mμ (in hexane) is the value used for the absorption maximum of butadiene,

TABLE 9. ULTRAVIOLET ABSORPTION MAXIMA OF VARIOUS ALIPHATIC SUBSTANCES
(hydrocarbons, carbonyl compounds, acids)

Substance	Position of maximum (mμ)	ε	Solvent (*)	Ref.
HYDROCARBON CHROMOPHORES				
$CH_2 : CH—CH : CH_2$	218.5		C	215
	217.5		E	
$CH_3—CH : CH—CH : CH_2$ *trans*	223	23,000	E	219
$CH_3—CH : CH—CH : CH—CH_3$ *trans* . . .	227	22,500	E	
$CH_3—CH(OH)—CH : CH—CH : CH_2$ *trans* . .	223	28,000	E	220
$(CH_3)_2C : CH—CH : CH_2$	234		C	215
	232.5		E	
$CH_3-(CH_2)_5-CH^t : CH-CH^t : CH-(CH_2)_7-CO_2H.$	231	29,000	E	221
$CH_3-(CH_2)_4-CH^c : CH-CH^c : CH-(CH_2)_8-CO_2H.$	235	24,100	E	222
$CH_3-CH^t : CH-C(CH_3)^t : CH-CH(CH_3)-CO_2H.$	234	15,000	E	213
$CH_2 : CH-(CH_2)_4-C \vdots C-C \vdots C-(CH_2)_7-CO_2H.$	227	370	E	
	237	240		223
	254	40		
$CH_2 : CH—CH : CH—CH : CH_2$	247.5	68,000	C	224
	257.5	79,000		
	267.5	56,000		
$CH_2 : CH—CH : CH—C(CH_3) : CH_2$	248	$>$ 21,000	E	225
	257	$>$ 28,000		
	267	$>$ 22,000		
$CH_2 : C(CH_3)—CH : CH—C(CH_3) : CH_2$	251	37,000	E	225
	261	46,000		
	271	34,000		
$CH_3—(CH_2)_3—CH : CH—CH : CH—CH : CH—$				
$(CH_2)_7—CO_2H$	261	34,000	E	
t *t* *c* . . .	270	48,000		226
	280	34,500		
t *t* *t* . . .	258	40,500	E	226
	268	57,000		
	279	44,000		
CARBONYL COMPOUNDS				
$CH_3—CO—CH_3$	275	17	E	227
$CH_2 : C(CH_3)—CH_2—CO—CH_3$	290	80	I	227
$CH_3—CH : CH—CH(OH)—CO—CH_2—CH_3$ . .	281	300	E	228

* C = cyclohexane   H = hexane   E = 96 % ethanol   M = methanol   I = isooctane.

Substance	Position of maximum (mμ)	ε	Solvent (*)	Ref.
$CH_3 - (CH_2)_2 - CH : CH - C(CH_3) : CH - CO - CH_3$	281.5	19,000	E	211
$CH_3 - (CH_2)_2 - CH : CH - CO - CH : C(CH_3) - CH_3$	248	13,000	E	237
$(CH_3)_2 CH—CH_2—CO—CH : C(CH_3)—CH : CH_2$	267.5	18,300	E	250
ACIDS, ESTERS				
$CH_3—(CH_2)_{14}—CO_2H$	210	50	E	239
$CH_3—CH : CH—CO_2H$ *trans*	208	13,000	H	240
	205	14,000	E	
cis	205.5	13,500	E	
$CH_3—(CH_2)_{22}—CH : CH—CO_2H$ Free acid . .	210	13,850	E	210
Me ester . .	210	13,600	E	
$CH_3—(CH_2)_{14}—CH : CH—CO_2 H$ *trans*. . . .	213	20,000	H	241
cis.	213	13,000	H	
$CH_3—C : C—COOH$ Free acid	205	6,400	E	240
Me ester	205.5	7,200	E	
$CH_3—(CH_2)_{15}—C : C—CO_2H$	210	1,400	H	242
$CH_3—(CH_2)_{17}—CH—CH_2—CH—CH : C—CO_2H$				
$\quad\quad\quad\quad \mid \quad\quad\quad \mid \quad\quad\quad \mid$				
$\quad\quad\quad\quad CH_3 \quad\quad CH_3 \quad\quad CH_3$				
(DL, *erythro*)				
trans Free acid	218	13,100	H	128
Me ester	215	12,925	H	
cis Free acid	220	10,700	H	
Me ester.	217	10,200	H	
$CH_3—(CH_2)_8—CH_2—C——COOH$ Free acid .	208	8,180	E	201
$\quad\quad\quad\quad\quad || $				
$\quad\quad\quad\quad CH_2$ Me ester . .	210		E	
$CH_3—(CH_2)_5—C(CH_3) : CH—CO_2H$ Free acid .	219	12,070	E	243
Me ester .	219	14,500	E	
$CH_3OOC—CH : CH—COOCH_3$ *trans*.	211	16,600	E	244
cis.	205	7,950	E	
$CH_3OOC—C(CH_3) : CH—COOCH_3$ *trans* . . .	222	12,880	E	244
cis	211	8,320	E	
$CH_3—(CH_2)_{12}—CO—CH : CH—CO_2C_2H_5$. . . .	222	11,900	E	245
$HO_2C—CH_2—CO—CH_2—CO—CH : CH—CO_2H$				
c	315	1,000	Water	249
t	315	13,500	pH 1	
$CH_3—CH : CH—CH : CH—CO_2H$				
t *t*	251	27,000	E	246
	257	27,400		
	263	25,800		

* C = cyclohexane   H = hexane   E = 96 % ethanol   M = methanol   I = iso-octane.

Substance	Position of maximum (mμ)	ε	Solvent (*)	Ref.
CH_3—CH : CH—CH : CH—CO_2H				
t *c.*	251	16,200	E	246
	257	17,000		
	260	16,200		
c *t* Free acid	260	22,500	E	240
Me ester	262	23,500		
c *c* Free acid	259	20,000	E	240
Me ester	263.5	19,000		
$(CH_3)_2$C : CH—CH^t : C(CH_3)—CO_2H.	273	26,171	M	248
$(CH_3)_2$C : CH—C($CH_3)^t$: CH—CO_2H.	200	6,056	M	248
	268	12,566	M	
$(CH_3)_2$C : CH—C(CH_3) : C(CH_3)—CO_2H	199	9,439	M	248
	249	5,293	M	
CH_3—C ⋮ C—CH : CH—CO_2H *trans* Free acid	245.5	16,000	E	240
Me ester .	257	19,000		
cis Free acid	244	11,000	E	240
Me ester .	258.5	14,000		
CH_3—CH : CH—C ⋮ C—CO_2H *trans* Free acid	247	11,500	E	240
Me ester	250	13,000		
cis Free acid	246	10,500	E	240
Me ester	249	11,500		
CH_3—(CH : CH)$_3$—CO_2H.	296		E	247
	302		H	
CH_3—(CH : CH)$_4$—CO_2H	328		E	247
	330		H	
β—KETO-ESTERS				
CH_3—CO—CH_2—$CO_2C_2H_5$	245	6,700	H	115
CH_3—$(CH_2)_{20}$—CO—CH_2—$CO_2C_2H_5$	248	4,000	H	115
CH_3—CH_2—CO—CH(CH_3)—$CO_2C_2H_5$	260	350	E	115
CH_3—$(CH_2)_{20}$—CO—CH($C_{20}H_{41}$)—CO_2CH_3 ...	260	305	H	115
	286	610	H + E—KOH	115

* C = cyclohexane   H = hexane   E = 96 % ethanol   M = methanol   I = iso-octane.

CH_2=CH—CH=CH_2, the calculated value of the absorption maximum of the acid [3] is given by: $214 + (2 \times 5) = 224$ mμ (found 225 mμ).

$$CH_3—(CH_2)_5—CH=CH—CH=CH—(CH_2)_7—COOH \qquad [3]$$

An analogous rule allows calculation of the position of the absorption maximum of aldehydes or of α,β-unsaturated ketones [214]: an α-substituent (relative to CH_2: CH-CHO or to CH_2: CH-CO-CH_3) causes a displacement of the absorption maximum towards longer wavelengths of about 10 mμ and a β-substituent of 12 mμ. Introduction of a second β-substituent gives rise to an even greater displacement[215] (see Table 9).

A similar rule was proposed by Fieser (ref. 216; see also ref. 217) concerning carotenoids, taking into account the existence of endo- or exo-cyclic double bonds.

A review on the absorption spectra of α,β-unsaturated acids has been published by Nielsen[218].

2. INFRARED SPECTROGRAPHY

Infrared spectrography has been extensively utilized during recent years in the study of bacterial lipids, either to follow the fractionation of lipid extracts (e.g. the lipids of Mycobacteria, refs 251-253), or to obtain information about the structure of definite substances (e.g. C_{27}-phthienoic acid, refs 254, 255), (Fig. 4).

It must be underlined that caution is required when applying infrared spectrographic information to elucidating the structure of a substance. The presence of an absorption band in an I.R. spectrum may sometimes have several origins. For example, the band characteristic of the trans-disubstituted double bond (10.3 μ), widely used for detecting the presence of trans-unsaturated acids in lipid fractions, can also arise from the presence of the P—O—C group in the molecule (phospholipids, for example)[256]. In consequence, certain authors have advanced the idea that in an I.R. spectrum the absence of a band is more significant than the presence of a band[257].

Moreover, although a difference between the I.R. spectra of two substances suggests that they are not identical, the identity of two I.R. spectra, particularly in the case of long-chain aliphatic compounds, does not necessarily imply the identity of the substances concerned (in the aliphatic series, the introduction of a chain longer than C_4 does not cause any modification of the spectrum).

Information on the interpretation of I.R. spectra of various organic compounds can be obtained from a number of sources (e.g. refs 258-262). In the particular case of lipids, several reviews may be consulted[263-266].

Within the lipid group, I.R. spectrographic studies have been carried out chiefly on the fatty acids and their simple derivatives (esters)[254,255,267-274] and in the region 0.9 to 3.0μ[275-277].

These studies show, among other things, the existence in the region 7.4-8.5μ of a series of regularly spaced bands, the number of which increases with the length of the chain ("band progression"). This phenomenon, observed in the spectra of solid-state acids (in nujol[269] or in potassium bromide[273]), permits the identification of straight-chain fatty acids (i.e. whether odd or even series). Meiklejohn et al.[273], comparing the spectra of straight-chain fatty acids from C_{10} to C_{36}, observed the following relation between the number of bands of the progression (N) and the number of carbon atoms in the chain (nC):

$$\text{Acids with an even number of carbon atoms} \qquad N = \frac{nC}{2}$$

$$\text{Acids with an odd number of carbon atoms} \qquad N = \frac{nC + 1}{2}$$

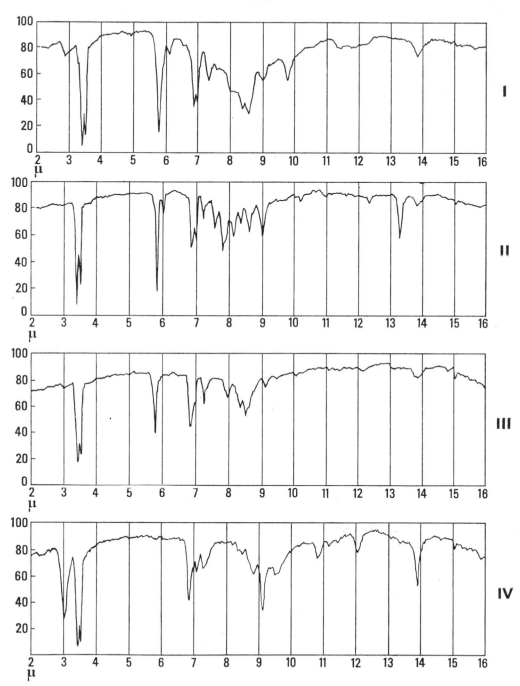

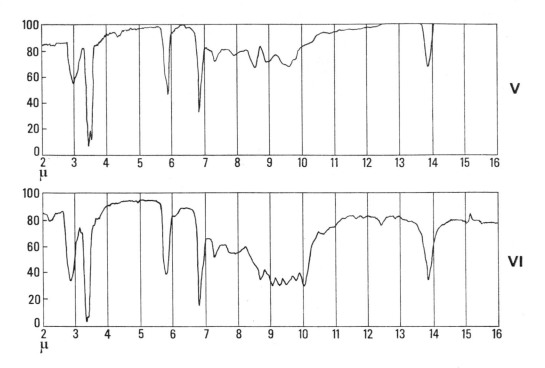

FIGURE 4. Infrared spectra of some compounds isolated from bacterial lipids.

   I Methyl lactobacillate (sample from K. Hofmann; p. 92).
   II Methyl C_{25}-+C_{27}- mycolipenate (p. 96).
  III Methyl mycocerosate (p. 102).
  IV Phthiocerol (sample from strain $H_{37}Ra$, p. 74).
   V Glyceryl mycolate (p. 156).
  VI Trehalose dimycolate ("cord factor", p. 174).

(The spectra were taken on films, melted and resolidified if necessary, with a Baird spectrophotometer equipped with a sodium chloride prism).

In the case of compounds of the type R—CO—(CH$_2$—CH$_2$)n—CO—R′ Primas & Günthard[278] observed an analogous phenomenon, a supplementary band appearing when the chain was lengthened by 4 CH$_2$ (passage from n to $n+2$).

Some observations have been made on the I.R. spectra of acids with branched chains[254, 255]. The presence of a substituent α to the carboxyl brings about a change in the relative intensities of the bands at 7.78 and 8.00 μ. An ethyl branch produces a band at 12.95 μ and a n-propyl branch one at 13.5 μ (see also ref. [279]). The presence of *iso*propyl or *t*-butyl groups is characterized by a doubling of the band at 7.3 μ (see in particular ref. 280). A longer aliphatic chain gives a band in the neighbourhood of 13.9 μ, the doubling of which can be observed in the case of certain crystalline forms[281].

TABLE 10. CORRELATION BETWEEN FUNCTIONAL GROUPS AND INFRARED ABSORPTION BANDS IN ALIPHATIC SERIES (compilation from data in the literature)

Absorption maximum		Functional group	Absorption maximum		Functional group
μ	cm⁻¹		μ	cm⁻¹	
2.75-2.80	3636-3571	Alcoholic —OH(free)	7.3	1370	—CH₃
2.80-3.00	3571-3333	Alcoholic —OH (bound)	7.75-7.80	1290-1282	C—O (acids) : doublet
3.00-3.05	3333-3279	—C ⋮ CH	8.40-8.45	1190-1183	
3.50-3.70	2857-2703	CH of aldehydes	8.3-8.9	1205-1124	Tertiary alcohol
3.4-3.7	2941-2703	OH of acids	8.9-9.2	1124-1087	Secondary alcohol
4.65-4.75	2150-2100	—C ⋮ CH	9.2-9.5	1087-1053	Primary alcohol
4.4-4.55	2260-2190	—C ⋮ C—	7.90-8.00	1266-1250	C—O (esters) . triplet
5.14	1950	—C : C : C—	8.3	1205	
5.55-5.65	1802-1770	γ-Lactone (saturated)	8.4-8.5	1190-1176	
5.70-5.75	1754-1739	γ-Lactone (unsaturated)	8.7-9.4	1149-1064	—O—(ether)
5.70	1754	Acid (monomer)	8.5-9.5	1176-1053	Anhydride (aliphatic)
5.75	1739	CO Ester	8.8	1136	Quaternary carbon
5.71-5.78	1750-1730	δ-Lactone (saturated)	10.10	990	Conjugated *trans, trans* double bonds
5.75-5.80	1739-1724	CO Aldehyde	10.3	970	—CH : CH— *trans*
5.80-5.85	1724-1709	CO Ketone (saturated) CO Ester (α,β-unsaturated)	10.7	934	—OH (acids)
5.80-5.90	1724-1695	Acid (dimer)	10.9-11.1	917-900	—CH : CH₂
6.0-6.05	1667-1653	CO Ketone (α,β-unsaturated)	11.1-11.3	900-885	>C : CH₂
6.01-6.2	1664-1613	C : C	11.2-12.0	893-833	Epoxide
6.10	1639	CO amide	13-14.9	769-671	—CH : CH— *cis*
6.21-6.45	1610-1550	Ionized carboxyl	13.3-13.4	751-746	—CH : C< (conjugated)
6.89-7.69	1450-1300		13.9	720	Poly-CH₂ (≥ 4)

Table 10 gives an indication of the values of absorption maxima observed for certain structural characteristics in the aliphatic series.

In the case of fatty acids of bacterial origin, infrared spectrography has been utilized particularly in studying the structure of C_{27}-phthienoic[254, 255] and lactobacillic[122] acids. This latter acid contains a cyclopropane ring, revealed by an absorption band at 9.8 μ. However, more recently the specificity of this band has been rendered doubtful[282]: bands at 1.63-1.65 and 2.22-2.27 μ seem to be more specific for a cyclopropane ring (ref. 283, and ref. 284); NMR spectrography is more reliable..

Finally, mention may also be made of some work carried out on the infrared spectra of glycerides[267, 285], of sphingomyelins and related substances[256] of lecithins[286, 287], of cerebrosides[288], and of lipo-proteins[289].

3. X-RAY DIFFRACTION

X-ray diffraction furnishes a convenient means for arriving at a precise identification of aliphatic compounds, and in particular of fatty acids. Since this method is based on the determination of the distance between the planes formed in the crystal by atomic groups of the same type, it furnishes results directly linked to the chain length of the aliphatic compound under study. This distance ("the principal lattice spacing") is easily measured on the diffraction patterns of the specimens (crystals "pressed" on a glass slide, or melted and resolidified), starting from the interval which separates the diffraction lines, regularly spaced, corresponding to the successive orders of reflection in accordance with the Bragg equation: $n\lambda = 2d\sin\theta$ (n = order of reflection; λ = wavelength of the radiation employed; d = lattice spacing; θ = angle of incidence).

Obtaining X-ray diffraction patterns of aliphatic compounds has been described in detail (see, e.g. refs. 290-293); an excellent review on the subject has been published by Malkin[294].

The patterns of pure acids (with a straight chain) show fine diffraction lines corresponding to a dozen orders of reflection, while for impure specimens only the first orders of reflection can be seen and the lines are broad. The intensity of these lines alternates regularly on the diagram, due to the fact that in the crystal lattice, the acid molecules are grouped in pairs with the carboxyls touching.

When side-chain substituents are present, the diffraction lines corresponding to certain orders of reflection disappear, and the nature of the missing orders permits calculation of the position of the substituent on the chain (e.g. refs. 295-297). But, for this determination a knowledge of the crystal structure is necessary. In particular, it may happen that the crystal lattice contains parts of several molecules or that the direction of the carbon chain may be different at the edges of the lattice: these cases are illustrated by optically active 2-methyloctadecanoic acid or by 9DL-methyloctadecanoic acid[298].

X-ray diffraction, depending on the arrangement of molecules in the crystal lattice, furnishes different results for the same substance according to the crystalline form and, consequently, according to the working conditions in the case of polymorphic substances. Polymorphism is very frequently encountered among long-chain aliphatic compounds and in particular among the fatty acids. Three crystalline forms, designated A, B, and C, can be exhibited by fatty acids. In general, the acids produce form B when crystallized slowly from a non-polar solvent such as benzene. Crystallization from a melted acid produces form C. A camera, as described by Stenhagen[299], can measure in a continuous manner the X-ray diffraction of a sample whose temperature is progressively varied, thus permitting exact determination of the points of transition. Information concerning the crystalline modifications of straight-chain fatty acids can be found in the publications of Francis & Piper (in particular ref. 300), and in the more recent ones of von Sydow[301] and Nyburg[302].

X-ray diffraction has been used for the identification of straight chain fatty acids of bacterial origin, either isolated from lipids or produced in the degradation of more complex compounds (refs 64, 303). Moreover, the method has been utilized during studies on the structures of the principal branched-chain constituents of the tubercle bacillus lipids: tuberculostearic acid [297], phthienoic acid [179, 304], mycolic acid [305, 306], and phthiocerol [307, 308]. The X-ray diffraction diagrams of palmitone and of methyl α-palmitoyl-palmitate, degradation products of corynomycolic acid from *C. diphteriae*, made possible the identification of this acid [309]. X-ray diffraction has also been employed in work on phytomonic acid from *Agrobacterium tumefaciens* [310].

4. MASS SPECTROMETRY

The improvements introduced during the last few years in mass spectrometry installations have permitted its application to the analysis of various organic substances. High resolution mass spectrometers which can be employed in the case of substances of high molecular weights (up to 1500) have been recently built.

Mass spectrometry permits, first of all, determination to within one unit, of the molecular weight of a compound, thanks to a parent peak due to the entire ionized molecule. "Molecule mass spectrography", which is a modification of mass spectrometry employing the negatively charged ions, may also be used for molecular weight determination [314]. On the other hand, under the influence of the electron bombardment in the ionization chamber, a large number of molecules of the compound being studied are broken into fragments, whose masses (or more exactly, the ratio of the mass to the charge m/e) are given by the peaks of the spectrum. An aliphatic molecule breaks preferentially near certain structural characteristics: breaking of the C_0—C_α bond in the case of a carbon branch (situated at C_0) on a chain or in the case of a keto group, breaking of the C_α—C_β bond in the case of an alcohol, etc. Knowing a certain number of rules of this type, established empirically, it is possible from the mass of the fragments formed to determine the structure of the whole molecule. This result is attained with less than one milligram of substance [315, 316].

The application of mass spectroscopy to organic chemistry has been developed mainly by McLafferty [317-319], Stenhagen and Ryhage [311, 315, 320, 321], and more recently, Djerassi [322], Biemann [323, 324], and Reed [324a].

As far as lipids are concerned, it is principally the esters of fatty acids that are capable of being analysed by this method. The spectra of methyl esters show two series of important peaks, arising, either from the methyl end of the molecule or from the carbomethoxy part (see fig. 5). With the aid of the parent peak furnished by each ester, it is possible to analyse quantitatively and qualitatively a mixture of esters, saturated or unsaturated [325, 326]. In the case of a complex mixture of esters, excellent results are obtained by combining gas chromatography and mass spectrometry [327]. The position of the double bond can be determined by comparison of the mass spectra measured before and after deuteration [328].

Mass spectrometry has been applied to the study of the structure of branched chain compounds isolated from the lipids of the tubercle bacillus: mycocerosic acid [145, 329], phthienoic acid [128, 330], phthiocerol [180, 331], and more recently, mycolic acids [312]. Spectacular results have been obtained on more complex molecules, such as the peptidolipid fortuitine [313].

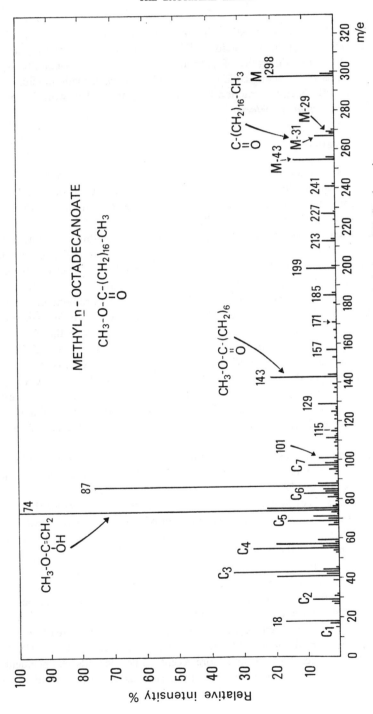

FIGURE 5a. Mass spectrum of methyl octadecanoate (R. Ryhage and E. Stenhagen).

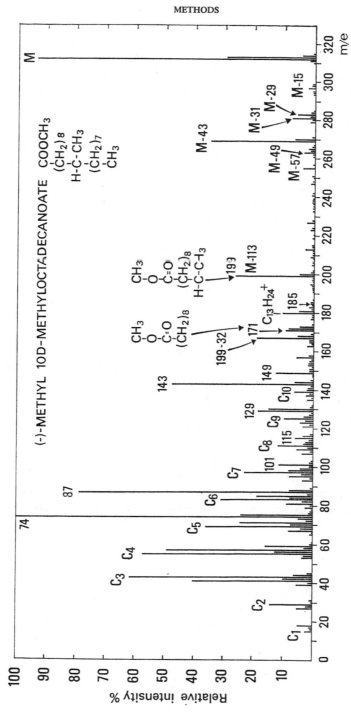

FIGURE 5b. Mass spectrum of methyl 10D-methyloctadecanoate (methyl tuberculostearate). This spectrum shows clearly the peaks at m/e 171 and 199, derived from the rupture of the carbon chain on each side of the carbon atom carrying the methyl branch (R. Ryhage and E. Stenhagen).

Because of the small quantities of substance that are required and the remarkable results that can be obtained, mass spectrometry is destined to achieve greater and greater importance, particularly in the field of bacterial lipids. Nevertheless, the very great expense of a high resolution mass spectrometer which can be used for products with a high molecular weight, is an obstacle to its widespread use.

The principal limitation of the method is due to the necessity of introducing the substance into the spectrometer in the vapour state. It must be remembered that in the case of substances of high molecular weight, the peaks observed in the mass spectrogram correspond to the fragments liberated both by electron bombardment and by cracking reactions produced during the volatilization of the product. On the other hand, in the aliphatic series, stereo-isomers furnish identical mass spectrograms (this can, however, be an advantage in comparing an optically active natural product with a racemic synthetic product).

5. N.M.R. (Nuclear magnetic resonance SPECTROGRAPHY)

This method is based on the possible induction of resonance in an atomic nucleus placed in a magnetic field and irradiated with energy in the form of radio waves. In consequence, the spectra can be expressed either in gauss (parts per million of the total magnetic field), or in cycles per second (frequency of the radio waves utilized).

In organic chemistry, N.M.R. spectrography is mainly limited to the resonance of the proton. It is possible, for example, to distinguish between aliphatic and cyclic CH_2 by this method, or between CH_3 on a trisubstituted carbon, CH_3 attached to an ethylene or acetylene carbon, or CH_3 of methoxyl, etc. Detailed information on this method can be found in the books written by Roberts[332] and Jackman[333]; see also[334-338].

Applications of N.M.R. spectrography to lipid compounds have been summarized by Hopkins in 1961[339] and a review limited to the glyceride field has been published by Chapman in 1963[340].

In the field of the bacterial lipids, N.M.R. spectrography has been used to study a sulphur-containing lipid from the tubercle bacillus[341], an unsaturated mycolic acid from *M. smegmatis*[342], a peptidolipid from *M. fortuitum*[343], and many other compounds. Quantitative determination of C-methyl groups has been used in the field of branched chain fatty acids[343a].

6. STUDY OF MONOMOLECULAR LAYERS

The properties of monomolecular layers depend on a number of factors, of which one of the most important is the structure of the molecules that constitute the film. Therefore, the study of a compound in a monomolecular layer is capable of furnishing information about its structure. However, "it is tempting to use measurements of surface area in monolayers as a means of determining molecular constitutions, but this should be done with great caution"[344]. It is for this reason, rather than simply a question of apparatus, that the utilization of monomolecular layers in studying the structure of a compound has remained in the hands of a limited number of specialists.

Two detailed reviews [344, 345] furnish all the essential information about the application of this method to lipids.

Curves expressing the changes in the surface of the film as a function of the pressure exerted on it show, according to the compounds studied, one or several points of transformation which correspond to changes of state. In fact, while the molecules remain in a film, i.e. in an essentially two dimensional form, they can exhibit properties approaching those of molecules in the solid, liquid, or gaseous state. When attempting to deduce information about the behaviour of a given substance in a monomolecular layer, it is essential to compare it with known substances studied under identical conditions of state.

Applications of this method to the study of bacterial lipid constituents (Mycobacteria) are essentially due to Ställberg-Stenhagen and Stenhagen. In the cases of phthiocerol [346] and of a mycolic acid [305], the authors arrived at conclusions which are entirely in accord with results obtained later by completely different ways.

In another example, Anderson and his collaborators isolated a C_{24} acid from the lipids of a bovine strain of *M. tuberculosis* [347] and a C_{25} acid by pyrolysis of an avian mycolic acid [348] (see page 136). The melting points of these two acids were lower than those of the corresponding straight-chain acids and this suggested the presence of a branch in their molecules. Since branched-chain acids are known to behave completely differently in the monomolecular layer form from unbranched acids, the two bacterial acids were studied by this method [349]. They were, in reality, mixtures of homologous unbranched acids. Later, a method based on the examination of pressure/temperature diagrams was introduced by Ställberg-Stenhagen & Stenhagen [350] for analysing the composition of mixtures of higher straight-chain acids.

7. MISCELLANEOUS METHODS

Although certain chromatographic methods are more conveniently classified as methods of analysis than of fractionation, for the sake of convenience chromatography has been dealt with as a whole in one of the previous sections (see page 32).

Among other physical methods of analysis that merit attention, there are polarimetry and a thermal method of analysis, both of which will be briefly discussed.

The optical rotation of a compound, by which it can be followed during fractionating operations can also contribute to its identification. On the other hand, the existence itself of a rotatory power implies certain structural peculiarities. It was on the basis of optical rotation considerations that Cason & Prout [351] rejected a formula, previously accepted, of "phthioic" acid from the tubercle bacillus (see page 95). Optical rotation measurements (see, refs 352, 353) are capable of furnishing useful information in certain cases.

The melting (or solidifying) point curves of binary mixtures of neighbouring homologues of fatty acids generally show two transition points due to the formation of an eutectic and of an equimolecular mixed compound. Working on binary mixtures of an iso or ante-iso acid and a straight-chain acid, Weitkamp [124] ascertained that to obtain two transition points on the solidification curves, the straight-chain fatty acid, which is mixed with the

Substance	Position of maximum (mμ)	ε	Solvent (*)	Ref.
CH_3—CO—CH_2—CO—CH_3	270	13,150	H	229
	273	9,550	E	
CH_3—$(CH_2)_{16}$—CO—CH_2—CO—$(CH_2)_{16}$—CH_3	275	10,000	H	230
$CH_3(CH_2)_{16}$-CO-$CH(C_{18}H_{37})$-CO-$(CH_2)_{16}$-CH_3.	290	2,000	H	230
CH_2 : CH—CHO	203		C	215
	207		E	
CH_3—CH : CH—CHO	213		C	215
	218		E	
CH_3—$(CH_2)_3$—CH : CH—CHO	223	14,000	E	213
$(CH_3)_2$C : CH—CHO	228		C	215
	235.5		E	
CH_3—CH_2—CH : $C(CH_3)$—CHO	229	13,600	E	213
CH_2 : CH—CO—CH_3.	205		C	215
	208.5		E	
CH_3—$(CH_2)_5$—CH : CH—CO—CH_3 *trans* . .	224	14,460	E	231
cis . . .	228	8,710		
CH_2 : $C(OCH_3)$—CO—CH_3	248		E	232
CH_3 - $(CH_2)_5$ - CO -CH : CH- CO - $(CH_2)_7$ - CO_2H.	230		E	233
$C_{21}H_{43}$—CH : $C(C_{20}H_{41})$—CO—$C_{19}H_{39}$.	235	15,200	H	234
CH_2 : CH—CH : CH—CHO.	258.5	27,800	E	235
	325	51		
CH_3—CH : CH—CH : CH—CHO	270	26,500	E	211
CH_3—$(CH_2)_6$—CH : CH—CH : CH—CHO . . .	274	32,900	E	235
OCH-$C(CH_3)$: CH-CH : CH-$C(CH_3)$-CHO .	234	13,400	H	236
t *c* *t*	306	33,100		
	319.5	50,800		
	336	43,000		
	237	10,600	M	
	327	43,400		
	337	39,500		
*t*** *t*** *t***.	225	3,680	H	236
	305	39,400		
	319	64,000		
	336	58,000		
	235	1,820	M	
	328	55,500		
	341	53,500		
CH_3—CH : CH—CH : CH—CO—CH_3	271	22,600	E	211
CH_2 : CH—$C(CH_3)$: CH—CO—CH_3.	269	20,000	E	211

* C = cyclohexane H = hexane E = 96 % ethanol M = methanol I = iso-octane.
** *Trans*, considering the principal chain as being —C : C—CHO [238].

iso or ante-iso C_N-acid, should be C_{N-2} or C_{N-3}, respectively (maximum number of carbon atoms):

$$\textit{Iso-}C_{20} + \textit{n-}C_{19} : \text{One transition point}$$
$$\textit{Iso-}C_{20} + \textit{n-}C_{18} : \text{Two transition points}$$
$$\textit{Iso-}C_{18} + \textit{n-}C_{17} : \text{One transition point}$$
$$\textit{Iso-}C_{18} + \textit{n-}C_{16} : \text{Two transition points}$$
$$\textit{Ante-iso-}C_{21} + \textit{n-}C_{19} : \text{One transition point}$$
$$\textit{Ante-iso-}C_{21} + \textit{n-}C_{18} : \text{Two transition points}$$

This observation thus permits the localization of the position of a methyl branch. The validity of this procedure has been confirmed by Cason & Winans [354].

Chemical methods of analysis are generally utilized without particular modification, and their description is outside the scope of the present work. However, mention may be made of an interesting method of determinating the C-methyl content of an aliphatic compound. This determination in fact furnishes a convenient means of demonstrating branches, and gives an approximate estimate of their number [355].

TABLE 11. RESULTS OF THE DETERMINATION OF METHYL GROUPS BY VARIOUS MODIFICATIONS OF THE KUHN-ROTH METHOD

Substance studied	Number of methyls		Ref.
	Calcd	Found	
n-Decanoic acid	1	0.99	359
n-Octadecanoic acid	1	0.96	359
n-Dodecanoic acid	1	0.83	358
n-Hexacosanoic acid	1	0.75	358
n-Tetratriacontane	2	1.47—1.60	358
DL-9-Methyloctadecanoic acid.	2	1.40—1.45	358
DL-4-Methylpentacosanoic acid	2	1.38—1.39	358
2-Heptylnonanoic acid	2	1.58—1.62	358
2,2-Dimethyloctanoic acid	3	1.64	359
4,4-Dimethyltetradecanoic acid	3	1.60—1.90	359
3-Methylbutan-2-one	3	1.62—1.68	359
Trimethylacetic acid	3	0.72	359
Methyl hexadecane-1,16-dicarboxylate	0	0,01	358
Methyl 3,3-dimethylglutarate	2	0.72,0.73	358
2-Eicosyl-3-hydroxytetracosanoic acid	2	1.60,1.70	358
C_{27}-Phthienoic acid (p. 96)	4	3.13,3.30	327,357
Lactobacillic acid (p. 93)	1	1.3,1.4	122
2-Methylenedodecanoic acid	1	1.05	201
Methyl oleate	1	1.5,1.6	362
Oleic alcohol.	1	1.53	362
Linoleic acid	1	1.29,1.16	362

The various procedures recommended for the determination of C-methyl are nothing more than adaptations or improvements of the Kuhn-Roth method[356], which consists in oxidizing the molecule by a sulpho-chromic mixture: only $CH_3—C\lessgtr$ groups furnish acetic acid, which is distilled off and titrated (see in particular refs. 357, note p. 411, and refs 358-360). Table 11 shows some results obtained by the use of this method. Two (or three) methyl branches on the same carbon atom, obviously can only furnish one molecule of acetic acid. The technique of Ginger[361] can lead to results that are too high. An eventual confirmation can be obtained from the intensity of the methyl group absorption band in the I.R. spectrum (e.g. refs. 254, 255, 363), or more conveniently from the intensity of the peak at 0.90 ppm in the N.M.R. spectrum[343a].

The use of quantitative paper chromatography allows the quantity of substance required for the determination of C-methyl to be reduced. Furthermore, the oxidation of an aliphatic compound by a dilute sulpho-chromic mixture can give rise to the entire series of lower n-acids from C_2 to C_8, detectable by paper chromatography. If a group containing oxygen (carbonyl, hydroxyl) is located in the part of the molecule that gives rise to these acids, the molecule will be preferentially split at this point and the higher member of the acids observed on the paper chromatogram will indicate the position of this group (from the CH_3 end of the molecule)[364-366]. This method was utilized by Demarteau-Ginsburg[367] to determine the position of the methoxyl group in phthiocerol.

The presence of a branch in the neighbourhood of a carboxyl group can be demonstrated by the influence it exerts on the properties of this carboxyl group and this effect has been studied by Cason et al.[368,369]: the rate of hydrolysis of the amide under well defined conditions can give useful information (see also the "rule of six", ref. 370, p. 206).

Various colour reactions are currently used to obtain an indication, at least qualitative, of the presence of certain groups in a molecule. The test for unsaturation for example, can be performed with tetranitromethane: often a response that may be difficult to evaluate is obtained with long-chain aliphatic compounds (a dilute solution of bromine in carbon tetrachloride frequently gives better results). α,β-Unsaturated acids give a negative test with tetranitromethane[371], as do α,β-unsaturated alcohols[372] and enol ethers (eg. ref. 373).

The Legal reaction (ref. 374, p. 56), which is very useful for detecting carbonyl groups, gives negative results with the higher ketones such as stearone $C_{35}H_{70}O$[375]; the same is the case with the Adachi test for methyl ketones[376]. These negative results may be due in part to the poor solubility of the higher aliphatic compounds.

It has often been claimed that long-chain oxo-compounds form oximes as sole characteristic derivatives (e.g. ref. 377). The reactivity of these compounds does not seem to be notably diminished and, provided that the ketone compound is kept in solution, various derivatives may be prepared. For example, the semicarbazones of 4,6-dimethyltetracosan-2-one $C_{26}H_{52}O$[128] and 4-methylhexacosan-2-one $C_{27}H_{54}O$[378] have been obtained with an alcoholic solution of free semicarbazide. Likewise, the 2,4-dinitrophenylhydrazones of a series of eicosanone isomer $C_{20}H_{40}O$[379], of palmitoine $C_{32}H_{64}O_2$, of stearoine $C_{36}H_{72}O_2$[380], and of symmetric dialkyl ketones from C_{21} to C_{43}[381] have been prepared.

V. METHODS OF DEGRADATION

Determination of the structure of an organic compound by chemical means depends upon methods involving fission of the molecule into identifiable fragments by as selective a process as possible. A brief description will be given here of the degradation methods commonly used in the study of lipid substances.

1. INITIAL REDUCTION OF COMPLEX SUBSTANCES TO SIMPLE CONSTITUENTS

The first step in the study of the structure of complex substances is to split them into simple constituents. For example, glycerides are hydrolysed to glycerol and fatty acids and waxes to aliphatic alcohols and fatty acids. Next, the problem is to determine how the isolated and identified simple constituents were linked together in the original complex substance.

Obtaining simple constituents from complex lipids is generally carried out by saponification. The conditions used are extremely variable and depend in particular on the solubility characteristics of the substances studied. Most frequently, saponification is effected by alcoholic potassium hydroxide, with the addition of water in the case of lipids rich in lower fatty acids or the addition of benzene in the case of long-chain substances not very soluble in alcohol (see, e.g. ref. 382). The structures of the substances to be saponified also play an important rôle in the choice of the conditions to be used. The esters of acids having branches near the carboxyl group are saponified more slowly: this is the case, for example, with the esters of mycocerosic acid (see page 102) (ref. 383, p. 26). The rule of six [370] shows that a methyl group in the β-position with respect to the carboxyl group introduces a steric hindrance greater than that of a methyl group in the α-position. It can be advantageous to make use of the differences in the rate of saponification and to proceed in stages, starting with the use of very mild conditions, which are made stronger in succeeding stages. This method has been employed in particular by Anderson et al. [384] in their work on the phosphatides of the tubercle bacillus (see also p. 162).

Although sphingomyelins do not seem to exist in bacterial lipids, it should be mentioned here that this type of phospholipid is much more stable to alkaline hydrolysis than are lecithins or cephalins: this difference in behaviour is due to the absence in sphingomyelins of free hydroxyl groups (or hydroxyl groups capable of being liberated in alkaline medium) in the α-position to the carbon carrying the phosphate residue, thus preventing the intermediate formation of a cyclic phosphate [385]. Sulphatides are specifically hydrolysed to sulphur free glycolipids on standing at room temperature for 4 hrs. in 0.05 N methanolic hydrochloric acid [386].

Trans-esterification phenomena can be observed when alcoholic potassium hydroxide is used: saponification (by methanolic potassium hydroxide) of a tubercle bacillus glycolipid (ester of mycolic acids and a polysaccharide) in a few minutes gives a precipitate of polysaccharide, while the mycolic acid methyl esters are found in the solution [387].

Acid hydrolysis can also be used (e.g. hydrolysis of the phosphatides of the tubercle bacillus [388]) and is essential for the study of compounds containing acetal linkages. With the aid of hydrochloric acid alcohol, Stendal [389] carried out the hydrolysis of phthiocerol esters, which resulted in the formation of the fatty acid ethyl esters: it is therefore also a transesterification phenomenon. This method seems preferable to the long alkaline saponification sometimes employed.

Lithium aluminium hydride is a convenient tool for the rapid cleavage of ester bonds, especially those which are difficult to saponify. The reaction is a hydrogenolysis, as the acid constituents are reduced to alcohols. Ester linkages are broken, but glycosidic linkages are left unchanged: it is therefore possible to verify that in a glycolipid containing a polysaccharide and hydroxy-acids, the latter are linked to the polysaccharide in the form of esters through their carboxyl group and not in the form of glycosides through their alcoholic hydroxyl group, (ref. 64, p. 104).

2. DEGRADATION OF SIMPLE CONSTITUENTS

Two cases will be considered: that of a saturated molecule with a single functional group, and that of a molecule containing several functional groups or multiple linkages.

a) *Saturated compounds with a single functional group*

Most aliphatic substances with a straight chain and a single functional group are known today, and their identification no longer raises any problem other than a functional analysis. In the case of complex substances, possessing one or more branches on the carbon chain and a reactive oxygen group, generally located at the extremity of the main chain, elucidation of the structure is made difficult by the lack of a weak point at which to attack the molecule.

In such a case, one can resort to a systematic degradation beginning at the extremity of the molecule which has the reactive oxygen group. This latter is first converted to an acid [4], which is then brominated in the α-position [5]. After elimination of a molecule of hydrobromic acid, the α,β-unsaturated acid obtained [6] is cleaved by ozonization or permanganate oxidation (mycoceranic acid, page 102) [390]. This procedure provides information about carbon atoms 2 and 3 (relative to the carboxyl): in particular, if R_2 is a hydrogen or an alkyl, the acid or ketone [7] will be obtained. It has also been suggested that the unsaturated acid [6] be split by alkaline fusion [391].

The acid [4] can be esterified, and the ester degraded by the Barbier Wieland procedure [10 → 11 → 12 → 13] (see, e.g. refs. 392, 393, 394 p. 110). A modification of this method, devised by Miescher [395], entails the elimination of three atoms of carbon : a second double bond, conjugated with the existing olefin bond [12], is introduced by allylic bromination with *N*-bromosuccinimide. This method of degradation was utilized [396] for the identification of 6L-methyloctanoic acid, an acid produced by *Bacillus polymyxa* (and which is transformed into (+)-3L-methylpentanoic acid; see page 83).

$$R_4\text{—CH—CH—CH—COOH} \quad [4]$$
$$\overset{|}{R_3} \quad \overset{|}{R_2} \quad \overset{|}{R_1}$$

$$R_4\text{—CH—CH—CH—COOCH}_3$$
$$\overset{|}{R_3} \quad \overset{|}{R_2} \quad \overset{|}{R_1} \qquad [10]$$

$$+ C_6H_5MgBr$$

$$R_4\text{—CH—CH—CH—C} \overset{C_6H_5}{\underset{C_6H_5}{<}}$$
$$\overset{|}{R_3} \quad \overset{|}{R_2} \quad \overset{|}{R_1} \quad \overset{|}{OH}$$
$$[11]$$

$$R_4\text{—CH—CH—C : C} \overset{C_6H_5}{\underset{C_6H_5}{<}}$$
$$\overset{|}{R_3} \quad \overset{|}{R_2} \quad \overset{|}{R_1}$$
$$[12]$$

$$R_4\text{—CH—C(Br)—C : C} \overset{C_6H_5}{\underset{C_6H_5}{<}}$$
$$\overset{|}{R_3} \quad \overset{|}{R_2} \quad \overset{|}{R_1}$$
$$[14]$$

$$R_4\text{—CH—CH—C : O}$$
$$\overset{|}{R_3} \quad \overset{|}{R_2} \quad \overset{|}{R_1}$$
$$[13]$$

$$\text{Br}$$
$$R_4\text{—CH—CH—C—COOH}$$
$$\overset{|}{R_3} \quad \overset{|}{R_2} \quad \overset{|}{R_1} \qquad [5]$$

$$R_4\text{—CH—C : C—COOH}$$
$$\overset{|}{R_3} \quad \overset{|}{R_2} \quad \overset{|}{R_1} \qquad [6]$$

$$R_4\text{—CH—C : O} \quad O : C\text{—COOH}$$
$$\overset{|}{R_3} \quad \overset{|}{R_2} \quad + \quad \overset{|}{R_1}$$
$$[7] \qquad\qquad [8]$$

$$R_1\text{—COOH} \qquad [9]$$

$$R_4\text{—C : C—C : C} \overset{C_6H_5}{\underset{C_6H_5}{<}} \longrightarrow R_4\text{—C : O} \quad + \quad O : C\text{—C : C} \overset{C_6H_5}{\underset{C_6H_5}{<}}$$
$$\overset{|}{R_3}\,\overset{|}{R_2}\,\overset{|}{R_1} \qquad\qquad \overset{|}{R_3} \qquad\qquad\qquad \overset{|}{R_2}\,\overset{|}{R_1}$$
$$[15] \qquad\qquad\qquad [16] \qquad\qquad\qquad\qquad [17]$$

Another method of carbon-by-carbon degradation of an aliphatic molecule has been devised by Darzens & Mentzer[397]:

$$R\text{—CH}_2\text{—COOH} \rightarrow R\text{—CH}_2\text{—CO—C}_6H_5 \rightarrow R\text{—C—CO—C}_6H_5 \rightarrow R\text{—CN} + HOOC\text{—C}_6H_5$$
$$\overset{\|}{NOH}$$
$$[18] \qquad\qquad [19] \qquad\qquad [20] \qquad\quad [21] \qquad [22]$$

The mono-oxime of an α-diketone [20] on pyrolysis at 200° splits into a nitrile [21] and benzoic acid [22]. This procedure has been applied to the degradation of fatty acids, especially in order to locate labelled carbon in the carboxyl group; labelled benzoic acid is formed, which is easily purified [398, 399].

Under sufficiently drastic conditions, the acid molecule [4] can be directly oxidized It will be preferentially oxidized at tertiary carbon atoms. This procedure was used, for example, by Spielman [400] to determine the constitution of tuberculostearic acid [23] (see page 87); the resulting n-decan-2-one [24] and azelaic acid [25] show that the branch is at C-10.

$$CH_3-(CH_2)_7-\underset{\underset{[23]}{\underset{|}{CH_3}}}{CH}-(CH_2)_8-COOH \rightarrow CH_3-(CH_2)_7-\underset{\underset{[24]}{\underset{|}{CH_3}}}{CO} + \underset{[25]}{HOOC-(CH_2)_7-COOH}$$

However, this procedure gives rise to complex mixtures of oxidation products and the results are sometimes difficult to interpret.

More recently, methods have been elaborated to study the structure of branched-chain esters on the milligram scale. The fragments obtained by oxidative degradation of the initial molecule are identified by gas chromatography. Cason et al. [401] developed a method based on oxidation with chromic acid in acetic acid. Good results were obtained in the case of fatty acids containing a single methyl branch (ref. 402); but the method failed in the case of poly-methyl-branched acids, such as the phthienoic acids (and their dihydro-derivatives) [175], which required chromyl acetate as oxidizing agent [175].

A quite different approach was proposed by Murray [403]. The fatty acid molecule is oxidized with an excess of potassium permanganate in acetone, giving rise to a complex mixture of acids which is analysed by vapour phase chromatography of the methyl esters. If, for instance, tuberculostearic acid (10-methyloctadecanoic acid) is oxidized by this procedure, branched-chain acids with 19 to 11 carbon atoms as well as straight-chain acids with 8 to 2 carbon atoms will be observed. The absence of the straight-chain C_9 acid shows that the branch is located on the 9th carbon atom from the methyl end of the molecule and the extent of the interval where no acid is observed in the gas chromatogram gives information about the size of the branch. Confirmation can be obtained by analysing the neutral fraction, which contains a C_{10} methyl ketone.

b) Compounds containing several functional groups

The presence of several reactive oxygen functions or double bonds in the molecule permits the employment of methods which break the carbon chain at the site of one of these groups. The problem is simplified it two oxygen functions are α to each other, since reagents such as periodic acid [404] and lead tetra-acetate [405] react specifically with these functions. Double bond migrations have been observed in the course of oxidations with periodic acid and lead tetra-cetate (see, e.g. ref. 406).

— Severing the carbon chain at a double bond

One of the methods most frequently used, because of its relative specificity, is ozonization (see the reviews by Bailey, ref. 407, and Kadesch, ref. 408b). According to the conditions under which the ozonide is hydrolysed, it is possible to preserve the aldehyde groups formed [408] or to transform them into acids [175]. Unsaturated esters, isolated by means of thin-layer chromatography on silica gel impregnated with silver nitrate and gas chromatography, were identified by ultramicro-ozonolysis followed by gas chromatography of the neutral aldehyde [408a]. Ozonization, however, gives rise to numerous secondary reactions [407, 409]. Among those which are most often encountered in the chemistry of lipids are the formation of acetaldehyde from compounds containing the unsaturated divinylmethane system [410] and the formation of the C_{n-1}-acid instead of the α-hydroxy- or α-oxo-C_n-acid. This last case is illustrated by the isolation of n-pentacosanoic acid instead of 2-oxohexacosanoic acid, from the products of ozonolysis of monoanhydromycolic acid (see page 128) [126]. By taking special precautions, the α-substituted acids can sometimes be obtained [196]. The rate of ozonization of the potassium salt of an α,β-unsaturated acid is higher than that of its ester [411].

Fission of the carbon chain at a double bond can also be achieved by permanganate oxidation (in acetone solution, for example). This method has been utilized to locate the double bond in corynomycolenic acid from the diphtheria bacillus [412] and to study the constitution of mycolipenic and mycoceranic acids from the tubercle bacillus [196, 390]. The specificity of this fission can be considerably increased by using a small quantity of permanganate in dilute solution and in the presence of periodic acid: the dilute permanganate causes dihydroxylation of the double bond and the periodic acid splits specifically the α-glycol as fast as it is formed. The permanganate consumed is regenerated by re-oxidation of the manganese salts with the excess periodic acid [413]. This procedure has been applied to unsaturated fatty acids by von Rudloff [414, 415] and by Jones & Stolp [416]. An anomalous case of the permanganate periodate oxidation has been observed in which one of the expected end products, β-hydroxyadipic acid undergoes oxidative decomposition [417]. Dihydroxylation of a double bond can also be achieved with osmic acid (ref. 418).

Hydroxy compounds can be dehydrated to unsaturated derivatives, which are treated as described above, but frequently the dehydration gives rise to a mixture of isomers and thus increases the complexity of the mixture of oxidation products. When the dehydration occurs preferentially in a given position, the procedure becomes very useful. An example of this is the mycolic acids of the tubercle bacillus which, since they are β-hydroxy-α-branched acids, on dehydration give an α,β-unsaturated acid [126]. With branched-chain molecules, dehydration can lead to rearrangements and it must be kept in mind that dehydration accompanied by rearrangement [26 → 27] is easier than simple dehydration (e.g. 28 → 29) [419].

$$(CH_3)_3C—CHOH—C(CH_3)_3 \longrightarrow (CH_3)_3C—C(CH_3) : C(CH_3)_2 + H_2O$$
$$[26] \hspace{5cm} [27]$$

$$CH_3—(CH_2)_3—CHOH—(CH_2)_3—CH_3 \to CH_3—(CH_2)_3—CH : CH—(CH_2)_2—CH_3 + H_2O$$
$$[28] \hspace{5cm} [29]$$

— Oxidation of hydroxy- or oxo-compounds

The controlled oxidation of a compound containing several oxygen functions can lead to carbonyl derivatives having particular properties. For example, the controlled oxidation (chromic acid in acetic acid) of a mycolic ester gives a β-keto ester [126], and mild oxidation (chromic acid in pyridine) of phthiocerol gives a β-diketone [367], the two types of ketone compound presenting characteristic ultraviolet absorption spectra (see page 76).

Further oxidation splits the molecule preferentially in the neighbourhood of the carbonyl groups and, according to the degree of substitution of the molecule near this position, ketones or acids are formed. For example, phthiocerol, which is a mixture of two β-glycols [30] and [33] (see page 75), on oxidation with chromic acid in acetic acid, gives the C_{22} and C_{24} straight-chain acids, accompanied by small quantities of the C_{21} and C_{23} acids [180, 367]:

$$CH_3-(CH_2)_{20}-CHOH-CH_2-CHOH-C_9H_{18}(OCH_3) \rightarrow CH_3-(CH_2)_{20}-COOH +$$
$$[30] \hspace{6cm} [31]$$

$$CH_3-(CH_2)_{19}-COOH$$
$$[32]$$

$$CH_3-(CH_2)_{22}-CHOH-CH_2-CHOH-C_9H_{18}(OCH_3) \rightarrow CH_3-(CH_2)_{22}-COOH +$$
$$[33] \hspace{6cm} [34]$$

$$CH_3-(CH_2)_{21}-COOH$$
$$[35]$$

It is also possible to submit the carbonyl compound (whether or not it arises from the oxidation of a hydroxy precursor) to more specific methods of degradation. In particular, Beckmann rearrangement of the oxime leads to a mixture of amides, thus permitting the carbon chain to be broken by hydrolysis. The nature of the two acids and the two amines which are liberated indicates the position of the oxygen function in the original substance.

This method has been used to study the constitution of hydroxy acids of bacterial origin (corynolic acid, see page 118) and others [420, 421]. A limitation of this procedure is the fact that long-chain amides are very resistant to hydrolysis: the Beckmann rearrangement effected on the dioxime of a diketone $C_{86}H_{70}O_2 \pm 5\ CH_2$, originating from the oxidation of a mycolic acid, gave a diamide which could not be hydrolysed [422].

Oxidation with peracids by the BAEYER-VILLIGER procedure does not seem applicable to higher aliphatic ketones [423].

VI. METHODS OF SYNTHESIS

Synthesis has been principally used in the study of bacterial lipid constituents, either to confirm the structure attributed to a substance (and perhaps clarify details of its stereochemistry), or to prepare model compounds in order to compare their chemical and biological properties with those of natural products.

1. SYNTHESIS OF SIMPLE LIPID CONSTITUENTS

Most of the simple constituents of bacterial lipids have been synthesized. The procedures employed are applications of classical organic reactions and their description is outside the scope of this work. Recent reviews have assembled the literature on this subject [424-428].

Nevertheless, some points merit special mention. Straight-chain fatty acids which are available commercially may contain a sizable proportion of homologous acids, since they are generally prepared from natural lipids. If such acids are used as starting materials for syntheses, it is particularly important to eliminate the homologous acids they may contain and to verify their homogeneity by sufficiently sensitive methods (gas chromatography, for example). Thus, the end products of the synthesis consist of long-chain aliphatic compounds for which a mixed melting point test (with the natural product) is often without value because of the ready co-crystallization of this type of substance. Recourse must therefore be made to more complicated physical methods in order to establish the identity of the synthetic and natural products; the possible presence of homologues in the final product makes the interpretation of results difficult.

Purification of a batch of fatty acids is a long and tedious task so that a guide to the choice of a method of synthesis is the ease with which the starting material can be obtained in a pure state. The numerous methods which exist today (see the reviews cited above) of extending chains allow the size of the intermediate products in the synthesis to be varied almost at will; for example, the malonic acid C_nH_{2n+1}—$CH(COOH)_2$ [35], may be obtained starting from any of the C_n [32], C_{n+1} [36], or C_{n+2} [38] fatty acids:

$$C_{n-1}H_{2n-1}\text{—COOH} \xrightarrow{\text{LiAlH}_4} C_{n-1}H_{2n-1}\text{—CH}_2\text{OH} \xrightarrow{\text{PBr}_3} C_{n-1}H_{2n-1}\text{—CH}_2\text{Br}$$

$$[32] \qquad\qquad\qquad\qquad [33] \qquad\qquad\qquad\qquad [34]$$

$$C_nH_{2n+1}\text{—COOH} \xrightarrow[\text{reaction (429)}]{\text{Hunsdiecker}} C_nH_{2n+1}\text{Br} \longrightarrow C_nH_{2n+1}\text{—CH(COOH)}_2$$

$$[36] \qquad\qquad\qquad\qquad [37] \qquad\qquad\qquad\qquad [35]$$

$$C_nH_{2n+1}\text{—CH}_2\text{—COOH} \dashrightarrow C_nH_{2n+1}\text{—CH}_2\text{—COOC}_2H_5 \xrightarrow[(430)]{} C_nH_{2n+1}\text{—CH—COOC}_2H_5$$
$$\text{CO—COOC}_2H_5$$

$$[38] \qquad\qquad\qquad\qquad [39] \qquad\qquad\qquad\qquad [40]$$

Synthesis of optically active substances, having an asymmetric carbon atom because of the presence of a methyl or hydroxyl group, is a frequently encountered problem. A simple solution consists in the use as starting material of optically active mono-esters of diacids containing the asymmetric carbon atom to be introduced. One of the carboxyls can be

TABLE 12. EXAMPLES OF ACIDS UTILIZED FOR THE SYNTHESIS OF LONG-CHAIN OPTICALLY ACTIVE ACIDS

Acid	Formula	Boiling point or melting point (b. p. or m. p.)	Optical rotation $[\alpha]_D$	Solvent	Temp.	Ref.
D-3-Methyl-4-methoxycarbonylbutanoic	$CH_3OOC—CH_2—CH—CH_2—CO_2H$ (CH_3)	B. p. 98°/0.4 mm	−0.58°	Homogeneous	22°	431,432
L-isomer		B. p. 101°/0.5 mm	+ 0.58°	Homogeneous	22°	
D-2-Methyl-4-carboxybutanoic	$HOOC—(CH_2)_2—CH—CO_2H$ (CH_3)	M. p. 81°	+21.25°	Water	17.5°	433
L-4-Methyl-5-acetoxypentanoic	$OCH_2—CH—CH_2—CH_2—CO_2H$ (CO, CH_3, CH_3)	B. p. 167.5°/15 mm	+ 4.02°	Ether	20°	433,440
D-2-Pent-4-enoic	$CH_2 : CH—CH_2—CH—CO_2H$ (CH_3)	B. p. 87—88°/12 mm	− 8.25°	Homogeneous	25°	435,434
L-isomer		B. p. 97—98°/16 mm	+ 8.24°	Homogeneous	19°	
D-3,5-dimethyl 6-methoxycarbonylhexanoic	$CH_2—CH—CH_2—CH—CH—CH_2$ (CH_3OOC, CH_3, CH_3, CO_2H)	B.p. 137—139°/0.3 mm	+ 1.96°	Homogeneous	22°	436
L-isomer		B.p. 137—139°/0.3 mm	− 1.96°	Homogeneous	22°	
D-3-Acetoxybutanoic	$CH_3—CH—CH_2—CO_2H$ ($O—COCH_3$)	B. p. 80—85°/0.25 mm	− 2.86°*	Homogeneous	24°	437
L-isomer			+ 2.78°*	Homogeneous	23°	
D-3-Acetoxy 4-methoxycarbonylbutanoic	$CH_3OOC—CH_2—CH—CH_2—CO_2H$ ($O—CO—CH_3$)	B.p.145—155°/0.5 mm	− 5.27° / − 6.2° / − 3.7°	Homogeneous / Chloroform / Ether	21°	438,439
L-isomer			− 5.28° / + 6.1° / + 3.7°	Homogeneous / Chloroform / Ether	25°	

* Value of α_D, tube 10 cm long.

replaced by other groups which allow extension of the carbon chain. It is necessary to emphasize that separation of the components of a racemic aliphatic substance having more than 10 carbon atoms is usually difficult. Table 12 gives some examples of mono-esters from which it has been possible to synthesize the optically active forms of branched-chain fatty acids.

2. SYNTHESIS OF COMPLEX LIPIDS

Glycerides, phospholipids, and glycolipids are discussed in succession. Here the problem consists of introducing, in a known position, an acyl residue (ether-soluble) into a polyhydric alcohol (water-soluble).

— Glycerides. — The general methods for synthesizing glycerides have been outlined in several recent reviews [441-444]. Attaching an acyl residue to a given hydroxyl group in glycero is helped by the fact that the treatment of glycerol with acetone produces 1,2-isopropylidene-glycerol[445] while with benzaldehyde it leads to 1,3-benzylidene-glycerol [446, 447]. On the other hand, since the primary alcohol groups are more reactive, partial esterification of glycerol leads preferentially to l-acyl-glycerol and then to 1,3-diacyl-glycerol [448].

In connection with the presence of branched α,β-unsaturated acids of the mycolipenic and phthienoic types in the lipids of the tubercle bacillus, Fray & Polgar [449] prepared the 1,2- and 1,3-glycerol diesters of 2-methyloctadec-2-enoic acid.

A 1-monomycolate of glycerol (see page 156) has been isolated from the waxes of the tubercle bacillus and synthesized from potassium mycolate and 1,2-isopropylidene-3 tosyl-glycerol (according to a method devised for the preparation of glycolipids; see below) [450].

— Phospholipids. — Information about methods which might be used for the synthesis of phospholipids in general can be found in three reviews [451, 452, 453] and some fairly recent papers [454-457]. Synthesis of amino acid esters of phosphatidylglycerols has also been described [457a].

— Glycolipids. — Of the glycolipids encountered in bacterial lipids, only one has been synthesized; viz. the "cord factor" or 6,6′-dimycolate of trehalose (see page 174).

This synthesis was accomplished by two different procedures:

(i) By the reaction of trehalose with previously acetylated mycolic acid chloride [458], according to the procedure earlier employed for the preparation of glucose, galactose, and glucosamine mycolates [459]. It was shown that esterification of a sugar by a fatty acid gives mainly the ester of the primary hydroxyl group (position 6) [460].

(ii) By reacting the potassium salt of mycolic acid with a 6,6′-ditosyl derivative of trehalose. 6,6′-Ditosyl-2,3,4,2′,3′,4′-hexaacetyltrehalose was used at first and the reaction carried out with synthetic α-branched β-hydroxy acids [461]. The "cord factor" was subsequently synthesized via the intermediate 6,6′-dimycolyl-2,3,4,2′,3′,4′-hexaacetyltrehalose [458]. Because of the low yield in the deacetylation step, condensation of the potassium mycolate with 6,6′-ditosyltrehalose has been proposed [462].

Esters of fatty acids and sugars, in which the acyl residues are attached to the primary hydroxyl group of the sugar may be obtained in good yield by trans-esterification between a fatty acid methyl ester and a sugar in the presence of potassium carbonate [463-465].

Simple specific constituents

This chapter will deal with the well-characterized simple constituents, straight- or branched-chained, which can be considered as specific to bacterial lipids.

The compounds are classed by function and, within each functional group, by the increasing number of carbon atoms they contain.

I. HYDROXY COMPOUNDS (alcohols and phenols)

1. PHTHIOCOL $C_{11}H_8O_3$

Although this substance is not a lipid, it is considered here because of its isolation from the lipids of the tubercle bacillus. Anderson & Newman [466] isolated a yellow crystalline substance, m.p. 173-174°, which they called phthiocol, from the saponification products of the fats from a human strain of the tubercle bacillus. This compound contained a phenol group, demonstrated by its solubility in aqueous alkalis and by the preparation of a light yellow mono-acetyl derivative, m.p. 101—102° [42]. The quinonoid character of phthiocol is shown by its reductive acetylation to a colourless triacetate m.p. 148° [43]. The oxidation of phthiocol gives rise to phthalic acid [44]. From these properties, Anderson & Newman [467] deduced that phthiocol is 2-methyl-3-hydroxy-1,4-naphthoquinone [41].

This conclusion was verified by the synthesis of phthiocol by chromic acid oxidation of 2-methylnaphthalene followed by air oxidation in alkaline medium [469], or by starting with naphthalene and proceeding via 1,4-naphthoquinone, 2,3-dibromo-1, 4-naphthoquinone, ethyl 2-(3-bromonaphthoquinone)-malonate, and 2-carbomethoxy-3-hydroxy-1, 4-naphthoquinone [470]. For preparation on a larger scale, Anderson & Creighton [471] used, in an improved form, the synthesis due to Madinaveitia [472], which consists in the oxidation of 2-methyl-1, 4-naphthoquinone by calcium hypochlorite and subsequent hydrolysis of the epoxide [45] thus obtained with sulphuric acid.

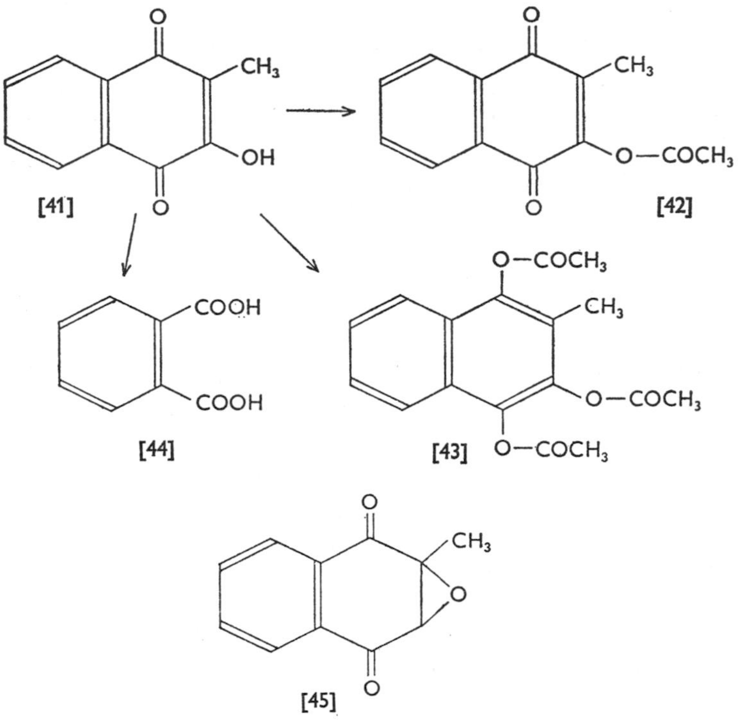

Anderson & Reeves [473] devised a colorimetric determination of phthiocol, based on the red colour developed in alkaline aqueous solution. The ultraviolet spectrum shows absorption maxima at 250, 278, 334 and 385 mμ (in 95 % ethanol) [474]. The redox potential has been studied by Ball [475, 476], by Hill [477], and by Lugg *et al.* [478].

Since it is a 2-methyl-1,4-naphthoquinone, phthiocol possesses vitamin K activity [479]. On the other hand, bostrycoidin, an antibiotic produced by *Fusarium bostrycoides* and active against *M. tuberculosis*, is a dihydroxy-1,4-naphthoquinone [480]: its antibiotic activity might be explained by an interference with the synthesis of phthiocol (or of the precursors of phthiocol) in the bacterial cell.

Phthiocol has also been isolated from the unsaponifiable fraction of the fats from *M. phlei* [481] and *Corynebacterium diphtheriae* [482]. Nevertheless, several authors [483-485] have been unable to isolate free phthiocol from the lipids of human strains of the tubercle bacillus, whereas a substance possessing the properties of a higher homologue of vitamin K, and capable of liberating phthiocol upon saponification, has been isolated [484, 486] (see page 80).

As early as 1939, Fieser *et al.* [487] considered that the formation of phthiocol might be an artefact, due to the degradation of a quinone related to the K vitamins.

Concerning the existence in the lipids of the tubercle bacillus of 1,4-naphthoquinone derivatives, the isolation by Aebi *et al.* [65] of phthalic acid [44], which might be derived from phthiocol by strong oxidation, may be mentioned.

2. 2D-OCTADECANOL $C_{18}H_{38}O$ AND 2D-EICOSANOL $C_{20}H_{42}O$

Since these two alcohols are generally encountered as a mixture, they will be discussed together.

The mixture of 2-octadecanol and 2-eicosanol was isolated by Anderson and his collaborators from waxes extracted with chloroform (waxes C and D, see page 239) from *Mycobacterium phlei* [488], *M. avium* [489], and a "leprosy bacillus" [490]; the same alcohols were again found in the hydrolysis products from the bound lipids of *M. avium* [491] and the "leprosy bacillus" [492]. By chromatography of the wax A from *M. phlei*, esters of these alcohols were isolated [493].

Whereas 2-eicosanol is rather easily obtained in a pure state (after 19 recrystallizations from the waxes of *M. phlei* [488],) 2-octadecanol is always very difficult to purify (more than 100 recrystallizations, in the form of the phenylurethan, from the waxes of *M. avium* [489]). It is therefore possible that a third alcohol, a lower homologue, may be present in the mixture; and, in fact, gas chromatography of the oxidation products of the mixture of secondary alcohols isolated from a *M. phlei* strain has shown the presence of 2-docosanone; so that 2-docosanol is also a component of the mixture [493].

The two alcohols were identified by their conversion to the corresponding methyl ketones and comparison with synthetic specimens [488]. Table 13 summarizes some properties of 2-octadecanol and 2-eicosanol and of the corresponding methyl ketones.

(+)-2-eicosanol has been synthesized by Serck-Hanssen *et al.* [437] from (+)-3L-acetoxybutanoic acid and stearic acid by Kolbe's reaction. This synthesis shows that the natural (+)-2-eicosanol has the D configuration.

The presence in waxes from *Corynebacterium diphtheriae* of (+)-3-octadecanol has been claimed [494]. This alcohol, m.p. 58.5°, $[\alpha]_D + 9.35°$, $n^{80}1.4337$, gives palmitic acid on mild oxidation. The antipode, synthesized a long time ago [495], has the following properties: m.p. 56°, $[\alpha]_D$—4.78° (ethanol); the rotation is significantly lower.

3. α- AND β- LEPROSOLS $C_{26}H_{46}O_2$ (or $C_{25}H_{44}O_2$?)

From the unsaponifiable fraction of the fats from a "leprosy bacillus", Crowder *et al.* [496] isolated two methoxylated phenolic substances, which they called α - and β-leprosol, by making use of their insolubility in petroleum ether. The smaller solubility of α-leprosol acetate in alcohol, enabled the two compounds to be separated from one another.

α- and β-leprosol have similar properties: they are insoluble in water and soluble in alkalis (while remaining extractable by ether); they give a green-blue colour with ferric chloride and, in the presence of a trace of ammonia, a deep blue colour with phosphomo-

TABLE 13. PROPERTIES OF SAMPLES OF 2D-EICOSANOL AND 2D-OCTADECANOL, SYNTHETIC AND ISOLATED FROM DIFFERENT STRAINS OF MYCOBACTERIA

Source	M. phlei			M. avium	
References	488			489	
	M. p.	$[\alpha]_D$	Temp*	M. p.	$[\alpha]_D$
2-Octadecanol	56°	+5.7° +7.3° (B)**	25°	53-54°	+4.84°
phenylurethan	72-73° then 76-77°	+7.9°	22°	76-76.5°	
3,5-dinitrobenzoate				71-72°	+25.3°
2-Octadecanone	52°			50-51°	
semi-carbazone	127.5°				
2-Eicosanol	62.5-63°	+4.2°		62-63°	+6.79° (E)**
acetate	35-37°	+1.5°			
benzoate	39-40°				
phenylurethan	78-78.5° then 81°				
3,5-dinitrobenzoate				77.5-78°	+23.4°
half-ester of phthalic acid	partially at 58° solidifies at 59° melts at 60-61°	+27.5°	18°		
2-Eicosanone	58-59°			60-61°	
oxime	73-74°				
semicarbazone	128°			130-131°	
2,4-dinitrophenyl-hydrazone					

Source	"Leprosy" bacillus		Synthetic				
References	490		437			488	379
	M.p.	$[\alpha]_D$	M.p.	$[\alpha]_D$	Temp*	M.p.	M.p.
2-Octadecanol	50°	+6.3°(E)**19°					
phenylurethan							
3,5-dinitrobenzoate							
2-Octadecanone	50-51°					52°	
semicarbazone	127-128°					127.5°	

* Temperature of the polarimetric measurement.
** Solvents: B = benzene, E = ether; where no indication is given, the measurement was made in chloroform.

TABLE 13 *(suite)*

Source	"Leprosy" bacillus		Synthetic				
References	490		437			488	379
	M.p.	[α]$_D$	M.p.	[α]$_D$	Temp.*	M.p.	M.p.
2-Eicosanol acetate	62-63°	+6.9°(E)**21°	61.8-61.9° 35.3-35.5° 31.6-31.9° 25.2-25.3°***	+3.9°	23°		DL 58.5-59°
benzoate phenylurethan 3,5-dinitrobenzoate half-ester of phthalic acid			59.2-59.7° 55.3-55.5° 25.7-26.3°***	+26.4°	22°		
2-Eicosanone oxime semicarbazone 2-4-dinitrophényl-hydrazone	60-61° 130-131°					58° 73-74° 128°	59.3-59.7° 94.5-94.8°

* Temperature of the polarimetric measurement.
** Solvents: B = benzene, E = ether; where no indication is given, the measurement was made in chloroform.
*** Polymorphism.

TABLE 14. THE PROPERTIES OF α-AND β-LEPROSOLS [496]

Compounds	α-Series			β-Series		
	Appearance	M. p.	2nd M. p.*	Appearance	M. p.	2nd M.p.*
Leprosol.	Globules	100-101°	100-101°	Powder	84-85°	84-85°
acetate	Powder	67-68°	69- 70°	Needles	47-48°	51-52°
3,5-dinitrobenzoate .					86-87°	
bromo-derivative . .	Needles	66-67°	73-74°		42-43°	45-46°
methyl ether	Needles	78-79°	80-81°	Needles	68-69°	70°
demethylation product	Needles	113-114°		Needles**	104-105°	
diacetate of the demethylation product					48°	

* Melting point of the solid product, after a first melting.
** λ_{max} 287 mμ (ether).

lybdic acid; they do not react with diazomethane, but are easily methylated with methyl sulphate under alkaline conditions.

In table 14 are listed the properties of the leprosols and their derivatives, as recorded by Crowder *et al.* [496]. These results show that the compounds are phenolic and this conclusion has been supported by Butenandt & Stodola [497], who compared the ultraviolet absorption spectra and colorations obtained with a number of reagents of demethyl-β-leprosol and of substituted resorcinol derivatives. These authors concluded that the leprosols are probably monomethyl ethers of 4, 5, 6-trialkyl-resorcinol [46].

Recently, a mixture of 5-nonadecyl- and 5-heneicosyl-resorcinol (m.p. 84-85°; dimethyl-ether m.p. 43-50°) has been isolated from wheat bran [497 a]; the properties of this mixture appears to be very close to that of β-leprosol.

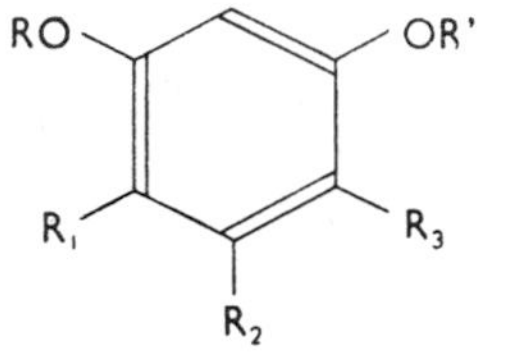

$$R \text{ or } R' = H \text{ or } CH_3$$
$$R_1 + R_2 + R_3 = C_{19}H_{41} \text{ or } C_{18}H_{39} \qquad [46]$$

The leprosols give an addition compound with digitonin which is only sparingly soluble in alcohol, but they do not show any of the colour reactions of sterols.

4. HENTRIACONTAN-16-OL $C_{31}H_{64}O$

From the unsaponifiable fraction of a strain of *Nocardia brasiliensis*, hentriacontan-16-ol m.p. 84-85° (acetate m.p. 47-49°) has been isolated [1256 a, b]. It was identified by comparison of the alcohol and of the corresponding ketone with synthetic compounds (the corresponding ketone, palmitone, is a component of the lipids of *Corynebacterium diphtheriae*).

Search of hentriacontanol in the lipids of another strain of *N. brasiliensis* gave negative results [1256 b].

5. C_{34} AND C_{36}-PHTHIOCEROLS, $C_{34}H_{70}O_3$ AND $C_{36}H_{74}O_3$, AND RELATED ALCOHOLS

The name "phthiocerol" was given in 1936 by Stodola & Anderson [498] to a methoxyglycol $C_{35}H_{72}O_3$, m.p. 73-74°, $[\alpha]_D$—4.8°, isolated from the waxes (extracted by chloroform) of a human strain of *M. tuberculosis**.

Phthyoglycol, described in 1934 by Stendal [389], seems to be identical with this (see

---

* I.R. spectrum, see page 45.

Table 15), in spite of some discrepancies in the carbon and hydrogen content (which led Stendal to suggest the formula $C_{26}H_{54}O_2$).

Fractionation of crude phthiocerol by chromatography and by use of Girard & Sandulesco's reagent T enabled Demarteau-Ginsburg et al.[199] to isolate a triol or phthiotriol, a keto-diol or phthiodiolone, and a methoxy keto-alcohol or phthiocerolone, in addition to the methoxyglycol for which the name *phthiocerol* is reserved. These alcohols, whose characteristics are listed in table 15, are isolated in various proportions principally from waxes A and C of human and bovine strains of *M. tuberculosis*, whether virulent or not [64, 72, 383, 499-502]. Phthiocerol is always the principal constituent of the mixtures thus isolated; it has never yet been isolated from bound lipids. Reports concerning the presence of phthiocerol in a *M. avium* strain [503] and related alcohols in a *M. phlei* strain [504] have not yet been confirmed.

TABLE 15. CHARACTERISTICS OF PHTHIOCEROL AND OF ITS "COMPANIONS"

Substance		Preparations containing phthiocerol and possible companions			Pure individual substances			
		"Phthioglycol"	Phthiocerol of Anderson	Phthiocerol of Acbi et al.	Phthiocerol	Phthiocerolone	Phthiodiolone	Phthiotriol
References		389	498	65	199 383	199 383	199 383	199 383
Free alcohol	m. p.	73°	73-74°	73-74°	72-73° 72°	72°	80°	90°
$[\alpha]_D$		—4.2°	—4.8°	—4.5°	—4.8°			
acetate	m. p.	34°	37-38°	35°	30°		30°	31°
phenylurethan	m. p.		91-92°					
isopropylidene derivative	m. p.				35°		35-40°	
oxime	m. p.					67°	71°	
product of reduction by LiAlH$_4$	m. p.					72°	74°	
$[\alpha]_D$							—3°	
phthiocerane	m. p.		59-60°					
$[\alpha]_D$			0					

Phthiocerane, the hydrocarbon corresponding to phthiocerol, has been prepared by Ginger & Anderson[505] by treating phthiocerol (contaminated with its "companions") with hydrogen iodide and subsequently reducing the iodide derivative with zinc amalgam and acetic acid. After catalytic hydrogenation and purification, the phthiocerane melted at 59.1-59.3° (product recrystallized from acetone); this hydrocarbon is optically inactive.

The structure of phthiocerol was first investigated with physical methods by Ställberg-Stenhagen & Stenhagen. From a study of monomolecular films of phthiocerol[346] and from X-ray examination of phthiocerane[506], these authors concluded that the phthiocerol molecule is composed of a long hydrocarbon chain carrying short branches and one or several polar groups near one extremity of the molecule.

Later, examination of phthiocerane by infrared spectrography led to the conclusion that the hydrocarbon could be 4-methyltritriacontane[279]: hydrocarbons possessing a 4-methyl group show an absorption band at 13.5 μ (740 cm^{-1}) in their infrared spectra, due to vibration of the propyl group (see page 46). The position of the methyl group was later confirmed chemically by Demarteau-Ginsburg & Lederer[507] (see below).

For comparison purposes, Ställberg-Stenhagen & Stenhagen[307] synthesized 12 hydrocarbons having a main chain of 33, 34, or 35 carbon atoms and a methyl group in the 2-, 3-, 4-, or 5-position. These hydrocarbons (racemic), the melting points of which are given in table 16, were prepared according to the following reaction scheme:

TABLE 16. MELTING POINTS OF RACEMIC HYDROCARBONS (AND OF THEIR KETO PRECURSORS)
SYNTHESIZED BY STÄLLBERG-STENHAGEN AND STENHAGEN[307]
IN THE COURSE OF THEIR STUDY OF PHTHIOCERANE

Keto compound	M. p.	Hydrocarbon	M. p.
2-Methyltritriacontanone-18	75.8-76.0°	2-Methyltritriacontane	66.1-66.3°
2-Methyltetratriacontanone- 19	78.8-79.2°	2-Methyltetratriacontane	68.1-68.3°
2-Methylpentatriacontanone-19	74.4-74.6°	2-Methylpentatriacontane	69.9-70.1°
3-Methyltritriacontanone-19	72.5°	3-Methyltritriacontane	61.8-61.9°
3-Methyltetratriacontanone- 19	69.9-70.1°	3-Methyltetratriacontane	64.1-64.2°
3-Methylpentatriacontanone -1	69.3-69.5°	3-Methylpentatriacontane	66.0-66.1°
4-Methyltritriacontanone-19	65.2-65.4°	4-Methyltritriacontane	58.6-58.7°
4-Methyltetratriacontanone-19	66.0°	4-Methyltetratriacontane	60.7-60.9°
4-Methylpentatriacontanone-19	66.2-66.4°	4-Methylpentatriacontane	63.0-63.1°
L-4-Methyltritriacontanone-26	65.0-65.1°	L-4-Methyltritriacontane	60.5-60.7°*
			61.6-61.8°**
5-Methyltritriacontanone-20	63.6-63.7°	5-Methyltritriacontane	55.5-55.7°
5-Methyltetratriacontane-20	63.3°	5-Methyltetratriacontane	58.0-58.1°
5-Methylpentatriacontanone-20	64.0-64.2°	5-Methylpentatriacontane	60.3-60.4°

* Recrystallized from acetone.
** Recrystallized from chloroform.

$H_2)_n$—CHOH—CH$_2$—CHOH—(CH$_2$)$_3$—CH=C—CH$_2$—CH$_2$—CH$_3$
                                                    |
                                                    CH$_3$

                         +

$H_2)_n$—CHOH—CH$_2$—CHOH—(CH$_2$)$_4$—CH—CH=CH—CH$_3$
                                          |
                                          CH$_3$

                    [63]
                    m. p. 72°   O$_3$

                                          CH$_3$—CO—CH$_2$—CH$_2$—CH$_3$ [64]

(acetic acid)
                                          + CH$_3$—CHO   [65]

       CH$_3$—(CH$_2$)$_n$—COOH   [56]

                    +

CH$_3$—CH$_2$—CH(OCH$_3$)—CH—(CH$_2$)$_4$—COOH
                          |
                          CH$_3$
                    [57]
          n_D^{21} 1,4432 [α]$_D^{17}$—3,2 (*)

O—CH—CH$_2$—CH$_2$—CH$_2$Br
   |
   CH$_3$
   [61]

tone [54][367, 503] and confirmed by the examination of the mass spectrum of phthiocerol [331, 510]. Stronger oxidation of phthiocerol yielded a long-chain fatty acid, at first identified as n-tetracosanoic acid [509], and then shown to be a mixture of n-tetracosanoic acid (51%) and n-docosanoic acid (38%), with small quantities of n-tricosanoic (9%) and n-heneicosanoic (2%) acids [511]. On the other hand, from the same products of oxidation, Hall & Polgar [509] isolated a "C_{11}-methoxy acid", at first thought to be 6-methoxy-6-methylnonanoic acid [503], but later identified as 7-methoxy-6-methylnonanoic acid [57] by degradation to 7-oxo-6-methylnonanoic acid [58], itself synthesized starting from methylallylacetic acid [59] [512-514]. Examination of this C_{11}-methoxy acid by gas chromatography showed that the 7-methoxy-6-methylnonanoic acid [57] constituted only two-thirds of the product; four other acids were also present [511]:

6-Methoxy-5-methyloctanoic acid,
5-Methoxy-4-methylheptanoic acid,
7-Hydroxy-6-methylnonanoic acid,
6-Hydroxy-5-methyloctanoic acid.

Position 3 was previously assigned to the methoxy group, based on the examination of the mass spectrum of phthiocerol [308] and on the absence of any acids possessing more than three atoms of carbon in the products of the chromic acid oxidation of phthiocerol by the method of Bickel, Schmid & Karrer (see page 55). It may be remarked here that the demethylation of phthiocerol by acetic anhydride in the presence of p-toluenesulfonic acid gives, along with a triol m.p. 75°, an ene-diol m.p. 72° [63], the ozonolysis of which leads to a mixture of 2-pentanone [64] and acetaldehyde [65] [507]. The unexpected production of 2-pentanone from the glycols [52] and [53] confirms chemically the position of the methyl branch.

A combination of gas chromatography and mass spectrometry finally showed that phthiocerane [62] consists of a ca. 3:2 mixture of 4-methyltetratriacontane ($C_{35}H_{72}$) and 4-methyldotriacontane ($C_{33}H_{68}$) [180, 315]. Since the repeated recrystallizations lead to enrichment of the higher homologue, the two glycols [52] and [53] are probably present in nearly equal proportions in the lipids of Mycobacteria [180].

The stereochemistry of phthiocerol has not yet been elucidated. However, the following evidence is suggestive of the configuration at carbons 3 and 4: the reduction of phthiodiolone, which has a 3-keto group in place of the methoxy of phthiocerol (see below), by sodium borohydride gives a triol apparently identical with the triol obtained on demethylation of phthiocerol [383]. The application of Cram's rule [516] to the reduction of the keto group shows that the hydroxyl formed will preferentially have the erythro position with respect to the 4-methyl substituent. The demethylation of phthiocerol probably occurs with inversion of the configuration, so that the 3-methoxy and the 4-methyl in phthiocerol would seem to be in the threo relation to one another.

Phthiocerol is synthesized by the tubercle bacillus from docosanoic acid (C_{34}-phthiocerol) or tetracosanoic acid (C_{36}-phthiocerol) by the addition of acetate and propionate units[517] (see page 148).

Phthiocerolone is reduced by sodium borohydride to a methoxyglycol, m.p. 72°, identical with phthiocerol according to a comparison of the infrared spectra. Phthiocerolone therefore differs from phthiocerol by the presence of a β-keto group in place of the β-glycol group[383]. The resistance of a compound of this kind to the prolonged saponification used in isolating these alcohols is remarkable *.

In phthiodiolone, the functional groups occupy the same places as in phthiocerol, since reduction with lithium aluminium hydride leads to a triol m.p. 74°, $[\alpha]_D$—3°, seemingly identical with the triol produced by the demethylation of phthiocerol (m-p. 75°, $[\alpha]_D$—5.3°). As phthiodiolone possesses a β-glycol group (*iso*propylidene derivative, m.p. 35-40°), the keto group is presumably located at position 3, and formula [66] can be attributed to the compound[383]:

$$CH_3-(CH_2)_{20 \text{ or } 22}-CHOH-CH_2-CHOH-(CH_2)_4-CH-CO-CH_2-CH_3$$

[66] CH_3

It has not been possible to correlate phthiotriol with the other constituents of the phthiocerol group.

The phthiocerol isolated by Anderson is therefore a mixture of at least 5, and more probably 8, substances (if the principal chain can be either C_{32} or C_{34} in phthiocerolone, phthiodiolone, and phthiotriol); (see also ref. 889).

6. PHENOL-GLYCOL B $C_{32}H_{58}O_4$

Bovine strains of the tubercle bacillus are characterized by the presence of a specific glycolipid mycoside B (see page 171), in their lipids. The hydrolysis of mycoside B affords a "phenol-glycol B", m.p. 55°, $[\alpha]_D$—3°, which contains one methoxy, two hydroxy, and one phenol groups, and which has the molecular formula $C_{32}H_{58}O_4$ [518]. From ultraviolet and mass spectrographic studies, formula [67] has been tentatively deduced[518, 518a].

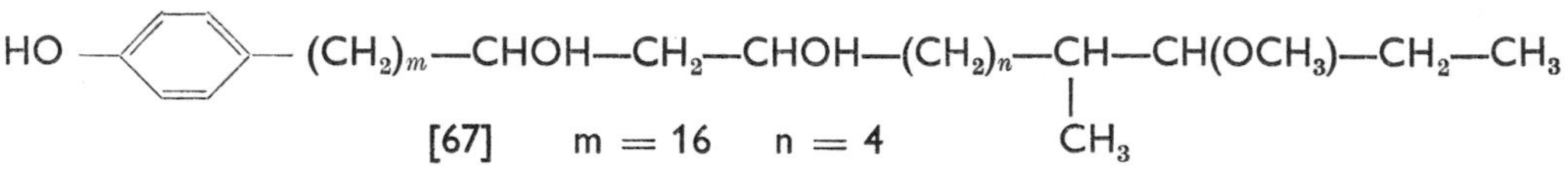

$$HO-\langle\rangle-(CH_2)_m-CHOH-CH_2-CHOH-(CH_2)_n-CH-CH(OCH_3)-CH_2-CH_3$$

[67]   m = 16   n = 4 CH_3

---

* Stenhagen (unpublished results) has found that the keto group is located at position 3 and the methoxy group in the β-glycol system.

7. NOCARDOLS, $C_{49}H_{96}O \pm 3 CH_2$

From the unsaponifiable part of the fat from *Nocardia asteroides*, Michel & Lederer [519] have isolated an alcohol fraction, $C_{49}H_{96}O \pm 3 CH_2$, m.p. 55-59°, $[\alpha]_D + 0.5°$, which they have called the nocardols.

The position of the hydroxyl group was determined by hydrogenation of the nocardols to the tetrahydronocardols [69], m.p. 92—93°, followed by oxidation to the tetrahydrono-cardones [70], m.p. 92°, and Beckmann rearrangement of their oximes to amides. Hydrolysis of the amides yielded an acidic fraction which after methylation was analysed by gas chromatography; it was found to be a mixture of methyl palmitate and methyl stearate. On the other hand, ozonization of the nocardols, followed by hydrolysis of the ozonides under oxidizing conditions, gave a mixture of substances in which the straight-chain acids with 9, 10, 11, and 12 carbon atoms were characterized [519].

From these results, partial formula [68] has been proposed for the nocardols.

$$CH_3—(CH_2)_m—CH = [C_{24}H_{45} (\pm 3 CH_2)] —CHOH—(CH_2)_n—CH_3$$

$$H_2/Pt \qquad [68] \qquad O_3$$

$$CH_3—(CH_2)_{m+1}—[C_{24}H_{48}]—CHOH—(CH_2)_n—CH_3$$
$$[69]$$

$$CH_3—(CH_2)_m—COOH$$
$$[71]$$

$$CrO_3/CH_3CO_2H$$

$$CH_3—(CH_2)_{m+1}—[C_{24}H_{48}]—CO—(CH_2)_n—CH_3$$
$$[70]$$

Beckmann rearrangement
(of the oximes)

$$CH_3—(CH_2)_{14}—COOH + CH_3—(CH_2)_{16}—COOH$$
$$[72] \qquad\qquad [73]$$

$$m = 7 — 10 \qquad n = 14 \text{ or } 16$$

Because of the similarities between the partial formula [68] and that of the nocardo-mycolic acids (see page 117), it has been suggested that the nocardols may be formed in the bacteria from the same β-keto ester as the nocardomycolic acids [519].

II. CARBONYL COMPOUNDS (Ketones and Quinones)

Fatty aldehydes were isolated from plasmalogen components of *Clostridium butyricum* and of rumen microörganisms; C_{17} and C_{19} cyclopropane fatty aldehydes were observed (see page 237).

1. PALMITONE $C_{31}H_{62}O$

From the lipids of *C. diphtheriae*, Pudles & Lederer [412] isolated 0.43 % palmitone [74], m.p. 80°, oxime m.p. 56°, identified by comparison of its properties with those of an authentic specimen.

$$CH_3—(CH_2)_{14}—CO—(CH_2)_{14}—CH_3$$
$$[74]$$

2. Δ^7-PALMITENONE $C_{31}H_{60}O$

In addition to palmitone, the same authors [412] isolated a ketone, m.p. 40°, which was identified as cis-Δ^7-palmitenone [75]. This ketone adds one mol. of hydrogen to form palmitone (m.p. 80°; oxime m.p. 56°).

$$CH_3—(CH_2)_5—CH : CH—(CH_2)_7—CO—(CH_2)_{14}CH_3$$
$$[75]$$

On ozonolysis, a lower acid is formed, the properties of which correspond to those of heptanoic acid (behaviour on a partition chromatography column; p-phenylphenacylate m.p. 54°). Moreover, cis-Δ^7-palmitenone has been synthesized and its properties found practically identical with those of the ketone m.p. 40° [520].

3. Δ^x-PALMITENONE $C_{31}H_{60}O$

A third ketone, mono-unsaturated, accompanies palmitone and Δ^7-palmitenone in the lipids of *C. diphtheriae* [412]. It has been isolated as a light yellow liquid, n_D^{21} 1.4710, which on hydrogenation gives palmitone [412]. Nevertheless, the ketone cannot be pure, since its U.V. spectrum has a maximum at 213.7 mµ ($\varepsilon = 1135$).

4. NAPHTHOQUINONES RELATED TO THE VITAMINS K

These compounds are outside the scope of this book, but their presence in mycobacterial lipids [486, 521, 525] may be mentioned as their degradation during the saponification of these lipids gives rise to phthiocol [486].

Some properties of the vitamins K isolated from Mycobacteria are listed in table 17; information about the presence of vitamins K and ubiquinone in other species of bacteria may be found in the papers by Bishop *et al.* [526, 527] (see also 1133 *a*).

TABLE 17. NAPHTHOQUINONES RELATED TO VITAMIN K ISOLATED FROM MYCOBACTERIA

	Compound isolated by :			Vitamin K_2 (45)	Dihydro-vitamin K_2(45)
	Snow	Noll	Brodie *et al.*		
Ref.	486	521	523	522	525
Source	*M. tuberculosis,* human strains		*M. phlei*	Synthetic	*M. phlei*
Appearance	Oil n_D^{91} 1.5286	Crystals M. p. 38-39°	Oil	Crystals M. p. 56-57°	Oil
Molecular formula .	$C_{56}H_{80}O_2$?	$C_{51}H_{72}O_2$ or $C_{56}H_{80}O_2$	$C_{46}H_{64}O_2$	$C_{56}H_{80}O_2$	$C_{56}H_{82}O_2$
UV spectrum $\lambda^{m\mu}$ (iso-octane) . .	243 248 260 269	243 249 260 270	243 249 261 270	243 (196)* 249.5 (208) 260 (204) 270 (200) 325 (37)	242.5 (192)* 247.5 (200) 260 (198) 270 (196) 325 (37)

* $E_{1\ cm}^{1\ \%}$

5. TUBERCULENONE $C_{60}H_{118}O$

Chromatography of the waxes C from two human strains of *M. tuberculosis* (strain R_1 and strain H-37 Rv streptomycin-resistant) has given a mono-unsaturated ketone, m.p. 72—74°, $[\alpha]_D$—12°, oxime m.p. 50—52°, for which the name tuberculenone has been proposed [528, 529]. Elementary analysis and degradation of the ketone suggested the empirical formula $C_{60}H_{118}O \pm 3\ CH_2$.

$$CH_3—(CH_2)_m—C : CH—(R_1)—CO—(R_2)—CH_3$$
$$| \atop (CH_2)_n$$
$$| \atop CH_3$$

[76]

m + n ~ 32

$$CH_3—(CH_2)_m—CO—(CH_2)_n—CH_3 \qquad [77]$$

$$CH_3—(R_1)—CO—(R_2)—COOH \qquad [78]$$

$R_1 + R_2 \sim C_{21}H_{41}$ (one of these two radicals contains either a branch or a cyclopropane ring).

Ozonolysis of tuberculenone gives on the one hand a monoketone m.p. 58—62° [77] and on the other hand a branched keto-acid m.p. 58—60° [78]. These results suggested formula [76] for tuberculenone [529].

Other C_{60} neutral substances have been isolated from the waxes of other human strains of *M. tuberculosis*, in particular a compound m.p. 70° from the human strain Test [528].

These compounds may well be intermediates in the metabolism of the mycolic acids (see page 148) as well as of a diol, m.p. 57-60°, $C_{84}H_{164}O_2 + 5\ CH_2$, diacetate m.p. 44—47° isolated from a strain of *M. avium* [530].

III. AMINO COMPOUNDS

From the hydrolysis products of a lipopolysaccharide from *Escherichia coli*, Ikawa *et al.* [531] isolated a long-chain diamine which they called necrosamine; it was obtained as a dihydrochloride, m.p. 275° (dec.), from which was prepared a dipicrate, m.p. 159—161°, and a benzoyl derivative, m. p. 72.5—73.5°. Formula [79] was proposed for necrosamine, and syntheses of the erythro and threo racemic compounds were carried out [532, 533]. However, in the course of a more recent investigation, necrosamine could not be isolated and its existence is therefore doubtful [534].

$$CH_3—(CH_2)_{14}—CH—CH—(CH_2)_2—CH_3$$
$$[79]\quad \underset{NH_2}{|}\ \underset{NH_2}{|}$$

There are several claims in the literature for the presence of sphingosine-like compounds in bacterial lipids, but so far no definite compound of this type has been isolated.

IV. ACIDS

The acids are here classified in two groups, according to whether their molecule contains an hydroxyl or not.

1. ACIDS DEVOID OF OTHER OXYGEN FUNCTIONS

a) *6-Methylheptanoic acid* $C_8H_{16}O_2$

By counter-current distribution of polymyxine B (an antibiotic produced by *Bacillus polymyxa*), Hausmann & Craig [535] isolated a polypeptide which on hydrolysis afforded, besides 6-methyloctanoic acid, a branched chain octanoic acid (amide m.p. 110—111°). This optically inactive acid has been shown to be 6-methylheptanoic acid by Wilkinson & Lowe [535a].

b) *(+)-6L-Methyloctanoic acid* $C_9H_{18}O_2$

Hydrolysis of various polymyxins gives, in addition to a mixture of amino acids, a $C_9H_{18}O_2$ fatty acid whose properties are shown in Table 18 [536, 537, 537a].

TABLE 18. PROPERTIES OF SAMPLES OF (+)–6–METHYLOCTANOIC ACID ISOLATED FROM POLYMYXINS [536, 537, 537a] OR SYNTHETIC [540, 541]

	Natural acid, % of the polymyxine	n_D^{20}	$[\alpha]$ (ether)	Amide, m.p.	p-Bromo-phenacy-late, m.p.	p-Bromoben-zylthiouro-nium salt, m.p.
Polymyxin A .	8—9.7	1.4390 (at 18°)	+8.6° (21°, 5461 A)	93°	57-57.5°	159°
B .	6.3	1.4330		93°		160°
C .	12.2					158-158.5°
M .		1.4320	+7.2 (16°, 5890 A)	94°		
Synthetic acid .		1.4330 1.4328' (at 21°)	+ 8.9°(21°, 5461 A) +9.2° (20°, 5890A)**	91° 92°***	58-59°	

*d^{24} 0.8761.   ** + 8.85° (homogeneous).   *** $[\alpha]_D^{20}$ + 10.1° (methanol).

Examination of the infrared spectrum shows it to be a branched-chain acid, because of the relatively strong absorption band corresponding to the methyl group [539]. Degradation of this acid by the Barbier-Wieland method as modified by Miescher (page 57) furnished (+)-3-methylpentanoic acid [84], identified by the mixed melting points of the amide and of the p-bromobenzylthiouronium salt with authentic specimens [396]. The $C_9H_{18}O_2$ branched-chain acid of polymyxin is therefore (+)-6-methyloctanoic acid [80]. The same acid has been identified in another antibiotic, colistin [535a].

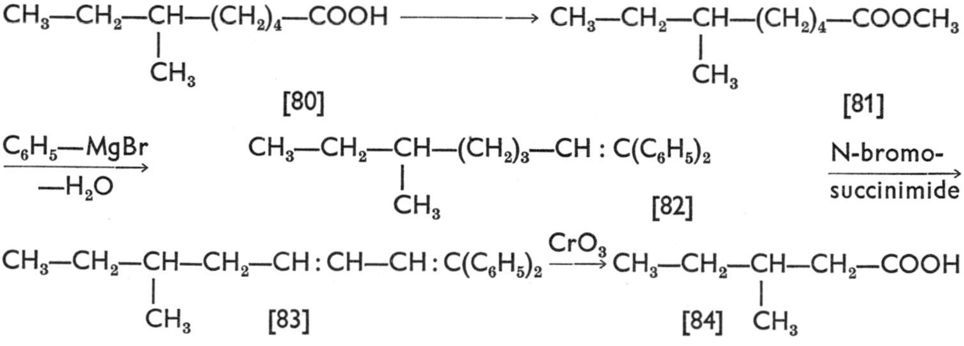

$$CH_3-CH_2-CH-(CH_2)_4-COOH \longrightarrow CH_3-CH_2-CH-(CH_2)_4-COOCH_3$$
$$| \qquad\qquad\qquad\qquad\qquad\qquad\qquad\qquad | $$
$$CH_3 \qquad\qquad\qquad\qquad\qquad\qquad\qquad\qquad CH_3$$
$$[80] \qquad\qquad\qquad\qquad\qquad\qquad\qquad [81]$$

$$\xrightarrow[-H_2O]{C_6H_5-MgBr} \qquad CH_3-CH_2-CH-(CH_2)_3-CH:C(C_6H_5)_2 \qquad \xrightarrow[\text{succinimide}]{\text{N-bromo-}}$$
$$| \qquad\qquad\qquad\qquad\qquad\qquad$$
$$CH_3 \qquad [82]$$

$$CH_3-CH_2-CH-CH_2-CH:CH-CH:C(C_6H_5)_2 \xrightarrow{CrO_3} CH_3-CH_2-CH-CH_2-COOH$$
$$| \qquad\qquad\qquad\qquad\qquad\qquad\qquad\qquad\qquad\qquad | $$
$$CH_3 \qquad [83] \qquad\qquad\qquad\qquad\qquad\qquad [84] \quad CH_3$$

(+)-6-Methyloctanoic acid has been synthesized by Crombie & Harper [540] from (—)-2-methylbutanol [85] via the intermediate 2-alkyl-3-chlorotetrahydrofuran [87]. The (+)-6-methyloctanoic acid [80] thus obtained belongs to the L series, since the initial (—)-2-methyl-butanol has the L configuration. Most of the natural ante-iso acids belong to the L series [542].

Another synthesis, lengthening the chain of (—)-2-methylbutanol [85] with malonate, has been described by Vogler & Chopard-dit-Jean [541].

[Reaction scheme with structures [85], [86], [87], [88], [89] and [90], [91], [92], [93], [80]]

$$
\begin{array}{ccc}
CH_2OH & CH_2MgBr & \\
| & | & \\
CH_3\!-\!C\!-\!H & CH_3\!-\!C\!-\!H & \\
| & | & \\
CH_2 & CH_2 & \\
| & | & \\
CH_3 & CH_3 & \\
(-) & & \\
[85] & [86] &
\end{array}
$$

$$
\begin{array}{ll}
Cl\!-\!CH\!-\!CH_2 & \\
| \quad\;\; | & \\
Cl\!-\!CH \quad CH_2 & \\
\quad\;\backslash O / &
\end{array}
$$

[87]:
$$
\begin{array}{l}
CH_2\!-\!CH_2\!\!\searrow O \\
| \qquad | \\
CH\!-\!CH \\
| \qquad | \\
Cl \qquad CH_2 \\
\qquad | \\
CH_3\!-\!C\!-\!H \\
\qquad | \\
\qquad CH_2 \\
\qquad | \\
\qquad CH_3
\end{array}
\xrightarrow[\text{(powder)}]{Na}
$$

[88]:
$$
\begin{array}{l}
CH_2OH \\
| \\
CH_2 \\
| \\
CH \\
\| \\
CH \\
| \\
CH_2 \\
| \\
CH_3\!-\!C\!-\!H \\
| \\
CH_2 \\
| \\
CH_3
\end{array}
\xrightarrow{H_2}
$$

[89]:
$$
\begin{array}{l}
CH_2OH \\
| \\
(CH_2)_4 \\
| \\
CH_3\!-\!C\!-\!H \\
| \\
CH_2 \\
| \\
CH_3 \\
(+)
\end{array}
$$

[90]:
$$
\begin{array}{l}
CH_2Br \\
| \\
CH_3\!-\!C\!-\!H \\
| \\
CH_2 \\
| \\
CH_3 \\
(+)
\end{array}
\xrightarrow{\text{Malonate}}
$$

[91]:
$$
\begin{array}{l}
COOH \\
| \\
(CH_2)_2 \\
| \\
CH_3\!-\!C\!-\!H \\
| \\
CH_2 \\
| \\
CH_3 \\
(+)
\end{array}
\xrightarrow{\text{LiAl}H_4}
$$

[92]:
$$
\begin{array}{l}
CH_2OH \\
| \\
(CH_2)_2 \\
| \\
CH_3\!-\!C\!-\!H \\
| \\
CH_2 \\
| \\
CH_3 \\
(+)
\end{array}
\xrightarrow{P\,Br_3}
$$

[93]:
$$
\begin{array}{l}
CH_2Br \\
| \\
(CH_2)_2 \\
| \\
CH_3\!-\!C\!-\!H \\
| \\
CH_2 \\
| \\
CH_3 \\
(+)
\end{array}
\xrightarrow{\text{Malonate}}
$$

[80]:
$$
\begin{array}{l}
COOH \\
| \\
(CH_2)_4 \\
| \\
CH_3\!-\!C\!-\!H \\
| \\
CH_2 \\
| \\
CH_3 \\
(+)
\end{array}
$$

c) *Subtilo-pentadecanoic acid* $C_{15}H_{30}O_2$

From the lipids of *B. subtilis*, Saito [543] isolated an optically inactive acid, m.p. 52.5-53°, which was identified as 13-methyltetradecanoic acid. The acid has been characterized by gas chromatography in the membranes of *B. megaterium* [544] and in the whole cells of *Staphylococcus aureus* [343], of *Propionibacterium freudenreichii* [544a] and of several strains of *Streptomyces* [544b].

d) *Sarcinic acid* $C_{15}H_{30}O_2$

From the lipids of a *Sarcina* species, Akashi and Saito [546] isolated an acid, m.p. 24°, $[\alpha]_D + 5.2°$, which may be 12L-methyltetradecanoic acid; this same acid has been identified by gas chromatography in the membranes of *B. megaterium*[544] and in the whole cells of *St. aureus*[545] and of *Streptomyces* sp.[544b].

e) *14-Methylpentadecanoic acid* $C_{16}H_{32}O_2$

Kaneda[547] has found *iso*-hexadecanoic acid in the fatty acids of *B. subtilis* by gas chromatography and has isolated it as crystals m.p. 60-61°. It was also characterised by gas-liquid chromatography in the lipids of several strains of *Streptomyces*[544b].

f) *cis-Δ^5-Hexadecenoic acid* $C_{16}H_{28}O_2$

This unusual hexadecenoic acid has been characterized in the whole cells of *B. megaterium* KM[547a].

g) *cis-Δ^{10}-Hexadecenoic acid* $C_{16}H_{28}O_2$

This acid was characterized in the lipids of *M. phlei* by oxidative cleavage to sebacic and caproic acids[46]. At least 80% of the hexadecenoic acid fraction in *M. phlei* consists of this unusual isomer of palmitoleic acid. Small amounts of the same acid were observed by Cason & Miller[548] in the lipids of the human strain H_{37} of *M. tuberculosis*.

h) *Subtilo-heptadecanoic acid* $C_{17}H_{34}O_2$

Partition chromatography of the fatty acids from *B. subtilis* gave, beside subtilo-pentadecanoic acid, an optically inactive acid, m.p. 61.0—61.5°, identified as 15-methylhexadecanoic acid[543]. This acid is a component of the whole cells of *St. aureus*[545].

i) *14-Methylhexadecanoic acid* $C_{17}H_{34}O_2$

The anteiso-heptadecanoic acid has been identified by gas chromatography in the membranes of *B. megaterium* and *Micrococcus lysodeikticus*[544], and in the whole cells of *St. aureus*[545]; it has also been isolated (m.p. 35.5—36°) from the lipids of *B. subtilis*[547].

j) *8-and 10-Methylhexadecanoic acids* $C_{17}H_{34}O_2$

Cason & Miller[548] isolated the branched-chain C_{17} acids from the human strain H_{37} of *M. tuberculosis*. By means of the oxidative micromethod elaborated by Cason *et al.*[401], this fraction was shown to contain a mixture of 8-methyl- and 10-methylhexadecanoic acids.

k) *10-Methylhexadec-9-enoic acid* $C_{17}H_{32}O_2$

The studies of Cason & Miller[548] on the C_{17} acid fraction of the human strain H_{37} of *M. tuberculosis*, just mentioned above, also led to the characterization of a methyl-branched unsaturated : acid 10-methyl-hexadec-9-enoic acid.

l) *9,10-Methylenehexadecanoic acid* $C_{17}H_{32}O_2$

In 1960, Dauchy & Asselineau[549] isolated a C_{17} cyclopropane fatty acid from the lipids of *E. coli*, by the technique of urea inclusion. The existence of the cyclopropane ring was demonstrated by the hydrogenolysis procedure previously used by Hofmann in the case of lactobacillic acid (see page 92). This result was confirmed by Chalk & Kodicek[550] in the

course of a study of the rôle of methionine in the biosynthesis of the fatty acids of *E. coli.*
The same acid was later found in the lipids of *Pasteurella pestis*[177] (see table 21).

The acid was subsequently identified as 9,10-methylenehexadecanoic acid [94] by
Kaneshiro & Marr[551] and Toubiana & Asselineau[552], by examining the oxidation products
of the natural and synthetic esters and by comparing the I.R. and mass spectra of the
natural and synthetic esters. The natural acid gives an amide, m.p. 70—72°, and the synthetic
(DL) acid, an amide, m.p. 79—81°[552]. The synthesis was achieved by addition of carbene
to cis-Δ^9-hexadecenoic acid (palmitoleic acid).

$$CH_3-(CH_2)_5-CH\underline{\qquad}CH-(CH_2)_7-COOH$$
$$CH_2 \qquad [94]$$

C$_{17}$ and C$_{19}$ cyclopropane fatty acids, are frequently encountered in bacterial lipids,
as is shown in table 21 (p. 95).

m) *Branched-chain octadecanoic acid* C$_{18}$H$_{36}$O$_2$

From the waxes extracted by chloroform from a bovine strain of the tubercle bacillus
(Vallée), Cason & Anderson[347] isolated an optically inactive acid, C$_{18}$H$_{36}$O$_2$, m.p. 0°, n_D^{25}
1.4436, tribromanilide m.p. 96°. A similar acid was observed by Agre & Cason[402], during
a study of the fatty acids from *M. tuberculosis* by vapour phase chromatography, and shown
to be mainly 10-methylheptadecanoic acid.

n) *Trans-Δ^2-Octadecenoic acid* C$_{18}$H$_{34}$O$_2$

Acid hydrolysis of mycobactin, a growth factor for *M. johnei* isolated from *M. phlei*, gives
among other substances trans-Δ^2-octadecenoic acid, m.p. 58.5°, *p*-bromophenacylate m. p.
88.5—89.5°, S-benzylthiouronium salt m.p. 152—153°, identified by comparison of the
natural acid and its derivatives with the corresponding synthetic compounds[553].

o) *cis-Δ^{11}-Octadecenoic acid* (cis-*vaccenic acid*) C$_{18}$H$_{34}$O$_2$

The unsaturated C$_{18}$ acid isolated from lipids of *Lactobacillus arabinosus*, m.p. 13.2—14.0°
amide m.p. 77.6—78.8°, *p*-phenylphenacylate m.p. 64.5—66°, was identified as cis-Δ^{11}-
octadecenoic acid [95] by the following properties : hydrogenation to stearic acid, m.p.
69.4—70.1°; formation of an epoxide by action of perphthalic acid, m.p. 46—47°; conversion
by performic acid to 11, 12-dihydroxyoctadecanoic acid, m.p. 91.8—93.8°, which on cleavage
by periodic acid gives heptanal (2,4-dinitro-phenylhydrazone m.p. 100—103°) and after
silver oxide oxidation undecanedioic acid (m.p. 109.4—111.2°)[122].

The same acid is the principal C$_{18}$ unsaturated acid of the lipids from *L. casei*[554],
Agrobacterium tumefaciens[555], and a strain of *Streptococcus hemolyticus*[556] (in the last
case, oleic acid, or cis -Δ^9-octadecenoic acid, is also present). It accounts for ca. 75 % of the
total fatty acids of a strain of *Leuconostoc mesenteroides*[556 a].

Cis -Δ^{11}-Octadecenoic acid [95] has been synthesized by the Kolbe reaction between palmitoleic acid and succinic acid monomethyl ester [557] and also by the following series of reactions [554, 558]:

$$CH_3—(CH_2)_5—C \equiv CH + I(CH_2)_9Cl \rightarrow CH_3—(CH_2)_5—C \equiv C—(CH_2)_9—Cl$$
$$[96] \qquad\qquad [97] \qquad\qquad [98]$$

$$\rightarrow CH_3—(CH_2)_5—C \equiv C—(CH_2)_9—CN \rightarrow CH_3—(CH_2)_5—C \equiv C—(CH_2)_9—COOH$$
$$[99] \qquad\qquad\qquad [100]$$

$$\rightarrow CH_3—(CH_2)_5—CH = CH—(CH_2)_9—COOH \quad [95]$$

p) *Tuberculostearic acid* $C_{19}H_{38}O_2$

Tuberculostearic acid, m.p. 10.3—11.7°, $[\alpha]_D$—0.03°, amide m.p. 76.5—77°, tribromanilide m.p. 94.5 95.1°, was the first branched chain acid to be isolated from the lipids of the tubercle bacillus, in 1929 [559]. The relatively high proportion of tuberculostearic acid in the total C_{10}—C_{20} fatty acids explains its easier isolation.

Tuberculostearic acid is present in the lipids from human and bovine strains (virulent and otherwise) of *M. tuberculosis* [76, 560, 561] and of *M. phlei* (115, see also 46). Examination of the fatty acids isolated from *M. avium* by vapour phase chromatography [562] has confirmed the presence of tuberculostearic acid, already made probable by the work of Anderson (60, p. 161). Tuberculostearic acid has also been detected in the lipids of *M. paratuberculosis* (*M. johnei*) [563]. Moreover, tuberculostearic acid has been found in the lipids of several strains of *Nocardia* [1256, 1256 b] and of *Streptomyces* [563a].

The structure of this acid [105] was deduced by Spielman [400] in 1934 from the isolation of azelaic acid and 2-decanone after chromic acid oxidation (see page 59) *. The synthesis of 10DL-methyloctadecanoic acid (the optical rotation of the natural acid was only detected later on) was carried out by the same author [400] as follows:

$$CH_3—(CH_2)_7—ZnCl + ClCO—(CH_2)_8—CO_2C_2H_5 \longrightarrow$$
$$[101] \qquad\qquad\qquad [102]$$

$$CH_3—(CH_2)_7—CO—(CH_2)_8—CO_2H \xrightarrow[CH_3MgI]{Ba\ salt} CH_3—(CH_2)_7—\underset{\underset{CH_3}{|}}{\overset{\overset{OH}{|}}{C}}—(CH_2)_8—CO_2H$$
$$[103] \qquad\qquad\qquad\qquad\qquad\qquad [104]$$

$$\xrightarrow[H_2/Pt]{-H_2O,} CH_3—(CH_2)_7—\underset{\underset{CH_3}{|}}{CH}—(CH_2)_8—CO_2H$$
$$[105]$$

---

* Mass spectrum : see page 51.

TABLE 19. THE PROPERTIES OF SYNTHETIC AND NATURAL 10-METHYLOCTADECANOIC ACID

	Tuberculoste-aric acid (natural)	10-methyloctadecanoic acids (synthetic)		
		DL	D	D
References	539	368	539	537
Free acid				
m.p.	10.3-11.7°	20-21°	12.8-13.4°	12.4-12.8°
[α]$_D$ (homogeneous)	—0.03°		—0.05°	—0.12°
Amide m.p.	76-77°	77.5-79.2°	75.1-76.3°	76.4-76.6°
Tribromanilide				
m.p.	94.5-95.4°	93.4-93.9°	94.0-95.3°	

The racemic acid thus obtained melted about 10° higher than the natural acid, although the other properties were practically the same (see Table 19). These results led Spielman [400] to assume that tuberculostearic acid is an optically active form of 10-methyloctadecanoic acid. This hypothesis, reinforced by comparison of the X-ray diffraction patterns of tuberculostearic acid and of 10DL-methyloctadecanoic acid [297], was verified by Prout et al. [564], who demonstrated the very low rotation of the natural acid.

The same authors [565] achieved the synthesis of the optical isomers of 10-methyloctadecanoic acid from (+)-2-decanol [106]. The identity of tuberculostearic acid and the D(-) isomer showed that the natural acid is (—)-10 D-methyloctadecanoic acid. The synthesis of this isomer is represented below:

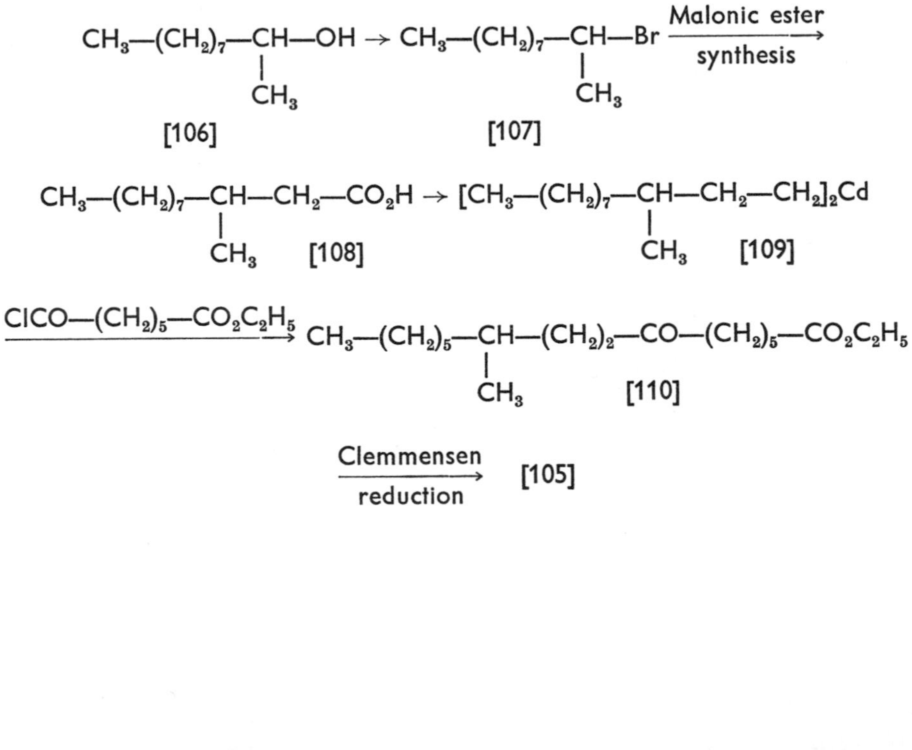

$$CH_3—(CH_2)_7—\underset{\underset{CH_3}{|}}{CH}—OH \rightarrow CH_3—(CH_2)_7—\underset{\underset{CH_3}{|}}{CH}—Br \xrightarrow[\text{synthesis}]{\text{Malonic ester}}$$

[106]   [107]

$$CH_3—(CH_2)_7—\underset{\underset{CH_3}{|}}{CH}—CH_2—CO_2H \rightarrow [CH_3—(CH_2)_7—\underset{\underset{CH_3}{|}}{CH}—CH_2—CH_2]_2Cd$$

[108]   [109]

$$\xrightarrow{ClCO—(CH_2)_5—CO_2C_2H_5} CH_3—(CH_2)_5—\underset{\underset{CH_3}{|}}{CH}—(CH_2)_2—CO—(CH_2)_5—CO_2C_2H_5$$

[110]

$$\xrightarrow[\text{reduction}]{\text{Clemmensen}} [105]$$

Almost simultaneously, Ställberg-Stenhagen [566] described a synthesis which did not involve a substitution reaction at the asymmetric carbon atom and which leaves no ambiguity at all about the configuration of the final product, since that of the starting substance, (—)-3L-methyl-4-carbomethoxy-butanoic acid [111], is known (see page 63) :

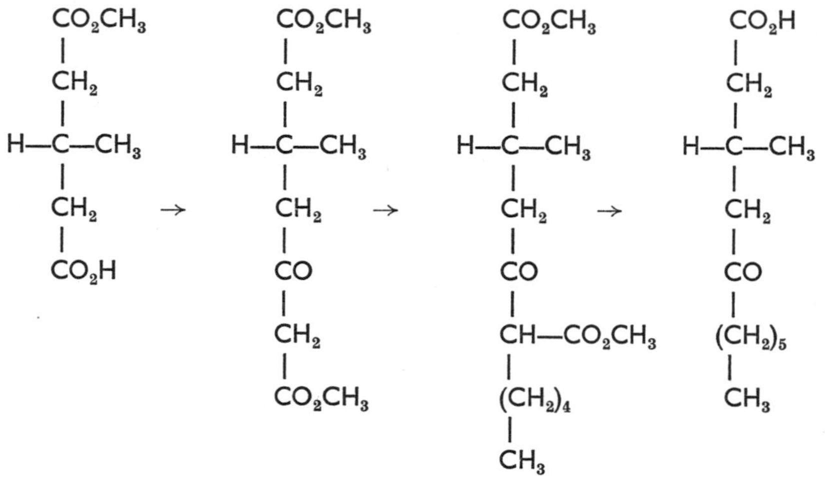

$$
\begin{array}{cccc}
CO_2CH_3 & CO_2CH_3 & CO_2CH_3 & CO_2H \\
| & | & | & | \\
CH_2 & CH_2 & CH_2 & CH_2 \\
| & | & | & | \\
H-C-CH_3 & H-C-CH_3 & H-C-CH_3 & H-C-CH_3 \\
| & | & | & | \\
CH_2 \;\rightarrow & CH_2 \;\rightarrow & CH_2 \;\rightarrow & CH_2 \\
| & | & | & | \\
CO_2H & CO & CO & CO \\
& | & | & | \\
& CH_2 & CH-CO_2CH_3 & (CH_2)_5 \\
& | & | & | \\
& CO_2CH_3 & (CH_2)_4 & CH_3 \\
& & | & \\
& & CH_3 & \\
\end{array}
$$

$$[111] \qquad\qquad [112] \qquad\qquad [113] \qquad\qquad [114]$$

$$
\begin{array}{cccc}
 & & CO_2CH_3 & \\
 & & | & \\
 & CO_2C_2H_5 & (CH_2)_5 & CO_2H \\
 & | & | & | \\
 & CH_2 & CH-CO_2C_2H_5 & (CH_2)_6 \\
CO_2H & | & | & | \\
| & CO & CO & CO \\
CH_2 \;\rightarrow & CH_2 \;\rightarrow & CH_2 \;\rightarrow & CH_2 \;\rightarrow [105] \\
| & | & | & | \\
H-C-CH_3 & H-C-CH_3 & H-C-CH_3 & H-C-CH_3 \\
| & | & | & | \\
(CH_2)_7 & (CH_2)_7 & (CH_2)_7 & (CH_2)_7 \\
| & | & | & | \\
CH_3 & CH_3 & CH_3 & CH_3 \\
\end{array}
$$

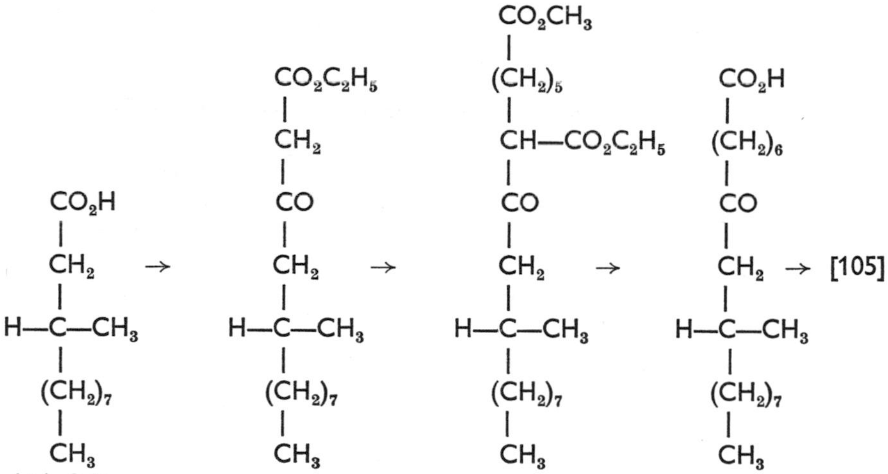

(+)-3 D —
—Methylunde-
canoic acid

$$[115] \qquad\qquad [116] \qquad\qquad [117] \qquad\qquad [118]$$

The identification of the synthetic and natural acids was made by examination of the X-ray patterns, mixed melting points, and comparison of the optical properties [536].

Linstead *et al.* [567] synthesized 10-DL-methyloctadecanoic acid by two Kolbe reactions from the monomethyl ester of β-methylglutaric acid. Then, using the laevorotatory isomer of the same ester [111], these authors [598] made an elegant synthesis of tuberculostearic acid:

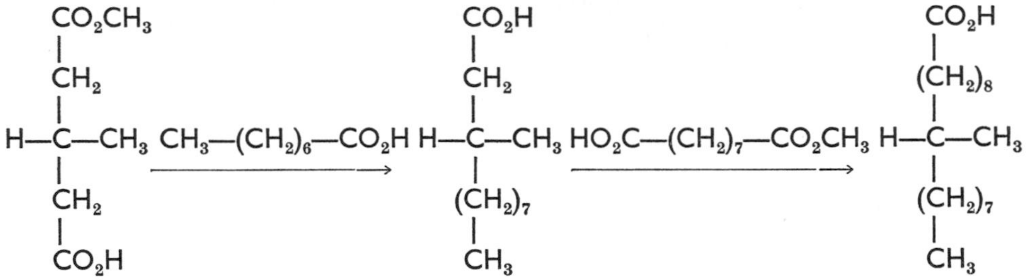

$$
\begin{array}{ccc}
\text{CO}_2\text{CH}_3 & \text{CO}_2\text{H} & \text{CO}_2\text{H} \\
| & | & | \\
\text{CH}_2 & \text{CH}_2 & (\text{CH}_2)_8 \\
| & | & | \\
\text{H—C—CH}_3 \;\;\; \text{CH}_3\text{—(CH}_2)_6\text{—CO}_2\text{H} & \text{H—C—CH}_3 \;\;\; \text{HO}_2\text{C—(CH}_2)_7\text{—CO}_2\text{CH}_3 & \text{H—C—CH}_3 \\
| \quad\quad\quad\quad\longrightarrow & | \quad\quad\quad\quad\longrightarrow & | \\
\text{CH}_2 & (\text{CH}_2)_7 & (\text{CH}_2)_7 \\
| & | & | \\
\text{CO}_2\text{H} & \text{CH}_3 & \text{CH}_3 \\
[111] & [118] & [105]
\end{array}
$$

The overall yield was about 15%, (calculated on the initial half-ester).

On page 90-91 are shown the schemes of several syntheses of 10-DL-methyloctadecanoic acid due to Asano & Ohta [568, 569], Schmidt & Shirley [570], Sy *et al.* [571], and Hünig & Salzwedel [572].

Since tuberculostearic acid has been isolated from tubercle bacillus lipids by a procedure involving hydrogenation, it may be asked, bearing in mind the isolation of a cyclopropane fatty acid from bacterial lipids (see lactobacillic acid, page 92), whether the 10-methyloc-

i) *Asano and Ohta* [569]

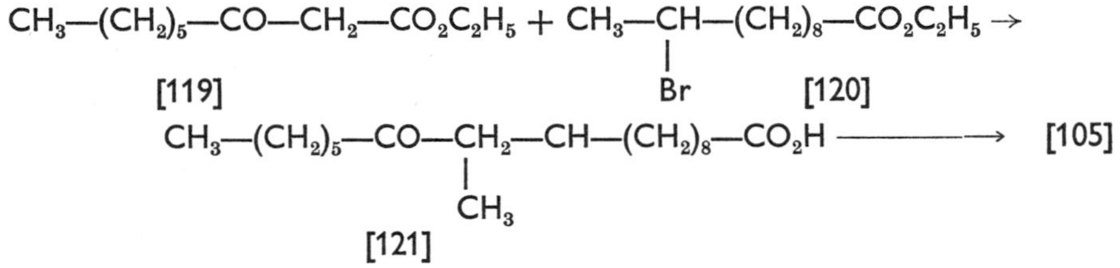

$$\text{CH}_3\text{—(CH}_2)_5\text{—CO—CH}_2\text{—CO}_2\text{C}_2\text{H}_5 + \text{CH}_3\text{—CH—(CH}_2)_8\text{—CO}_2\text{C}_2\text{H}_5 \rightarrow$$

$$\underset{[119]}{} \quad\quad\quad\quad\quad\quad \underset{\text{Br} \quad\quad [120]}{|}$$

$$\text{CH}_3\text{—(CH}_2)_5\text{—CO—CH}_2\text{—CH—(CH}_2)_8\text{—CO}_2\text{H} \longrightarrow [105]$$

$$\underset{\text{CH}_3}{|}$$

$$[121]$$

ii) *Schmidt and Shirley* [570]

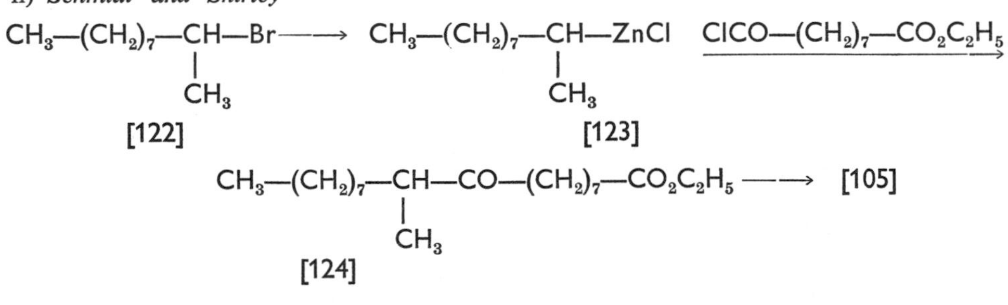

$$\text{CH}_3\text{—(CH}_2)_7\text{—CH—Br} \longrightarrow \text{CH}_3\text{—(CH}_2)_7\text{—CH—ZnCl} \quad \overset{\text{ClCO—(CH}_2)_7\text{—CO}_2\text{C}_2\text{H}_5}{\longrightarrow}$$

$$\underset{\text{CH}_3}{|} \quad\quad\quad\quad\quad\quad\quad \underset{\text{CH}_3}{|}$$

$$[122] \quad\quad\quad\quad\quad\quad\quad [123]$$

$$\text{CH}_3\text{—(CH}_2)_7\text{—CH—CO—(CH}_2)_7\text{—CO}_2\text{C}_2\text{H}_5 \longrightarrow [105]$$

$$\underset{\text{CH}_3}{|}$$

$$[124]$$

iii) *Sy et al.* [571]

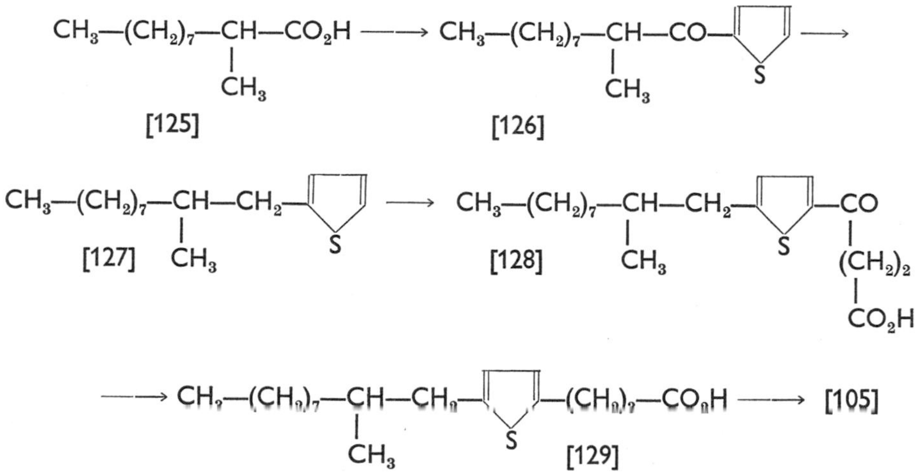

$$CH_3-(CH_2)_7-\underset{\underset{CH_3}{|}}{CH}-CO_2H \longrightarrow CH_3-(CH_2)_7-\underset{\underset{CH_3}{|}}{CH}-CO-\underset{S}{\square} \longrightarrow$$

[125]   [126]

$$CH_3-(CH_2)_7-\underset{\underset{CH_3}{|}}{CH}-CH_2-\underset{S}{\square} \longrightarrow CH_3-(CH_2)_7-\underset{\underset{CH_3}{|}}{CH}-CH_2-\underset{S}{\square}-\underset{\underset{CO_2H}{\overset{|}{(CH_2)_2}}}{CO}$$

[127] CH₃   [128]   CH₃

$$\longrightarrow CH_3-(CH_2)_7-\underset{\underset{CH_3}{|}}{CH}-CH_2-\underset{S}{\square}-(CH_2)_2-CO_2H \longrightarrow [105]$$

                                       [129]

iv) *Hünig and Salzwedel* [572]

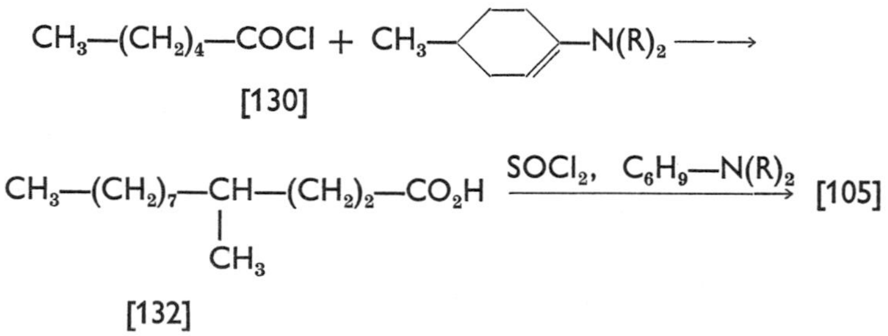

$$CH_3-(CH_2)_4-COCl + CH_3-\langle\text{—}\rangle-N(R)_2 \longrightarrow$$

[130]

$$CH_3-(CH_2)_7-\underset{\underset{CH_3}{|}}{CH}-(CH_2)_2-CO_2H \xrightarrow{SOCl_2, \ C_6H_9-N(R)_2} [105]$$

[132]

tadecanoic acid may not have arisen by hydrogenation of a 9,10- or 10,11-methyleneoctade-canoic acid present in the bacterial cell. This possibility has been eliminated by the isolation of tuberculostearic acid without prior hydrogenation and by examination of the product thus obtained (physical properties, *C*-methyl content, infrared spectrum) [560, 573].

The biosynthesis of tuberculostearic acid will be discussed on page 146.

For the purpose of studying their bacteriostatic activity, a series of amides of 10DL-methyloctadecanoic acid with amines such as 4,4'-diaminodiphenylsulphone or *p*-amino-benzoic acid were prepared [574], and more recently, 18-fluoro-10DL-methyloctadecanoic acid has been synthesized from ω-fluoro-octanoic acid [575].

From the fats of a human strain of the tubercle bacillus (residual bacilli from the manu-facture of tuberculin), Edens *et al.* [576] isolated a $C_{19}H_{38}O_2$ acid, $[\alpha]_D$—1.2° (ether), methyl ester, n_D^{25} 1.4368, which is therefore an isomer of tuberculostearic acid. No other details are reported.

q) *Lactobacillic acid* $C_{19}H_{38}O_2$

In 1950, Hofmann & Lucas [577] isolated the ester of a $C_{19}H_{36}O_2$ acid, by fractional distillation of the ester mixture obtained from the total lipids of *Lactobacillus arabinosus* (distillation curve, p. 30), which they called *lactobacillic acid;* it constitutes about 15% of the total lipids. The acid has the following properties: m.p. 28—29°, no measurable optical activity, methyl ester b.p. 187.5°/3 mm, amide m.p. 80—82°. The X-ray diffraction pattern shows a lattice spacing of 41.0A, different from, but close to, that of a normal C_{18} acid; the I.R. spectrum is reproduced on p. 45.

Lactobacillic acid [133] remains unaltered after treatment with permanganate in acetone, unlike an unsaturated acid. It adds hydrobromic acid and on catalytic hydrogenation consumes one molecule of hydrogen to give a solid acid, m.p. 68—68.5°, identified as n-nonadecanoic acid [134] by its X-ray diffraction spectrum, and a liquid acid, m.p. 13—14°, which is a mixture of the two branched acids [135] and [136]. This behaviour is characteristic of cyclopropane derivatives [122].

This conclusion is in accord with the existence of a band at 9.8 μ (1020 cm^{-1}) in the infrared spectrum of lactobacillic acid, which is absent from the spectrum of the hydrogenation products.

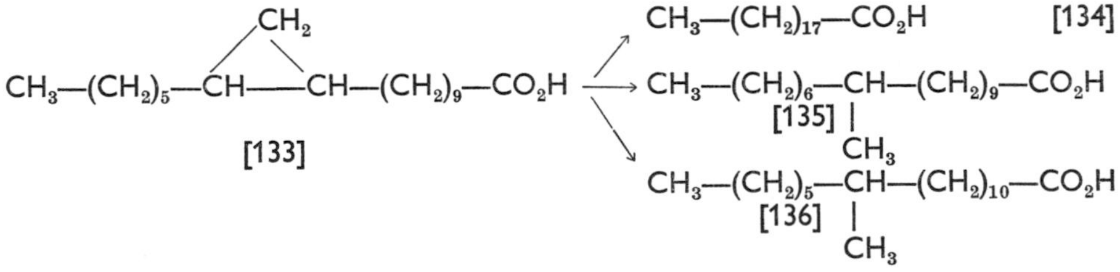

$$CH_3-(CH_2)_5-\overset{\displaystyle CH_2}{\overset{\diagup\ \diagdown}{CH——CH}}-(CH_2)_9-CO_2H$$

[133]

$$CH_3-(CH_2)_{17}-CO_2H \qquad [134]$$

$$CH_3-(CH_2)_6-CH-(CH_2)_9-CO_2H$$
[135] |
$$CH_3$$

$$CH_3-(CH_2)_5-CH-(CH_2)_{10}-CO_2H$$
[136] |
$$CH_3$$

The position of the cyclopropane ring on the aliphatic chain was determined by opening the ring with hydrobromic acid, dehydrobromination of the monobromo derivatives obtained, performic acid dihydroxylation of the unsaturated acids formed, and fission of the latter by periodic acid followed by silver oxide oxidation of the aldehydes. The diacids thus obtained were analysed and isolated by partition chromatography using the method of Klenk & Bongard [578]. The C_{10} diacid, m.p. 126.5—128.0°, and the C_{11} diacid, m.p. 109.0—110.0°, were obtained from lactobacillic acid as well as from synthetic 11,12-methyleneoctadecanoic acid. A synthetic 9,10-methylene-octadecanoic acid, treated in the same manner, afforded C_8 and C_9 diacids. Hofmann *et al.* [579] concluded from this that the cyclopropane ring is located on carbon atoms 11 and 12.

TABLE 20. THE PROPERTIES OF CIS— AND TRANS-METHYLENE-OCTADECANOIC ACIDS (SYNTHETIC AND NATURAL)

Acid	Free acid		Amide		Ref.
	M.p.	$d*$	M.p.	$d*$	
Methylene-octadecanoic acid					
trans-DL-9,10-	33.6-35°	41.1	86.2-87.2°	39.1	580
trans-DL-11.12-	36.5-37.2°	41.3	84-85°	39.1	
cis-DL-9,10	38.6-39.6°	43.4	86.4-87.6°	37.6	582
cis-DL-11,12	31.0-33.6°	43.3	84.0-87.6°	39.3	
Lactobacillic acid	28-29°	41.0	80-82°	37.5	122,580

*d = Main spacing, expressed in Angstroms.

Hofmann et al. [580] prepared DL-trans-11,12-methylene-octadecanoic and -9,10-methylene-octadecanoic acids from trans-cyclopropane-1,2-dicarboxylic acid [137] (see table 20), by the chain-lengthening procedure of Ställberg-Stenhagen [581]. Since the properties of the trans synthetic acids were distinctly different from those of lactobacillic acid, Hofmann et al. [582] carried out the synthesis of the DL-cis-isomers, using as starting material cis-cyclopropane-1,2-diacetic acid [138]; the sequence of reactions used is shown on page 94. The DL-cis-11,12-methylene-octadecanoic acid [144] thus obtained had an infrared spectrum identical with that of lactobacillic acid, but differed in melting point and X-ray diffraction pattern. Nevertheless, the synthetic acid possessed half the growth-promoting power for L. delbrückii of the natural acid (the trans isomer is inactive). This observation shows that lactobacillic acid is one of the optical isomers of DL-cis-11,12-methylene-octadecanoic acid and this conclusion has been confirmed by a two-dimensional crystal structure analysis [583]. The preparation of cis-cyclopropane-1,2-diacetic acid [138] has been described in detail [584]; the same starting material was used by Hofmann et al. [585] to synthesize DL--dihydrosterculic acid (9,10-methylene-octadecanoic acid).

A very convenient procedure for preparing dialkyl-cyclopropanes has been devised more recently by Simmons & Smith [586]. Methylene iodide in the presence of the zinc copper couple can act as a carbene donor and reacts with an unsaturated compound to give a cyclo-

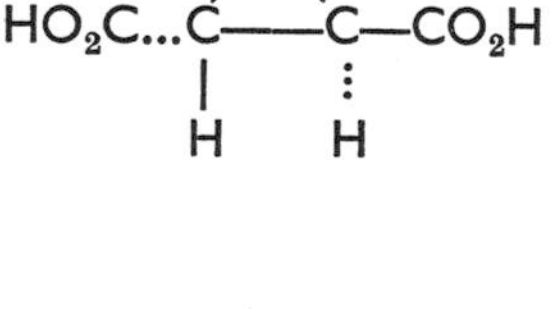

$$HO_2C...C——C—CO_2H \qquad [137]$$

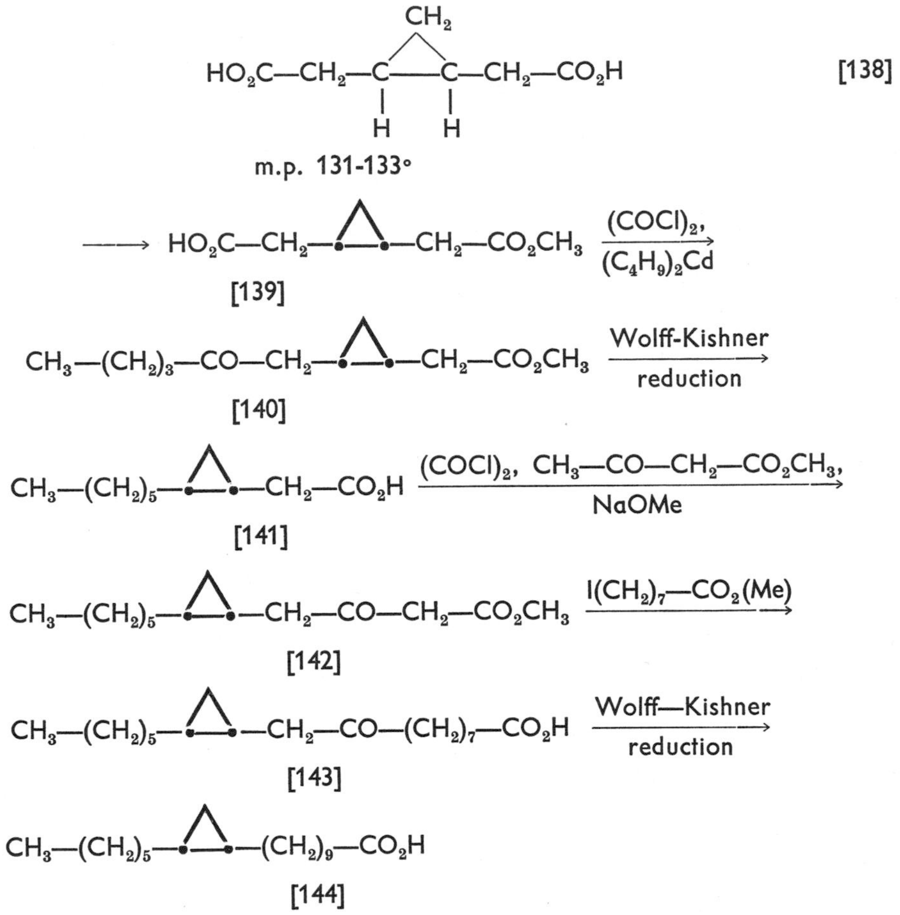

$$\text{HO}_2\text{C}-\text{CH}_2-\overset{\displaystyle\text{CH}_2}{\underset{\text{H}}{\text{C}}}\text{---}\overset{}{\underset{\text{H}}{\text{C}}}-\text{CH}_2-\text{CO}_2\text{H} \qquad [138]$$

m.p. 131-133°

$$\longrightarrow \text{HO}_2\text{C}-\text{CH}_2-\triangle-\text{CH}_2-\text{CO}_2\text{CH}_3 \xrightarrow[\text{(C}_4\text{H}_9)_2\text{Cd}]{\text{(COCl)}_2,}$$

[139]

$$\text{CH}_3-(\text{CH}_2)_3-\text{CO}-\text{CH}_2-\triangle-\text{CH}_2-\text{CO}_2\text{CH}_3 \xrightarrow[\text{reduction}]{\text{Wolff-Kishner}}$$

[140]

$$\text{CH}_3-(\text{CH}_2)_5-\triangle-\text{CH}_2-\text{CO}_2\text{H} \xrightarrow[\text{NaOMe}]{\text{(COCl)}_2, \text{ CH}_3-\text{CO}-\text{CH}_2-\text{CO}_2\text{CH}_3,}$$

[141]

$$\text{CH}_3-(\text{CH}_2)_5-\triangle-\text{CH}_2-\text{CO}-\text{CH}_2-\text{CO}_2\text{CH}_3 \xrightarrow{\text{I(CH}_2)_7-\text{CO}_2\text{(Me)}}$$

[142]

$$\text{CH}_3-(\text{CH}_2)_5-\triangle-\text{CH}_2-\text{CO}-(\text{CH}_2)_7-\text{CO}_2\text{H} \xrightarrow[\text{reduction}]{\text{Wolff---Kishner}}$$

[143]

$$\text{CH}_3-(\text{CH}_2)_5-\triangle-(\text{CH}_2)_9-\text{CO}_2\text{H}$$

[144]

propane derivative. The reaction is stereospecific and the geometry of the unsaturated compound used governs the stereochemistry of the cyclopropane derivative formed: oleic acid (cis compound) gives *cis*-9,10-methylene-octadecanoic acid. The zinc copper couple can be prepared in aqueous medium [587]. This simple procedure was used to prepare DL-*cis*-9,10-methylenehexadecanoic acid [551, 552].

The biosynthesis of lactobacillic acid will be dealt with on page 146.

r) *Phytomonic acid* $C_{19} H_{36} O_2$

The existence of branched-chain acids in the lipids of *Agrobacterium tumefaciens (Phytomonas tumefaciens)* was observed in 1938 by Chargaff & Levine [588] and later by Geiger & Anderson [33]. By distillation of the methyl esters of the "liquid saturated" acids, Velick & Anderson [589] isolated the ester of an acid which they called phytomonic acid.

Velick [310] suggested the structure to be 10- or 11-methylnonadecanoic acid, based on examination of the X-ray diffraction pattern; but optical isomers of 11-methylnonadecanoic acid, synthesized by Cavanna & Ställberg-Stenhagen [590], differed from phytomonic acid.

In 1955, Hofmann & Tausig [591] isolated phytomonic acid by a procedure that did not involve hydrogenation. They obtained an acid, m.p. 27.8—28.8°, amide m.p. 79.2—81.2°, hydrazide m.p. 59.6—61.2°, whose properties were identical with those of lactobacillic acid. Moreover, Hofmann & Tausig [591] observed no depression of the melting point of the hydrazide of their acid when mixed with a sample of the hydrazide of phytomonic acid provided by Velick.

Table 21 lists the bacterial species from which cyclopropane fatty acids have been isolated or characterised.

TABLE 21. SPECIES OF BACTERIA CONTAINING CYCLOPROPANE FATTY ACIDS

Main cyclo-propane acid	Gram-negative species	Ref.	Main cyclo-propane acid	Gram-positive species	Ref.
C_{19}	*Agrobacterium tumefaciens*.	591	C_{17}, C_{19}	*Clostridium butyricum* . .	597
C_{17}	*Aerobacter aerogenes* . . .	592	C_{19}	*Lactobacillus*	
				acidophilus.	544
C_{19}	*Brucella abortus*	593		*arabinosus*.	577
C_{17}	*Escherichia coli*.	549		*casei*	554
		550		*delbrückii*	153
		551	C_{19}	*Streptococcus*:	
C_{17}	*Pasteurella pestis*	177		*lactis var. maltigenes* . .	598
C_{17}	*Proteus P 18 (L form)*. . .	594		*cremoris*	598
C_{17}	*Salmonella typhimurium* . .	595			
C_{17}	*Serratia marcescens*	596			

s) *2L, 4L-Dimethyldocosanoic acid* $C_{24}H_{48}O_2$

The methyl ester of this acid was isolated by vapour phase chromatography of the crude mixture obtained by saponification of the lipids of the human strain H_{37} of *M. tuberculosis* [598a]; the properties of the free acid, m.p. 43.0-44.5°, $[\alpha]_D + 2.2°$, show that partial racemization had occurred during saponification (the synthetic acid has $[\alpha]_D + 7.4°$).

The name "C_{24}-mycosanoic acid" was proposed by Cason *et al.* [598a] for this acid.

t) *Mycolipenic and phthienoic acids*, $C_{25}H_{48}O_2$, $C_{27}H_{52}O_2$, and $C_{29}H_{56}O_2$

No other constituent of bacterial lipids, with the exception of the mycolic acids, has given rise to such an amount of work—recorded in about forty publications. In fact these acids were the first adequately characterized constituents isolated from the tubercle bacillus able, after injection into animals (see p. 270), to bring about tissue modifications resembling those which can be observed in a tubercle.

Two principal phases can be distinguished in the study of these acids. The first extends from 1929, date of the isolation of "phthioic" acid by Anderson [599], to 1950, when the unsaturation of these acids was demonstrated. Since that date, the structures of the mycolipenic acids have been established and, more recently, their identity with the phthienoic acids.

When he isolated phthioic acid, a dextrorotatory branched acid, from the lipids of the tubercle bacillus, Anderson [599, 600] thought he had a saturated acid with the empirical formula $C_{26}H_{52}O_2$. In order to have model compounds for comparison, Chargaff [601] in 1932 synthesized a series of $C_{26}H_{52}O_2$ α-branched-chain acids, but all these acids showed higher melting points than phthioic acid.

Phthioic 'acid has the following constants: m.p. 20—21°, $[\alpha]_D^{25} + 12.5°$, n_D^{25} 1.4628, d_4^{25} 0.8763, amide m.p. 45° [602]. From the products of chromic acid oxidation, an unidentified C_{11} acid [602] and azelaic acid [603] were isolated. By comparison with synthetic products, it was thought that the C_{11} acid was 6-methyldecanoic acid [604, 605]. In the light of present knowledge it seems that the C_{11} acid and azelaic acid probably arose from impurities present in the samples of phthioic acid (azelaic acid possibly arising from tuberculostearic acid).

In 1941, after study of monomolecular layers and X-ray diffraction patterns, a trialkylacetic acid structure was proposed for phthioic acid. On the basis of this hypothesis, several syntheses were accomplished, [605-612] which only led to its rejection: in particular, trialkylacetic esters are much more difficult to saponify than the phthioic esters.

A second structure, based on the isolation of the C_{11} and azelaic acids after oxidation of phthioic acid, was proposed in 1945, viz. 3, 13,19-trimethyltricosanoic acid [604, 605]. Such an acid (mixture of stereoisomers) was synthesized [605, 613]. However, in 1948, Cason & Prout [351] observed that the maximum molecular rotation that could be calculated for a 3,13,19-trimethyltricosanoic acid is about 12°, whereas the value found for phthioic acid is close to 50°.

Simultaneously, observations were made which indicated the heterogeneity of phthioic acid. In 1937, from a preparation of phthioic acid, Wagner-Jauregg [603] isolated a tribromanilide m.p. 66-69°, of the formula $C_{35}H_{60}NBr_3$, i.e. corresponding to a derivative of a $C_{29}H_{58}O_2$ acid. Later, Ginger & Anderson [614] obtained four fractions on distilling a sample of methyl phthioate obtained from the fat of cell residues from the manufacture of tuberculin. The four corresponding acids showed analytical data in agreement with the formulae $C_{24}H_{48}O_2$, $C_{25}H_{50}O_2$, $C_{26}H_{52}O_2$, and $C_{27}H_{54}O_2$; the determination of C-methyl groups showed the presence of three methyl groups in each acid and the optical rotation varied from +5.17° to +17.11°.

In 1950, Chanley & Polgar [615] and Cason & Sumrell [616] established simultaneously that the phthioic acid of Anderson is a mixture of α,β-unsaturated acids. The unsaturation in these acids had escaped observation up till this time because of the very weak fixation of halogen by double bonds conjugated with carboxyl: it was UV spectrophotometry which made this discovery very easy (see p. 39).

Polgar called these α,β-unsaturated acids mycolipenic acids and Cason phthienoic acids. Each series of investigations will be discussed separately.

— Mycolipenic Acids

The "phthioic acid" fraction from the tubercle bacillus (mixture of strains used in the manufacture of tuberculin), isolated by fractional distillation, was separated into three α,β-unsaturated acids by recrystallization of the semicarbazones of the acetol esters (see p. 38). One of these acids, called mycolipenic acid-I, had the molecular formula $C_{27}H_{52}O_2$. Its properties are given in Table 22, and its constitution, studied by Polgar & Robinson [617, 196], was established in 1951.

TABLE 22. THE PROPERTIES OF C_{27}-MYCOLIPENIC AND PHTHIENOIC ACIDS

	Natural acids			Synthetic acids		
	C_{27}-Phthienoic acid	Myco-lipenic acid-I	$C_{25}+C_{27}$-Mycoli-penic acids	2, 4, 6-Trimethyl-Δ^2-tetracosenoic acid		
				4(L), 6(L) trans	DL-*erythro*	
					cis	*trans*
References	357	196	643	623	128	128
Free acid m.p.	39.5-42° or 19-21°	Oil*		28°	66.9-68.0°	44.5-47.2° or 22.4-23.1°
$[\alpha]_D$ (CHCl$_3$)	+17.8°	+10.3°**		+19.3°		
$\lambda_{max}^{m\mu}$ (hexane) . . .	218	220		216	221	218
	13,200	11,000		13,900	10,720	13,100
Methyl ester .						
m.p.	30-32.5° or 13-15°		12.3-13.2°		35.2-36.6° or 16.3-16.6°	30.5-31.5° or 14.3-14.7°
$[\alpha]_D$	+14.7°		+14.6°	+16.4°		
$\lambda_{max}^{m\mu}$	218		216	217	217	215
	12,330		13,000	13,600	10,230	12,900
n_D^{25}	1.4600		1.4600	1.4632	1.4587	1.4600
Phthianoic acid... . .						
m.p.	22.5-23.5° or 30-32°	Oil			14.7-15.2°	
$[\alpha]_D$	+2.85°	+1.7°				
n_D^{25}	1.4565				1.4500	

* In ref. 623, m.p. 27° and $[\alpha]_D$ +19.3° are attributed to mycolipenic acid.
** At 16°.

The ozonization of mycolipenic acid, at low temperatures, gave rise to pyruvic acid along with a $C_{23}H_{47}$—COOH acid, which demonstrated the presence of the terminal grouping —CH=C(CH$_3$)—COOH. On the other hand, permanganate oxidation of mycolipenic acid afforded, along with the same $C_{23}H_{47}$—COOH acid, a methyl ketone $C_{21}H_{43}$—CO—CH$_3$, which demonstrated the existence of a methyl group at the position 4 in mycolipenic acid (or at position 2 in the $C_{23}H_{47}$—COOH acid).

The $C_{23}H_{47}$—COOH acid [145], after α-bromination and dehydrobromination, was transformed into an α,β-unsaturated α-branched acid [146] (methyl ester: $[\alpha]_D +13.3°$).

$$C_{23}H_{47}\text{—COOH} \xrightarrow[\text{—HBr}]{Br_2} C_{21}H_{43}\text{—CH=C—COOH}$$
$$\underset{CH_3}{|}$$

[145]   [146]

$$\xrightarrow{KMnO_4} C_{18}H_{37}\text{—CH—COOH} + C_{18}H_{37}\text{—CO—CH}_3$$
$$\underset{CH_3}{|}$$

[147]   [148]

Permanganate oxidation of the unsaturated acid [146] yielded a mixture of acid [147] and methyl ketone [148], which shows that the acid [147] possesses a methyl branch in the α-position with respect to the carboxyl. Consequently, mycolipenic acid [149] possesses a third methyl group in position 6. The α-branched chain acid [147] is also dextrorotatory: $[\alpha]_D +7°$. The methyl ketone [148], semicarbazone m.p. 122°, was identified as 2-eicosanone by comparison of the X-ray diffraction patterns with those of an authentic sample[618]. This completes the proof of structure [149] for mycolipenic acid-I.

$$CH_3\text{—}(CH_2)_{17}\text{—CH—CH}_2\text{—CH—CH = C—COOH}$$
$$\underset{CH_3}{|} \qquad \underset{CH_3}{|} \qquad \underset{CH_3}{|} \qquad [149]$$

Since the α-branched chain acids [145] and [147] obtained in the course of the degradation are dextrorotatory and since it has been shown that long-chain acids with a 2-methyl group belong to the L series when they are dextrorotatory, the configuration 4(L),6(L) was suggested[619] and subsequently verified by synthesis (see below). The high optical rotation of mycolipenic acid is explained by the existence of an asymmetric centre in the α-position with respect to the double bond; hydrogenation of the latter considerably lowers the rotation to $[\alpha]_D +1.7°$. This explanation is confirmed by the great difference in optical activity between (—)-2,4,8-trimethyl-Δ^2-nonenoic acid ($[\alpha]_D -24.6°$) and the corresponding saturated acid ($[\alpha]_D -3.8°$), whereas in the case of (—)-2,5,9-trimethyl-Δ^2-decenoic acid the optical activity ($[\alpha]_D <-0.1°$) remains unchanged on hydrogenation[620].

By comparing the IR spectra of tiglic and angelic acids and cis and trans 2,4- or 2,5-disubstituted α,β-unsaturated long-chain acids with that of mycolipenic acid, Ställberg-

Stenhagen [619] arrived at the conclusion that the natural acid possesses the trans structure, i.e. the carboxyl and the main chain are trans with respect to each other.

The synthesis of 2,4,6-trimethyl-Δ^2-tetracosenoic acid (mixture of stereoisomers) was described in 1953 [618]. Later, Ahlquist et al. [621, 128] synthesized the cis-and trans-isomers of DL-erythro-2,4,6-trimethyl-Δ^2-tetracosenoic acid [149], from monomethyl meso-3,5-dimethylpimelate [436], according to the reaction schemes described on p. 100. The synthetic trans acid shows a close similarity in its properties to the natural acid, while the synthetic cis acid shows distinct differences. The trans structure of the natural acid is, therefore, confirmed. Moreover, Fray & Polgar [622] synthesized (+)-2(L), 4(L)-dimethyldocosanoic acid, $[\alpha]_D +7.0°$ (ether), p-bromophenacylate m.p. 71°, i.e. the acid [145], which is the first product in the degradation of mycolipenic acid. This work confirmed the L-configuration of the asymmetric centres 4 and 6 in mycolipenic acid. Subsequently, Millin & Polgar [623] converted the [145] acid, obtained by degradation of mycolipenic acid, back into natural mycolipenic acid.

Thus the structure and the stereochemistry of mycolipenic acid I has been well established by degradation and synthesis. In spite of the initial isolation of several α,β-unsaturated acids [615], Bailey et al. [618] claimed shortly afterwards that only one mycolipenic acid existed. Nevertheless, the mass spectrum of a methyl mycolipenate sample, isolated from the human strain Test and purified by chromatography (for its constants, see Table 22, p. 97), showed the presence, of a lower homologue $C_{25}H_{48}O_2$ besides the $C_{27}H_{52}O_2$ acid (see ref. 128); thus at least two acids exist : the C_{25}- and C_{27}-mycolipenic acids.

— Phthienoic acids

By fractional distillation of a 24 g sample of methyl phthioate prepared by Anderson, Cason & Sumrell [357] were able to isolate a dozen acids in which the number of carbon atoms varied from 23 to 31; at least six of these acids are α,β-unsaturated and α-branched [202]. Quantitatively the two most important constituents have 27 and 29 carbon atoms (besides those with 25 and 26) and are called the C_{27}- and C_{29}-phthienoic acids [357, 202].

The characteristics of the C_{27}-phthienoic acid and of its methyl ester are given in Table 22, (page 97*). At first, its constitution was studied only by physico-chemical methods [357, 624]. From the position of the UV absorption maximum (λ_{max} 218mμ), the presence of a substituent on a double bond conjugated with the carboxyl may be deduced. This substituent is situated in the α-position to the carboxyl, according to a comparison between the rates of saponification of the phthianamide (amide of the dihydro-acid) and of α-and β-methyl-substituted amides. The substituent is presumed to be a methyl because of the absence in the IR spectrum of a band due to an ethyl, propyl, or butyl group and because of the absence of any known natural compounds with longer branches. The optical rotation of the C_{27}-phthienoic acid, $[\alpha]_D +18°$, decreases considerably after hydrogenation to $[\alpha]_D +2.8°$, which shows that there must be an asymmetric centre at position 4 or 5. At 200°, C_{27}-phthienoic acid gives rise to only a very small amount of a β,γ-unsaturated acid

---

* I. R. spectrum, see page 45.

$$HOOC-CH_2-CH-CH_2-CH-CH_2-COOCH_3 \longrightarrow CO-CH_2-CH-CH_2-CH-CH_2-COOH$$

$$\underset{CH_3}{|} \quad \underset{CH_3}{|} \qquad \underset{CH_3}{|} \quad \underset{CH_3}{|} \quad \underset{CH_3}{|}$$

[150]   [153]

$$C_{16}H_{33}-CO-CH_2-CH-CH_2-CH-CH_2-COOH$$

$$\underset{CH_3}{|} \quad \underset{CH_3}{|}$$

[151]

$$CH_3-(CH_2)_{17}-CH-CH_2-CH-CH_2-COOH \longrightarrow CH_3-(CH_2)_{17}-CH-CH_2-CH-CH_2-CO$$

$$\underset{CH_3}{|} \quad \underset{CH_3}{|} \qquad\qquad \underset{CH_3}{|} \quad \underset{CH_3}{|} \quad \underset{CH_3}{|}$$

[152]   [154]

$$CH_3-(CH_2)_{17}-CH-CH_2-CH-CH_2-\overset{OH}{\underset{|}{C}}-COOH \leftarrow CH_3-(CH_2)_{17}-CH-CH_2-CH-CH_2-\overset{OH}{\underset{|}{C}}-CN$$

$$\underset{CH_3}{|} \quad \underset{CH_3}{|} \quad \underset{CH_3}{|} \qquad\qquad \underset{CH_3}{|} \quad \underset{CH_3}{|} \quad \underset{CH_3}{|}$$

[156]   [155]

$$CH_3-(CH_2)_{17}-CH-CH_2-CH-CH=C-COOH \quad [149]$$

$$\underset{CH_3}{|} \quad \underset{CH_3}{|} \quad \underset{CH_3}{|}$$

$$CH_3-(CH_2)_{17}-CH-CH_2-CH-CH=C-CHO \leftarrow CH_3-(CH_2)_{17}-CH-CH_2-CH-CH=C-CH_2O$$

$$\underset{CH_3}{|} \quad \underset{CH_3}{|} \quad \underset{CH_3}{|} \qquad\qquad \underset{CH_3}{|} \quad \underset{CH_3}{|} \quad \underset{CH_3}{|}$$

[163]   [162]

$$CH_3-(CH_2)_{17}-CH-CH_2-CH-CH_2-C=CH_2 \rightarrow CH_3-(CH_2)_{17}-CH-CH_2-CH-\overset{Br}{\underset{|}{CH}}-C=CH_2$$

$$\underset{CH_3}{|} \quad \underset{CH_3}{|} \quad \underset{CH_3}{|} \qquad\qquad \underset{CH_3}{|} \quad \underset{CH_3}{|} \quad \underset{CH_3}{|}$$

[160]   [161]

$$HOOC-CH_2-CH-CH_2-CH-CH_2-\overset{O-COCH_3}{\underset{|}{C}}-CH_3 \leftarrow CH_3OOC-CH_2-CH-CH_2-CH-CH_2-\overset{O-COCH_3}{\underset{|}{C}}-CH_3$$

$$\underset{CH_3}{|} \quad \underset{CH_3}{|} \quad \underset{CH_3}{|} \qquad\qquad \underset{CH_3}{|} \quad \underset{CH_3}{|} \quad \underset{CH_3}{|}$$

[159]   [158]

$$CH_3OOC-CH_2-CH-CH_2-CH-CH_2-COOH \rightarrow CH_3OOC-CH_2-CH-CH_2-CH-CH_2-\overset{OH}{\underset{|}{C}}-CH$$

$$\underset{CH_3}{|} \quad \underset{CH_3}{|} \qquad\qquad\qquad \underset{CH_3}{|} \quad \underset{CH_3}{|} \quad \underset{CH_3}{|}$$

[150]   [157]

isomer (determined by the diminution in absorption at 218 mμ) and only very little
lactone is formed. Cason & Sumrell therefore conclude that the second substituent (methyl
for the reasons given above) is at the 5- rather than the 4-position. The determination of
C-methyl groups by the Kuhn-Roth method or by the measurement of the intensity of
absorption at 7.3 μ in the infrared spectrum, shows that there is a third substituent in the
molecule. Taking into account the absence of iso- or neo-groups and of a tetrasubstituted
carbon atom (according to the IR spectrum), the formula [164] was proposed :

$$C_4H_9-(CH_2)_{15}-\underset{\underset{CH_3}{|}}{CH}-CH_2-\underset{}{CH}=\underset{\underset{CH_3}{|}}{C}-COOH \quad [164]$$

$$\underset{CH_3}{}$$

Subsequently, on the basis of the optical rotation of model synthetic acids, Cason *et
al.* [201, 625] placed the second methyl substituent at position 4. The trans nature of the double
bond was established by the work of Cason & Kalm [626], which was based on examination
of the IR spectra of model acids of known configuration (for other syntheses in this field,
see also refs. 627, 628). The partial formula of C_{27}-phthienoic acid put forward by Cason in
1961 was therefore [165]. This structure was in accord with that of mycolipenic acid [149],

$$C_4H_9-(CH_2)_{16}-\underset{\underset{CH_3}{|}}{CH}-CH=\underset{\underset{CH_3}{|}}{C}-COOH \quad [165]$$

established since 1951. On the other hand, the similarity in properties exhibited by the methyl
C_{27}-phthienoate of Cason, the mixture of methyl C_{25} -and C_{27}-mycolipenates isolated by
Asselineau, and the trans synthetic ester (see Table 22, page 97) were all in favour of the
identity of the C_{27}-phthienoic and C_{27}-mycolipenic acids; and this identity was rendered
more probable by the fact that each of these two acids are the main α,β-unsaturated branched-
chain acids isolated from the batch of bacilli studied.

Because of the isolation of a C_{16} diketone from the ozonolysis products of C_{27}-phthienoic
acid, Cason *et al.* [179] suggested in 1957 that the latter acid might have a structure such as [166].
However, more recently, Cason *et al.* [175] have concluded from a very careful examination
of the oxidation products of pure C_{27}-phthienoic acid samples that this acid has the 2,4,6-
trimethyltetracos-2-enoic acid structure [149] proposed ten years ago by Polgar.

$$CH_3-(CH_2)_6-\underset{\underset{C_5H_{11}}{|}}{CH}-(CH_2)_8-\underset{\underset{CH_3}{|}}{CH}-CH=\underset{\underset{CH_3}{|}}{C}-COOH \quad [166]$$

In the course of the same study, Cason *et al.* [175] isolated pure samples of C_{25} -phthienoic
acid, m.p. 29—30°, $[\alpha]_D$ +20.6°, λ_{max} 218 mμ, ε = 14,900, and assigned to it the structure
of a 2,4,6-trimethyldocos-2-enoic acid.

From a mass-spectrometric study of methyl C_{27}-phthianoate samples provided by Cason and of synthetic model esters, Ryhage *et al.*[330] confirmed the structure [149] for C_{27}-phthienoic acid. On the other hand, Murray[629] arrived at the same conclusion by permanganate oxidation studies.

As the identity of mycolipenic and phthienoic acids is now established, it appears reasonable to retain the single name phthienoic acid, which is the most directly related to the original name "phthioic acid" used by Anderson.

Dextrorotatory α,β-unsaturated acids of the phthienoic acid type have been isolated from human[196, 65, 202, 357, 625] and bovine[202] virulent strains of *M. tuberculosis*; these acids are mostly localized in the fats (see particularly ref. 139) and the phosphatides. However, such acids seem to be absent from the lipids of non-virulent human strains[76, 561] and the attenuated bovine strain BCG[561, 630]. Likewise, no α,β-unsaturated acids could be detected in the lipids from a strain of *M. phlei*[115], from *M. avium*[562], or from *M. johnei*[563] by UV spectrographic examination and optical rotation measurements.

The influence of streptomycin resistance on the content of phthienoic acids will be discussed on p. 265, and the biological properties of these acids on p. 270. Analogues of methyl phthienoate in which the end of the carbon chain is blocked against ω-oxidation have been synthesized, viz. methyl cis- and trans-Δ^2-2,4(L),21,21-tetramethyldocosenoates[631a].

u) *Mycocerosic acids* $C_{29}H_{58}O_2$, $C_{30}H_{60}O_2$, $C_{32}H_{64}O_2$

Anderson and his collaborators repeatedly observed the presence of laevorotatory branched acids of high molecular weight in the lipid fractions of the tubercle bacillus. Wieghard & Anderson[500], for example, isolated a $C_{31}H_{62}O_2$ acid, m.p. 37—38°, $[\alpha]_D$—7.2°, from the waxes A of a human strain and Cason & Anderson[347] a $C_{30}H_{60}O_2$ acid, m.p. 33—40°, $[\alpha]_D$—5.3°, from the waxes C + D of a bovine strain.

In 1945, Ginger & Anderson[631] proposed the name mycocerosic acid for a $C_{30}H_{60}O_2$ acid, m.p. 27-28°, $[\alpha]_D$—5.7°, *p*-bromophenacylate m.p. 47—48°, isolated from the waxes C + D of residual bacilli (human strain) from the manufacture of tuberculin. The probable presence of 4 methyl groups was established by a modification of the Kuhn-Roth method[358].

In 1953, Polgar[632] isolated a laevorotatory branched-chain acid from the lipids of residual bacilli (human strain) from the manufacture of tuberculin. He gave the name mycoceranic acid to this acid, which had m.p. 30°, $[\alpha]_D$—9.2° and *p*-bromophenacylate m.p. 31.5°. The structure was determined by a sequence of reactions similar to that utilized in the case of mycolipenic acid (p. 98). Mycoceranic acid, after α-bromination and dehydrobromination, yielded an α,β-unsaturated acid [167], whose methyl ester had $[\alpha]_D$—10.2°, λ_{max} 218 mμ, log ε 4.06. The acid [167] gives pyruvic acid (2,4-dinitrophenylhydrazone m.p. 214—215°) on ozonolysis which demonstrates the presence of a branch in the α-position with respect to the carboxyl of mycoceranic acid. Permanganate oxidation of the acid [167] yields a $C_{28}H_{56}O_2$ acid [168], $[\alpha]_D$—5.8°, *p*-bromophenacylate m.p. 68°, and a methylketone $C_{27}H_{54}O$

[169], semicarbazone m. p. 92.5°. The acid [168] is transformed into an α,β-unsaturated acid [170] $C_{28}H_{54}O_2$, $[\alpha]_D$—9.1°, in the same manner as above, and the unsaturated acid [170] on oxidation with potassium permanganate gives a $C_{25}H_{50}O_2$ acid [171], p-bromophenacylate m.p. 82—83°, and a methylketone $C_{24}H_{28}O$ [172], semicarbazone m.p. 126°, considered most likely to be n-tetracosan-2-one. These results led to the tentative formula [173] for mycoceranic acid [632, 390].

Marks and Polgar [378] synthesized n-tetracosan-2-one, m.p. 67—68°, semicarbazone m.p. 131—131.5°, and (+)-4(D)-methylhexacosan-2-one [174], m.p. 52.5—53.5°, $[\alpha]_D$ +4.9° semicarbazone m.p. 101-102°, which might be identical to the methyl ketones [172] and [169], respectively, obtained in the course of the degradation of mycoceranic acid. No conclusion could be drawn from the comparison of the X-ray diffraction patterns of the semicarbazones derived from these two ketones, and mycoceranic acid "is tentatively regarded as" represented by [173] [347].

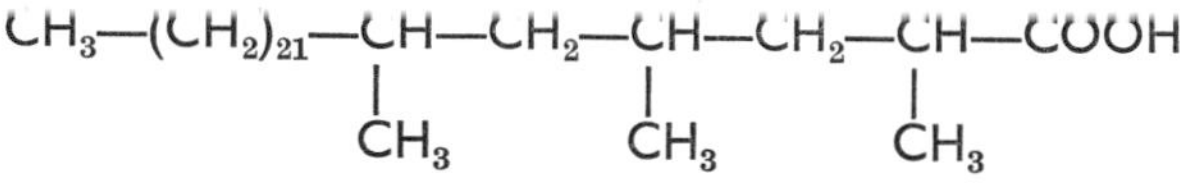

$$CH_3-(CH_2)_{21}-\underset{\underset{CH_3}{|}}{CH}-CH_2-\underset{\underset{CH_3}{|}}{CH}-CH_2-\underset{\underset{CH_3}{|}}{CH}-COOH \quad [173]$$

As the two α-branched chain acids [168] and [171] obtained during the degradation of mycoceranic acid are laevorotatory and as 2-methyl-substituted laevorotatory acids have been related to D-glyceraldehyde by the work of Ställberg-Stenhagen & Stenhagen [633], mycoceranic acid would be 2(D), 4(D), 6(D)-trimethyloctacosanoic acid.

A 2, 4, 6(D)-trimethyloctacosanoic acid [182] was synthesized from the dextrorotatory half ester of β-methylglutaric acid [175], according to the reaction scheme represented on p. 104 [378]. As the acid obtained was a mixture of stereoisomers, no conclusion could be drawn from its comparison with the natural acid.

Examination by mass spectrometry of a specimen of methyl mycocerosate obtained from Anderson and purified by chromatography (m.p. 20.8—21.4°, $[\alpha]_D$—7.8°) confirmed the presence of methyl groups in positions 2, 4, and 6 and showed that mycocerosic acid has the empirical formula $C_{32}H_{64}O_2$ [329]. A similar result was obtained with a sample of methyl mycocerosate isolated from the human strain Test [329]. Anderson's mycocerosic acid, mycoceranic acid, and probably also a laevorotatory acid called mycosanoic acid, m.p. 19—21° and 28—29.5° (dimorphism), $[\alpha]_D$—7.8°, isolated by Cason & Fonken [202] from the lipids of a human strain of the tubercle bacillus, are thus probably all identical.

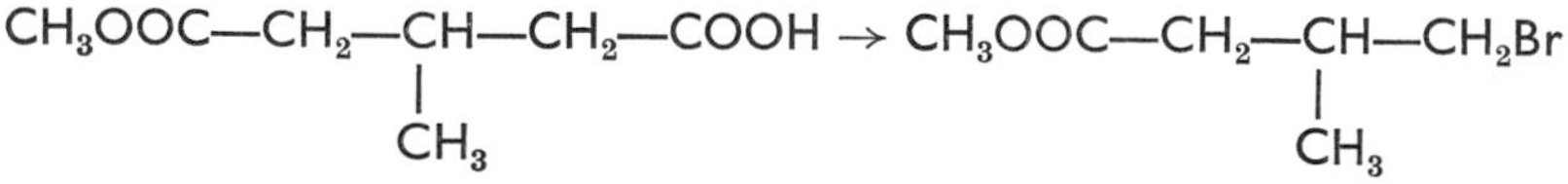

$$CH_3OOC-CH_2-\underset{\underset{CH_3}{|}}{CH}-CH_2-COOH \rightarrow CH_3OOC-CH_2-\underset{\underset{CH_3}{|}}{CH}-CH_2Br$$

$$[175] \qquad\qquad\qquad [176] \quad [\alpha]_D-2.54°$$

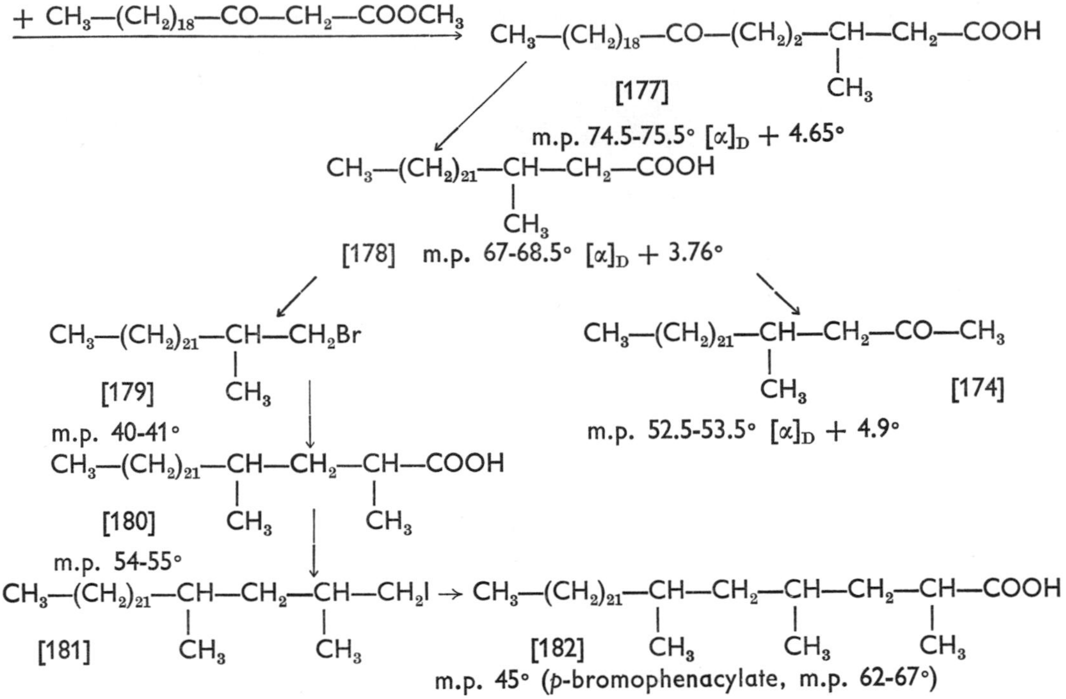

$$+ \ CH_3\text{---}(CH_2)_{18}\text{---}CO\text{---}CH_2\text{---}COOCH_3 \longrightarrow CH_3\text{---}(CH_2)_{18}\text{---}CO\text{---}(CH_2)_2\text{---}CH\text{---}CH_2\text{---}COOH$$

[177] CH_3

m.p. 74.5-75.5° $[\alpha]_D$ + 4.65°

$$CH_3\text{---}(CH_2)_{21}\text{---}CH\text{---}CH_2\text{---}COOH$$
$$CH_3$$
[178]   m.p. 67-68.5° $[\alpha]_D$ + 3.76°

$$CH_3\text{---}(CH_2)_{21}\text{---}CH\text{---}CH_2Br \qquad\qquad CH_3\text{---}(CH_2)_{21}\text{---}CH\text{---}CH_2\text{---}CO\text{---}CH_3$$

[179] CH_3 CH_3 [174]

m.p. 40-41°   m.p. 52.5-53.5° $[\alpha]_D$ + 4.9°

$$CH_3\text{---}(CH_2)_{21}\text{---}CH\text{---}CH_2\text{---}CH\text{---}COOH$$

[180] CH_3 CH_3

m.p. 54-55°

$$CH_3\text{---}(CH_2)_{21}\text{---}CH\text{---}CH_2\text{---}CH\text{---}CH_2I \rightarrow CH_3\text{---}(CH_2)_{21}\text{---}CH\text{---}CH_2\text{---}CH\text{---}CH_2\text{---}CH\text{---}COOH$$

[181] CH_3 CH_3 [182] CH_3 CH_3 CH_3

m.p. 45° (p-bromophenacylate, m.p. 62-67°)

The synthesis of methyl 2(D),4(D),6(D)-trimethylnonacosanoate [188] was achieved by Asselineau *et al.*[145] by the following sequence of reactions:

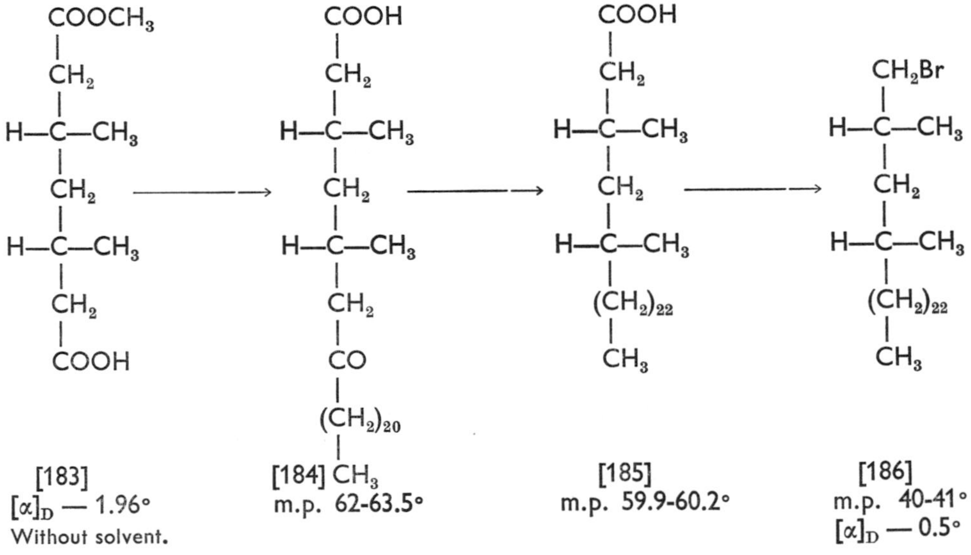

COOCH₃	COOH	COOH	CH₂Br
COOCH$_3$	COOH	COOH	CH$_2$Br
CH$_2$	CH$_2$	CH$_2$	H—C—CH$_3$
H—C—CH$_3$	H—C—CH$_3$	H—C—CH$_3$	CH$_2$
CH$_2$	CH$_2$	CH$_2$	H—C—CH$_3$
H—C—CH$_3$	H—C—CH$_3$	H—C—CH$_3$	(CH$_2$)$_{22}$
CH$_2$	CH$_2$	(CH$_2$)$_{22}$	CH$_3$
COOH	CO	CH$_3$	
	(CH$_2$)$_{20}$		

[183]   [184] CH₃   [185]   [186]
$[\alpha]_D$ — 1.96°   m.p. 62-63.5°   m.p. 59.9-60.2°   m.p. 40-41°
Without solvent. $[\alpha]_D$ — 0.5°

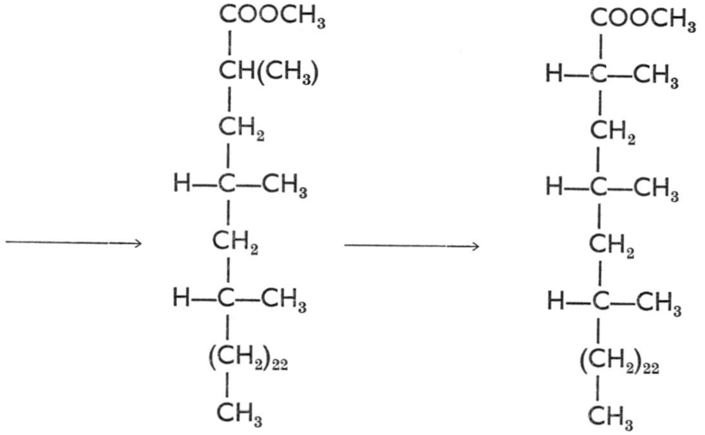

$$
\begin{array}{c}
COOCH_3 \\
| \\
CH(CH_3) \\
| \\
CH_2 \\
| \\
H—C—CH_3 \\
| \\
CH_2 \\
| \\
H—C—CH_3 \\
| \\
(CH_2)_{22} \\
| \\
CH_3
\end{array}
\qquad
\begin{array}{c}
COOCH_3 \\
| \\
H—C—CH_3 \\
| \\
CH_2 \\
| \\
H—C—CH_3 \\
| \\
CH_2 \\
| \\
H—C—CH_3 \\
| \\
(CH_2)_{22} \\
| \\
CH_3
\end{array}
$$

$\longrightarrow$ $\longrightarrow$

[187]   m.p. 37.9-38.2° [100]

$[\alpha]_D — 7.2°$

The methyl ester [188] melts about 17° higher than the natural methyl mycoserosate. The latter (a sample from Anderson) was purified by chromatography and the separate fractions, after reduction to the alcohols with lithium aluminium hydride, were then submitted to vapour-phase chromatographic analysis combined with mass spectrometry. Three main components were observed: a C_{29} acid with three branches, a C_{30} acid with 4 branches, and a C_{32} acid with 4 branches. The latter acid, which constitutes about 65 % of the initial mycocerosic acid, is a 2,4,6,8-tetramethyloctacosanoic acid [189], which is called C_{32}-mycocerosic acid [147].

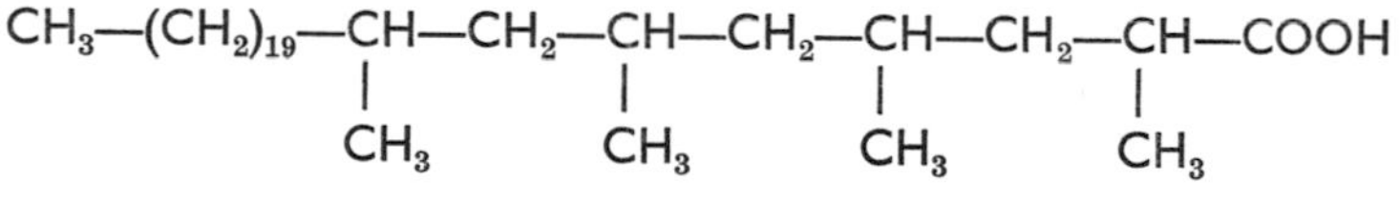

$$
CH_3—(CH_2)_{19}—\underset{\underset{CH_3}{|}}{CH}—CH_2—\underset{\underset{CH_3}{|}}{CH}—CH_2—\underset{\underset{CH_3}{|}}{CH}—CH_2—\underset{\underset{CH_3}{|}}{CH}—COOH
$$

[189]

The same conclusion was reached more recently by Polgar & Smith [634] from a gas-chromatographic analysis of the esters of the acids containing only one methyl branch (in the α-position), obtained by chemical degradation of the crude mycocerosic acid. The synthesis of methyl 2(D),4(D),6(D),8(D)-tetramethyloctacosanoate (contaminated with some 2(L),4(D),6(D),8(D)-isomer) has been described [635].

Mycocerosic acids are found in the lipids of human and bovine strains of *M. tuberculosis*, principally in the form of diesters of phthiocerol [528, 636, 637], but also as triglyceride [139]. In mycoside B, a glycolipid isolated from BCG (p. 171), the mycocerosic acid fraction appears to be a mixture of 15 % 2,4-dimethyltetracosanoic acid, 70 % 2,4,6-trimethylhexacosanoic acid, and a few percent of 2,4,6,8-tetramethyloctacosanoic acid[518]. However, analysis of the mycocerosic fraction obtained from crude BCG fat shows that 2,4,6-trimethylhexacosanoic and 2,4,6,8-tetramethyloctacosanoic acids (along with some 2,4,6,8-tetramethylhexacosanoic acid) are the most important components[630].

Pure C_{32}-mycocerosic acid has been isolated by Cason *et al.*[1162], and the following properties are given: m.p.: 31-32.5°, $[\alpha]_D$—3.3°, amide m.p. 54-57°.

The same authors[1162] have also described 2(D),4(D),6(D)-trimethylhexacosanoic acid, as white crystals, m.p. 45.5-48°, $[\alpha]_D$—6.1°. They used for this acid the name "C_{29}-phthianoic acid" which is misleading, as phthianoic acids are *dextrorotatory* dihydroderivatives of phthienoic acids.

The strains of *Mycobacterium* that do not contain phthiocerol or related alcohols (*M. avium*, saprophytic *Mycobacterium*) seem to be devoid of mycocerosic acids.

The biosynthesis of the mycocerosic acids will be discussed on p. 147.

In connection with the presence of this type of methyl-branched fatty acids in the lipids of the tubercle bacillus, mention may be made of the isolation of methyl 2,4,6,8-tetramethyldecanoate [190a], $[\alpha]_D$—33.3°, and methyl 2,4,6,8-tetramethylundecanoate [190b] $[\alpha]_D$—24.9°, from the lipids of the preen gland of the goose[638, 639]; it may be noted that saponification of these acids gives rise to a slight racemization.

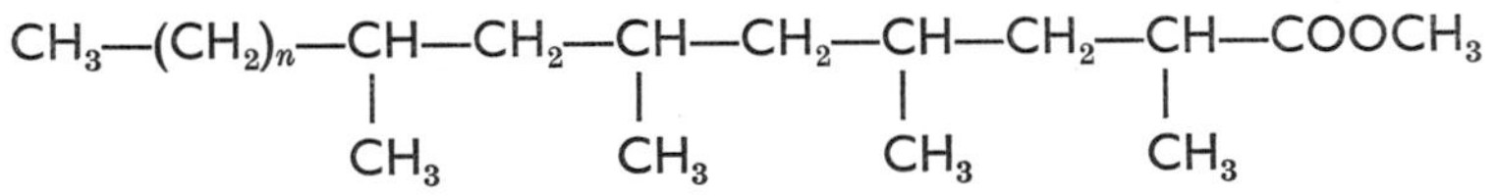

$$CH_3-(CH_2)_n-\underset{\underset{CH_3}{|}}{CH}-CH_2-\underset{\underset{CH_3}{|}}{CH}-CH_2-\underset{\underset{CH_3}{|}}{CH}-CH_2-\underset{\underset{CH_3}{|}}{CH}-COOCH_3$$

[190] a : n = 1

b : n = 2

v) Diphtheric and corinnic acids $C_{35}H_{68}O_2$

From the fats of *Corynebacterium diphtheriae*, Chargaff[640] isolated a mono-unsaturated acid, the potassium salt of which is soluble in ether. This acid, called diphtheric acid, melts at 35—36° and distills at 260°/0.003 mm. The optical rotation, $[\alpha]_D$—2.6°, shows that it is a branched-chain acid; the analytical data are in agreement with the molecular formula $C_{35}H_{68}O_2$.

The same acid, m.p. 35—36°, was later isolated by Asano & Takahashi[641]. Catalytic reduction gives a dihydrodiphtheric acid, m.p. 65°, anilide m.p. 73°. Permanganate oxidation yields a dihydroxydiphtheric acid, m.p. 46°, which is oxidized by chromic acid with formation of a C_{26} acid, m.p. 46°, and a 8-oxononanoic acid, m.p. 40.5°, semicarbazone m.p. 134.5°. From these data, the formula [191] is proposed for diphtheric acid.

$$(C_{25}H_{51})—CH = \underset{\underset{CH_3}{|}}{C}—(CH_2)_6—COOH$$

[191]

The $C_{25}H_{51}$ radical should contain a branch, as is indicated by the optical rotation of diphtheric acid and the low melting point of the C_{26} acid obtained by oxidation.

Gubarev et al.[642] mention the isolation of α-corinnic acid, m.p. 64°, $C_{35}H_{68}O_2$, and β-corinnic acid, m.p. 44—45°, $C_{34}H_{66}O_2$, from the lipids of C. diphtheriae. These mono-unsaturated acids, whose empirical formulae are only approximate, seem to be different from diphtheric acid because of their melting points. No other information is given about their structure. Earlier on, Chargaff[640] observed the presence of an acid, m.p. 62—64°, mol. wt. 514, which may be identical with the α-corinnic acid of Gubarev.

w) *Mycobacteric acids* $C_{42}H_{80}O_2 \pm 3\ CH_2$

From the lipids of two human strains of the tubercle bacillus, Asselineau et al.[643] isolated the methyl ester of an acid, b.p. 280°/0.1 mm, m.p. 40-42°, $[\alpha]_D—4°$.

Methoxyl and C-H determinations, titration and NMR spectroscopy lead to propose the empirical formula $C_{42}H_{80}O_2 \pm 3\ CH_2$. At least one cyclopropane ring is present in the molecule.

An acid $C_{42}H_{80}O_2$ ($\pm 3\ CH_2$) (methyl ester m.p. 27—32°, $[\alpha]_D—4.7°$) was isolated from the lipids of *M. phlei*. It is devoid of cyclopropane ring, but contains double bonds. Oxidative degradation gives palmitic acid (and small amounts of homologs) and branched chain acids[643].

The name "mycobacteric acid" is proposed for this group of acids.

An oxo member of this group, mycobacteronic acid, was isolated from B.C.G. (see page 117).

2. HYDROXY ACIDS

Of the fifteen hydroxy acids mentioned in this section, twelve are β-hydroxy acids. In all cases where the steric configuration of the asymmetric carbon atom bearing the hydroxyl has been studied, it has been observed that these β-hydroxy acids belong to the D-series, but 2-methyl-3-hydroxypentanoic acid which belongs to the L-series of 3-hydroxy-acids.

a) 3 D-*Hydroxybutyric acid* $C_4H_8O_3$ and "*Poly-β-hydroxybutyrate*" $(C_4H_6O_2)_n$

The production of (—)-3-hydroxybutyric acid by *Bacillus megaterium* has long been known[644]. This acid is obtained as very hygroscopic crystals with m.p. 45—48° and $[\alpha]_D—25°$, (water). It can be conveniently prepared by hydrazinolysis of poly-β-hydroxybutyrate through the hydrazide, m.p. 126—128°, $[\alpha]_D—30.0°$ [645].

Correlation of its configuration with D-glyceraldehyde results from the work of Levene *et al.* (see particularly ref. 646). Subsequently, this acid was isolated from the fermentation products of other *Bacillus* species (*B. cereus, B. mycoides, B. anthracis*) [647]. β-hydroxybutyric acid can be identified in the bacterial cell by IR spectrography [648].

The extraction of bacterial cells, by a procedure using an acid hydrolysis, was first used to obtain "poly-β-hydroxybutyrate" ("lipide β-hydroxybutyrique"): an amorphous powder insoluble in water, alcohol, and ether, soluble in chloroform and benzene, the melting point of which varied, according to the preparation, from 115° to 157°. Lemoigne *et al.* [649] showed that on saponification this lipid affords a mixture of crotonic acid (m.p. 72°) and (—)-3-hydroxybutyric acid in a ratio of about 1 to 3. On pyrolysis, it gives crotonic acid. These results led Lemoigne *et al.* [649] to suggest an estolide type structure [192] for this lipid ;

[192]

In 1952, Képès & Péaud-Lenoël [650] showed that the poly-β-hydroxybutyrate could be obtained by extraction of powdered bacteria with a mixture of dioxan and chloroform, without any hydrolysis. Such preparations have a melting point of 179°, which is higher than that observed by Lemoigne *et al.* and which is due to a higher degree of polymerization.

The structure [192] attributed to the poly-β-hydroxybutyrate was confirmed by Kepes & Peaud-Lenoel [650]. Potentiometric titration, carried out in aqueous dioxan on samples with m.p. 179°, revealed the presence of one carboxyl group for a molecular weight of about 10000 (corresponding to 110 β-hydroxybutyric residues). The presence of a terminal hydroxyl is demonstrated by the isolation of acetylacetic acid (2,4-dinitrophenylhydrazone, m.p. 123°) after chromic acid oxidation and saponification. A physico-chemical study of this lipid led to the assumption that the estolide chain must be coiled or branched [650].

The lipids of *B. megaterium* mostly consist of poly-β-hydroxybutyrate [649] which, under appropriate conditions, can reach up to 50 % of the dry weight of these bacilli [647].

Poly-β-hydroxybutyrate has been detected in a large number of bacteria: *B. cereus, B. mycoides, B. anthracis* [651], *Azotobacter chroococcum* [652], *Actinobacillus mallei* [643], *Chromobacterium* sp. [653], *Hydrogenomonas* sp. [654], *Micrococcus halodenitrificans* [655], *Nitrobacter* [655a], a group of *Pseudomonas* [656], *Rhizobium trifolii* [657], *Rhodospirillum rubrum* [658], *Sphaerotilus natans* [659, 660], *Spirillum* sp., and *Vibrio* sp. [653]. Poly-β-hydroxybutyrate has been most often isolated either by extraction with a mixture of dioxan and chloroform or by treatment of the cell with hypochlorite (see, e.g. ref. 661); however the latter procedure gives samples of low molecular weight. Samples of molecular weight as high as 250,000 were obtained by solvent extraction [661b]. Infrared spectrography has been used for its direct detection in the bacterial cell; [648, 662]; see also ref. 663.

This polymer accumulates in the cell during exponential growth (see, e.g. ref. 655) and can be observed under the microscope as refringent globules. These globular inclusions are pure poly-β-hydroxybutyrate [655] or poly-β-hydroxybutyrate containing 8—11 % of ether-soluble lipids [664, 661]. Their microscopic structure was studied by Merrick et al. [661a, 663a].

Glucose, pyruvate, and β-hydroxybutyrate (but not glycerol) are suitable substrates for its synthesis in washed cells of *B. megaterium* [665]. Its synthesis from carbon dioxide and water by *Hydrogenomonas* was studied by Schlegel et al. [666, 666a] and from organic nitrogen compounds by *M. halodenitrificans* by Sierra & Gibbons [665]. This polymer "represents a means for the rapid and massive intracellular accumulation of exogenous organic carbon, when this organic carbon cannot be immediately converted to cell material" [658, 658a]. It may be used as an energetic substrate and is completely oxidized to carbon dioxide and water [667]; this degradation requires a depolymerase (sensitive to *p*-nitrophenyl phosphate) and a NAD-linked dehydrogenase (isolated from a strain of *Hydrogenomonas* [668]).

A review on the distribution, rôle, and biosynthesis of poly β hydroxybutyrate was published by Schlegel & Gottschalk in 1962 [669]; (see also 669 a).

b) (—)-2-*Methyl-3-hydroxypentanoic acid* $C_6H_{12}O_3$

From the hydrolysis products of mycobactin (growth factor for *M. johnei* synthesized by *M. phlei*) Snow [670] isolated (—)-2-methyl-3-hydroxypentanoic acid [193] as a viscous oil, b.p. 90—100° (bath)/0.1/mm, $[\alpha]_D^{25}$—14.8° (methanol), *p*-bromophenocylate m.p. 80.5— 90° and $[\alpha]_D^{18}$—15° (methanol).

This acid was transformed into 2-methylpentanoic acid [194] (anilide m.p. 89.5— 90.5°, $[\alpha]_D^{18}$—19° (methanol)) by reduction of an intermediate iodo derivative. The anilide was identified by comparison of its IR spectrum with that of a synthetic product [670].

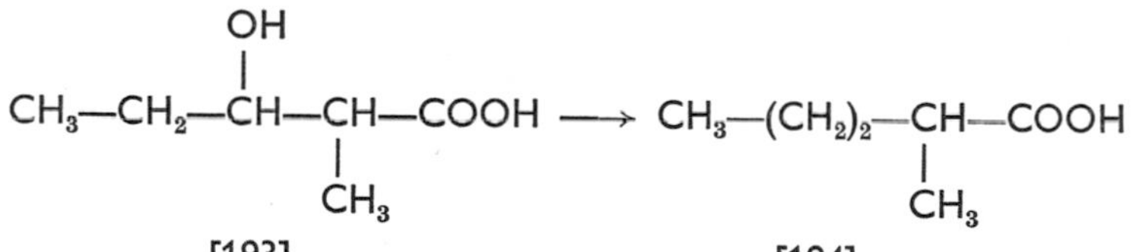

$$CH_3-CH_2-\underset{\underset{CH_3}{|}}{\overset{\overset{OH}{|}}{CH}}-CH-COOH \longrightarrow CH_3-(CH_2)_2-\underset{\underset{CH_3}{|}}{CH}-COOH$$

[193] [194]

A 2-methyl-3-hydroxypentanoic acid was synthesized by Snow [670] by the Reformatsky reaction of propionic aldehyde with ethyl α-bromopropionate. The hydroxy acid obtained differed from the natural acid in the melting point of its *p*-bromophenacylate (m.p. 62.5— 63°) and in its IR spectrum: "it was apparently the racemic form of the other epimer" [670]. Actually, the products obtained by the Reformatsky reaction and by the hydrogenation of the β-keto ester ethyl 2-methyl-3-oxopentanoate are a mixture of erythro-and threo-isomers which are difficult to separate [671]. Recently, Snow [672] has obtained conclusive evidence for the threo-configuration of the natural acid; the asymmetric centre in position 3 belongs to the L-series. This acid is then 2(D)-methyl-3(L)-hydroxypentanoic acid or 2R-methyl-3s-hydroxypentanoic acid [672].

An acid such as [193] can be synthesized *in vivo* by condensation of two molecules of propionic acid (see p. 147).

c) *Mevalonic acid* $C_6H_{12}O_4$

This acid, which is a precursor of terpene and sterol compounds, exists in most living creatures and cannot therefore be considered as a specific constituent of bacteria. Nevertheless, we mention its existence here by reason of the isolation, from certain species of *Lactobacillus*, of hiochic acid, quinine salt m.p. 137—138°, *S*-benzylthiouronium salt m.p. 122—123°; lactone, oil n_D^{19} 1.474 $[\alpha]_D^{20}$—19.9° [673]. Hiochic acid was identified as mevalonic acid [674], the constitution [195] of which had been previously elucidated by Folkers *et al.* [675, 676].

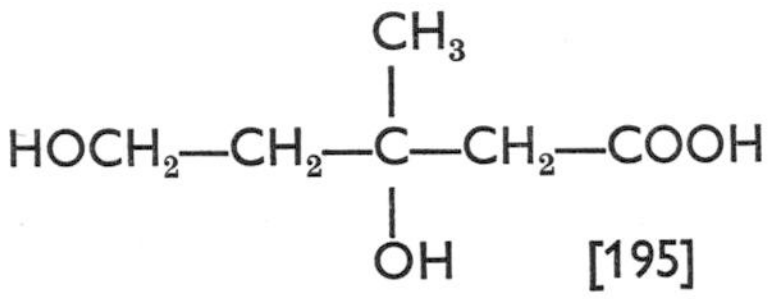

$$HOCH_2—CH_2—\overset{\overset{\displaystyle CH_3}{|}}{\underset{\underset{\displaystyle OH}{|}}{C}}—CH_2—COOH \qquad [195]$$

d) (—)-3(D)-*Hydroxydecanoic acid* $C_{10}H_{20}O_3$

The acid or alkaline hydrolysis of pyolipic acid (a rhamnoside produced by *Pseudomonas pyocyanea*, see p. 170) gives a hydroxy acid which has been identified as (—)-3-hydroxydecanoic acid [196]. The free acid melts at 46—47°, hydrazide m.p. 134—136°, *S*-benzylthiouronium salt m.p. 131—132°. The methyl ester , b.p. 97°/0.9 mm $[\alpha]_D$— 18.9°, affords a mono-azoate, which demonstrates the presence of a hydroxyl group. The chromic acid oxidation of the acid, which consumes 5 atoms of oxygen, gives n-octanoic acid. In pyolipic acid, 3-hydroxydecanoic acid is accompanied by small quantities of lower and higher homologues (3-hydroxyoctanoic and 3-hydroxydodecanoic acids) [677].

The same acid, m.p. 47—48°, $[\alpha]_D$ —21°, was obtained by hydrolysis of a crystalline rhamnolipid synthesized by *Pseudomonas aeruginosa* [678] (see p. 170).

The hydrolysis of viscosin, an antibiotic produced by *Pseudomonas viscosa*, gives, besides amino-acids, (—)-3-hydroxydecanoic acid (accompanied by some Δ^2-decenoic acid, probably arising from dehydration of the β-hydroxy acid) [679]. In this antibiotic, the hydroxydecanoic acid is bound to the peptide fraction in the amide form. The same is the case with serratamic acid, isolated from a species of *Serratia* (p. 188), which is the amide of (—)-3-hydroxydecanoic acid and L-serine [680]. 5.2 % of the total fatty acids extracted from *Serratia marcescens* consists of 3-hydroxydecanoic acid [681]. It has also been found in the bound lipids of *Azotobacter agilis* [682].

(+)-3(L)-Hydroxydecanoic acid [199], the antipode of the natural acid [196], was synthesized by Serck-Hanssen & Stenhagen [438] by Kolbe's reaction using methyl (—)-3(L)-acetoxy-4-carboxybutanoate [197] and heptanoic acid [198].

```
COOH              COOCH₃                                    COOH
 |                  |                                         |
CH₂                CH₂               COOH                    CH₂
 |                  |                  |                       |
H—C—OH         CH₃COO—C—H    +      (CH₂)₅     ⟶        HO—C—H
 |                  |                  |                       |
(CH₂)₆             CH₂                CH₃                    (CH₂)₆
 |                  |                                          |
CH₃               COOH                                       CH₃
[196]             [197]              [198]                   [199]
```

The (+)-L synthetic acid has the following properties: m.p. 48.4°, $[\alpha]_D$ + 20° (chloroform), +13° (ethanol). With an equimolecular amount of the natural acid, it gives the racemic acid, m.p. 56.6°. The laevorotatory natural acid therefore belongs to the D-series.

e) *2-Hydroxydodecanoic acid* $C_{12}H_{24}O_3$

This acid was characterized in the bound lipids of *Azotobacter agilis*, along with the 3-hydroxy isomer [682].

f) *3-Hydroxydodecanoic acid* $C_{12}H_{24}O_3$

This acid has been observed in the hydrolysis products of pyolipic acid, along with 3-hydroxydecanoic acid [677] (p. 170). It has been more recently characterized in the lipids of *Serratia marcescens* [681], where it forms up to 2.5 % of the total fatty acids, and in the bound lipids of *Azotobacter agilis* [682].

g) *3-Hydroxydodec-5-enoic acid* $C_{12}H_{22}O_3$

This acid has been isolated from the total fatty acids of a strain of *Serratia marcescens* obtained by saponification of the crude lipids. Its structure [200] is deduced from the formation of 3-hydroxydodecanoic acid on hydrogenation, of decanoic acid on permanganate oxidation of the dihydro-acid, and of heptanoic acid on permanganate oxidation of the unsaturated acid [681]. 1.5 % of 3-hydroxydodec-5-enoic acid was isolated from the total fatty acids; this acid has a biotin-sparing effect on *Lactobacilli*, which can be explained by its possible rôle as precursor of *cis*-vaccenic acid [681].

$$CH_3—(CH_2)_5—CH = CH—CH_2—CHOH—CH_2—COOH \qquad [200]$$

h) *3(D)-Hydroxytetradecanoic acid* $C_{14}H_{28}O_3$

The hydrolysis of a phospholipid present in a lipopolysaccharide isolated from *Escherichia coli* (see p. 195) yields, besides normal saturated acids, (—)-3-hydroxytetradecanoic acid, m.p. 73—74°, $[\alpha]_D$—16° (chloroform), —9.6° (pyridine), *p*-bromophenacylate m.p. 112.5—113°, benzyl-ammonium salt m.p. 84—86° [683]. Its structure has been elucidated by reduction to tetradecanoic acid and permanganate oxidation to dodecanoic acid.

DL-β-Hydroxytetradecanoic acid (m.p. 78—79°) has been synthesized by the Reformatsky reaction of ethyl bromoacetate with lauraldehyde and has been resolved by recrystallization of its D-α—methyl-β-phenylethylamine salt: the laevorotatory acid obtained has the same properties as the natural acid.

Comparison of the specific rotation of this acid with those of 3(D)-hydroxyhexanoic and 3(D)-hydroxydecanoic acids favours the D-configuration of (—)-3(D)-hydroxytetradecanoic acid [683].

i) (—)10-Hydroxyoctadecanoic acid $C_{18}H_{36}O_3$

From the lipids of human strains of *M. tuberculosis*, Polgar & Smith [683a]) isolated 10-hydroxyoctadecanoic acid; its methyl ester has a m.p. 52—54° and $[\alpha]_D$—0.25°. According to the sign of rotation, it is likely to belong to the D-series.

j) 10-Oxoöctadecanoic acid $C_{18}H_{34}O_3$

Beside the above hydroxy-acid, Polgar & Smith [683a] found the corresponding keto acid, whose methyl ester has a m.p. 45—46°.

k) Dihydroxyoctadecanoic acid $C_{18}H_{36}O_4$

Crowder & Anderson [684] isolated from the lipids of *Lactobacillus acidophilus* a dihydroxyoctadecanoic acid, m.p. 106—107° (diacetate oily) because of its low solubility in ether. The treatment of this acid with hydrogen iodide gave stearic acid (octadecanoic acid).

The samples of dihydroxyoctadecanoic acid obtained by Crowder and Anderson [584] showed an optical rotation $[\alpha]_D$ varying from + 7.78° to 0° (methanol); these authors mention the easy racemization of this acid by simply heating in alcohol.

The existence of cis-vaccenic acid ($\Delta^{11,12}$-octadecenoic acid) in strains of *Lactobacilli* might suggest that the hydroxyl groups in the dihydroxyoctadecanoic acid are at carbon atoms 11 and 12. Moreover, the high melting form of 11,12-dihydroxyoctadecanoic acid melts at 106—108° [685]. Nevertheless, the very easy racemization of natural dihydroxyoctadecanoic acid would indicate more plausibly the presence of an α-ketol group, for example.

l) "3-Hydroxy-C_{27}-acid", $C_{27}H_{54}O_3$

By chromatography of the high-boiling methyl ester fractions obtained from the lipids of the human strain Test of *M. tuberculosis*, Asselineau [643] isolated a hydroxy-ester with m.p. 41—43.5° and $[\alpha]_D$ +9°. The elementary composition of the ester led to the formula $C_{27}H_{54}O_2(\pm CH_2)$ for the free acid. The position of the hydroxyl, β with respect to the carboxyl, results from the dehydration to an α,β-unsaturated acid (λ_{max} 220 mμ, ε = 10 000) and from the relatively high position of the carbonyl band in the infrared spectrum (5.87 μ) of the hydroxy-ester. The carbon skeleton of this acid is branched, as the *C*-methyl determination shows the presence of at least three C—CH$_3$.

This acid might be a precursor of acids of the phthienoic type; however the infrared spectrum of the dehydrated ester differs slightly from that of methyl C_{27}-phthienoate [643].

m) *Corynomycolic acid* $C_{32}H_{64}O_3$

The lipids of *Corynebacterium diphtheriae* contain about 6% of a hydroxy acid, present in the free state, which has been named corynomycolic acid [686, 309]. This acid, purified by chromatography of its methyl ester, has the molecular formula $C_{32}H_{64}O_3$. Its properties are given in Table 23; the alkali salts are soluble in ether.

TABLE 23. C_{32}-β-HYDROXY-ACIDS FROM THE DIPHTHERIA BACILLUS

	Corynomycolic acid			Corynomycolenic acid	
	Natural acid		Synthetic DL-acid (β-isomer)	Natural acid	Synthetic acid (mixture of isomers)
Reference	309	686	693	412	695
Free acid	$C_{32}H_{64}O_3$			$C_{32}H_{62}O_3$	
m.p.	70°		70°	—15°	
				n_D^{19} 1.4758	
$[\alpha]_D$	+7.5°			+9.5°	
Methyl ester	$C_{33}H_{66}O_3$			$C_{33}H_{64}O_3$	
m.p.	61°		57-59°	n_D^{19} 1.4680	n_D^{21} 1.4678
$[\alpha]_D$	+5.7°			+9.0°	
Diol (from reduction by LiAlH₄) . . .	$C_{32}H_{66}O_2$				
m.p.	43-44°		44-45°		
$[\alpha]_D$	+12°				
Anhydro-acid. . . .	$C_{32}H_{62}O_2$				
m.p.	60°		58-60°		

The structure of corynomycolic acid [201] has been established through the series of reactions schematized below [686, 309]. The similarity between the formula of corynomycolic acid [201] and the partial formula common to the mycolic acids of the *Mycobacteria* (p. 123) justifies the name given to it.

Determination of the exact length of the aliphatic chains in corynomycolic acid depends on examination of the X-ray diffraction diagrams of the palmitic acid [207] formed on pyrolysis and of palmitone [204], m.p. 80°, which is obtained on chromic acid oxidation.

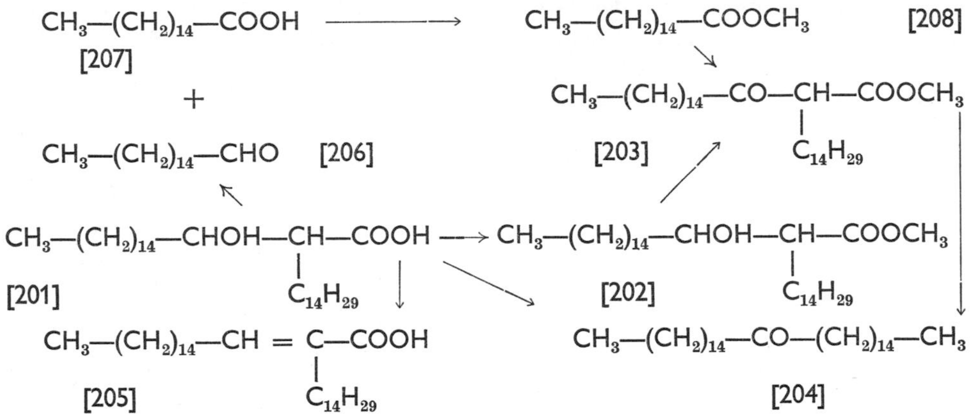

$$CH_3—(CH_2)_{14}—COOH \longrightarrow CH_3—(CH_2)_{14}—COOCH_3 \qquad [208]$$

$$[207]$$

$$+$$

$$CH_3—(CH_2)_{14}—CO—CH—COOCH_3$$
$$\qquad\qquad\qquad\qquad\qquad |$$
$$CH_3—(CH_2)_{14}—CHO \quad [206] \qquad\qquad [203] \qquad C_{14}H_{29}$$

$$CH_3—(CH_2)_{14}—CHOH—CH—COOH \longrightarrow CH_3—(CH_2)_{14}—CHOH—CH—COOCH_3$$
$$\qquad\qquad\qquad\qquad |$$
$$[201] \qquad\qquad C_{14}H_{29} \qquad\qquad [202] \qquad C_{14}H_{29}$$

$$CH_3—(CH_2)_{14}—CH = C—COOH \qquad CH_3—(CH_2)_{14}—CO—(CH_2)_{14}—CH_3$$
$$\qquad\qquad\qquad\qquad |$$
$$[205] \qquad\qquad C_{14}H_{29} \qquad\qquad\qquad [204]$$

Corynomycolic acid was again found in *C. diphtheriae* by Pustovalov [687] and more recently in the lipids of *C. ovis* by Diara & Pudles [688] and closely related hydroxy-acids were characterized in the lipids of *Corynebacterium* 506 and *C. rubrum* [688a]. It appears that corynomycolic acid is a characteristic component of the lipids of *Corynebacteria* (just as mycolic acids are characteristic constituents of the lipids of *Mycobacteria*). Cmelik [31] observed in the bound lipids of *C. diphtheriae* the presence of a hydroxy acid $C_{32}H_{64}O_3$, m.p. 68°, different from corynomycolic acid (mixed melting point depression).

Acetylation of corynomycolic acid [201] gives a mixture of the acetyl derivative [209], m.p. 86—88°, and of the anhydride of acetylcorynomycolic acid, $C_{68}H_{130}O_7$, m.p. 33—34°, $[\alpha]_D$ +11.2°. The lactone [210], m.p. 44—45°, $[\alpha]_D$ +33°, was prepared from the acetyl derivative by the Arndt-Eistert reaction. As the optical rotation of this lactone is higher than that of the corresponding hydroxy-acid, the asymmetric centre 3 is likely to belong to the D series [689].

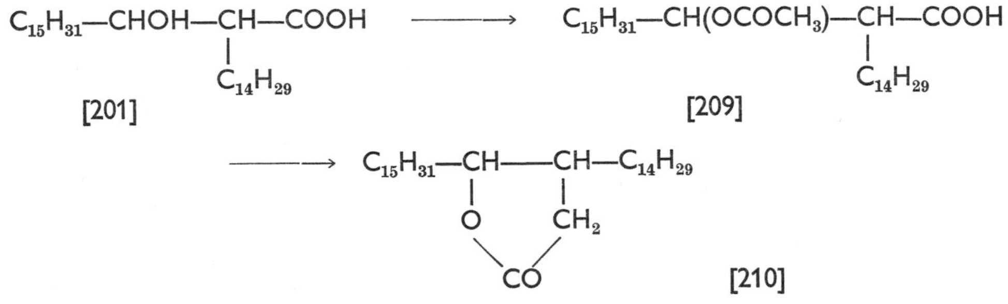

$$C_{15}H_{31}—CHOH—CH—COOH \longrightarrow C_{15}H_{31}—CH(OCOCH_3)—CH—COOH$$
$$\qquad\qquad\qquad |$$
$$\qquad\qquad C_{14}H_{29} \qquad\qquad\qquad\qquad\qquad C_{14}H_{29}$$
$$[201] \qquad\qquad\qquad\qquad\qquad\qquad [209]$$

$$\longrightarrow C_{15}H_{31}—CH——CH—C_{14}H_{29}$$
$$\qquad\qquad\qquad | \qquad |$$
$$\qquad\qquad\qquad O \quad CH_2$$
$$\qquad\qquad\qquad \diagdown CO \diagup \qquad\qquad [210]$$

Lederer *et al.* [690] synthesized methyl α-palmitoylpalmitate [203] by condensing two molecules of methyl palmitate [208] in the presence of sodium hydride, according to Hansley's method [691]. This procedure was used again a little later by Clement [692], who was apparently unaware of the work of Lederer *et al.* Methyl α-palmitoylpalmitate shows an X-ray diffraction pattern identical with that of the keto-ester [203] arising from the degradation of corynomycolic acid [309].

The reduction of methyl α-palmitoylpalmitate by sodium borohydride, or catalytically in the presence of Raney nickel, gives a mixture of isomeric acids $C_{32}H_{64}O_3$ [690]. Chromatography on alumina separates this mixture into the two diastereoisomers: isomer α, m.p. 73—75° (eluted first), and isomer β, m.p. 68—69° [693]. This latter acid is racemic corynomycolic acid, as is shown by examination of the properties of some derivatives (see Table 24), and by comparison of the X-ray diffraction patterns [693].

Using Hansley's method, the following lower and higher racemic homologues of corynomycolic acid have been synthesized: the acids $C_{14}H_{28}O_3$ and $C_{16}H_{32}O_3$, from methyl heptanoate and octanoate, respectively; $C_{36}H_{72}O_3$, from methyl stearate; $C_{44}H_{88}O_3$, from methyl behenate; $C_{48}H_{96}O_3$, from methyl tetracosanoate; and $C_{52}H_{104}O_3$, from methyl hexacosanoate [690, 693, 694] (see Table 24). Two di-unsaturated acids were prepared in the same way from methyl palmitoleate and oleate [695, 693].

TABLE 24. THE PROPERTIES OF SYNTHETIC α-BRANCHED-β-HYDROXY-ACIDS OF THE CORYNOMYCOLIC ACID TYPE

Acid	Diastereo-isomer	Molecular formula	Free acid, m.p.	Methyl ester, m.p.	Anhydro-acid			Ref.
					M.p.	$\lambda_{max}^{m\mu}$ (hexane)	ε	
2-n-Tetradecyl-3-hydroxy octadecanoic	α	$C_{32}H_{64}O_3$	73-75°	70°	58-60°	215.5	12,600	690
	β		68-69°	57-59°				693
2-n-Hexadecyl-3-hydroxy-eicosanoic	α	$C_{36}H_{72}O_3$	78-79°	71-73°	68-70°	215.5	13,600	690
	β		72-74°	58-60°				693
2-n-Eicosyl-3-hydroxy-tetracosanoic	α	$C_{44}H_{88}O_3$	88-89°	82-83°				693
	β		83-85°	74-76°				
2-n-Docosyl-3-hydroxy-hexacosanoic	α	$C_{48}H_{96}O_3$	91-92.5°					694
	β		86-88°					
2-n-Tetracosyl-3-hydroxy-octacosanoic	α	$C_{52}H_{104}O_3$	92-93.5°	86.5-88°	90-90.5°			694
	β		87-89°	77-78°				

The mixture of the $C_{32}H_{64}O_3$ acids and their higher homologues are acid-fast (p. 255); no acid-fast testing seems to have been made on the isolated diastereoisomers. The lower homologues have not been tested because of pratical difficulties. The α,β-unsaturated acids arising from the dehydration of the β-hydroxy acids lose the acid-fastness of their precursors [690].

The biosynthesis of corynomycolic acid will be discussed on p. 149.

Esters of corynomycolic acid with N-acetyl-D-glucosamine or α-D-trehalose have been prepared (p. 174).

n) *Corynomycolenic acid* $C_{32}H_{62}O_3$

The lipids of *C. diphtheriae* contain, besides corynomycolic acid, an unsaturated hydroxy-acid, $C_{32}H_{62}O_3$, which on catalytic hydrogenation gives rise to corynomycolic acid [412]. Some properties of this unsaturated acid, known as corynomycolenic acid, are given in Table 23.

The carbon skeleton and the hydroxyl position are determined by the observation that corynomycolic acid is obtained on hydrogenation. The double bond, which is not in the side chain because pyrolysis of corynomycolenic acid gives palmitic acid, was located by permanganate oxidation. The isolation of n-heptanoic acid and azelaic acid as oxidation products shows that it is at the 11:12-position. Corynomycolenic acid therefore has the structure [211] [412]. According to its infrared spectrum, this unsaturated hydroxy-acid is a cis compound.

The formation of corynomycolic acid, $[\alpha]_D$ +7.5°, by hydrogenation of corynomycolenic acid, $[\alpha]_D$ +9.5°, shows that the asymmetric centres at positions 2 and 3 have the same configuration in both acids.

The synthesis of 2-n-tetradecyl-3-hydroxy-cis-Δ^{11}-octadecenoic acid (mixture of stereoisomers) was achieved by the following sequence of reactions:

$$CH_3-(CH_2)_5-CH=CH-(CH_2)_7-COCl \; + \; CH_3-(CH_2)_{13}-\underset{\underset{\textstyle CO_2C_2H_5}{|}}{CH}-CO_2(C_5H_9O)$$

[212 a]   [212 b]

$$\longrightarrow \; CH_3-(CH_2)_5-CH=CH-(CH_2)_7-CO-\underset{\underset{\textstyle C_{14}H_{29}}{|}}{CH}-CO_2C_2H_5 \; \xrightarrow{\; NaBH_4, \; KOH \;}$$

[213]

$$CH_3-(CH_2)_5-CH=CH-(CH_2)_7-CHOH-\underset{\underset{\textstyle C_{14}H_{29}}{|}}{CH}-CO_2H$$

[211]

The infrared spectrum of the methyl ester from the synthetic acid is "practically identical" with that of methyl corynomycolenate [695].

A C_{34}-corynomycolenic acid (giving palmitic acid by pyrolysis) was isolated from the lipids of *Corynebacterium* 506 [688a].

o) *Hydroxycorinnic acids* $C_{34}H_{68}O_3$

Several hydroxy acids have been isolated from the lipids of *C. diphtheriae* by Gubarev and his collaborators.

α-*Hydroxycorinnic acid*, $C_{34}H_{68}O_3$, m.p. 70° [642], may be identical with corynomycolic acid. All the acids isolated in Gubarev laboratory are characterized only by the determination of various values, in particular the neutralization and acetyl values, and no additional data are given.

β-*Hydroxycorinnic acid*, m.p. 59°, was isolated at the same time.

In 1946, Gubarev [696] described a hydroxydiphtheric acid, $C_{30}H_{58}O_3$, m.p. 50°, $[\alpha]_D$ —9.4°, which was later separated by the same author [697] into three hydroxy acids, α, β, and γ. The γ acid melts at 45°; its molecular weight (titration) is 385, iodine number 49.1, and acetyl number 105.9. No other information is given about their structure.

p) *Mycobacteronic acid* $C_{42}H_{80}O_3 \pm 3 CH_2$

From the fat of BCG (a bovine strain of the tubercle bacillus), Bennet & Asselineau [630] isolated a mono-unsaturated keto acid, m.p. 36—37°, $C_{42}H_{80}O_3 \pm 3 CH_2$ (methyl ester m.p. 30—32° and $[\alpha]_D$ + 1.1°). NMR spectrography shows the presence of three C—CH_3 groups and of—CH_2—CO—CH_2—. From chemical studies, the carbonyl group is farther from the carboxyl than position 5. The UV spectrum of the initial keto acid indicates the absence of conjugation.

This keto acid has about the same molecular weight as the dienic acids isolated from other types of *Mycobacteria* (p. 107), so that the occurrence of C_{42} acids may well be a common feature of the *Mycobacteria*.

q) *Nocardomycolic acids (nocardic acids)* $C_{50}H_{96}O_3$

From the lipids of *Nocardia asteroides*, Michel *et al.* [698] isolated an oily hydroxy-acid, $C_{50}H_{96}O_3$, $[\alpha]_D$ +5°, which they called nocardic acid; its potassium salt is soluble in aqueous alkali. This acid contains two double bonds and on hydrogenation gives tetrahydronocardic acid, $C_{50}H_{100}O_3$, m.p. 78—82°, methyl ester m.p. 64°. That the position of the hydroxyl is β with respect to the carboxyl, is shown by the formation of an α,β-unsaturated acid on dehydration and of a neutral ketone on oxidation. Pyrolysis (p. 127) of tetrahydronocardic acid gives a mixture of myristic and palmitic acids. On the basis of the results obtained with the mycolic acids (p. 122), this acid appears to be a mixture of acids [214 *a*] and [214 *b*]. Ozonolysis of the nocardic acids furnishes nonanoic acid, which suggests the presence of the grouping CH_3—$(CH_2)_7$—CH = in the radical R [698].

$$R—CHOH—CH—CO_2H$$
$$|$$
$$R' \quad [214]$$

$$a : R' = C_{12}H_{25}$$
$$b : R' = C_{14}H_{29}$$

The nocardic acids thus belong to the family of mycolic acids (p. 122) and we therefore propose to use the name nocardomycolic acids, by analogy to corynomycolic acid.

From a mass spectroscopic investigation of the aldehydes obtained by pyrolytic splitting of a sample of nocardomycolic acid from *N. asteroides*, Bordet *et al.* [698 a] concluded that the radical R in formula [214] consists of a normal aliphatic chain with 35, 37 or 41 carbon atoms. Nocardomycolic acid is a mixture of di- and tri- unsaturated acids.

Simultaneously, Lanéelle *et al.* [1256 b] arrived at the same results by studying a sample of methyl nocardomycolate from *N. brasiliensis* by NMR spectroscopy and thin-layer chromatography on silica-gel impregnated with silver nitrate. The same authors [1256 b] also observed the presence of nocardomycolic acids in strains of *N. pellegrino* and *N. rhodocrous*. Lanéelle *et al.* [1256 b] found stearic acid in the mixture of acids obtained by pyrolysis of various samples of nocardomycolic acid. Stearic acid is likely to be also formed from nocardomycolic acid from *N. asteroides*, as Michel and Lederer [519] have shown that degradation of nocardols (see page 79) gives rise to a mixture of C_{16} and C_{18} acids.

The biosynthesis of nocardomycolic acids is considered on page 148.

r) *Corynolic acid* $C_{52}H_{104}O_4$

In 1933, Chargaff [640] isolated from the phospholipids of *C. diphtheriae* a hydroxy acid, $C_{50}H_{100}O_4$, m.p. 70—71°, diacetate m.p. 75—76°, which he called corynin; the potassium salt is soluble in large amounts of ether.

A hydroxy acid possessing the same properties (m.p. 70—71°, $[\alpha]_D^{31}$ —26.3°) was obtained from the same source by Asano & Takahashi [699] in 1945; the name of this acid was altered to corynolic acid.

On mild chromic oxidation, corynolic acid [215] gives a keto-lactone [216], m.p. 79°, the oxime (m.p. 83°) of which undergoes a Beckmann rearrangement with the formation after hydrolysis of monomethylamine. The partial formula [215] could therefore be attributed to it.

$$
C_{47}H_{93} \left\{ \begin{array}{l} -CHOH-CH_3 \\ -OH \\ -COOH \end{array} \right. \qquad C_{47}H_{93} \left\{ \begin{array}{l} -CO-CH_3 \\ -O \\ \quad | \\ -C=O \end{array} \right.
$$

[215]   [216]

Study of the structure of corynolic acid was pursued by Takahashi [700]. Treatment of corynolic acid with hydrogen iodide reduces the hydroxy groups and deoxycorynolic acid, $C_{52}H_{104}O_2$, m.p. 50°, is obtained. From examination of the chromic oxidation products of corynolic and deoxycorynolic acids, Takahashi [700] suggested the formula [217] for corynolic acid. This very unusual structure is based, in part, on the elucidation of the structure of the keto-lactone [218] and the ketone [221].

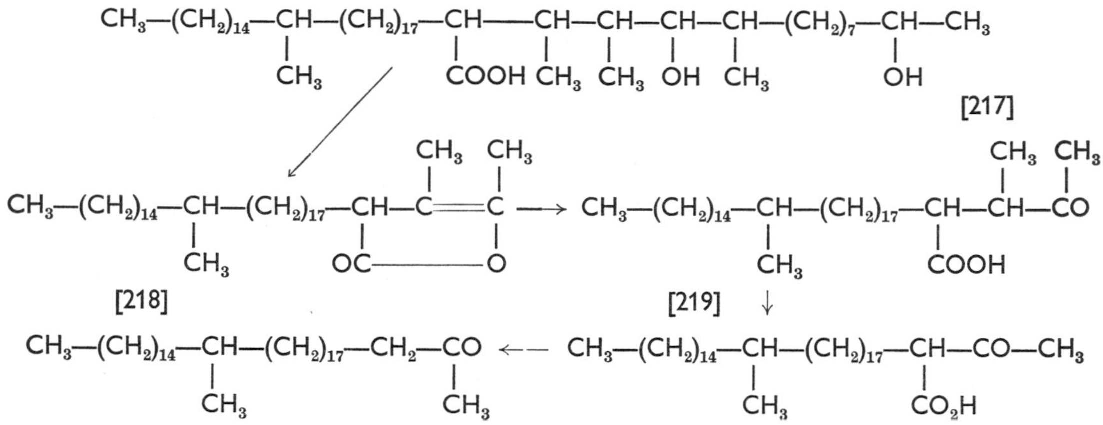

$$CH_3-(CH_2)_{14}-CH-(CH_2)_{17}-CH--CH-CH-CH-CH-(CH_2)_7-CH-CH_3$$

with substituents: CH_3 ; $COOH$ CH_3 CH_3 OH CH_3 ; OH

[217]

$$CH_3-(CH_2)_{14}-CH-(CH_2)_{17}-CH-C=C$$

with substituents CH_3 ; CH_3 CH_3 ; $OC-----O$

[218]

$$\longrightarrow CH_3-(CH_2)_{14}-CH-(CH_2)_{17}-CH-CH-CO$$

with substituents CH_3 ; CH_3 CH_3 ; $COOH$

[219] ↓

$$CH_3-(CH_2)_{14}-CH-(CH_2)_{17}-CH_2-CO \longleftarrow CH_3-(CH_2)_{14}-CH-(CH_2)_{17}-CH-CO-CH_3$$

with substituents left: CH_3 ; CH_3 ; right: CH_3 ; CO_2H

[221]   [220]

The stability of the δ-hydroxy acid [217] compared to the easy formation of the keto-lactone [216] is puzzling.

Very little information was given by Takahashi about the methods used in the determination of the structure of the complex oxidation products, particularly of the keto-lactone [218] and the ketone [221]. Therefore, Toubiana & Asselineau carried out the synthesis of the ketone [221] through the intermediates [222]—[226] [701] to give the racemic form and

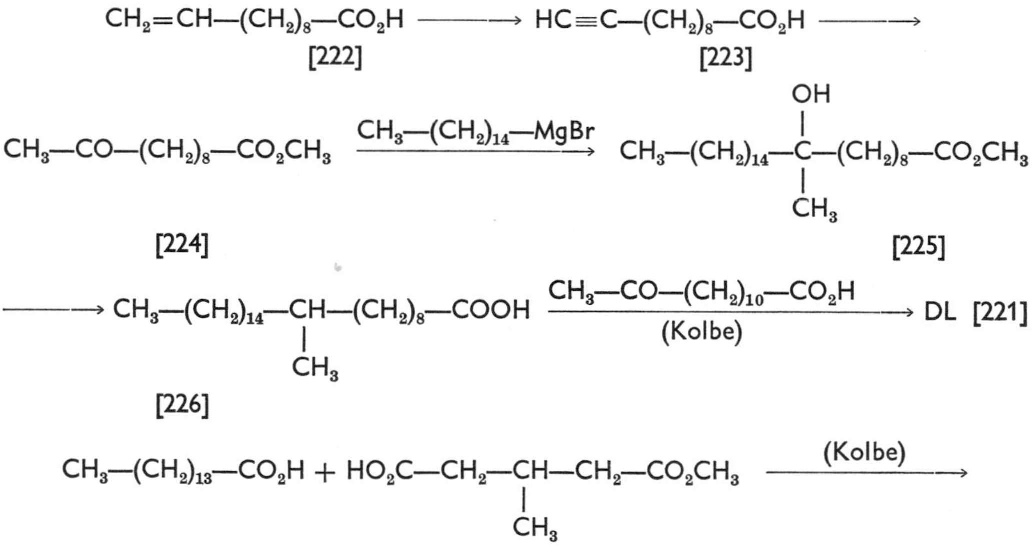

$$CH_2=CH-(CH_2)_8-CO_2H \longrightarrow HC\equiv C-(CH_2)_8-CO_2H \longrightarrow$$
[222]   [223]

$$CH_3-CO-(CH_2)_8-CO_2CH_3 \xrightarrow{CH_3-(CH_2)_{14}-MgBr} CH_3-(CH_2)_{14}-\overset{\overset{\displaystyle OH}{|}}{\underset{\underset{\displaystyle CH_3}{|}}{C}}-(CH_2)_8-CO_2CH_3$$

[224]   [225]

$$\longrightarrow CH_3-(CH_2)_{14}-CH-(CH_2)_8-COOH \xrightarrow[\text{(Kolbe)}]{CH_3-CO-(CH_2)_{10}-CO_2H} DL [221]$$

with substituent CH_3

[226]

$$CH_3-(CH_2)_{13}-CO_2H + HO_2C-CH_2-CH-CH_2-CO_2CH_3 \xrightarrow{\text{(Kolbe)}}$$

with substituent CH_3

[227]   [228]

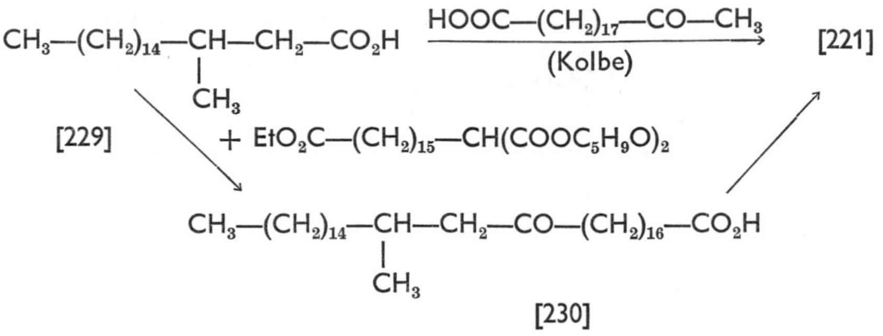

$$CH_3-(CH_2)_{14}-\underset{\underset{CH_3}{|}}{CH}-CH_2-CO_2H \quad\xrightarrow[\text{(Kolbe)}]{HOOC-(CH_2)_{17}-CO-CH_3}\quad [221]$$

[229]

$$+\ EtO_2C-(CH_2)_{15}-CH(COOC_5H_9O)_2$$

$$CH_3-(CH_2)_{14}-\underset{\underset{CH_3}{|}}{CH}-CH_2-CO-(CH_2)_{16}-CO_2H$$

[230]

through the intermediates [227]—[230] [702], [703] to give an optically active form. The melting points of the synthetic free ketone and its semicarbazone are very different from those of the ketone and its semicarbazone obtained by oxidative degradation of corynolic acid (Table 25).

TABLE 25. THE MELTING POINTS OF 21-METHYLHEXATRIACONTAN-2-ONE AND TAKAHASHI'S PRODUCT FROM CORYNOLIC ACID

	21-Methylhexatriacontan-2-one [221]		Takahashi's product
	DL	D	
Free ketone m.p.	49—51°	64—65°	79°
Semicarbazone m.p.	104—105°	110—113°	75°

The ketone m.p. 79° obtained by Takahashi thus cannot have the structure [221], and the structure [217] proposed for corynolic acid is therefore doubtful.

s) *Diphtherocorynic acid* $C_{53}H_{104}O_3$

From a chloroform extract of *C. diphtheriae*, Gubarev & Pustovalova [704] isolated a mono-unsaturated hydroxy acid, $C_{53}H_{104}O_3$, m.p. 29.0—29.6°, which might be a dehydration product of corynolic acid. No information is given about its constitution.

t) "C_{60} *hydroxy acid*" $C_{60}H_{120}O_3$

From the unsaponifiable residue of two human strains of *M. tuberculosis*, Asselineau [528], [139] isolated two saturated hydroxy acids, $C_{60}H_{120}O_3$ ($\pm\ 3CH_2$):

α) Strain Brévannes: free acid m.p. 43—49°, methyl ester m.p. 41—44°.

β) Strain H_{37} Rv S.r: free acid m.p. 45—47°.

These acids, which represent only about 0.01 % of the dry weight of the bacilli, have a branched carbon skeleton, as shown by *C*-methyl determinations. According to the position

TABLE 26. THE CHARACTERISTICS OF MYCOLIC ACIDS ISOLATED FROM HUMAN STRAINS OF *M. tuberculosis*

Strain	Order of Elution	Free acid Melting Point	$[\alpha]_D$	Molecular formula	Functional groups at C-3	Functional groups at C-x	No. of methyl-groups	Methyl-ester, m.p.	Acetate, m.p.	Anhydro-acid, m.p.	Bis anhydro-acid, m.p.	Neutral ketone, m.p.	Ref.
Test	1	55–56°	+2.3°	$C_{88}H_{176}O_4$	OH	OCH_3	3	43–46°	40–42°	36–38°	36–38°	64–67°	126
	2	71–73°	+2.2°	$C_{88}H_{176}O_4$	OH	OCH_3	3	52–55°	66–70°	36–38°		83–87°	710
	3	56–57°		$C_{87}H_{174}O_3$	OH		3	42–43°					
	4	59–60°		$C_{88}H_{176}O_3$	OCH_3			39–42°					
R_1	1	45–59°	+3.0°	$C_{87}H_{174}O_3$	OH	OH	4	45–49°		36–39°	42–43°	72–74°	710
	2	56–58°		$C_{87}H_{174}O_4$	OH	C=O	4	45–49°		50–52°			
	3	68–73°		$C_{87}H_{172}O_4$	OH			50–55°					
L_{25}	1	51–53°		$C_{87}H_{174}O_3$	OH		3	40–42°		39–41°			710
	2			$C_{88}H_{176}O_3$	OCH_3			42–44°					
				$C_{87}H_{174}O_3$	OH								
$H_{37}Ra$	1	61–63°	+2.5°	$C_{87}H_{174}O_3$	OH	OH	3	49–50°	42–44°			76–78°	724
	2	72–74°		$C_{87}H_{174}O_4$	OH	OCH_3	3	55–56°					
	3	61–64°		$C_{88}H_{176}O_4$	OH			48–50°					
$H_{37}Rv$	1	53–54°		$C_{88}H_{176}O_4$	OH	OCH_3	3	44–45°			37–38°		724
	2	56–57°		$C_{87}H_{174}O_4$	OH	OH	3	43–44°					
	3	70–72°		$C_{87}H_{174}O_4$	OH	OH	3						
	4	55–57°		$C_{87}H_{174}O_3$	OH								
$H_{37}RvS.r.$	1	56–57°	+3.0°	$C_{88}H_{176}O_4$	OH	OCH_3	3	45–46°	39–41°			68–71°	724
	2	56–57°		$C_{87}H_{174}O_4$	OH	OH	3					88–92°	
	3	70–76°		$C_{87}H_{174}O_4$	OH	OH	4						
	4	50–54°		$C_{87}H_{174}O_3$	OH								
Brévannes	1	54–55°	+1.4°	$C_{87}H_{174}O_4$	OH	OH	3				46–48°	81–83°	65
	2	75–76°		$C_{88}H_{176}O_4$	OH	OCH_3	3						
	3	56–57°		$C_{88}H_{176}O_4$	OH	OCH_3	3						
				$C_{87}H_{174}O_3$	OH								
				$C_{88}H_{176}O_3$	OCH_3								
Canetti	1	56–59°	+2.5°	$C_{87}H_{174}O_3$	OH	C=C	4	47–48°					731
	2	75–76°		$C_{87}H_{172}O_3$	OH	OCH_3		48–51°					
	3			$C_{88}H_{176}O_4$	OH	OH		46–48°					
	4			$C_{87}H_{174}O_4$	OH			49–51°					
	5			$C_{88}H_{176}O_4$	OH			53–55°					

of the carbonyl band in the IR spectra of the esters, the hydroxyl is probably sited in the β-position with respect to the carboxyl. Presence of cyclopropane rings is likely.

u) *Mycolic acids* $C_{88}H_{172}O_4$, $C_{87}H_{170}O_3$, etc.

The mycolic acids are hydroxy acids with branched chains and high molecular weights, at least two representatives of which have been found in every strain of *Mycobacterium* studied (*M. tuberculosis, M. avium, M. phlei, M. smegmatis*, etc.).

The first representative of this group of acids, isolated from a human strain of *M. tuberculosis*, was described in 1938 by Stodola *et al.*[705]. In an impure form, called "unsaponifiable wax", it had already been studied by Anderson[706] in 1929. Subsequently, the same author demonstrated the presence of mycolic type acids in a bovine strain[347], an avian strain[348, 491], the saprophytic *M. phlei*[707], and a "lepra bacillus"[490, 492].

Isolation of the "mycolic acid fraction" from the lipids of *Mycobacteria* (mainly the lipids extracted by chloroform, p. 239) is relatively simple using chromatographic techniques to eliminate the neutral impurities which may be present. The 72 h saponification utilized by Stodola *et al,*[705] can be reduced to 16—18 h[64]; the mycolic acids are found in the unsaponifiable part, since their alkali salts are soluble in ether.

Chromatography, utilized for the first time in 1949 for the separation and fractionation of mycolic acids[708], has, since that date, been widely used in studying the mycolic acids from various strains (for references, see Tables 26, 27 and 28). The fractionation of these acids,

TABLE 27. THE CHARACTERISTICS OF MYCOLIC ACIDS ISOLATED FROM BOVINE STRAINS
OF *M. tuberculosis*

| Strain | | Free acid | | | | Methyl ester, m.p. | Anhydro-acid, m.p. | Neutral ketone, m.p. | Ref. |
| | | M.p. | Molecular formula | Functional groups: | | | | | |
				at C-3	at C-x				
Vallée	1	65-67°	$C_{87}H_{174}O_3$	OH		50-53°	47-53°	76°	
	2	54-56°	$C_{88}H_{176}O_4$	OH	OCH_3	41-43°	46-49°	54-58°	721
	3	62-64°	$C_{87}H_{172}O_4$	OH	C=O	52-54°			722
Marmorek . .	1	57°	$C_{87}H_{174}O_3$	OH		44°		74°	
	2	56°	$C_{87}H_{174}O_4$	OH	OH	41-43°			383
	3	60°	$C_{88}H_{176}O_4$	OH	OCH_3	45-47°			722
	4	62-64°	$C_{87}H_{172}O_4$	OH	C=O	50°		50°	
BCG.	1	50-52°	$C_{87}H_{174}O_3$	OH		42-45°		74-77°	
	2	50-53°	$C_{87}H_{174}O_4$	OH	OH	40-46°		68-72°	723
	3	70-72°	$C_{87}H_{172}O_4$	OH	C=O	54-56°	42-45°	74-78°	

which are always isolated in the form of more or less complex mixtures, is achieved by means of a preliminary chromatographic separation of the free acids on alumina followed by methylation of the fractions obtained, separation of the methyl esters by chromatography on alumina, magnesium silicate, or silicic acid. The separation can be checked by thin-layer chromatography [709]. Some analytical criteria (such as percentage composition, methoxyl content etc.) can also be utilized to follow the fractionation of these acids. Nevertheless, it remains very difficult to evaluate the homogeneity of a mycolic acid preparation. Because of the long paraffin chains in the molecules, there are too many arrangements possible in the crystal lattice to give a clearly defined crystalline substance with a sharp

TABLE 28. THE CHARACTERISTICS OF MYCOLIC ACIDS ISOLATED FROM AVIAN AND SAPROPHYTIC STRAINS OF MYCOBACTERIA

Strain		Free acid					Methyl ester, m.p.	Anhydro-acid, m.p.	Bisanhydro-ester, m.p.	Ref.
		M.p.	$[\alpha]_D$	Molecular Formula	Functional groups	Acid by pyrolysis				
Avian. . . .	1	58-59°		$C_{84}H_{168}O_3$	1 COOH 1 OH					
	2	52-57°	+2.0°	$C_{84}H_{168}O_4$	1 COOH 2 OH	C_{24}	48-52°			530
	3	66-69°	+3.9°	$C_{84}H_{164}O_6$	2 COOH 1 OH 1 CO	C_{24}	50-51°	49-51°		
	4	56-59°	+4.5°	$C_{84}H_{166}O_6$	2 COOH 1 OH 1 ?	C_{24}	46-49°			
M. paratuber culosis (M. johnei)	1						42-45°			
	2		+5.2°*	$C_{84}H_{168}O_3$	1 COOH 1 OH	C_{24}	54-55°			
	3			$C_{84}H_{168}O_4$	1 COOH 1 OH 1 CO		47-49°			709
	4		+4.2°*	$C_{84}H_{166}O_6$	2 COOH 2 OH	C_{24}	52-53°			
M. phlei "Pasteur".	1	55°	+5.5°	$C_{83}H_{166}O_4$	1 COOH 2 OH	C_{24}	45°	50-53°		150
	2	55°	+5.5°	$C_{83}H_{166}O_4$	1 COOH 2 OH	C_{24}	45°	53°		
"I.C.I.". .	1	61-64°	+6.9°	$C_{83}H_{166}O_4$	1 COOH 2 OH	C_{24}	48-50°			115
	2	55°	+6°	$C_{68}H_{132}O_6$	2 COOH 1 OH CO	$C_{22} + C_{24}$	45-47°	38-40°		734
M. smegma-tis. . . .	1	61°	+5.5°	$C_{83}H_{166}O_4$	1 COOH 2 OH	C_{24}	53°		37°	
	2	61°	+5.5°	$C_{83}H_{166}O_4$	1 COOH 2 OH	C_{24}	53°			150
	3	70°	+5.5°	$C_{83}H_{166}O_4$	1 COOH 2 OH	C_{24}	45-48°		45°	
"Leprosy bacillus" .	1	63-64°	+4°	$C_{88}H_{176}O_6$	2 COOH 1 OH 1 ?		51-52°			
	2**	64°	+5.4°	$C_{58}H_{116}O_4$	1 COOH 1 OH 1 ?		54°			490
	3**	57-60°	+5.7°	$C_{58}H_{116}O_4$	1 COOH 1 OH 1 ?		47°			492

* Measured on the methyl ester.   ** Isolated from bound lipids.

TABLE 29. DERIVATIVES OF α-MYCOLIC ACID *Test* (3-HYDROXY-x-METHOXY MYCOLANIC ACID [1-TEST]) (AFTER REFS. 64, 149, 727)

Derivatives	Molecular formula	M.p.	$[\alpha]_D$	Partial formula	% calculated C	H	OCH_3	N	% found C	H	OCH_3	N
Free acid	$C_{88}H_{176}O_4$*	55–56°	+2.3°	231	81.40	13.66	2.39		81.47	13.28	2.36	
									81.53	13.42		
methyl ester	$C_{89}H_{178}O_4$	43–46°	+2.0°	232	81.52	13.58			81.48	13.17		
acetate	$C_{90}H_{178}O_5$	40–42°	+3.4°		80.64	13.38			80.89	13.32		
acetate of methyl ester	$C_{91}H_{180}O_5$	33–35°	+6.2°		80.70	13.40			81.03	13.04		
Mycolic alcohol	$C_{88}H_{178}O_5$	50–52°	+4.5°		82.29	13.97			82.66	13.66		
diacetate	$C_{92}H_{182}O_5$	32–36°			80.81	13.32			80.79	13.11		
Mycolane	$C_{87}H_{176}$				85.51	14.50			85.69	14.25		
Amide	$C_{88}H_{177}O_3N$	75–78°			81.47	13.75		1.08	81.72	13.71		1.25
Mycolic amine	$C_{88}H_{179}O_2N$	44–46°			82.19	14.19		1.1	82.06	13.89		1.4
N-Acetyl-O-acetyl amine	$C_{92}H_{183}O_4N$	37–39°			80.80	13.49		1.0	81.00	13.42		1.6
Products of demethylation												
Dihydroxymycolanoic acid	$C_{87}H_{174}O_4$	57–59°	+3.0°	241	81.36	13.65	0		81.27	13.65	0	
methyl ester	$C_{88}H_{176}O_4$	45–46°	+3.1°		81.41	13.66	2.39		81.45	13.40	2.73	
mono-acetate	$C_{89}H_{178}O_5$	43–46°			80.47	13.50			80.89	13.67		
Products of dehydration												
2-Anhydromycolic acid	$C_{88}H_{174}O_3$	36–38°	≥0	233	82.55	13.69	2.42		82.68	13.46	2.56	
									82.58	13.55		
methyl ester	$C_{89}H_{176}O_3$	34–36°			82.66	13.62			82.52	13.53		
alcohol	$C_{88}H_{176}O_2$	44–48°			83.46	14.01			83.40	13.96		
Products of dehydration and demethylation												
x-Hydroxymycol-2-enoic acid	$C_{87}H_{172}O_3$	41–43°		239	82.52	13.69	0		82.85	13.64	0	
									82.63	13.35		
methyl ester	$C_{88}H_{174}O_3$	37–38°			82.55	13.69	2.42		82.54	13.50	2.86	
									82.52	13.08		
acetate	$C_{89}H_{174}O_4$	37–38°			81.70	13.40			81.44	13.30		
alcohol	$C_{87}H_{174}O_2$	46–48°			83.44	14.01	0		83.70	14.13	0	
		51–52°							83.75	13.81		
mono-acetate of alcohol	$C_{89}H_{176}O_3$	32–33°			82.66	13.62			82.58	13.57		
									82.49	13.72		

* $C_{88}H_{172}O_4$: % calculated C 81.66 H 13.40

Derivatives	Molecular formula	M.p.	$[\alpha]_D$	Partial formula	% calculated C	% calculated H	% calculated OCH_3	% calculated N	% found C	% found H	% found OCH_3	% found N
Products of dehydration and decarboxylation (continued).												
x-Anhydro-3-hydroxymycolanoic acid	$C_{87}H_{172}O_3$	57–60°		244	82.52	13.59			82.45 82.73	13.54 13.41		
acetate	$C_{89}H_{174}O_4$	42–44°			81.70	13.40			81.34 81.27	12.88 13.43		
Bis-anhydromycolic acid	$C_{87}H_{170}O_2$	36–38°	0	240	83.71	13.73	0		83.73 83.49	13.40 13.62	0	
methyl ester	$C_{88}H_{172}O_2$	35.37°	0		83.73	13.74	2.46		83.55 84.37	13.35 14.02	2.89	
alcohol	$C_{87}H_{172}O$	37–40°			84.66	14.04			84.65 84.72	14.07 13.76		
acetate of alcohol	$C_{89}H_{174}O_2$	29–32°			83.75	13.74			83.95	13.94		
Products of dehydration and decarboxylation.												
x-Hydroxy-normycolene-25	$C_{88}H_{172}O$	58–62°		242	84.50	14.14			84.84	14.11		
Nor-mycol-25,x-diene	$C_{88}H_{170}$	61–65°		243	85.77	14.22			85.70	13.84		
Products of oxidation												
x-Methoxy-nor-mycolanone	$C_{87}H_{174}O_2$	64–67°		235	83.44	14.01			83.65	14.01		
Methoxy-nor-mycolanol acetate	$C_{89}H_{178}O_3$	32–34°										
x-Hydroxy-nor-mycolanone	$C_{88}H_{172}O_2$	72–74°		245	83.41	14.00			83.62 83.66	13.84 13.62		
oxime	$C_{87}H_{173}O_2N$	48–50°			82.41	13.91		1.12	82.17	13.64		1.8
x--Anhydronormycolanone	$C_{86}H_{170}O$	69–73°			84.65	14.04			84.59	14.06		
oxime	$C_{86}H_{171}ON$	49–50°			83.61	13.95		1.13	83.92	14.00		1.25
Nor-mycoldione	$C_{86}H_{170}O_2$	76–78°			83.55	13.86			83.85 83.73	13.56 13.51		
dioxime	$C_{86}H_{174}O_2N_2$	58–60°			81.44	13.83		2.21	81.68	13.72		2.21
Methyl 3-oxo-x-methoxymycolanoate	$C_{89}H_{176}O_4$	40–43°		234	81.58	13.54			81.37	13.53		

melting point. The melting points of the different mycolic acids are concentrated in a relatively narrow temperature range (many melt between 55 and 60°) and a mixture of mycolic acids does not give any significant depression of the melting point. The optical properties lie very close to one another ($[\alpha]_D$ +2° to + 3°) and the IR spectra rarely show significant differences. Mostly, therefore, one must be satisfied with "chromatographic homogeneity", i.e. the apparent absence of further fractionation by thin-layer chromatography. Furthermore, this behaviour makes difficult the comparison of two mycolic acids with similar properties and different origins. No conclusion can be drawn as to their identity without a detailed chemical study. Thin-layer chromatography may be very useful in this field [709].

Some properties of mycolic acids isolated from human and bovine strains of *M. tuberculosis* are given in Tables 26 and 27; those of acids isolated from an avian strain and from saprophytic *Mycobacteria* in Table 28.

The molecular formula $C_{88}H_{176}O_4$ proposed by Stodola *et al.*[705] for the first mycolic acid isolated from a human strain remains valuable as a tentative formula for other acids isolated from human or bovine strains. However, because of the presence of cyclopropane rings or of double bonds (see below), probably 4 hydrogen atoms have to be substracted in these empirical formulas (in particular, in table 29). The precision of the analytical determinations carries with it an uncertainty of $\pm$ 5CH_2 (see ref. 64 and 126). Mycolic acids isolated from avian and saprophytic strains have different molecular formulae.

The various mycolic acids can be differentiated as follows :

(*a*) By their melting points; some acids melt between 55 and 60° and others between 70 and 75°.

(*b*) By the number, nature, and position of the functional oxygen groups; some acids may have two carboxyl groups (avian and saprophytic strains), while others may have a second hydroxyl sometimes in the form of the methyl ether (methoxyl) and sometimes replaced by a carbonyl.

(*c*) By the number, nature, and positions of the carbon branches. An approximate indication of the number of branches is given by *C*-methyl determinations. Depending on the acid, 3 or 4 methyl groups (including that of the main chain) may be found. Owing to the imprecision of the method, the difference between 3 and 4 groups may not necessarily be significant.

All the mycolic acids possess in the α-position to the carboxyl a branch which has 24 carbon atoms in the case of mycolic acids of human and bovine strains and 22 or 20 carbon atoms in the case of mycolic acids of avian * and saprophytic strains (see Tables 26-28). However, by using more precise techniques (vapour-phase chromatography, mass spectrometry), it has been found that the mycolic acids are mixtures of homologues and that these figures for the carbon atoms of the α-branch correspond to the main acid of the mixture.

The different mycolic acids, isolated from the same *Mycobacterium* strain, were first

---

* Nevertheless, in the case of an avian strain, a mycolic acid with a C_{24} α-chain has been described [348,720].

classified by the use of a Greek letter, the name of the strain being placed behind the name of the acid: for example, α-mycolic acid Test [126], β-mycolic acid R_1 [710], etc. Later, the increasing number of mycolic acids isolated and described necessitated modification of this nomenclature. Two rules are now utilized [711]:

(a) Each mycolic acid is considered as a derivative of a "mycolanoic acid", an acid devoid of oxygen functions other than carboxyl.

(b) The name of the acid is followed by a number, which corresponds to the order of elution of that acid during the chromatographic fractionation of the crude acid, and the name of the strain. The α-mycolic acid Test thus becomes 3-hydroxy-α-methoxymycolanoic acid [1-Test], β-mycolic acid R_1 becomes 3-x-dihydroxymycolanoic acid [2-R_1], etc. By convention, a C_{88} formula is utilised in the case of methoxylated mycolic acids and a C_{87} formula for acids without a methoxyl.

Stodola et al. [705] showed that pyrolysis of mycolic acid (by heating to 300° under vacuum) liberates a molecule of n-hexacosanoic acid. On the other hand, by chromic oxidation of this mycolic acid, Lesuk & Anderson [712] obtained a mixture of fatty acids among which were identified stearic acid (m.p. 68.5°), n-hexacosanoic acid (m.p. 87—88°), and octadecanedioic acid (hexadecane-1,16-dicarboxylic acid, m.p. 121—122°).

Studying the structure of α-mycolic acid Test, which constitutes about 70 % of the crude mycolic acid from this strain, Asselineau [713] obtained by dehydration an α,β-unsaturated acid (λ_{max} 218 mμ, ε = 13,000) called anhydromycolic acid [233]. On the other hand, the chromic oxidation of methyl mycolate [232] gives a β-keto-ester [234] (λ_{max} 260 mμ, ε = 520) which on saponification is decarboxylated to a neutral ketone [235]. The same ketone is obtained directly by oxidation of free mycolic acid. These reactions prove that the hydroxyl of this mycolic acid is in the β-position with respect to the carboxyl [713].

The β-position of the hydroxyl explains the pyrolytic reaction of mycolic acids, first observed by Anderson [706]. It is indeed well known [714-719] that β-hydroxy acids having one or two branches in the α-position are split by pyrolysis according to the following reaction, which constitutes the inverse of Claisen's reaction:

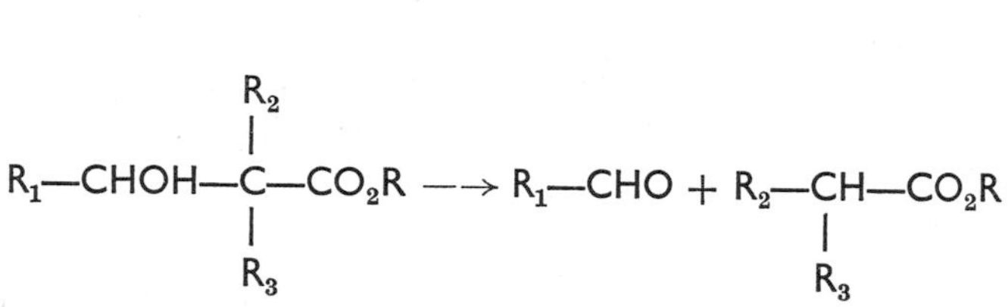

$$R_1\text{—CHOH—}\underset{\underset{R_3}{|}}{\overset{\overset{R_2}{|}}{C}}\text{—CO}_2R \longrightarrow R_1\text{—CHO} + R_2\text{—}\underset{\underset{R_3}{|}}{CH}\text{—CO}_2R$$

The pyrolysis of mycolic acids is a particular case of this general reaction. The non-volatile aldehyde [237], $C_{62}H_{124}O_2$, may undergo secondary reactions because of the prolonged heating but may be isolated. An almost quantitative yield of n-hexacosanoic acid [236] is obtained by pyrolysis of the free mycolic acid [64]. When the hydroxyl in position 3 is etherified or acetylated, the pyrolytic reaction no longer takes place.

R—CO—CH$_2$—C$_{24}$H$_{49}$ ⟵————   R—CO—CH—CO$_2$CH$_3$ [234]
 [235] |
                                                  C$_{24}$H$_{49}$

                                            R—CHOH—CH—CO$_2$CH$_3$ [232]
                                                  |
                                                  C$_{24}$H$_{49}$

R—CHOH—CH—CO$_2$H
        |
        C$_{24}$H$_{49}$ ————————⟶   R—CH=C—CO$_2$H   [233]
   [231] |
        ↓   C$_{24}$H$_{49}$
                                                    ↓
R—CHO + C$_{24}$H$_{49}$—CH$_2$—CO$_2$H   C$_{24}$H$_{49}$—CO$_2$H
 [237]   [236]   [238]

Obtaining hexacosanoic acid on pyrolysis of acids of human and bovine strains implies the existence of a branch with 24 carbon atoms in the α-position to the carboxyl of the mycolic acids. α-Mycolic acid Test was dehydrated to anhydromycolic acid [233], which was then ozonized. By carrying out the decomposition of the ozonide under oxidizing conditions, n-pentacosanoic acid [238] was obtained instead of 2-oxohexacosanoic acid. Identification of this acid by its X-ray diffraction pattern provides proof of the partial formula [231] of α-mycolic acid Test[126].

The pyrolytic reaction, easy to carry out on small quantities of acid (see for example [720 a]), showed that all the mycolic acids isolated (including those which were described by Anderson) possess a structure of the type [231], i.e. they are β-hydroxy acids carrying a long aliphatic chain at the α-position. This conclusion was verified by the ozonolysis of two other anhydromycolic acids[150]. Moreover, this reaction affords a convenient means of determining the nature of the α-branch in a mycolic acid (see Table 26, p. 121). Ställberg-Stenhagen & Stenhagen[305] studied a sample of Anderson's mycolic acid (human strain H$_{37}$) by monomolecular layer techniques and by X-ray diffraction. These authors conclude that "the structure of the molecule probably allows access to the water of at least one of the other polar groups (besides the carboxyl)", and that "the cross-section of the molecule at no part of its length can be larger than that occupied by three parallel hydrocarbon chains".

1) Mycolic acids isolated from human and bovine strains

Everytime that enough material was obtained to make possible a thorough fractionation of a mixture of mycolic acids isolated from any strain, at least three different acids were obtained: an O$_4$ acid melting at about 55°, an O$_4$ acid melting at about 73° and an O$_3$ acid melting at about 55°. In all cases, it is the O$_4$ acid with m.p. 55° which is the main component of the mixture. According to their chromatographic behaviour, there exist two types of O$_3$ acids, one only weakly adsorbed on alumina and the other very strongly adsorbed; such a difference in adsorption should correspond to an important difference in chemical structure*. The weakly adsorbed O_3 acids are isolated principally from slightly virulent or non-virulent strains, while the strongly adsorbed O_3 acids are usually encountered in virulent strains.

A number of mycolic acids have, in addition to the hydroxyl in position 3, a carbonyl group, indicated by formation of an oxime. These acids are called mycolonic acids [722]. From every bovine strain studied, a mycolonic acid has been isolated (Table 28); of nine human strains examined, only one (strain R_1) contained a mycolonic acid [710].

No relation was observed between the composition of the mixture of mycolic acids present in a strain and its virulence; likewise, no significant difference was detected between streptomycin-sensitive and resistant strains [724].

The partial formula [231] has two asymmetric carbon atoms and it may be asked whether the O_4 acids m.p. 55° and the O_4 acids m.p. 73°, apparently isomers, are not more likely to be diastereoisomers. The two asymmetric centres can be removed either by formation of an anhydro-acid [233] or by transformation into a decarboxylated ketone [235]. In the case of the Test mycolic acids, the IR spectra of the anhydro-acids (with the same melting point) are different, and the neutral ketones also have very different melting points [725]. An analogous observation has been made with the acids m.p. 55° and m.p. 73° of a streptomycin-resistant H_{37} Rv strain; the two acids give rise to two ketones with very different melting points [724]. It is clear, therefore, that the radical R in the formula [231] is different in the low and in the high melting O_4 acids.

All the mycolic acids, having about the same rotation, probably have the same configuration at the asymmetric centres 2 and 3. The changes observed in the optical properties of the mycolic acids, either with the nature of the solvent or by acetylation and/or methylation, are in the same direction as those observed in the case of corynomycolic acid where the centre 3 belongs to the D series [689].

Recently, Gastambide-Odier et al. [725a] have shown by NMR spectroscopy that three mycolic acids from human strains (α_2-mycolic acid H_{37} Rv S.r., α-mycolic acid Brévannes, and a sample of mycolic acid H_{37} from Anderson) and one bovine mycolic acid (from strain Marmorek) contain cyclopropane rings. In the author's laboratory, similar observations have been made on α-mycolic acid Test, α_2-mycolic acid R_1 and a mixture of mycolic acids from the bovine strain BCG. It is thus likely that cyclopropane rings occur in all mycolic acids of human or bovine strains.

The biosynthesis of mycolic acids will be discussed on p. 148.

Four mycolic acids, isolated from human strains of *M. tuberculosis*, have been more intensively studied. They are the α-mycolic acids Test and Brévannes, the 3,x-dihydroxymycolanoic acid [2-R_1], and the 3,x-dihydroxymycolanoic acid [4-Canetti]; all these are low melting O_4 mycolic acids.

α-Mycolic acid Test (3-hydroxy-x-methoxymycolanoic acid 1-Test)

We have explained above how the partial formula [231] was demonstrated in the case of this

---

* A strongly adsorbed O_3 acid (γ-mycolic acid Test [710]) was studied in parallel with a weakly adsorbed O_3 acid (α_1-mycolic acid R_1 [710]) in monomolecular films : the Test acid "differs from the acid R_1 in that the minimum areas are smaller and the curves (surface/pressure) have a slightly different appearance" (E. Stenhagen, personal communication).

acid. Asselineau [727] studied in greater detail the nature of the products formed when α-mycolic acid *Test* is treated with boiling acetic anhydride in the presence of potassium hydrogen sulphate. Besides the 2-anhydromycolic acid [233] already mentioned, compounds [239] to [243] are formed, often in considerable amounts depending on the conditions used, arising by demethylation, dehydration and decarboxylation reactions. However, the cyclopropane rings might be split in the course of this reaction.

$$C_{60}H_{116}\begin{cases} -OH \\ -CH=C-CO_2H \\ \quad\quad | \\ \quad\quad C_{24}H_{49} \end{cases}$$

[239]

$$C_{60}H_{116}\begin{cases} -OH \\ -CHOH-CH-CO_2H \\ \quad\quad\quad\quad | \\ \quad\quad\quad\quad C_{24}H_{49} \end{cases}$$

[241]

$$C_{60}H_{116}\begin{cases} -OH \\ -CH=CH \\ \quad\quad | \\ \quad\quad C_{24}H_{49} \end{cases}$$

[242]

$$C_{58}H_{115}\begin{cases} >C \\ \;\| \\ >C \\ -CH=C-CO_2H \\ \quad\quad | \\ \quad\quad C_{24}H_{49} \end{cases}$$

[240]

$$C_{58}H_{115}\begin{cases} >C \\ \;\| \\ >C \\ -CH=CH \\ \quad\quad | \\ \quad\quad C_{24}H_{49} \end{cases}$$

[243]

On treatment with acetyl chloride, the dihydroxy acid [241] gives an x-anhydromycolic acid [244], the structure of which is in accord with the liberation of hexacosanoic acid on pyrolysis. On the other hand, chromic oxidation of the same dihydroxy acid [241] affords the hydroxy-ketone [245] as the main product. These results were interpreted in favour of the tertiary nature of the hydroxyl in position x, i.e. the position of the methoxyl in the original mycolic acid.

From the products of ozonolysis of x-anhydromycolic acid [244], Asselineau & Lederer [149] isolated *n*-pentacosanoic acid, an acid which is probably *n*-heptadecanoic acid, and a waxy acid fraction with m.p. 53—58° and a molecular weight of about 1,000. If the dihydroxy acid [241] possesses the structure [246 b], its dehydration could lead to the x-anhydromycolic acids [247], [248], and [249], ozonolysis of which would give the three acids mentioned above. The α-mycolic acid Test, according to *C*-methyl determinations, has 3 methyl groups; it could therefore have the formula [246 a], in which R = —(CH₂)₁₅— [149]. Such a structure would explain the formation of hexadecane-1,16-dicarboxylic acid observed by Lesuk & Anderson [712].

$$C_{58}H_{115}\begin{cases} >C \\ \;\| \\ >C \\ -CHOH-CH-CO_2H \\ \quad\quad\quad\quad | \\ \quad\quad\quad\quad C_{24}H_{49} \end{cases}$$

[244]

$$C_{60}H_{116}\begin{cases} -OH \\ -CO-CH_2 \\ \quad\quad\; | \\ \quad\quad\; C_{24}H_{49} \end{cases}$$

[245]

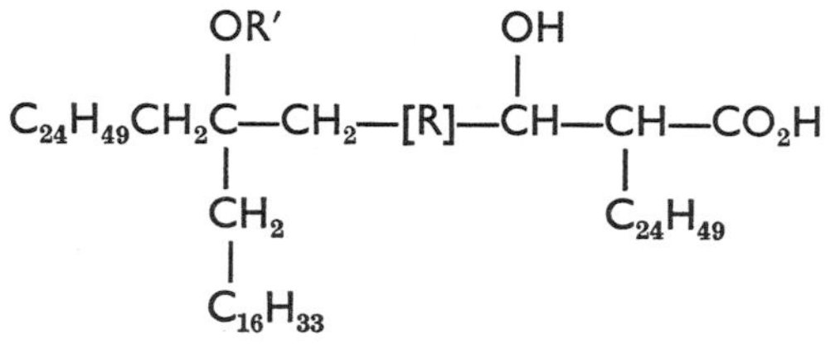

$$\begin{array}{c}
\overset{\displaystyle OR'}{|} \qquad \overset{\displaystyle OH}{|} \\
C_{24}H_{49}CH_2\overset{|}{\underset{\underset{\underset{C_{16}H_{33}}{|}}{\overset{|}{CH_2}}}{C}}{-}CH_2{-}[R]{-}CH{-}\overset{|}{\underset{C_{24}H_{49}}{CH}}{-}CO_2H
\end{array}$$

[246] $a : R' = CH_3$
         $b : R' = H$

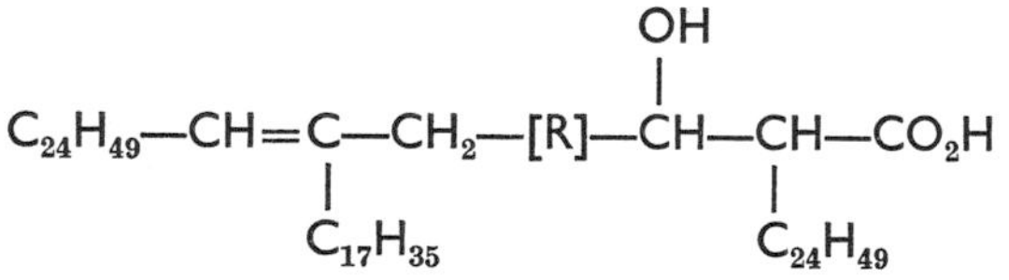

$$C_{24}H_{49}{-}CH{=}\overset{|}{\underset{C_{17}H_{35}}{C}}{-}CH_2{-}[R]{-}\overset{\overset{\displaystyle OH}{|}}{CH}{-}\overset{|}{\underset{C_{24}H_{49}}{CH}}{-}CO_2H$$

[247]

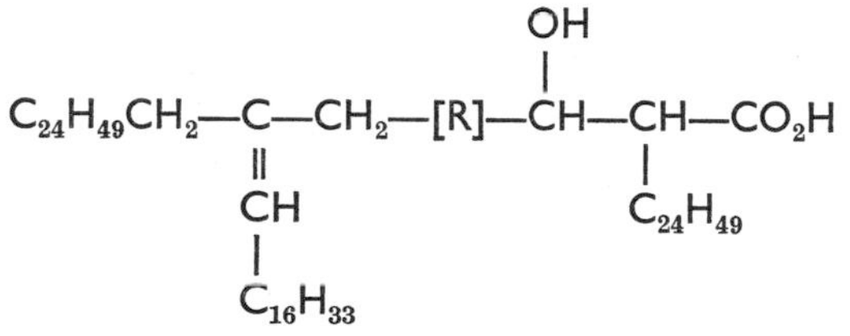

$$C_{24}H_{49}CH_2{-}\overset{\displaystyle ||}{\underset{\underset{C_{16}H_{33}}{|}}{C}}{-}CH_2{-}[R]{-}\overset{\overset{\displaystyle OH}{|}}{CH}{-}\overset{|}{\underset{C_{24}H_{49}}{CH}}{-}CO_2H$$

[248]

$$C_{25}H_{51}{-}\overset{|}{\underset{C_{17}H_{35}}{C}}{=}CH{-}[R]{-}\overset{\overset{\displaystyle OH}{|}}{CH}{-}\overset{|}{\underset{C_{24}H_{49}}{CH}}{-}CO_2H$$

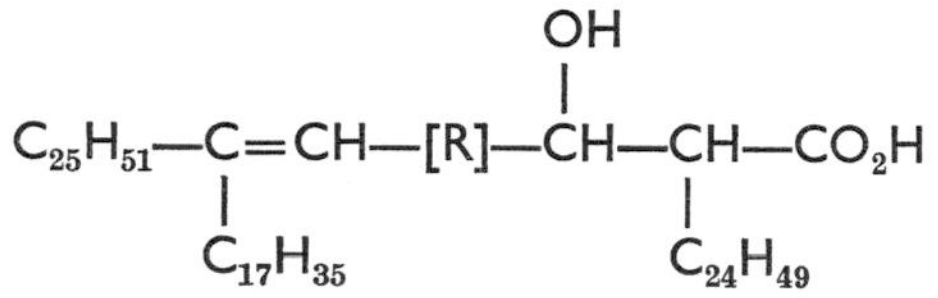

[249]

Nevertheless, the isolation of a dihydroxy acid having a tertiary alcohol group, after treatment of α-mycolic acid with boiling acetic anhydride in the presence of potassium hydrogen sulphate, is astonishing. Moreover, chromic oxidation of the non-demethylated mycolic acid with excess reagent subsequently furnished a diketone $C_{86}H_{170}O_2$, m.p. 76—78° (dioxime m.p. 58—60°)* . It is therefore more probable that the methoxyl in position x of the α-mycolic acid Test corresponds to a secondary alcohol. The results obtained on ozonolysis of the x-anhydromycolic acid can easily be explained by taking into account the results in the case of phthiocerol (p. 77). Elimination of the methoxyl at position 3 of phthiocerol [250] gave a mixture of ene-diols having a double bond at position 3 [251] or at position 4 [252] :

---

* The demethylation of a secondary hydroxyl in the course of a chromic oxidation was demonstrated in the case of the oxidation of phthiocerol (see p. 77) [511].

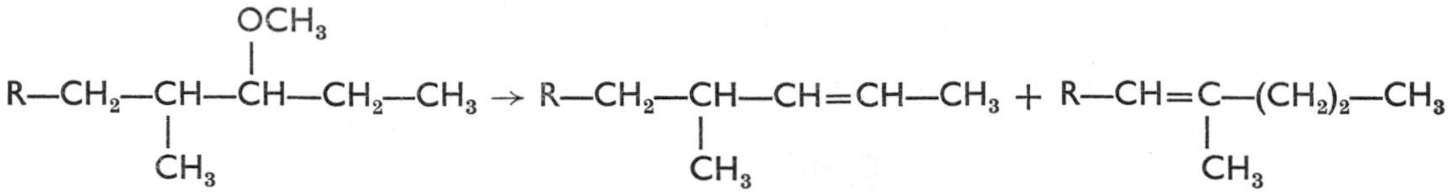

$$R-CH_2-\overset{\overset{\displaystyle OCH_3}{|}}{CH}-\underset{\underset{\displaystyle CH_3}{|}}{CH}-CH_2-CH_3 \rightarrow R-CH_2-\underset{\underset{\displaystyle CH_3}{|}}{CH}-CH=CH-CH_3 + R-CH=\underset{\underset{\displaystyle CH_3}{|}}{C}-(CH_2)_2-CH_3$$

$$[250] \qquad\qquad\qquad\qquad [251] \qquad\qquad\qquad\qquad [252]$$

A similar process of demethoxylation allows us to obtain the same x-anhydromycolic acids [247], [248], and [249] from a mycolic acid with the formula [253] :

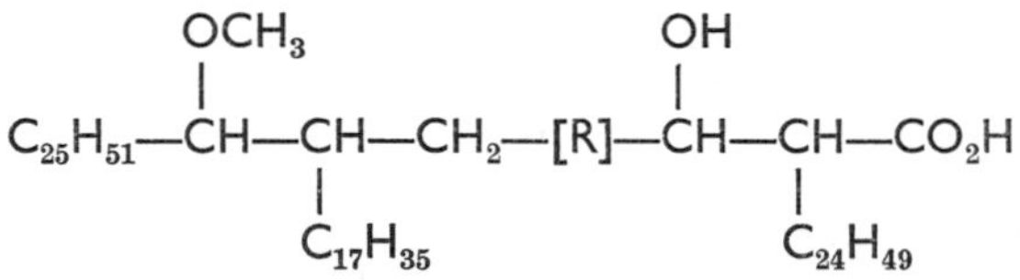

$$C_{25}H_{51}-\overset{\overset{\displaystyle OCH_3}{|}}{\underset{\underset{\displaystyle C_{17}H_{35}}{|}}{CH}}-CH-CH_2-[R]-\overset{\overset{\displaystyle OH}{|}}{CH}-\underset{\underset{\displaystyle C_{24}H_{49}}{|}}{CH}-CO_2H \qquad [253]$$

Such a structure (with cyclopropane rings) is much more acceptable from the biogenetic point of view.

A last problem still remains : in the course of the preparation of mycolic esters of sugars, Asselineau & Lederer [459] obtained derivatives containing a sulphite group. Such sulphites were studied by Asselineau & Ginsburg [728] in the case of mycolic acids H_{37} Rv S.r. and Marmorek; they behave like intramolecular derivatives, having the structure [254].

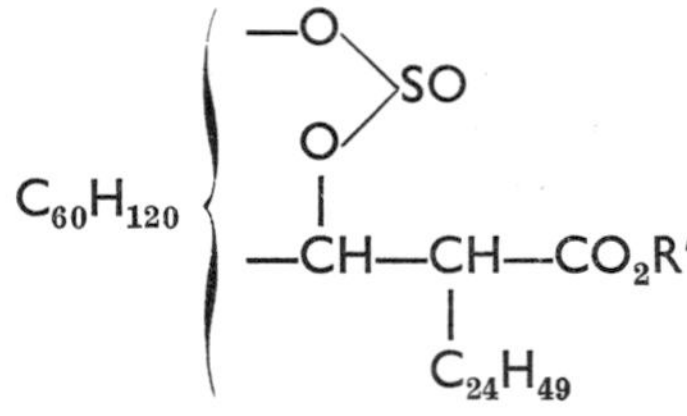

$$C_{60}H_{120}\left\{\begin{array}{c}-O\\ \qquad\diagup SO\\ O\\ |\\ -CH-CH-CO_2R'\\ |\\ C_{24}H_{49}\end{array}\right. \qquad [254]$$

The production of such a compound would indicate that the hydroxyl at 3 is in the neighbourhood of the methoxyl; the possibility of an internal sulphite with a large ring, although not excluded, is not very probable. In this case, the radical R of the formula [253] would be branched.

3,x-Dihydroxymycolanoic acid [2-R$_1$]

The properties of this acid are mentioned in Table 26 (p. 121). Its pyrolysis, with liberation of *n*-hexacosanoic acid, shows that it has the partial formula [231]. Dehydration leads to a 2-anhydromycolic acid m.p. 36—39° (λ_{max} 216 mμ, ε = 13,300) and to a bis-anhydromycolic acid m.p. 42—43° (λ_{max} 216 mμ, ε = 12,350). Ozonolysis of bis-anhydromycolic acid gives rise to 1.4 moles of *n*-pentacosanoic acid, which shows the presence of a chain of 25 carbon atoms linked to carbon x [255] [729]. Chromic oxidation of this mycolic acid leads to a diketone $C_{86}H_{170}O_2$, m.p. 72—74° (dioxime m.p. 54—57°), the subsequent oxidation of which gives as the main product a mixture of keto-acids $C_{60}H_{118}O_3$ which is separable by chromatography of the methyl esters. The stability of the keto-acids shows that they are not β-keto-acids and that, consequently, in the initial mycolic acid the second hydroxyl is located beyond position 5. The production, besides these keto-acids, of a C_{60} diketone can be explained by the existence of an α-branch in the diketone $C_{68}H_{170}O_2$ [256][729].

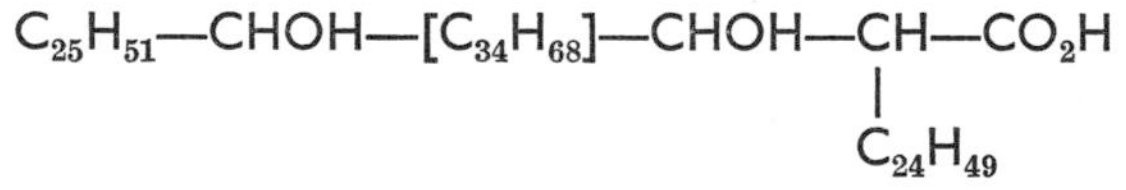

$$C_{25}H_{51}-CHOH-[C_{34}H_{68}]-CHOH-CH-CO_2H \qquad [255]$$
$$\underset{C_{24}H_{49}}{|}$$

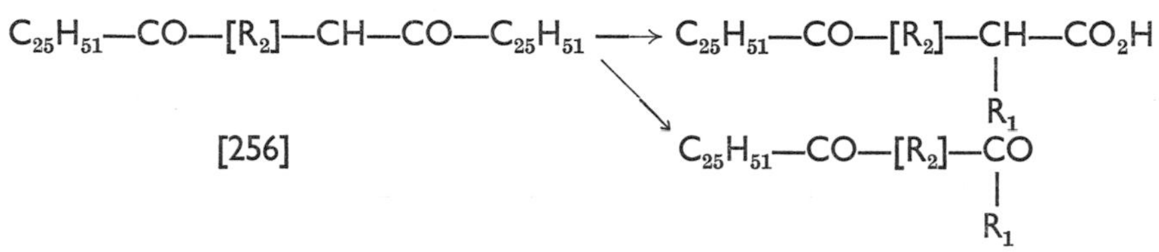

$$C_{25}H_{51}-CO-[R_2]-CH-CO-C_{25}H_{51} \longrightarrow C_{25}H_{51}-CO-[R_2]-\underset{\underset{R_1}{|}}{CH}-CO_2H$$

$$[256] \qquad C_{25}H_{51}-CO-[R_2]-\underset{\underset{R_1}{|}}{CO}$$

$$C_{24}H_{49}-CH_2CHOH-\underset{\underset{R_2}{|}}{CH}-[R]-\underset{\underset{R_1}{|}}{CH}-CHOH-\underset{\underset{C_{24}H_{49}}{|}}{CH}-CO_2H \qquad [257]$$

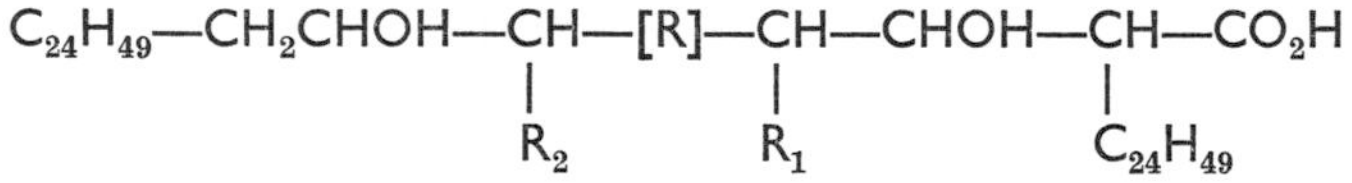

From biogenetic considerations and from the existence of 4 methyl groups, the tentative formula [257] was suggested for 3,x-dihydroxymycolanoic acid [2-R₁][729]. Nevertheless, the behaviour of this acid in a monomolecular layer shows that "there cannot be more than three chains parallel when the molecule is compressed in the monolayer. The results suggest that the distance between the carbon atom carrying the side chains R_1 and R_2 must be longer than one methylene group, or else one of the side chains must be very short if the side chain R_1 is to remain in γ position to the carboxyl group" (E. Stenhagen, personal communication). Moreover, cyclopropane rings are present.

α-Mycolic acid Brévannes

α-Mycolic acid Brévannes is a mixture of monohydroxy-monomethoxy and dihydroxy-acids, the separation of which has not been attempted [65]. Pyrolysis of this product gives n-hexacosanoic acid, which shows that these acids possess a structure of the type [231].

Chromic oxidation of this mixture gives a diketone $C_{86}H_{170}O_2$, m.p. 83—85° (dioxime m.p. 44—46°), containing 3 methyl groups. It has not been possible to isolate any pure methoxylated monoketone: this result can be related to the obtaining of hydroxy acids from the methoxylated part of phthiocerol by oxidation [511], and of a diketone from α-mycolic acid Test (see above). Besides the diketone $C_{86}H_{170}O_2$, Aebi et al. [730] isolated a monoketone $C_{60}H_{120}O$, m.p. 68—70° (oxime m.p. 44—46°), which does not have more than two methyl groups, and n-pentacosanoic acid. The same monoketone $C_{60}H_{120}O$, was obtained by Asselineau [528] by chromic oxidation of the diketone $C_{86}H_{170}O_2$. These results can most easily be interpreted by assigning positions 3 and 5 to the hydroxyls of mycolic acid [258]; the diketone $C_{86}H_{170}O_2$ would then be a β-diketone [259], the subsequent oxidation of which would lead to the monoketone $C_{60}H_{120}O$ [261] through an intermediary β-keto-ester [260]:

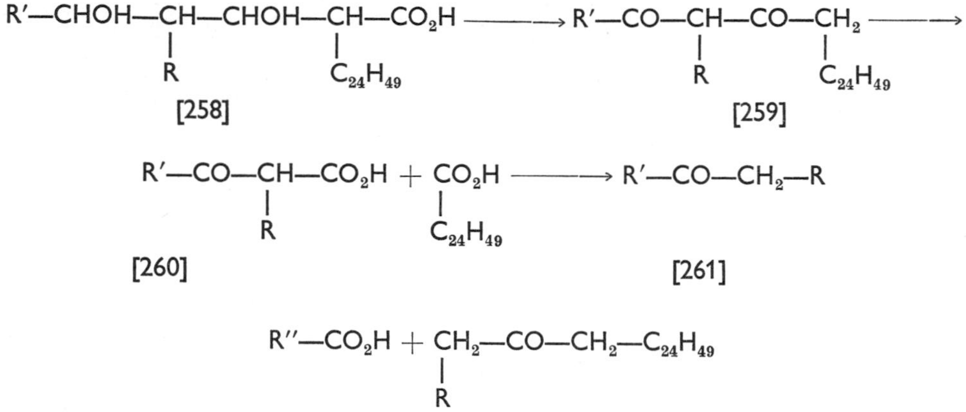

$$R'—CHOH—CH—CHOH—CH—CO_2H \longrightarrow R'—CO—CH—CO—CH_2 \longrightarrow$$

$$\underset{R}{|} \qquad \underset{C_{24}H_{49}}{|} \qquad\qquad \underset{R}{|} \qquad \underset{C_{24}H_{49}}{|}$$

$$[258] \qquad\qquad\qquad\qquad [259]$$

$$R'—CO—CH—CO_2H + CO_2H \longrightarrow R'—CO—CH_2—R$$

$$\underset{R}{|} \qquad \underset{C_{24}H_{49}}{|}$$

$$[260] \qquad\qquad\qquad\qquad\qquad [261]$$

$$R''—CO_2H + CH_2—CO—CH_2—C_{24}H_{49}$$

$$\underset{R}{|}$$

$$[262]$$

Dihydroxymycolanoix acid [*4-Canetti*]

From the complex mixture of mycolic acids obtained from the waxes of the Canetti strain, a dihydroxy acid $C_{86}H_{170}O_4$, m.p. 56—59°, was isolated [731]. Pyrolysis of this acid gives *n*-hexacosanoic acid, which demonstrates the partial formula [231]. By chromic oxidation, it is transformed into a diketone $C_{86}H_{170}O_2$, m.p. 80—83° (dioxime m.p. 44—46°), having 4 methyl groups. The subsequent oxidation of this diketone provides a complex mixture of substances, from which have been isolated [422] a monoketone $C_{60}H_{120}O$, m.p. 67—69° (oxime m.p. 45—47°), which has 3 methyl groups; a monoketone $C_{31}H_{62}O$, m.p. 78—80°, unbranched and having two methyl groups; a diketone $C_{60}H_{118}O_2$, m.p. 66—69°; a keto-acid $C_{60}H_{118}O_3$; methyl ester m.p. 48—50°; and *n*-pentacosanoic acid.

These results were interpreted by proposing the structure [263] for this mycolic acid, and structures [264] and [265] respectively for the C_{86}-diketone and the C_{60}-monoketone. It has been shown (table 11, page 54) that a cyclopropane ring gives a positive value in the Kuhn-Roth C-methyl determination. Thus, the presence of cyclopropane rings is likely to give too high results in the determination of the number of branches in such types of mycolic acid.

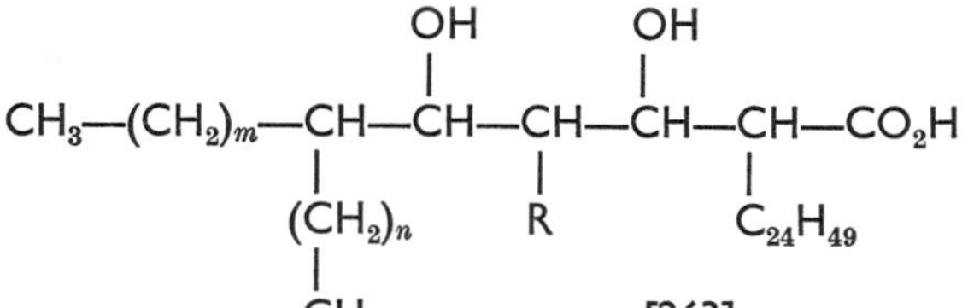

$$\overset{\textstyle OH}{\underset{\textstyle |}{}} \qquad \overset{\textstyle OH}{\underset{\textstyle |}{}}$$

$$CH_3—(CH_2)_m—CH—CH—CH—CH—CH—CO_2H$$

$$\underset{\underset{CH_3}{\overset{\displaystyle |}{(CH_2)_n}}}{|} \qquad \underset{R}{|} \qquad \underset{C_{24}H_{49}}{|}$$

$$[263]$$

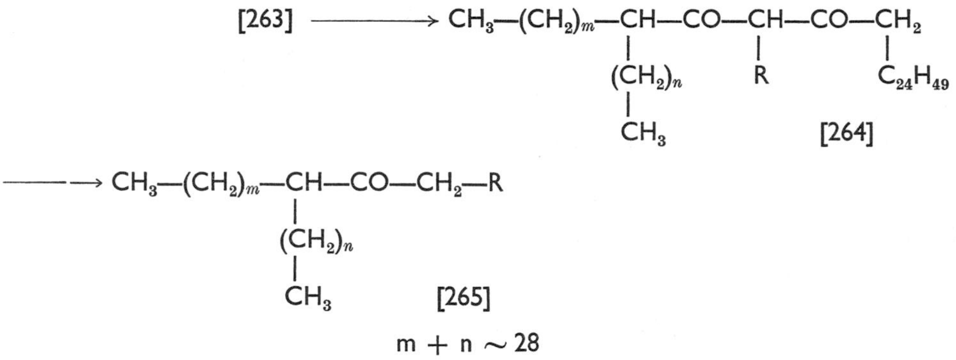

$$[263] \longrightarrow CH_3-(CH_2)_m-\underset{\underset{CH_3}{\overset{|}{(CH_2)_n}}}{\overset{|}{CH}}-CO-\underset{R}{\overset{|}{CH}}-CO-\underset{\underset{[264]}{\overset{|}{C_{24}H_{49}}}}{\overset{|}{CH_2}}$$

$$\longrightarrow CH_3-(CH_2)_m-\underset{\underset{CH_3}{\overset{|}{(CH_2)_n}}}{\overset{|}{CH}}-CO-CH_2-R \qquad [265]$$

$$m + n \sim 28$$

The diketone [264] does not have the UV and IR spectra characteristic of a β-diketone; this is in accord with the properties of long-chain 1,3-diketones branched at the 2-position, synthesized by Toubiana & Asselineau [703]. The fact that a 2,4-dienic acid is not formed by dehydration of an acid such as [263] was studied by Asselineau & Asselineau [213], with the aid of simple models (p. 141).

Mixture of mycolic acids

From the lipids of bacilli from a mixture of several human strains Morgan & Polgar [732] obtained a mycolic acid, which was probably very heterogeneous because of the nature of the starting material and because O_3 mycolic acid and high melting O_4 acid, were not separated.

This mycolic acid (hydroxy-methoxymycolanoic acid) was dehydrated by alkali treatment of its tosylate and the anhydromycolic acid obtained, m.p. 39—42°, was oxidized by potassium permanganate. Isolation of *n*-pentacosanoic acid from the oxidation products confirmed the partial formula [231]. Besides the pentacosanoic acid, Morgan & Polgar [732] obtained a methoxy C_{60} acid called O-methyl-meromycolic acid m.p. 45—47°, $[\alpha]_D^{20} + 1.4°$ (amide m.p. 64—70°). The methoxy acid distills without decomposition at 300-320° (bath)/ 0.06 mm, which excludes the presence of methoxyl in the α-position to the carboxyl, i.e. position 4 in the initial mycolic acid. Demethylation by heating in acetic anhydride in the presence of *p*-toluenesulphonic acid affords meromycolic acid, m.p. 40°. This hydroxy acid does not give a γ-lactone and on dehydration does not give an α,β-unsaturated acid. The hydroxyl of meromycolic acid, therefore, cannot be in the β- or γ-position with respect to the carboxyl. Thus, in the original mycolic acid, the methoxyl is sited farther down than position 6.

More recently, Malani & Polgar [733], working with a more homogeneous material, prepared a new batch of *O*-methylmeromycolic acid, m.p. 38—40° [268]. This acid was demethylated by means of acetic anhydride and *p*-toluenesulphonic acid and pyrolysis of the resulting acetoxy-acid gave a mixture of unsaturated acids which was hydrogenated. The deoxymeromycolic acid m.p. 48—50° [269] so obtained was brominated and dehydrobromination of the α-bromo-ester thus formed gave an α,β-unsaturated ester with λ_{max} 215 mμ*, $\varepsilon = 7,540$ [270]. Oxidation of this unsaturated ester by means of potassium permanganate in acetone furnished a mixture of acids containing as main components docosanoic and tetracosanoic acids [271]. These results suggest the partial formula [266] for the initial mycolic acid, which thus contains a branch in the γ-position [733].

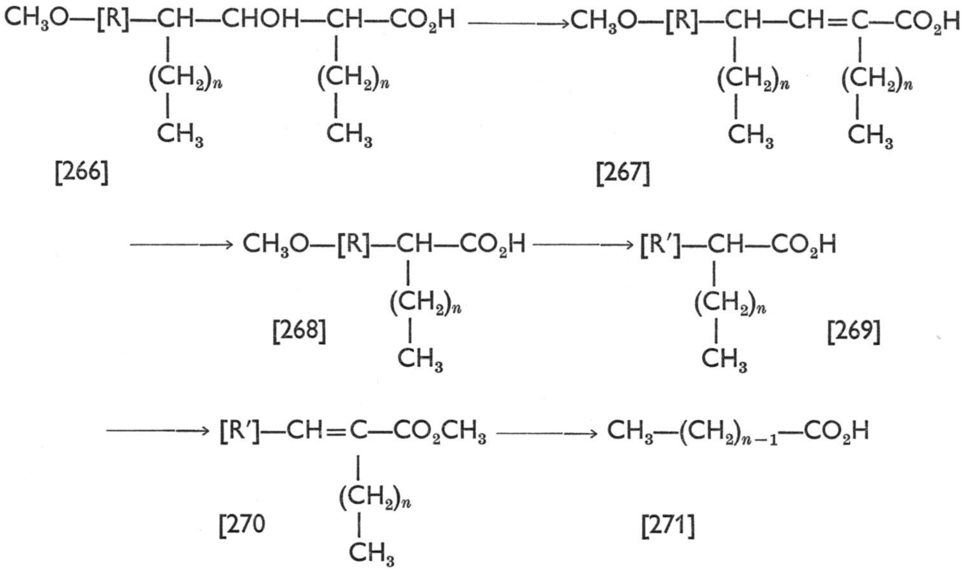

$$CH_3O—[R]—\underset{\underset{\underset{CH_3}{|}}{\underset{(CH_2)_n}{|}}}{CH}—CHOH—\underset{\underset{\underset{CH_3}{|}}{\underset{(CH_2)_n}{|}}}{CH}—CO_2H \longrightarrow CH_3O—[R]—\underset{\underset{\underset{CH_3}{|}}{\underset{(CH_2)_n}{|}}}{CH}—CH=\underset{\underset{\underset{CH_3}{|}}{\underset{(CH_2)_n}{|}}}{C}—CO_2H$$

[266]   [267]

$$\longrightarrow CH_3O—[R]—\underset{\underset{\underset{CH_3}{|}}{\underset{(CH_2)_n}{|}}}{CH}—CO_2H \longrightarrow [R']—\underset{\underset{\underset{CH_3}{|}}{\underset{(CH_2)_n}{|}}}{CH}—CO_2H$$

              [268]   [269]

$$\longrightarrow [R']—CH=\underset{\underset{\underset{CH_3}{|}}{\underset{(CH_2)_n}{|}}}{C}—CO_2CH_3 \longrightarrow CH_3—(CH_2)_{n-1}—CO_2H$$

        [270]   [271]

$$n = 21 \text{ and } 23$$

2) *Mycolic acids isolated from avian and saprophytic strains of Mycobacteria*

Mycolic acids isolated from avian or saprophytic strains maintain the same structural pecularities as the mycolic acids of human or bovine strains : they are again branched-chain acids with a high molecular weight (about 1,000), β-hydroxylated and substituted with a long aliphatic chain in the α-position [272]. Nevertheless, three differences should be noted :

(i) the α side chain [R' in 272] usually has only 22 carbon atoms (for the main component of the mixture) (see Table 28, p. 123);

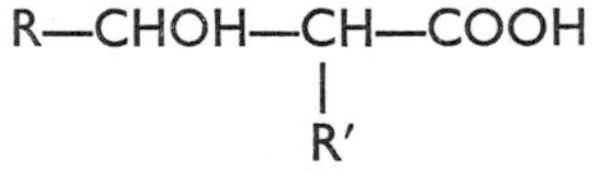

$$R—CHOH—\underset{\underset{R'}{|}}{CH}—COOH$$

[272]

* The position of the maximum shows that the double bond is only trisubstituted.

(ii) dicarboxylic mycolic acids (R containing a second carboxyl group) frequently exist in a strain (avian or saprophytic) besides monocarboxylic mycolic acids.

(iii) these mycolic acids are often devoid of cyclopropane rings, but contain double bonds.

In the case of a strain of *M. phlei* (strain "ICI"), dicarboxylic mycolic acid was studied in greater detail by Clermonté & Lederer [734]. This acid, $C_{68}H_{132}O_6$, m.p. 55°, contains two carboxyls, one hydroxyl and a keto group. The following derivatives have been prepared :

TABLE 30

Compound	Formula	M.p.	UV spectrum
Methyl diester.	$C_{70}H_{136}O_6$	45-47°	
Acetate of the diester.	$C_{72}H_{138}O_7$	31°	
Tetrol	$C_{68}H_{138}O_4$	54°	
Oxime of the anhydroacid	$C_{68}H_{131}O_5N_2$	38-40°	
Monoanhydromycolate, diester	$C_{70}H_{134}O_5$	38-40°	λ_{max} 220 mμ $\varepsilon = 11,200$
Methyl diketo-diester	$C_{70}H_{134}O_6$	42-43°	λ_{max} 260 mμ $\varepsilon = 800$
Methyl ester of the diketo-monoacid . .	$C_{68}H_{132}O_4$	70-73°	

Pyrolysis gives a mixture of *n*-docosanoic acid (about 60 %) and *n*-tetracosanoic acid (about 40 %), indicating the existence of two mycolic acids [272], one with $R' = C_{20}H_{41}$, the other with $R' = C_{22}H_{45}$.

A dicarboxylic acid, $C_{84}H_{164}O_6$, m.p. 66—69°, $[\alpha]_D + 3.9°$, has been isolated from a strain of *M. avium* [530]; several derivatives have been prepared, which show the presence of an hydroxyl in position 3, with respect to one carboxyl, and of a carbonyl group. The formation of a lactone under appropriate conditions could not be observed. Elementary composition and melting points show that this acid is different from the dicarboxylic mycolonic acid studied by Clermonté & Lederer.

A dicarboxylic acid, $C_{83}H_{164}O_6$, (methyl ester m.p. 52—53°) was isolated from the waxes of a strain of *M. paratuberculosis* : this acid has no carbonyl group [709].

The structure of 3,x-dihydroxymycolanoic acid [1-*smegmatis*] $C_{83}H_{166}O_4$, was more fully investigated [150]. Chromic acid oxidation gave a diketone $C_{82}H_{162}O_2$, m.p. 69° (dioxime m.p. 53°). The bis-anhydromycolic acid $C_{83}H_{162}O_2$ (methyl ester m.p. 37°) was ozonized: 1.6 moles of *n*-tricosanoic acid (m.p. 78—80°) were obtained. Structure [273] was then suggested [150].

$$C_{23}H_{47}-CHOH-[C_{34}H_{68}]-CHOH-\underset{\underset{C_{22}H_{45}}{|}}{CH}-CO_2H \qquad [273]$$

The analysis of the crude mycolic acid isolated from a new batch of *M. smegmatis* gave different results. The main component was a di-unsaturated mycolic acid m.p. 56—61.5°, $C_{81}H_{158}O_3$ (methyl ester m.p. 46—52°) [342]. Pyrolysis of the tetrahydro-acid (m.p. 56.5—64°) gave mainly *n*-tetracosanoic acid. Results obtained by oxydative degradation and mass spectrometric examination of the fragments were in agreement with structure [274]. In this case, the exact number of carbon atoms was determined [342].

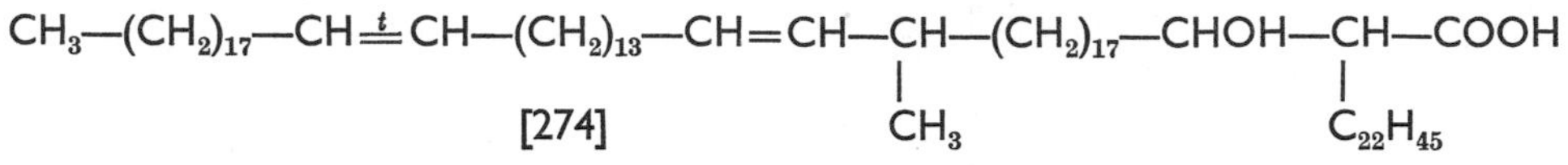

$$CH_3-(CH_2)_{17}-CH \triangleq CH-(CH_2)_{13}-CH=CH-CH-(CH_2)_{17}-CHOH-CH-COOH$$

$$[274] \qquad\qquad \underset{CH_3}{|} \qquad\qquad \underset{C_{22}H_{45}}{|}$$

It has to be noted that the acid [274] has no branching in position γ.

From the wax D of *M. kansasii*, Etemadi *et al.* [312] isolated a methyl α-kansamycolate, $C_{80}H_{156}O_3$, m.p. 45—47°, containing cyclopropane rings. Pyrolysis of this ester gave an aldehyde which was oxidized into meromycolic acid, still containing cyclopropane rings. Mass spectrometry showed that methyl meromycolate was a mixture of esters having the general structure [275]; α-kansamycolic acid has therefore the structure [276].

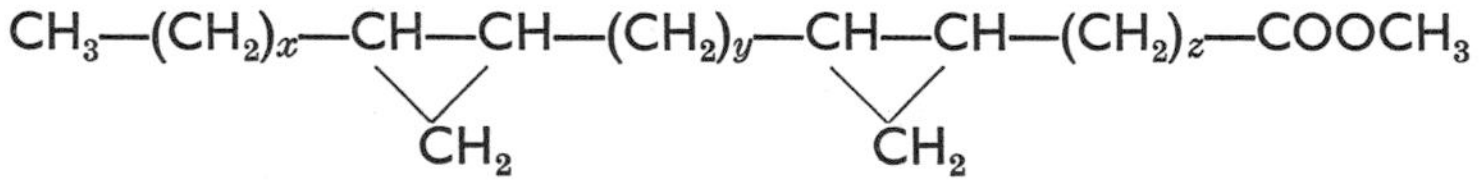

$$CH_3-(CH_2)_x-\underset{\underset{CH_2}{\diagdown/}}{CH-CH}-(CH_2)_y-\underset{\underset{CH_2}{\diagdown/}}{CH-CH}-(CH_2)_z-COOCH_3$$

$$[275]$$

$$CH_3-(CH_2)_x-\underset{\underset{CH_2}{\diagdown/}}{CH-CH}-(CH_2)_y-\underset{\underset{CH_2}{\diagdown/}}{CH-CH}-(CH_2)_z-CHOH-\underset{\underset{C_{22}H_{45}}{|}}{CH}-COOH$$

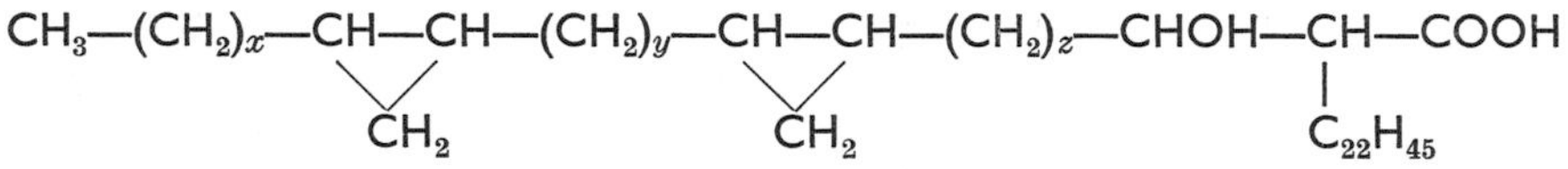

$$[276]$$

$$x + y + z = 46, 48, 50$$

The location of the cyclopropane rings was obtained by investigation of the structure of methyl meromycolate [275] by high resolution mass spectrometry [312]. The main acid in the sample of α-kansamycolic acid has the structure [277] :

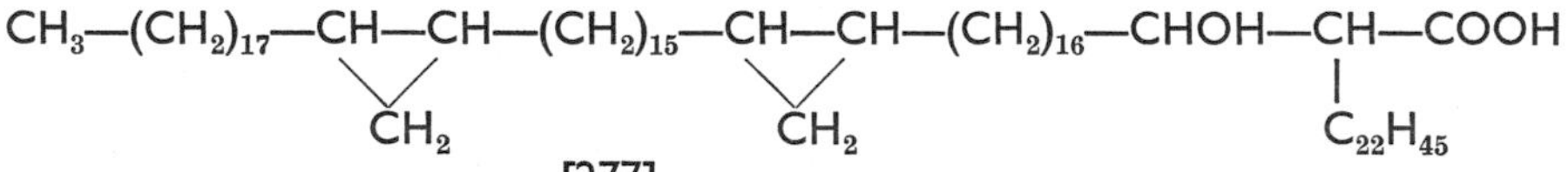

$$CH_3-(CH_2)_{17}-\underset{\underset{CH_2}{\diagdown/}}{CH-CH}-(CH_2)_{15}-\underset{\underset{CH_2}{\diagdown/}}{CH-CH}-(CH_2)_{16}-CHOH-\underset{\underset{C_{22}H_{45}}{|}}{CH}-COOH$$

$$[277]$$

The main mycolic acid isolated from the waxes of a non-photochromogenic strain of mycobacteria (methyl ester: m.p. 43—45°, $[\alpha]_D +3.8°$) contains 2 double bonds (methyl tetrahydromycolate m.p. 48—50°) [1217]. On the other hand, cyclopropane rings were observed in mycolic acids isolated from *M. paratuberculosis* [734a].

3) *Syntheses of compounds related to mycolic acids*

Syntheses of 3,5-dihydroxy-2,4-dialkyl acids
In connection with the work on α-mycolic acid Brévannes (see p. 133) the synthesis of an acid having two hydroxyls in positions 2 and 5, and two aliphatic chains in positions 2 and 4 was undertaken.

Eisner *et al.*[735] prepared from 3-acetoxy-2-tetradecyloctadecanoic acid [278], a β-keto ester $C_{54}H_{104}O_5$ [280] (colourless liquid, n_D^{20} 1.4645), which could not be reduced to a β-hydroxy-ester. A similar failure was obtained by Toubiana & Asselineau[703] in the case of ethyl 2-octadecyl-3-oxo-4-eicosyl-5-acetoxyhexacosanoate.

$$
\begin{array}{ccc}
\text{O-COCH}_3 & \text{O—COCH}_3 & \text{CO}_2\text{C}_2\text{H}_5 \\
| & | & | \\
\text{CH}_3\text{—(CH}_2)_{14}\text{—CH—CH—CO}_2\text{H} \rightarrow \text{CH—(CH}_2)_{14}\text{—CH—CH—CO—C—COO(C}_5\text{H}_9\text{O)} \\
| & | & | \\
[278] \quad \text{C}_{14}\text{H}_{29} & \text{C}_{14}\text{H}_{29} \quad \text{C}_{16}\text{H}_{33} & [279]
\end{array}
$$

$$
\begin{array}{c}
\text{O—COCH}_3 \\
| \\
\rightarrow \text{CH}_3\text{—(CH}_2)_{14}\text{—CH—CH—CO—CH—CO}_2\text{C}_2\text{H}_5 \\
| \quad\quad | \\
\text{C}_{14}\text{H}_{29} \quad \text{C}_{16}\text{H}_{33} \quad [280]
\end{array}
$$

Morgan & Polgar[736] synthesized a model of 3-hydroxy-5-methoxy acid. The preparation of the required β-methoxy acid was troublesome because of its easy transformation into an α,β-unsaturated acid. The chloride of the β-methoxy acid [282] could only be obtained by action of thionyl chloride in the presence of pyridine, the acid medium favouring formation of the α,β-unsaturated acid.

$$
\begin{array}{cc}
\text{OCH}_3 & \text{OCH}_3 \\
| & | \\
\text{CH}_3\text{CH}_2\text{CH—Cl} \xrightarrow{+\text{CH}_3\text{—(CH}_2)_2\text{—CH(CO}_2\text{C}_2\text{H}_5)_2} \text{CH}_3\text{CH}_2\text{—CH—CH—CO}_2\text{H} \\
& | \\
[281] \quad\quad\quad [282] & \text{C}_3\text{H}_7
\end{array}
$$

$$
\begin{array}{c}
\text{CO}_2\text{C}_2\text{H}_5 \quad\quad\quad \text{OCH}_3 \\
| \quad\quad\quad\quad | \\
\xrightarrow{+\text{C}_{18}\text{H}_{37}\text{—CH—CO}_2(\text{C}_5\text{H}_9\text{O})} \text{CH}_3\text{—CH}_2\text{—CH—CH—CO—CH—CO}_2\text{C}_2\text{H}_5 \\
| \quad\quad | \\
\text{C}_3\text{H}_7 \quad \text{C}_{18}\text{H}_{37} \quad [283]
\end{array}
$$

$$
\begin{array}{c}
\text{OCH}_3 \\
| \\
\xrightarrow{\text{NaBH}_4} \text{CH}_3\text{—CH}_2\text{—CH—CH—CHOH—CH—CO}_2\text{C}_2\text{H}_5 \\
| \quad\quad\quad | \\
\text{C}_3\text{H}_7 \quad\quad \text{C}_{18}\text{H}_{37} \quad [284]
\end{array}
$$

The ethyl 3-hydroxy-5-methoxy-2-octadecyl-4-propylheptanoate [284] melts at 63—65°; its infrared spectrum has a band at 1 093 cm^{-1} which may be due to the group $>$CH-OCH$_3$.

Oüra [737, 738] was successful in synthesizing 3,5-dihydroxy acids substituted at the 2 and 4 positions by long aliphatic chains. 3,5-Dihydroxy-2,4-ditetracosyl-triacontanoic acid [288], for example, was prepared from 3-acetoxy-2-tetracosyloctacosanoic acid [285] as follows:

$$
\begin{array}{cc}
\text{O—COCH}_3 & \text{CO}_2\text{C}_2\text{H}_5 \\
| & | \\
\text{C}_{24}\text{H}_{49}\text{—CH}_2\text{—CH—CH—CO}_2\text{H} \ + \ \text{C}_{24}\text{H}_{49}\text{—CH—CO}_2\text{CH}_2\text{—C}_6\text{H}_5 \ \longrightarrow \\
| \\
[285] \qquad \text{C}_{24}\text{H}_{49} \qquad\qquad\qquad [286]
\end{array}
$$

$$
\begin{array}{c}
\text{O—COCH}_3 \\
| \\
\text{C}_{24}\text{H}_{49}\text{—CH}_2\text{—CH—CH—CO—CH—CO}_2\text{C}_2\text{H}_5 \\
\qquad\quad | \qquad\quad | \\
[287] \qquad \text{C}_{24}\text{H}_{49} \quad \text{C}_{24}\text{H}_{49}
\end{array}
$$

$$
\begin{array}{c}
\text{OH} \\
| \\
\longrightarrow \text{C}_{24}\text{H}_{49}\text{—CH}_2\text{—CH—CH—CHOH—CH—CO}_2\text{H} \\
\qquad\qquad | \qquad\qquad\qquad | \\
\qquad\qquad \text{C}_{24}\text{H}_{49} \qquad\qquad \text{C}_{24}\text{H}_{49} \\
[288] \quad \text{m.p. } 63\text{-}64°
\end{array}
$$

The benzyl half-ester [286] was preferred to the monopyranyl derivative for the purpose of effecting the reaction at a higher temperature. Reduction of the acetoxy-keto-ester [287] to the dihydroxy-ester [288] was achieved by refluxing for 32 hours with an excess of sodium borohydride in a mixture of dioxan and alcohol. It is remarkable that under these conditions, partial reduction of the carboxyl group was not observed, although in the case of the reduction of methyl 3-keto-2-eicosyltetracosanoate Polonsky & Lederer [693] and Toubiana & Asselineau [703] observed it after only 3 hours' refluxing.

The melting points of the two 3,5-dihydroxy acids synthesized by Oura, compared with those of the α- and β-mycolic acids Brévannes, are as follows:

	3,5-Dihydroxy acids		Mycolic acids *Brévannes*	
	2,4-ditetracosyl-triacontanoic	2-tetracosyl-4-hexacosyldotria-contanoic	α	β
Free acid : molecular formula m.p. . . . . Methyl ester : m.p.	C$_{78}$H$_{156}$O$_4$ 82.5-83.5° 73-75°	C$_{82}$H$_{164}$O$_4$ 77.5° 68-70°	C$_{87}$H$_{174}$O$_4$ 55-56° 43-45°	C$_{88}$H$_{176}$O$_4$ + 73-75° 53-55°

The distinctly higher melting points of the synthetic products compared to those of the mycolic acids Brévannes (the number of carbon atoms of which is, however, greater), suggests for these latter a more branched structure than that [258] proposed by Aebi et al.[730].

Synthesis of long chain 2-substituted 1,3-diketones

The diketones $C_{86}H_{170}O_2$ obtained by degradation of the mycolic acids Brévannes and Canetti (see above) exhibit some reactions of β-diketones, but their UV and IR spectra do not have any characteristics of 1,3-diketones. To study this apparently abnormal behaviour, Toubiana & Asselineau[703] synthesized the branched β-diketones $C_{63}H_{124}O_2$ [291] and $C_{55}H_{108}O_2$ [295].

$$CH_3-(CH_2)_{20}-\underset{\underset{C_{20}H_{41}}{|}}{\overset{\overset{O-COCH_3}{|}}{CH}}-CH-CO_2H \rightarrow CH_3-(CH_2)_{20}-\underset{\underset{C_{20}H_{41}}{|}}{\overset{\overset{O-COCH_3}{|}}{CH}}-CH-CO-C_{19}H_{39}$$

[289]   [290]

$$\rightarrow CH_3-(CH_2)_{20}-CO-\underset{\underset{C_{20}H_{41}}{|}}{CH}-CO-C_{19}H_{39}$$

[291]   m.p. 58-59°

$$CH_3-(CH_2)_{16}-CO-CH_3 + CH_2-(CH_2)_{16}-CO_2C_2H_5 \rightarrow$$
[292]   [293]

$$C_{17}H_{35}-CO-CH_2-CO-C_{17}H_{35} \rightarrow C_{17}H_{35}-CO-\underset{\underset{C_{18}H_{37}}{|}}{CH}-CO-C_{17}H_{35}$$

[294]   [295]   m.p. 59-62°

While the unbranched diketone [294] has an absorption maximum at 275 mμ ($\varepsilon = 10\,000$), the branched diketones [291] and [295] have a maximum at 290 mμ ($\varepsilon \leqslant 2\,000$). Moreover, the band at 6.2 μ, characteristic of the enol form of β-diketones, is visible in the infrared spectrum of the unbranched β-diketone [294] and absent in the spectra of the branched β-diketones [291] and [295].

The two branched β-diketones, treated with hydroxylamine, give a dioxime (like the mycolic diketones), while the unbranched β-diketone gives a mixture of the dioxime and the iso-oxazole derivative.

Synthesis and dehydration of models of anhydromycolic acids

Asselineau & Asselineau[213] synthesized the esters [296] to [300] to study their dehydration, in relation with that of the mycolic acids Brévannes and Canetti.

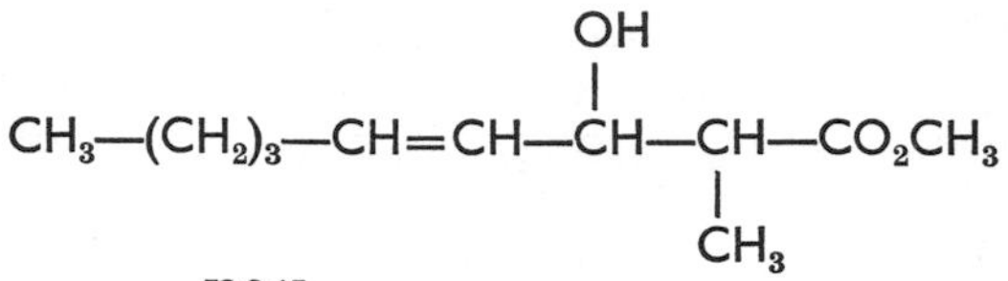

$$\underset{\text{[296]}}{CH_3-(CH_2)_3-CH=CH-\overset{\overset{\displaystyle OH}{|}}{CH}-\underset{\underset{\displaystyle CH_3}{|}}{CH}-CO_2CH_3}$$

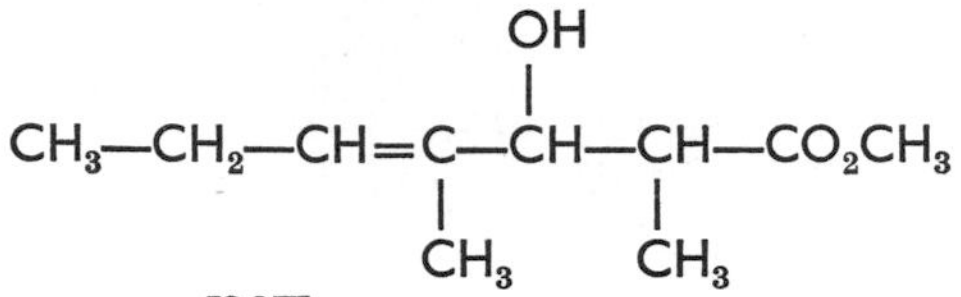

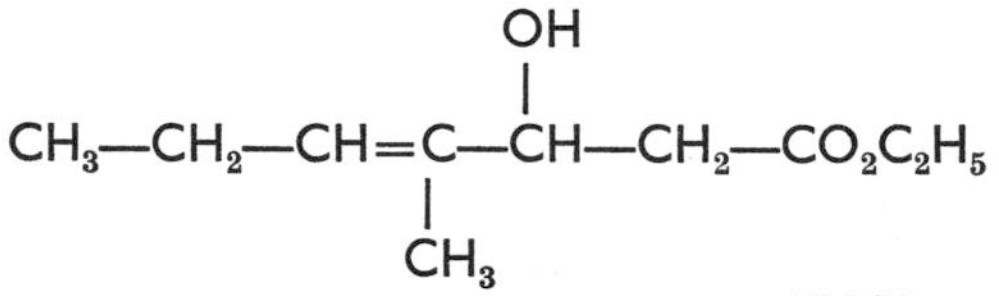

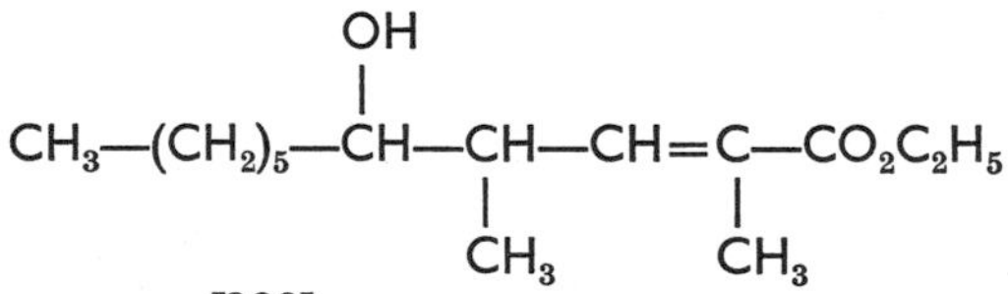

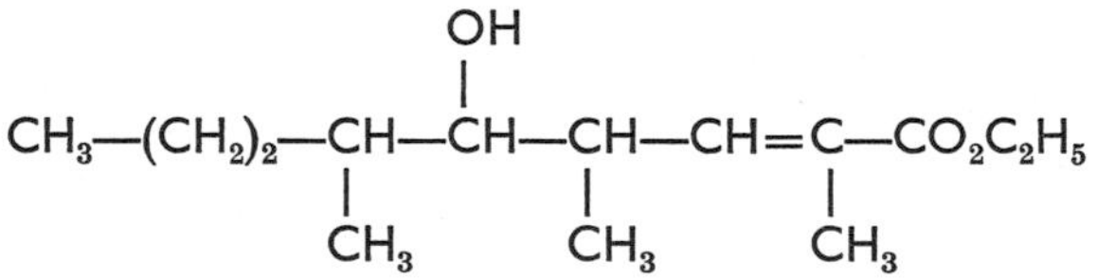

$$\underset{\text{[297]}}{CH_3-CH_2-CH=\underset{\underset{\displaystyle CH_3}{|}}{C}-\overset{\overset{\displaystyle OH}{|}}{CH}-\underset{\underset{\displaystyle CH_3}{|}}{CH}-CO_2CH_3}$$

$$\underset{\text{[298]}}{CH_3-CH_2-CH=\underset{\underset{\displaystyle CH_3}{|}}{C}-\overset{\overset{\displaystyle OH}{|}}{CH}-CH_2-CO_2C_2H_5}$$

$$\underset{\text{[299]}}{CH_3-(CH_2)_5-\overset{\overset{\displaystyle OH}{|}}{CH}-\underset{\underset{\displaystyle CH_3}{|}}{CH}-CH=\underset{\underset{\displaystyle CH_3}{|}}{C}-CO_2C_2H_5}$$

$$\underset{\text{[300]}}{CH_3-(CH_2)_2-\overset{\overset{\displaystyle OH}{|}}{CH}-\underset{\underset{\displaystyle CH_3}{|}}{CH}-\underset{\underset{\displaystyle CH_3}{|}}{CH}-CH=\underset{\underset{\displaystyle CH_3}{|}}{C}-CO_2C_2H_5}$$

Dehydration followed by equilibration in alkaline medium gives a 2,4-dienic acid from the α-methyl branched ester [296], and a mixture of 2,4- and 3,5-dienic acids from the γ-methyl branched ester [298] and the dimethyl branched esters [297], and [299]. It should be noted that the presence of 2,4-dienic acids in the dehydration products from 2,4-dimethyl branched esters [297] and [299] cannot be determined from the UV spectrum: steric hindrance caused by the methyl branches at positions 2 and 4 is strong enough to make the coplanarity of the conjugated system incomplete, so that the UV absorption of both the 3,5-dienic acid and its 2,4-isomer is the same as that of butadiene.

The trimethyl branched ester [300] gives a 2,5-dienic acid which cannot be isomerized in alkaline medium. This last example shows that the substitution in positions 2, 4, and 6 of simple methyl groups can discourage the formation of an entirely conjugated acid. The esters [299] and [300] are very resistant to dehydration.

"Mycolic acids" of diverse origins

Several mentions have been made of the existence in *spermatozoa* of an "acid-fast lipid fraction which resembles mycolic acid" (in particular, ref. [739] and [740]). This comparison with a mycolic compound is based on the acid-fast staining property (see p. 255), and on the production of tissue modifications resembling a granuloma by injection into animals. The only attempt, to our knowledge, to isolate this acid-fast factor was made by Berg[741]: this author obtained, from human spermatozoa, a waxy substance, m.p. 123—127°, which however differed from the mycolic acids in its solubility properties, being soluble in acetone, and insoluble in ether and benzene. The infrared spectrum of this compound, although considered by Berg to be compatible with that of an "ester of an aliphatic acid similar to mycolic acid", is very different. There is therefore, no sure indication of the presence of substances related to mycolic acids in spermatozoa.

Nethercott & Strawbridge[742] isolated from sarcoides (small tubercles found in sarcoidosis) an acid-fast waxy substance which was considered a derivative of mycolic acid because of the similarity of its infrared spectrum to that of a preparation from waxes C. This conclusion, therefore, rests entirely on examination of the infrared spectra: because of the inconclusiveness of the IR spectra of long-chain aliphatic compounds, confirmation of this result by another method is necessary.

The presence of compounds of mycolic acid type in pollen[743] has not been confirmed.

V. BIOSYNTHESIS

As it has been shown in several cases[744-748] that the biosynthesis of straight-chain fatty acids proceeds in bacteria through the usual acetate pathway, attention will be focused here on the biosynthesis of unsaturated acids and branched-chain acids (or alcohols). However, puzzling observations have recently been made by Kanemasa and Goldman[784 a] about the synthesis of straight-chain fatty acids in the tubercle bacillus: $1\text{-}C^{14}$-octanoyl-CoA is condensed by a partially purified enzyme system from H_{37} Ra bacilli to C_{16} and C_{24} fatty acids having respectively one-half and one-third of the total ^{14}C in the carboxyl carbon (these acids being straight-chain ones, according to their gas chromatographic behaviour). The possibility is suggested that "in *M. tuberculosis*, synthesis of long chain fatty acids may be accomplished through direct condensation of shorter chain length acyl-CoA's rather than only through a stepwise elongation mechanism"[784 a].

1. UNSATURATED FATTY ACIDS

The biosynthesis of unsaturated acids in micro-organisms has been systematically studied in recent years in the laboratory of K. Bloch.

Two separate pathways appear to exist for the synthesis of monounsaturated fatty acids[749, 749 b]:

(i) *Some aerobic* bacteria (in particular Mycobacteria) are able to desaturate palmitic and stearic acids [46]. This direct oxygen-dependent conversion is similar to that found in higher forms of life; however, it has been shown that the desaturation of palmitic and stearic acids by *M. phlei* requires Fe^{++} and a flavin derivative in addition to TPNH and O_2 [749 a]. The unsaturated C_{18} acid is then oleic acid. The mechanism of desaturation of stearic acid has been studied by Schroepfer & Bloch [750] in the case of *Corynebacterium diphtheriae* : the 9D-hydrogen appears to be the first to be removed by the enzyme in a rate-limiting reaction. Afterwards there occurs a non-rate-limiting stereospecific loss of the 10D-hydrogen.

Fulco *et al.* [749c] have observed that *B. megaterium* KM desaturates stearic and palmitic acids to cis-5-octadecenoic and cis-5-hexadecenoic acids, respectively. Here again, oxygen appears to be an absolute requirement for these desaturation reactions.

(ii) *Anaerobic, facultatively aerobic,* and some obligate aerobic bacteria are unable to desaturate palmitic or stearic acid, either in the absence or presence of oxygen. These organisms lack the ability to interconvert long-chain saturated and unsaturated fatty acids. Scheuerbrandt *et al.* [751] have observed that monounsaturated acids are synthesized by *Clostridium butyricum* from shorter-chain precursors [301 → 310]:

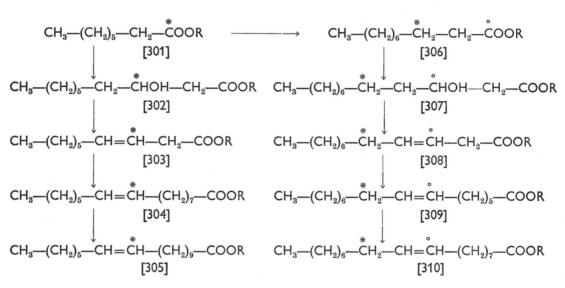

Carbon ^{14}C * originates from C—1 of octanoic acid,
Carbon ^{14}C ° originates from C—1 of decanoic acid.

This scheme of synthesis is in agreement with observations of Hofmann *et al.* [752] who observed that some short-chain unsaturated acids can replace vaccenic acid [305] or oleic acid [310] as a growth factor for Lactobacilli.

More recently, Norris & Bloch[753] have isolated from *E. coli* B an enzyme that acts specifically on β-hydroxydecanoate thioesters [302] and gives mixtures of α,β- and β,γ-decenoates [β,γ-isomer: 303]. "We conclude that this dehydrase accounts for the formation of cis-vaccenic acid by the *E. coli* synthetase"[753].

The nature of the main monounsaturated fatty acids synthesized by some species of aerobic and anaerobic bacteria is given in Table 31.

TABLE 31. THE NATURE OF THE UNSATURATED ACIDS FOUND IN SOME SPECIES OF BACTERIA (MAINLY FROM SCHEUERBRANDT & BLOCH[754])

Bacterial species	Number of carbon atoms in the acids		
	14 Δ	16 Δ	18 Δ
Aerobic bacteria			
Mycobacterium phlei		9 (3 %) 10 (32 %)	9 (7 %)
Corynebacterium diphtheriae		9 (42 %)	9 (8 %)
Corynebacterium ovis		9 (14 %)	9 (6 %)
Anaerobic bacteria:			
Escherichia coli B		9 (7 %)	11 (19 %)
Lactobacillus arabinosus		? (4 %)	11 (36 %)
Pseudomonas fluorescens		9 (31 %)	11 (12 %)
Rhodopseudomonas spheroides			
anaerobic culture (light)	7 (6 %)	9 (3 %)	11 (69 %)
aerobic culture (dark)	7 (3 %)	9 (3 %)	11 (78 %)
Clostridium butyricum	7 (0.3 %)	9 (8 %) 7 (8 %)	11 (2 %) 9 (1 %)
Clostridium pasteurianum	7 (1 %)	9 (3 %) 11 (1 %)	11 (2 %)

The values between brackets refer to the approximate content of unsaturated acids, in per cent of the total fatty acids (not including acids of the mycolic acid type).

Polyunsaturated fatty acids do not occur in significant amounts in the lipids of bacteria, whether anaerobic or not. Scheuerbrandt and Bloch[754] suggest that "the appearance of these compounds was a still later evolutionary event". On the other hand, polyunsaturated acids have been characterized in the lipids of protozoa[755-758]; about 48 % of the total fatty acids of *Ochromonas danica* (grown on a synthetic medium) consists of polyunsaturated acids (including a docosapentaenoic acid)[755].

2. BRANCHED-CHAIN FATTY ACIDS

The biosynthesis of bacterial branched-chain acids has been reviewed recently[759, 760].

a) *Iso and ante-iso fatty acids*

These branched chain acids are synthesized by condensation of short-chain iso or ante-iso fatty acid coenzyme A esters with malonylcoenzyme A in the presence of NADPH (TPNH). Conclusive evidence for such a pathway was given by Allison *et al.* [761] in the case of *Ruminococcus flavefaciens* and *R. albus*, by Wegner & Foster [762] in the case of *Bacteroides succinogenes*, and by Kaneda [763] in the case of *Bacillus subtilis*.

Labelled isobutyrate is incorporated mainly in isotetradecanoic and isohexadecanoic acids, and isovalerate in isopentadecanoic and isoheptadecanoic acids. Labelled α-methylbutyric acid gives rise to anteisoheptadecanoic acid. *M. tuberculosis* is unable to synthesize iso fatty acids from isobutyric acid [784].

b) *Branched-chain acids formed from methionine*

The biosynthesis of lactobacillic acid [133] and other cyclopropane fatty acids has been studied extensively. The basic work in this field is due to Hofmann, and is described in a recent book [764] and in a review [764a].

By using either labelled cis-vaccenic acid or CH_3-^{14}C-methionine, it was shown that lactobacillic acid is formed by addition of a one-carbon unit (arising from the methyl group of methionine) to the double bond of cis-vaccenic acid [765, 766].

Law *et al.* [767] found that cyclopropane fatty acids are synthesized by *E. coli*, *S. marcescens*, and *A. tumefaciens* mainly at the end of the logarithmic phase of growth and during the stationary phase. Carbon and hydrogen of the methyl group of methionine are both incorporated into the cyclopropane acid. By using CH_3-^2H-methionine, Pohl *et al.* [770] showed that two hydrogen atoms of the methyl group are incorporated. The rôle of methionine is specific, as no effect of isotope dilution is observed when other non-labelled C_1-donors (formate, formaldehyde, serine) are added with the labelled methionine to the culture medium.

Extracts of *S. marcescens* or *Cl. butyricum* are able to transform unsaturated precursors into cyclopropane acids when *S*-adenosylmethionine is added to the medium [768]; the rôle of *S*-adenosylmethionine was previously demonstrated in the case of the synthesis of a cyclopropane C_{17} fatty acid by whole cells of *Aerobacter aerogenes* [769]. The enzyme system of *Cl. butyricum* differs from that of *S. marcescens* by its requirement for phospholipids containing unsaturated acids. In both cases, cyclopropane fatty acids are obtained as components of phosphatidylethanolamine [768].

By using as substrate phosphatidylethanolamines with a known distribution of unsaturated fatty acid residues, and by analyzing the distribution of cyclopropane fatty acids in the phospholipids produced by the cyclopropane synthetase of *Cl. butyricum*, Hildebrand and Law [770a] observed that the enzyme has "a definite, but not absolute, specificity for an unsaturated fatty acid in the γ-position".

A similar pathway exists in *M. phlei* for the formation of tuberculostearic acid (10-methyloctadecanoic acid) [105] from oleic acid: methionine supplies the methyl side-chain [46]. Similar results were obtained in the case of the virulent human strain $H_{37}Rv$ and the attenuated bovine strain BCG; no inhibition of biosynthesis was observed in the presence of a large excess of ethionine or norleucine [760]. Jauréguiberry *et al.* [771a] have shown that only 2 hydrogen atoms from the methyl of methionine are incorporated into the tuberculo-stearic acid molecule.

These results are in agreement with those obtained in 1956 by Karlsson[771]: a tuberculo-stearic acid auxotrophic mutant of *M. tuberculosis* can grow when oleic acid is added to the medium.

Cason & Miller[552] have isolated 10-methylhexadec-9-enoic acid in addition to 10-methyl-hexadecanoic acid (and other members of this group) from the lipids of *M. tuberculosis*. It is therefore feasible that the addition of the methyl group of methionine to the double bond of the monounsaturated C_n precursor proceeds via an unsaturated C_{n+1} intermediate.

c) *Branched-chain acids formed from propionate*

In 1956 Woodward[772] proposed a "propionate rule" to explain the occurrence of methyl side-chains in the aglycones of macrolide antibiotics which are produced by bacteria of the genus Streptomyces. According to this rule, propionate may replace acetate units in the build-ing of the carbon skeleton of these molecules, one methyl side-chain occurring every time a propionate unit is incorporated. Recently, this hypothesis has received support from work on the aglycones of erythromycin [311][773-775] and methymycin [312][776], by using doubly labelled propionate. It was observed that 2-methylmalonate is a much better precursor of the preterminal C_3-units than of the terminal or primer C_3-unit[776a].

[311] Erythronolide
(7 propionate units)

Methynolide [312]
(5 propionate units + 1 acetate unit)

As early as 1951, Polgar & Robinson[617] suggested that C_{27}-phthienoic acid might be produced by the tubercle bacillus by addition of 3 propionate units to a stearic acid unit. This hypothesis, strengthened by the results obtained in the macrolide field, was verified by Gastambide-Odier *et al.*[777]: [1-^{14}C, 3-^{3}H]-propionic acid was incorporated into the myco-cerosic acid fraction [containing 313] of the avirulent human strain H_{37}Ra. The ratio ^{3}H/^{14}C in this fraction was about the same as that of the propionic acid initially added to the medium. 75 per cent of the tritium incorporated was found in the methyl branches[777]. It is likely that such a pathway operates in the case of phthienoic acids, but with different enzyme systems, because the configuration of the asymmetric centres are opposite in the case of mycocerosic acids and phthienoic acids. It was found that H_{37} Rv cells growing on a medium supplemented with propionate have a content of phthienoic acids much higher than that of control cells[784].

$$CH_3-(CH_2)_{18}-COOH + CH_2-COOH + CH_2-COOH + CH_2-COOH + CH_2-COOH \longrightarrow$$
$$\begin{array}{ccccc} & | & | & | & | \\ & CH_3 & CH_3 & CH_3 & CH_3 \end{array}$$

$$CH_3-(CH_2)_{19}-CH-CH_2-CH-CH_2-CH-CH_2-CH-COOH$$
$$\begin{array}{cccc} | & | & | & | \\ CH_3 & CH_3 & CH_3 & CH_3 \end{array}$$

[313]

Propionate is also used by vertebrates to build branched-chain acids: Noble *et al.*[778] have found that 2,4,6,8-tetramethyldecanoic acid, produced by the preen gland of the goose (see p. 106), is synthesized by condensation of 4 propionate units and 1 acetate unit.

The methyl branch of phthiocerol [314] (see p. 75) also arises from the incorporation of one propionate unit[517], whereas the methyl of the methoxyl group comes from methionine.

$$CH_3-(CH_2)_n-CHOH-CH_2-CHOH-(CH_2)_4-CH-CH(OCH_3)-CH_2-CH_3$$
$$\begin{array}{c} | \\ CH_3 \end{array}$$

[314] n = 20 or 22

Nothing is known about the mechanism of these condensations. Propionate is probably first carboxylated to methylmalonate: propionylCoA-carboxylase has been characterized in *M. smegmatis*[779], and the rôle of methylmalonic acid in the biosynthesis of erythromycine has recently been demonstrated[780].

d) *Acids of the mycolic type*

The partial formula [318] common to all the mycolic acids suggests that these acids might be formed in the bacterial cell by condensation of two fatty acid molecules according to a process related to Claisen's reaction[64]:

$$R-COOH + CH_2-COOH \rightarrow R-CO-CH-COOH \rightarrow R-CHOH-CH-COOH$$
$$\begin{array}{ccc} | & | & | \\ R' & R' & R' \end{array}$$

[315]   [316]   [317]   [318]

Such a scheme of biosynthesis can explain the formation of 2-methyl-3-hydroxypentanoic acid ([318], R = C_2H_5, R′ = CH_3) (see p. 109) from two molecules of propionic acid, of corynomycolic acid ([318], R = $C_{15}H_{31}$, R′ = $C_{14}H_{29}$) from two molecules of palmitic acid and of corynomycolenic acid ([318], R = $C_{15}H_{29}$, R′ = $C_{14}H_{29}$) from one molecule of palmitic acid and one molecule of palmitoleic acid.

The following observations substantiate such a biosynthetic pathway in the case of corynomycolic and corynomycolenic acids.

(i)   Palmitic and palmitoleic acids are the most important straight-chain acids isolated from the lipids of *C. diphtheriae*.

(ii) Palmitone and Δ^7-palmitenone, which can derive by decarboxylation of the intermediate β-keto acid [317], were isolated from the neutral fractions of the lipids[412]. Furthermore, these ketones might arise from saponification (followed by decarboxylation) of a β-keto ester derived from [317] in the course of the isolation steps.

(iii) From diphtheria bacilli grown in the presence of [1-^{14}C]-palmitic acid, a labelled corynomycolic acid has been isolated: half of the radioactivity of this acid is localized in the carboxyl as found by chromic acid oxidation [320 → 321]. The second half of the radioactivity is localized in the carbon atom of the keto group of palmitone [321], i.e. C-3 of corynomycolic acid, as is to be expected[781]:

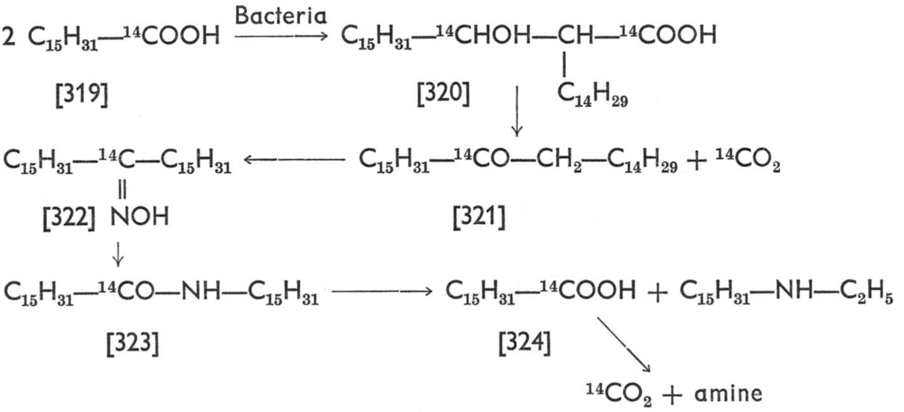

$$2\ C_{15}H_{31}-^{14}COOH \xrightarrow{\text{Bacteria}} C_{15}H_{31}-^{14}CHOH-CH-^{14}COOH$$

[319]   [320] | $C_{14}H_{29}$

$$C_{15}H_{31}-^{14}C-C_{15}H_{31} \longleftarrow C_{15}H_{31}-^{14}CO-CH_2-C_{14}H_{29} + ^{14}CO_2$$

[322] NOH   [321]

$$C_{15}H_{31}-^{14}CO-NH-C_{15}H_{31} \longrightarrow C_{15}H_{31}-^{14}COOH + C_{15}H_{31}-NH-C_2H_5$$

[323]   [324]

$$^{14}CO_2 + \text{amine}$$

Extension of this scheme of biosynthesis could explain the existence of acids of the type [325], $C_{48}H_{96}O_4$, in the lipids of *C. diphtheriae*. In this connection the isolation from the lipids of the diphtheria bacillus of a dihydroxy acid $C_{50}H_{100}O_4$ and a monohydroxy mono-unsaturated acid with the approximate molecular formula $C_{53}H_{104}O_3$ (see p. 120) may be noted.

$$CH_3-(CH_2)_{14}-CHOH-CH-CHOH-CH-COOH$$

[325] $C_{14}H_{29}$ $C_{14}H_{29}$

The same mechanism explains the incorporation of 2 molecules of palmitic acid into nocardomycolic acid (page 117) [781a].

The biosynthesis of mycolic acids from Mycobacteria may be explained by a similar series of condensations. The number of carbon atoms in the mycolic acids of human and bovine strains, 88, corresponds to the sum: (2 × 18) + (2 × 26); therefore, these acids might be produced by condensation of 2 molecules of stearic (or palmitic) acid and 2 molecules of hexacosanoic acid.

In support of this scheme of biosynthesis, which is an extension of that which has just been outlined for corynomycolic acid, the following observations may be made.

(i) Hexacosanoic and palmitic (or stearic) acids are very frequently encountered in the lipids of human or bovine strains of the tubercle bacillus. Moreover, Karlsson[771] found, with the aid of mutants that require some lipid substances for their growth, that a biogenetic relation exists between *n*-hexacosanoic acid and mycolic acids.

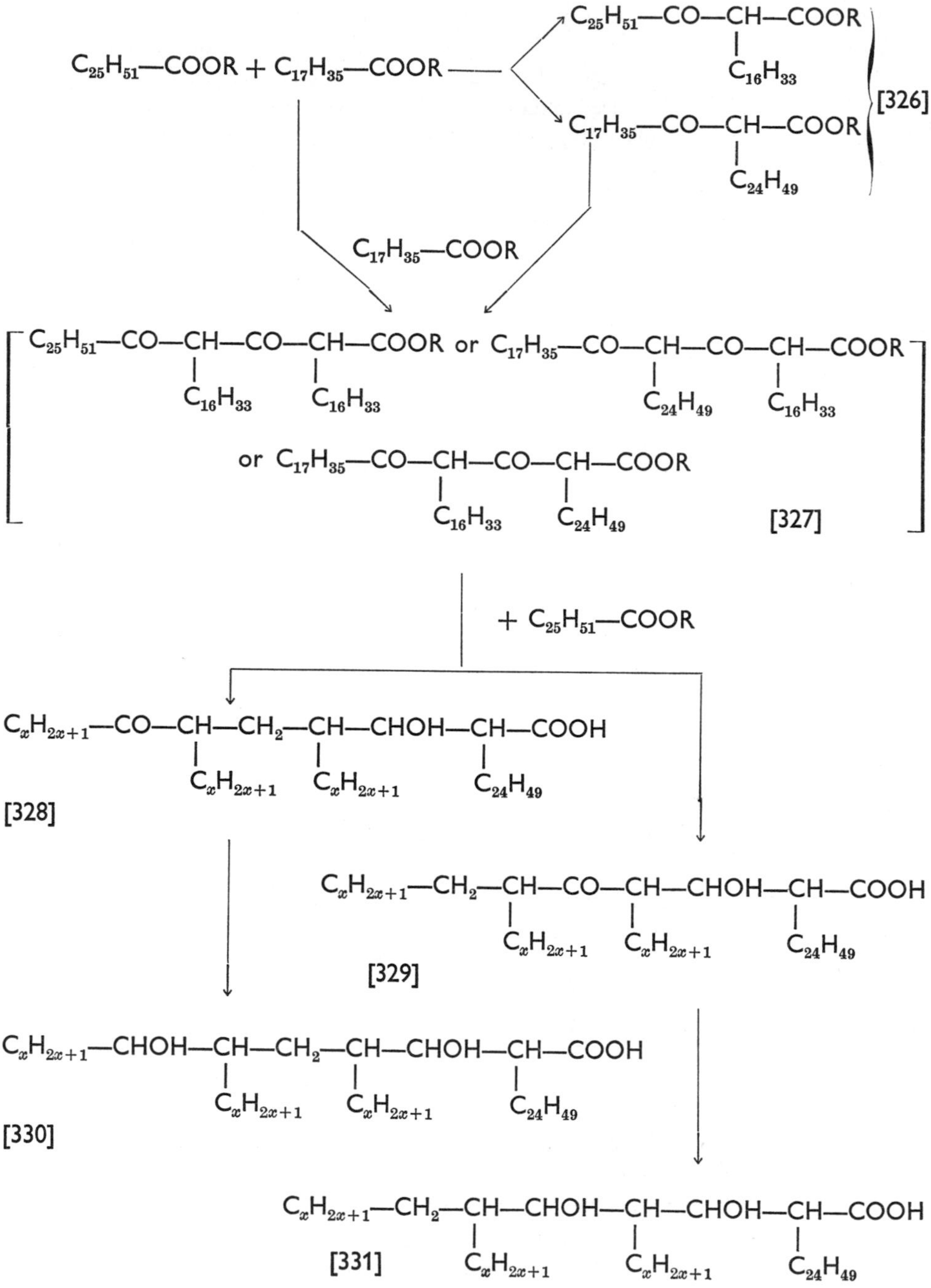

$$C_{25}H_{51}\text{—COOR} + C_{17}H_{35}\text{—COOR} \longrightarrow
\begin{cases}
\begin{array}{l}
C_{25}H_{51}\text{—CO—CH—COOR} \\
\qquad\qquad\quad | \\
\qquad\qquad\; C_{16}H_{33} \\[4pt]
C_{17}H_{35}\text{—CO—CH—COOR} \\
\qquad\qquad\quad | \\
\qquad\qquad\; C_{24}H_{49}
\end{array}
\end{cases} \text{[326]}$$

$$C_{17}H_{35}\text{—COOR}$$

$$\left[
\begin{array}{l}
C_{25}H_{51}\text{—CO—CH—CO—CH—COOR or } C_{17}H_{35}\text{—CO—CH—CO—CH—COOR} \\
\qquad\qquad\;| \qquad\quad | \qquad\qquad\qquad\qquad\qquad\qquad | \qquad\quad | \\
\qquad\quad C_{16}H_{33} \quad C_{16}H_{33} \qquad\qquad\qquad\qquad\qquad C_{24}H_{49} \quad C_{16}H_{33} \\[8pt]
\qquad\text{or } C_{17}H_{35}\text{—CO—CH—CO—CH—COOR} \\
\qquad\qquad\qquad\qquad\; | \qquad\quad | \\
\qquad\qquad\qquad\; C_{16}H_{33} \quad C_{24}H_{49} \qquad\qquad \text{[327]}
\end{array}
\right]$$

$$+ \; C_{25}H_{51}\text{—COOR}$$

$$C_xH_{2x+1}\text{—CO—CH—CH}_2\text{—CH—CHOH—CH—COOH}$$
$$\qquad\qquad\qquad | \qquad\qquad | \qquad\qquad\quad | $$
$$\qquad\qquad\; C_xH_{2x+1} \quad C_xH_{2x+1} \qquad C_{24}H_{49}$$

[328]

$$C_xH_{2x+1}\text{—CH}_2\text{—CH—CO—CH—CHOH—CH—COOH}$$
$$\qquad\qquad\qquad\qquad | \qquad\quad | \qquad\qquad\quad | $$
$$\qquad\qquad\qquad\; C_xH_{2x+1} \quad C_xH_{2x+1} \qquad C_{24}H_{49}$$

[329]

$$C_xH_{2x+1}\text{—CHOH—CH—CH}_2\text{—CH—CHOH—CH—COOH}$$
$$\qquad\qquad\qquad\quad | \qquad\qquad | \qquad\qquad\quad | $$
$$\qquad\qquad\quad\; C_xH_{2x+1} \quad C_xH_{2x+1} \qquad C_{24}H_{49}$$

[330]

$$C_xH_{2x+1}\text{—CH}_2\text{—CH—CHOH—CH—CHOH—CH—COOH}$$
$$\qquad\qquad\qquad\qquad | \qquad\qquad\quad | \qquad\qquad\quad | $$
$$\qquad\text{[331]} \qquad C_xH_{2x+1} \qquad C_xH_{2x+1} \qquad C_{24}H_{49}$$

(ii) The degradation of mycolic acids leads to products which can generally be considered as derived from hexacosanoic or palmitic (or stearic) chains.

(iii) Two C_{60} hydroxy acids with branched chains were isolated from lipids of human strains of *M. tuberculosis* (see p. 121): these acids may arise from the condensation of 3 molecules of fatty acids [(2 × 18) + 26 = 62] and correspond to compounds of type [327]. C_{60} neutral compounds (see p. 120) were also isolated: they might be formed by decarboxylative degradation of acids [327].

(iv) Acids with about 40 carbon atoms, containing cyclopropane rings or double bonds (mycobacteric acids, page 107) have been isolated from the lipids of several strains of mycobacteria; they may correspond to one of the early steps [326] in the series of condensation reactions.

(v)   Mycolonic acids (3-hydroxy-*x*-oxomycolanoic acids) isolated from a number of strains (particularly bovine strains) may correspond to intermediaries of type [328] or [329].

(vi) Mycolic acids isolated from human or bovine strains give on pyrolysis a molecule of *n*-hexacosanoic acid: the principal straight-chain higher fatty acid present in these strains is hexacosanoic acid. Pyrolysis of mycolic acids from saprophytic mycobacteria usually gives *n*-tetracosanoic acid: the principal straight-chain higher fatty acid found in the lipids of these bacilli is tetracosanoic acid (ref. 150; Asselineau, unpublished results quoted in ref. 711).

This scheme of biosynthesis has the advantage of explaining the existence of two types of mycolic acids one being 3,5-dihydroxy acids [331], the other 3,7-dihydroxy acids [330]. Now it has been shown that some mycolic acids (Brévannes, Canetti) have their hydroxy groups at positions 3 and 5, while in the case of other acids (Test, R_1), the second hydroxyl is farther removed than position 5. Moreover, Malani and Polgar [733] have demonstrated the presence of a long chain branch in position 4.

However, examination of monomolecular films of mycolic acids showed that the cross section of the molecule correspond to only three hydrocarbon chains. A structure of the type [332] would then appear more plausible for mycolic acids of human or bovine strains (the radical R containing or not one more oxygen group, and cyclopropane rings).

$$R-CH-CHOH-CH-COOH$$
$$\mid \qquad\qquad\quad \mid$$
$$(CH_2)n \qquad\quad C_{24}H_{49} \qquad\qquad [332]$$
$$\mid$$
$$CH_3$$

Intermediate compounds such as [326] or [327] would have one branch less and would contain cyclopropane rings (cf. mycobacteric acids).

In the case of mycolic acids from saprophytic strains of mycobacteria, Etémadi and Lederer [781b] have shown that tetracosanoic acid gives rise to the α-branch of α-smegmamycolic acid [274] and that the methyl branch arises from the methyl of methionine.

In the French edition of this book, we suggested that dicarboxylic mycolic acids might be produced by oxidative cleavage of a monocarboxylic mycolic acid precursor.

Lipid groups occurring in bacterial lipids

All the lipid groups existing in animals and in higher plants seem to occur in bacterial lipids, with the exception of sterols and of derivatives of sphingosine (sphingomyelins, glycosides of N-acyl sphingosine). Reports of sphingomyelin being present in the lipids of several bacterial species not seem significant, because the sphingosine was not isolated: the sole evidence has been the value of the nitrogen/phosphorus ratio.

I. HYDROCARBONS

Mixtures of hydrocarbons have been isolated from the lipids of several species of bacteria. The possibility of contamination from an outside source cannot always be ruled out: nevertheless, the synthesis of hydrocarbons by bacteria was demonstrated in one case [782, 783].

Asselineau & Moron [139] have isolated from the fats of a human strain of *M. tuberculosis* (Canetti), grown on Sauton's synthetic medium, a mixture of hydrocarbons, b.p. 110 to 150° under 0.05 mm, the average composition of which corresponds to $C_{21}H_{42}$; although no characteristic band for a double bond is visible in the infrared spectrum, at least a part of these hydrocarbons is unsaturated (according to the tetranitromethane test).

Chromatography of the unsaponifiable part of fats isolated from a strain of *M. phlei* (strain "ICI") gave a mixture of hydrocarbons, the major part of which distilled at 150—160° under 0.1 mm: colourless liquid $[\alpha]_D^{20} + 13.5°$. The elementary composition is in agreement with the formula $C_{25}H_{48}$; the shortage of hydrogen indicates the presence of double bonds: the infrared spectrum shows in particular bands at 3.7, 6.1, and 11.3 μ, attributable to the group $>C = CH_2$. The optical rotation shows that it is a branched-chain hydrocarbon [115]. Nevertheless, the bacilli used, residue from the preparation of Mycobactine, were grown in a non-synthetic medium [785]: therefore contamination by compounds from the medium remains possible.

Hydrocarbons were isolated from the lipids of *Sarcina lutea* : they mainly consist of saturated straight-chain hydrocarbons with 25, 26, 27, 28 and 29 carbon atoms. In the whole fraction, 37 components were detected [785a].

Other hydrocarbon fractions have been isolated from the lipids of *Corynebacterium ovis* [786] and *Escherichia coli* (Dauchy & Asselineau, unpublished results).

From the unsaponifiable matter of *Lactobacillus casei* grown in a medium with added [2-^{14}C]-acetate, Kodicek [782] isolated a mixture of radioactive hydrocarbons (separable into four constituents by paper chromatography): the ultraviolet spectrum of the mixture showed absorption maxima at 230 and 280 mμ, indicating the presence of conjugated double bonds.

More recently, a mixture of hydrocarbons has been isolated from BCG; they were included in urea, but the high intensity of the vibration band at 7.3 μ in their infrared spectrum shows that the carbon skeleton is branched [784].

II. GLYCERIDES

The saponification of neutral fats often gives glycerol as the principal water-soluble constituent. The presence of glycerides was shown, in this indirect manner, in the lipids of *Lactobacillus acidophilus* [787]; *Agrobacterium tumefaciens* [589]; *Brucella melitensis*, *B. suis*, and *B. abortus* [788]; *Actinobacillus mallei* [789]; *Pasteurella pestis* [177]; and in *Salmonella ballerup* [155], *S. typhi* [790], and *S. paratyphi C* [791].

Only in the case of the lipids of Mycobacteria have some glycerides been isolated and characterized. These lipids contain a large number of mono-, di-, and tri-glycerides, although the first analyses of the fats of Mycobacteria had shown glycerol to be absent [60].

Monoglycerides

A 1-glycerol ester (monostearin type) was identified in the fats of a human strain (Brévannes) of *M. tuberculosis* [140, 252]. From the waxes of BCG [792, 793] a 1-glyceryl monomycolate, m.p. 45—46°, $[\alpha]_D + 10°$, $C_{91}H_{182}O_6$, was isolated; in the case of glyceryl monomycolate isolated from the human strain Brévannes, Noll [794] gives m.p. 38-39°, $[\alpha]_D + 6.4°$ (benzene). The structure of this glyceride was determined by examination of the infrared spectrum, by the identification of glycerol as the sole water-soluble component after saponification, and by study of the periodic oxidation (consumption of one molecule of periodic acid). A 1-glyceryl monomycolate was synthesized by Defaye & Lederer [450] by condensation of potassium myco- late with 1-tosyl-2:3-isopropylidene-DL-glycerol. The synthetic product, m.p. 45—46°, showed the same optical activity ($[\alpha]_D + 10°$) as the natural ester in spite of the fact that it is a mixture containing D or L-glycerol.

The monomycolates were isolated by chromatography: it has been demonstrated that by this procedure, 2-monoglycerides are easily isomerized into 1-monoglycerides [795]. There- fore a doubt exists as to the nature of the ester present in the crude lipids.

Diglycerides

A mixture of diglycerides of the approximate formula $C_{55}H_{108}O_5$, m.p. 54—62°, $[\alpha]_D + 5°$, was isolated from the waxes of BCG; saponification gave principally hexacosanoic acid [792].

From the same waxes, a fraction of diglycerides containing one molecule of mycolic acid and one molecule of a lower fatty acid (about C_{16}), $C_{107}H_{212}O_7$, m.p. 50—53°, $[\alpha]_D + 8°$, was obtained [792].

A diglyceride, probably 1-stearo-3-palmitin, $C_{37}H_{72}O_5$, m.p. 67—68°, (acetyl derivative m.p. 49—50°), showing no measurable optical activity, was isolated from the fats of the human strain Brévannes [140]. This diglyceride is identical with "Compound C" of Smith *et al.* [252].

A diglyceride containing one molecule of phthienoic acid and one molecule of an acid about C_{18} was isolated from the fats of the human strain Canetti: $C_{48}H_{92}O_5$, m.p. 60—62°, $[\alpha]_D^{18} + 14°$, λ_{max} 220 mμ ($\varepsilon = 8,820$) [139].

Diglycerides have been characterized in the fat of *Staphylococcus aureus* [545] and *B. cereus* [796].

Triglycerides

A fraction of triglycerides, m.p. 52—55°, $[\alpha]_D + 2°$, was isolated from the waxes of BCG; its saponification gave a mixture (2:1) of hexacosanoic acid and lower acids (about C_{16}) [792]. A similar preparation, m.p. 50—58°, was described by Noll & Jackim [140] in the course of their study of the fats of the Brévannes strain; the average molecular weight of the acids obtained corresponds to that of a C_{24} acid.

A fraction rich in tripalmitin, m.p. 52—54°, was obtained from the waxes of BCG [792] and the waxes A of *M. marianum* [141]: in both cases, a mixture is indicated, since pure tripalmitin melts at 65°.

Oleo-tetracosano-palmitin was identified in the waxes A of *M. marianum* [141] by its oxidation to azelao-tetracosano-palmitin. A complex mixture of triglycerides, m.p. 48—50°; $[\alpha]_D + 1°$, was isolated from the waxes A of *M. phlei* [115].

A triglyceride fraction containing mycocerosic acid was observed in the fats of the human strain Canetti [139].

Esters of ethyleneglycol were detected in the fats of Mycobacteria [383, 530] and of *C. diphtheriae* [863] by paper chromatography of the hydrosoluble fraction obtained by saponification. These results were confirmed by isolation of ethyleneglycol as its dibenzoate m.p. 68—70° [816]. Esters of ethyleneglycol were recently characterized in the lipids of ox lung [817].

III. CERIDES

In spite of the very widespread use of the term "waxes" to designate some bacterial lipid fractions, true waxes or cerides (esters of long-chain acids with higher aliphatic alcohols) are rarely encountered.

The normal chain C_{16} and C_{18} alcohols have been detected in the unsaponifiable part of the lipids of *B. cereus* [796] and esters of palmitic and stearic acids with hentriacontanol-16 have been isolated from the lipids of a strain of *Nocardia brasiliensis* [1256 b]; however, the presence of cerides is rather limited to the lipids of Mycobacteria and Corynebacteria.

a) *Mycobacteria*

Human and bovine strains of *M. tuberculosis* contain diesters of mycocerosic acid (see p. 102) and alcohols of the phthiocerol group (see p. 75) [525, 636, 794]. Since mycocerosic acid is a mixture of at least three acids and phthiocerol of at least five alcohols, the number of diesters possible is rather high. The mixture is isolated as a colourless powder, m.p. 30—32°, $[\alpha]_D - 6°$.

In the case of *M. avium* and *M. phlei*, the saponification of a few lipid fractions gives a mixture of 2-eicosanol and 2-octadecanol, besides a complex mixture of fatty acids [488, 489]. The ester mixture was recently isolated by chromatography of the waxes A of *M. phlei* (strain ICI) [115]: colourless powder, m.p. 39—42°, $[\alpha] + 3.5°$.

b) *Corynebacteria*

Gubarev & Vakulenko [797] isolated from *C. diphtheriae* fractions that, on saponification, gave fatty acids and corinnic alcohol $C_{35}H_{70}O$, m.p. 54°. On the other hand, Asano & Takahashi [699] claimed that a fraction of wax extracted by chloroform is constituted of esters of palmitic and stearic acids with a C_9 or C_{10} alcohol, with octadecanol (m.p. 56°) and with docosanol (m.p. 82°).

IV. STEROLS

Much research has been directed to the search for sterols in bacterial lipids.

First investigations, made in 1930-1935, recognized the absence of sterols in the lipids of *C. diphtheriae* [640, 798], *E. coli* [798, 801] and Mycobacteria [802, 803].

More recently, the absence of sterols was confirmed in the case of *Bacillus M* [804], *Salmonella typhi* [790], *S. paratyphi* C [791], *Neisserria gonorrhoeae* [805], *M. tuberculosis* [485], *Micromonospora* sp. [806], *Rhodospirillum rubrum* [806], and *Lactobacillus casei* [782, 783].

Nevertheless, in several instances, sterols have been isolated from bacterial lipids. Crowder & Anderson [787] identified cholesterol in the lipids of *Lactobacillus acidophilus*; however, since milk was added to the culture medium, a doubt remains as to its origin. Likewise, a sterol $C_{27}H_{48}O_2$ m.p. 130—132°, was isolated from lipids extracted from the bacteria of the rumen of sheep [807], but here again numerous causes of contamination are possible. The sole case where the synthesis of a sterol by a bacteria seemed to be established was that presented by *Azotobacter chroococcum* : Sifferd & Anderson [808] isolated, from the unsaponifiable part of the lipids of a large number of bacilli grown on a synthetic medium, a sterol (precipitable by digitonin), m.p. 156—158°, $[\alpha]_D - 16°$. However, Bloch & Amdur (personnal communication) examined the unsaponifiable part of the lipids of several species of bacteria (in particular, *Azotobacter chroococcum*) grown on media containing labelled acetate, and these authors "have in no case observed any significant incorporation of ^{14}C into non-saponifiable materials".

Recently, Dauchy & Kayser [809] isolated from the unsaponifiable part of the lipids of a strain of *E. coli*, a compound m.p. 132—134°, precipitating with digitonin and giving a positive Liebermann-Burchard reaction. The colorimetric determination by this latter reaction indicates a proportion of about 1 part of "sterol" for 20 000 parts of dry bacilli. The infrared spectrum given by these authors shows that the product isolated is still impure. 2 parts of a mixture of sterols (m.p. 133—135°) for 900,000 parts of dry cells were obtained by Schubert et al. [809a] from E. coli. These sterols were identified as usual phytosterols by gas chromatography and mass spectrometry (sitosterol, stigmasterol, campesterol, cholesterol).

A different approach was used by Aaronson [809b]: hypocholesteraemic agents (benzmalecene, triparanol) inhibit the multiplication of Rhodopseudomonas palustris. This inhibition is reversed by oleic acid, ergosterol, squalene, farnesol, but not by geranyl acetate or mevalonic acid. Only oleic acid annuls the inhibition produced by higher concentrations of the inhibitors. The role of oleic acid is particularly puzzling. It must be added that Jensen [809c] isolated a triterpene, paluol (m.p. 282°; acetate m.p. 306°) from two strains of R. palustris (and that another triterpene, friedeline, was detected in the lipids of mycobacteria [64] and of Salmonella species [790, 791]).

It can be concluded from all these investigations that no significant amount of sterol is present in the lipids of bacteria. It must be noted that when the culture medium contains sterols, bacteria can bind them tightly [810]: this cause of error explains a report on the presence of cholesterol in L forms of Proteus P18 [811] which was not substantiated by further work on bacteria grown on synthetic medium [812, 813]. It is probably also the reason why sterols were found in tubercle bacilli isolated from infected mice [53] whereas mycobacteria grown on synthetic medium are devoid of sterol.

Pleuropneumonia-like organisms, when grown in the absence of cholesterol, contain no sterol in the non-saponifiable lipids [814]; the recent isolation of cholesterol and cholesterol esters from the pleuropneumonia-like organism Mycoplasma gallisepticum [815] is probably due to sterol contamination of the culture medium.

V. PHOSPHOLIPIDS

The phosphatide content of bacteria is likely to vary considerably according to the species, the extreme values being observed in the case of various species of the genus Bacillus that have a very low content of phospholipids [649], and Escherichia coli, which contains more than 5 % of phospholipids [800]. It should also be noted that the percentage figures found in the literature deal with fractions, the purity of which may greatly vary.

In the case of Salmonella, Čmelik [818] found that virulent strains contained definitely less phosphatides than the attenuated or non-virulent strains. On the other hand, Asselineau [38] observed that in the case of M. tuberculosis the phosphatide content of "young" bacilli is definitely higher than that of the older bacilli (see also ref. 819).

a) Phosphatidic acids

K. Bloch [820, 821], then Macheboeuf & Faure [822], showed the presence of phosphatidic acids in the phospholipids of the tubercle bacillus. More recently, from a streptomycin-resistant strain of $H_{37}Rv$, Vilkas & Lederer [142] isolated by chromatography and dissolving in a (1:1) mixture of chloroform and methanol, a magnesium salt of phosphatidic acids. The magnesium salt melts at 161-164° and contains 4.3 % of phosphorus; the free acid melts at 48—51° (the free acid of K. Bloch melts at 30°). Saponification gives palmitic and stearic acids.

Weibull [804] characterized phosphatidic acids in a strain of *Bacillus "M"*, Čmelik [154] in a strain of *Salmonella typhi*, Saito & Akashi [823] in a strain of *Alcaligenes faecalis* and Huston *et al.* [823a] in a strain of *Sarcina lutea*.

It is possible that these compounds arise from the hydrolysis of more complex phospholipids in the course of the operations required for their isolation. It must be kept in mind that some enzymes may easily hydrolyze glycerophosphatides into phosphatidic acids in organic solvents such as moist ether (see ref. 68 and 824).

b) *Lecithins and cephalins*

Saponification of the phosphatide of *Agrobacterium tumefaciens* gave fatty acids, glycerophosphoric acid, choline (characterized by its chloroplatinate) and ethanolamine (identified by its picrolonate) [33]. Geiger & Anderson [33] concluded that the phosphatide is a mixture of lecithins and cephalins, a conclusion that has been recently confirmed [825]. Choline was also found in the phospholipids of *Agrobacterium radiobacter* and *A. rhizogenes* [874]. Velick [826] observed in addition the presence of an unidentified amino-acid. A mixture of choline and ethanolamine was also found in the water-soluble fraction obtained by saponification of the phospholipids of *Brucella abortus* [827, 828].

Usually, a sole nitrogen base is present in the phospholipids of a bacterial species. Choline alone was detected in three cases, *Lactobacillus acidophilus* [829], *Neisseria gonorrhoeae* [805] and *Sarcina lutea* [823a]. Choline was also observed in the phospholipids of *Streptococcus lactis* [823b]. Ethanolamine alone is much more frequently encountered: it was identified in the phospholipids of *Alcaligenes faecalis* [823], *Azotobacter agilis* [825], *Azotobacter vinelandii* [830] *Bacillus cereus* [796], *Clostridium butyricum* [831], *Micrococcus halodenitrificans* [832], *Pseudomonas denitrificans* [823], *Staphylococcus aureus* [545, 833], *Salmonella typhi* [154, 834], and *Vibrio cholerae* [835]. Ethanolamine was also detected in the phospholipid A of *Escherichia coli* [531, 836].

Phospholipids of various species of Mycobacteria only contain a small amount of ethanolamine [837] which was isolated as its 2,4-dinitrophenyl derivative (m.p. 86—89°) in the case of *M. marianum* [838].

The hydrolysate of phospholipids of *Alcaligenes faecalis* contains an unidentified base which does not react with ninhydrin and differs from choline [823]. By chromatography of the phospholipids of *Clostridium butyricum* on silicic acid, Goldfine [831] obtained a fraction, eluated just behind the phosphatidylethanolamines, the hydrolysis of which gave a new base, N-methylethanolamine, weakly coloured by ninhydrin.

Phosphatidylserine has been found in the lipids of *E. coli* [839], of *Serratia marscescens* [840a], and in the endotoxin of *Pseudomonas aeruginosa*, a serine-containing phospholipid has been detected [840].

c) *Phosphatidylglycerols*

Phosphatidylglycerols and diphosphatidylglycerols (cardiolipin-like compounds) have been detected in the phospholipids of *Staphylococcus aureus*, *Micrococcus lysodeikticus* [841], *Thiobacillus thiooxidans* [841a], and *Streptococcus faecalis* [841 b]. Phosphatidylglycerols have also been characterized in the phospholipids of *Bacillus cereus* [796], [843], *B. megaterium* [843], *Micrococcus halodenitrificans* [832], and of the tubercle bacillus [842], [842a]. The structure of the cardiolipin fraction of *M. phlei*, as established by LeCoq and Ballou [842 b], is shown below:

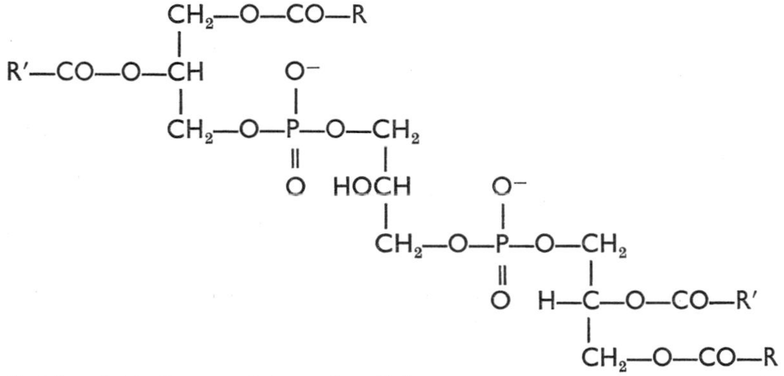

$$CH_2-O-CO-R$$
$$R'-CO-O-CH \qquad O^-$$
$$CH_2-O-\overset{\parallel}{\underset{O}{P}}-O-CH_2$$
$$HOCH \qquad O^-$$
$$CH_2-O-\overset{\parallel}{\underset{O}{P}}-O-CH_2$$
$$H-C-O-CO-R'$$
$$CH_2-O-CO-R$$

d) *Phospholipids containing ether linkages*

Virtually no ester linkage was detected in the phospholipids of *Halobacterium cutirubrum*; the main component (73 % of the crude phosphatides) appears to be a "long-chain ether analog of diphosphatidylglycerol" [844].

This phosphatide was isolated by Faure *et al.* [845] as a potassium salt: $[\alpha]_D - 4°$ (methanol), $+ 2.5°$ (chloroform). Structure [333] was established by chemical degradation [846].

It is split by 2.5 % HCl in methanol into a diether of glycerol and 1,3-glycerodiphosphoric acid [845] (see also ref. 846). The alcohol R-OH, linked to glycerol residues, is dihydrophytol [846].

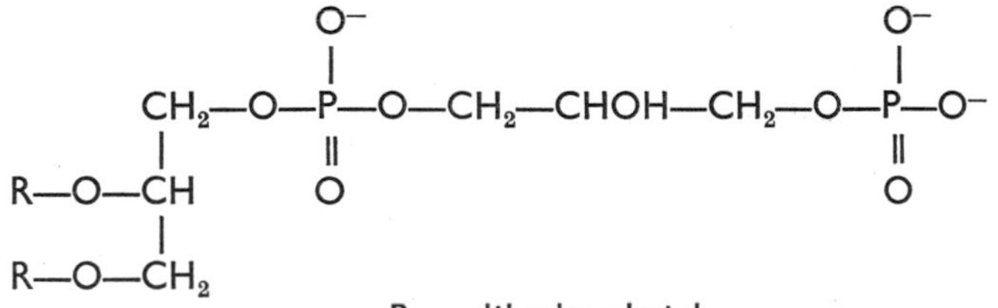

$$CH_2-O-\overset{O^-}{\underset{\parallel}{\underset{O}{P}}}-O-CH_2-CHOH-CH_2-O-\overset{O^-}{\underset{\parallel}{\underset{O}{P}}}-O^-$$
$$R-O-CH$$
$$R-O-CH_2$$

$$R = \text{dihydrophytyl}$$

[333]

L - α, β - di - O - dihydrophytylglycerol, $C_{43}H_{88}O_3$, has $[\alpha]_D + 7.8°$.

e) *Plasmologens*

Small amounts of fatty aldehydes (mainly pentadecanal) were detected by Allison *et al.* [761] in the products obtained by hydrolysis of phospholipids from *Ruminococcus flavefaciens*.

Wegner & Foster [762] characterized ethanolamine plasmalogen in the phospholipids of *Bacteroides succinogenes* by degradation with 90 % acetic acid (v/v) at 38° for 18hrs according to Gray [828a]; a mixture of normal chain and iso aldehydes were obtained.

Böhm [847] was unable to detect any plasmalogen in the lipids of the tubercle bacillus. Recently, it has been shown that the N-methylethanolamine-phosphatides of *Cl. butyricum* are mainly in the form of plasmalogens [847a]. So far, the presence of plasmalogens in bacteria appears to be restricted to anaerobes.

f) *Sugar containing phosphatides*

Saponification of phosphatides of *Lactobacillus acidophilus* gives 55 % fatty acids, about 20 % of a phosphorylated polysaccharide, glycerophosphoric acid, and choline [829]. The composition of this phosphorylated polysaccharide (after purification) corresponds to that of a phosphoric diester of a trisaccharide $C_{18}H_{28}O_{16}(H_2PO_3)_2$. After dephosphorylation by ammonia, the polysaccharide was obtained in crystalline form, m.p. 160—170°, $[\alpha]_D + 69°$ → 72° (water, equilibrium). Hydrolysis of the polysaccharide gives D-galactose (m.p. 164— 167°, $[\alpha]_D + 82.3°$ (water)) and two other hexoses which are probably glucose and fructose [829].

Galactose-phosphoric acid was isolated from a fraction of the phosphatides of *Salmonella typhi* [154]. Phosphatidylglucose derivatives were characterized in the lipids of *Mycoplasma laidlawii* [829a].

g) *Phosphoinositides*

Phosphatides of Mycobacteria contain fractions from which complete hydrolysis gives inositol and an aldose, identified with mannose. In 1930, Anderson demonstrated the presence in the phosphatide of the tubercle bacillus of inositol (human strain H_{37}) [848] and of mannose (human strain [849], bovine and avian strains [850]). By alkaline saponification, Anderson & Roberts [851] split the phosphatide (from a human strain) into fatty acids, an organophosphoric acid (different from glycerophosphoric acid), and a phosphorylated polysaccharide: the acid hydrolysis of the latter gave a mixture (about 2:1) of mannose and inositol. This polysaccharide received the name of manninositose.

The products obtained by alkaline saponification of the whole phosphatide were studied in greater detail by Anderson *et al.* [384]: the organophosphoric acid gave a barium salt whose composition corresponds to $C_9H_{16}O_{14}P_2Ba_2$; its hydrolysis gives mannose. It behaves then as a mannoglycerodiphosphoric acid. The polysaccharide was dephosphorylated by ammonia, and the free manninositose was obtained: $[\alpha]_D + 74.1°$ (water, no mutarotation). Its acetyl derivative had the following properties: m.p. 112° (ill defined), $[\alpha]_D + 47.8°$ (methanol), molecular weight (Rast) about 950. Although no conclusion was given by Anderson, these data already showed that manninositose contains only 1 mole of inositol and 2 moles of mannose (the dodecaacetate $C_{42}H_{56}O_{28}$ has the molecular weight 1008.8). A polysaccharide similar to manninositose was obtained from the phosphatides of *M. avium* [852].

From the phosphatides obtained from two lots of tubercle bacilli remaining after preparation of tuberculin [853], De Sütö-Nagy & Anderson [854, 855] isolated, besides other products of hydrolysis, inositomonophosphoric acid from one batch, and inositoglycerodiphosphoric acid from the second. De Sütö-Nagy & Anderson [855] concluded that "each lot of bacilli cultivated on artificial media elaborates different organo-phosphoric compounds".

For their part, Macheboeuf & Faure [822] arrived at the conclusion that the phosphatides of the tubercle bacillus are "glycerophosphoric acids bound by esterification, on the one hand to fatty acids, and on the other hand to non-nitrogenous polyols". The preparations obtained by these authors were in the form of sodium, calcium, and magnesium salts. As salts, the products are soluble in water and insoluble in acetone; the free acids are insoluble in water and soluble in acetone.

The phospholipids of a streptomycin-resistant strain of $H_{37}Rv$ were fractionated by Vilkas and Lederer [142] by chromatography on silicic acid; one fraction has been purified by making use of its insolubility in a mixture (1:1) of chloroform and methanol. The product thus obtained behaved like the magnesium salt of a phosphatidyl-inositodimannoside. The purest samples had the following properties: m.p. 209—210°, $[\alpha]_D + 34°$, P 2.45 %. Microbiological determination (with *Neurospora crassa*) showed that the inositol is the myo form. Saponification gave palmitic and stearic acids.

From the BCG (cultivated on Sauton's medium), Vilkas [856] isolated, by methanol extraction of bacilli defatted with acetone, a phosphatidyl-inositodimannoside, m.p. 215—217°, $[\alpha]_D + 32°$, which constituted 2 % of the dry bacilli. Saponification gave palmitic, stearic, hexadecenoic, octadecenoic and tuberculostearic acids. From the water soluble part, a dimannosidoinositol was isolated as a dodecaacetate, m.p. 137—139°, $[\alpha]_D + 52.6°$. (methanol), the properties of which show that it is purer than the dodecaacetate of manninositose obtained by Anderson [384].

The structure of the phosphatidylinositol dimannoside was studied by Vilkas and Lederer [857-859] by methylation and hydrolysis. This careful study, completed by further work done by Ballou and Lee [860], [861 a-c], established the structure of this phosphatide as [334]:

[334] M = mannopyranosyl

The glycerol phosphate moiety is linked to the L-1-position of the myoinositol ring, so that the stereochemistry of this phosphatide is identical with that of the phosphatidyl-myoinositols of plants and animals.

The structure of the manninositose is then different from that of the product synthesized by Angyal & Shelton [861] (synthetic product: m.p. 248—253°, $[\alpha]_D + 77°$ (water); dodecaacetate m.p. 134—137°, $[\alpha]_D + 52.3°$ (CHCl₃)).

From the pyridine extracts of bacilli defatted with acetone, Pangborn [862], isolated, by solvent precipitation or by chromatography on silicic acid, a fraction $[\alpha]_D + 55.6°$ (1.73 % P, 10.5 % inositol, 50 % mannose) insoluble in ether, which behaved like a phosphatidylinositol pentamannoside: this fraction constitutes about 3 % of the dry weight of the bacilli. From a preparation of wax D of BCG, Nojima [151] isolated phosphatidylinositol polymannosides: deacyclation gave a mixture of glycerophosphorylinositol di-, tetra-, and penta-mannosides

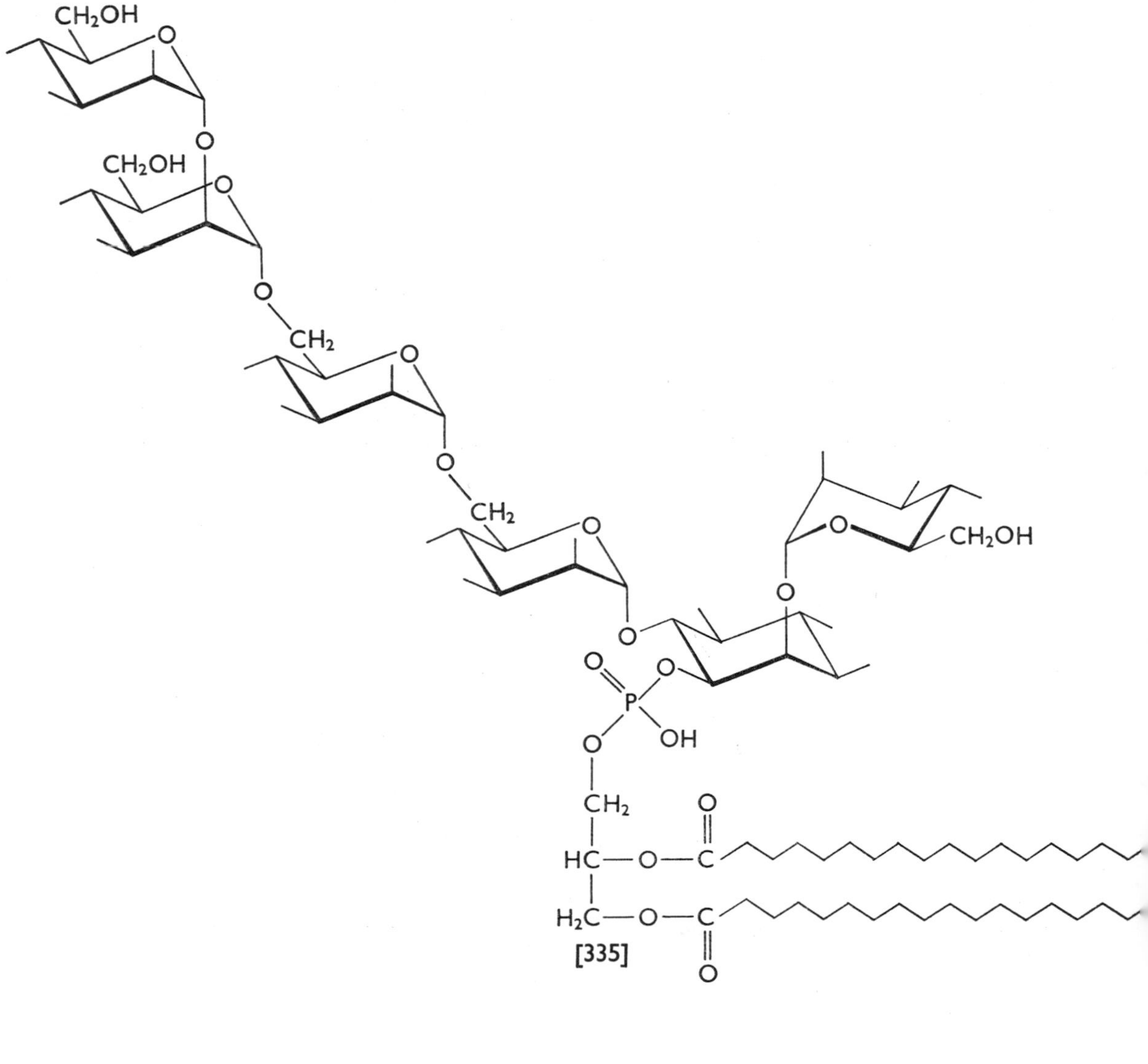

[335]

which was separated by ion-exchange chromatography. The pentamannoside derivative, isolated as a barium salt, was obtained in the form of very hygroscopic crystals melting at about 225°, $[\alpha]_D^{27} + 103°$ (water), $C_{39}H_{68}O_{36}PBa_{0.5}$. Only two fatty acids were found in the saponification products: palmitic acid and an unidentified acid which might be tuberculo-stearic acid [151]. Re-examination of the phosphoinositides of BCG showed the presence of phosphatidylinositol monomannoside, dimannoside and pentamannoside [860]. It must be noted that, whereas phosphatidylinositol is cleaved by heating in 98 % acetic acid at 100° for 30 minutes (with the formation of a diglyceride and inositol phosphate), the penta-mannoside is unchanged by refluxing in 98 % acetic acid for 2 hours. Heating in N HCl is required to cleave the molecule [860]. The complete structure of phosphatidylinositol penta-mannoside has been established as [335] by Ballou and Lee [861 c].

Previous claims of the existence of phosphatidylinositol polyglucosides in the lipids of some strains of Mycobacteria [856, 857] could not be substantiated by further investigations: the presence of glucose in the hydrolysis products was ascribed to a contamination of the phospholipids by trehalose dimycolate [860].

Inositol and mannose were detected in the hydrolysis products of the crude phospho-lipids from *Corynebacterium diphtheriae* [863].

Thiobacillus thiooxidans releases in its culture medium a phospholipid which appears to act as a wetting agent in the oxidative metabolism of sulphur [864]; this lipid, previously thought to be a phosphatidylinositol [864], has been identified as phosphatidylglycerol [841a].

From the microbiological determination of myoinositol in the hydrolyzates of phospho-lipids, it was concluded that *Lactobacillus casei, L. plantarum, Leuconostoc mesenteroides, Pediococcus cerevisiae*, and *Streptococcus faecalis* are devoid of inositol-containing lipids [865]. Phosphatidylinositol was detected in the lipids of the protoplast membranes or of the whole cells of *Micrococcus lysodeikticus* [841] and the whole cells of *Sarcina lutea* [823 a].

h) *Amino-acid-containing phospholipids*

Amino-acids have frequently been detected in the hydrolysis products of bacterial phospho-lipids. Barbier & Lederer [866] identified hydroxylysine (hydrochloride m.p. 210—218°; picrate m.p. 110-115° and 195°) in a sample of phosphatide from *M. phlei* (strain "Pasteur"), but ornithine was found in place of this amino-acid in later preparations of phosphatides from the same strain [481]. Gendre & Lederer [867] isolated L-ornithine from the phosphatides of *M. tuberculosis* (hydrochloride m.p. 228°, $[\alpha]_D + 17.8°$ (water); picrate m.p. 205—208°; dibenzoyl derivative m.p. 185—187°). Ornithine was determined in the hydrolysates of phosphatides of various strains of *M. tuberculosis* (0 to 1.42 % of initial phosphatide), of *M. avium* (4.7 % in strain no. 802), of *M. phlei* (strain "Pasteur": 2.2 %) and of *M. smegmatis* (traces). The same amino-acid was found in the phospholipids of *Vibrio cholerae* [835] and of *Brucella abortus* [828]. α,ε-diaminopimelic acid was observed in phospholipid fractions of *M. marianum* [838]: this is the only report on the presence of this amino-acid in a phosphatide preparation.

Several amino acids have been detected in phosphatides of *Salmonella ballerup* [155], *S. typhi* [154], *S. paratyphi* C [791], and *Alcaligenes faecalis* [823].

It is important to ensure the removal of non-bound amino-acids that might contaminate the phospholipid preparations: this step is achieved either by paper electrophoresis [868] or by filtration on cellulose powder [869] or by filtration on Sephadex [870].

MacFarlane [871] has recently isolated phospholipids containing amino-acids (in particular alanine, lysine, and ornithine) from *Clostridium welchii* (type A) and *Staphylococcus aureus*. These fractions are ninhydrin-positive; deacylation with 0.1 N methanolic sodium hydroxide/chloroform (1:1 v/v) gave glycerylphosphorylglycerol and free amino-acids. These results (combined with other tests) indicated that these fractions consisted of a series of O-amino-acid esters of phosphatidylglycerol.

The same conclusion was reached by Houtsmuller and van Deenen [872] in the case of an ornithine-containing phospholipid isolated from *Bacillus cereus*. Indications of the occurrence of small amounts of similar components in *B. megaterium*, *Pseudomonas stutzeri* and *Serratia marcescens* were obtained [872]. From *B. megaterium*, an ester of arginine and phosphatidylglycerol was isolated as a reineckate salt [873].

D-Alanine was found in the phospholipids of *Leuconostoc mesenteroides*, and L-lysine. in the phospholipids of *Lactobacillus casei*, *L. plantarum*, *Streptococcus faecalis*, and *Pediococcus cerevisiae;* however, paper chromatography of the deacylated phospholipids of *L. casei* and *L. plantarum* showed only a slight amount of lysine: most of the ninhydrin-positive material migrated differently from lysine [865].

It must be noted that these esters of amino-acids and phosphatidyl-glycerol are labile compounds. MacFarlane [871] increases the yield of the isolation step by acidification of the medium to pH 3 before harvesting the bacteria: this simple process might act by arresting enzymic degradation. By shaking an ethereal solution of these compounds with an equal volume of N/15 aqueous sodium hydroxide at 20° for 30 minutes, a phospholipid free of amino-acid is obtained [873].

A polar lipid-amino acid complex has been isolated from *Pseudomonas aeruginosa* by Shina & Gaby [873a]. This lipid contains an amino alcohol (mainly ethanolamine) and one mole of amino acid (mainly alanine). The following structure was proposed [873a] :

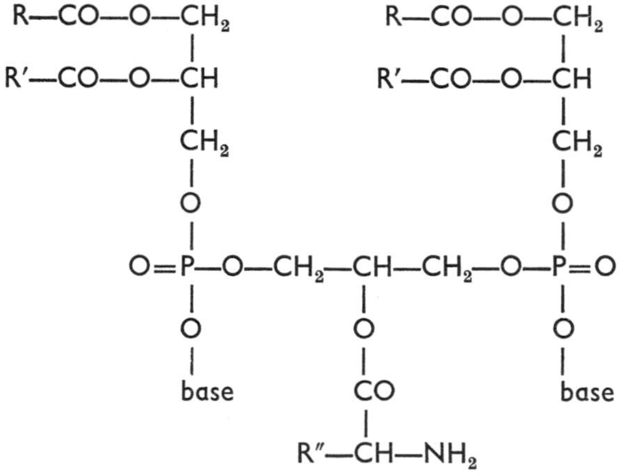

$$
\begin{array}{ccc}
R\!-\!CO\!-\!O\!-\!CH_2 & & R\!-\!CO\!-\!O\!-\!CH_2 \\
| & & | \\
R'\!-\!CO\!-\!O\!-\!CH & & R'\!-\!CO\!-\!O\!-\!CH \\
| & & | \\
CH_2 & & CH_2 \\
| & & | \\
O & & O \\
| & & | \\
O\!=\!P\!-\!O\!-\!CH_2\!-\!CH\!-\!CH_2\!-\!O\!-\!P\!=\!O \\
| & | & | \\
O & O & O \\
| & | & | \\
base & CO & base \\
& | & \\
& R''\!-\!CH\!-\!NH_2 &
\end{array}
$$

Most of the amino-acids found in these phospholipids are basic amino-acids: lysine, ornithine, arginine. Working recently on the lipids of a strain of atypical Mycobacteria, we isolated a phospholipid fraction containing ornithine. Repeated chromatography of this compound increased the nitrogen and decreased the phosphorous content, but we were unable to obtain a sample free of phosphorous. Deacylation of this product gave an ether soluble ornithine derivative, m.p. 85—90°, $[\alpha]_D$ + 15°, 3.6 % N, free of phosphorus; its IR spectrum showed amide bands [875, 1217]. In this case, it appears that we are dealing with a different lipophilic form of ornithine. Gorschein [875a] obtained similar results on an ornithine containing lipid isolated from *Rhodopseudomonas spheroides*. It should be noted that an alkali-stable relatively polar lipid, containing amino acids, has been characterized in the lipids of broad-bean leaves [875b].

Two types of amino acid containing lipids appear to exist: one alkali-labile (ester linkage of the amino acid residue), the other alkali-stable (amide linkage).

Phospholipids containing amino-acids have been observed in materials of very diverse origin: *Eremothecium ashbyii*, *Penicillium chrysogenum*, *Drosophila melanogaster*, chicken eggs, and rat's brain [868, 876-878]. These phospholipids "appear to play an important role as an intermediate in the metabolism of amino acids and possibly other compounds" [876]. An isolated membrane of *B. megaterium* and a spheroplast membrane of an *E. coli* strain, actively incorporated ^{32}P-labelled orthophosphate into the phospholipids. Hydrolysis and chromatography of the butanol and alcohol-ether extracts indicated that the amino-acids are intimately associated with the phospholipid components [879].

i) *Phospholipids A*

Water-soluble lipopolysaccharides from gram-negative bacteria contain two distinct lipid fractions.

(i) *Phospholipids B* (about 10 % of the initial complex), which are easily eliminated without loss of essential biological properties.

(ii) *Phospholipids A* (5-25 % of the initial complex), which can be isolated only after degradation of the lipopolysaccharide (see Table 32) and the loss of certain of its biological properties [880].

A few properties of phospholipids A isolated from several bacterial species are given in Table 42, p. 196).

Acid hydrolysis of the phospholipid A of *Escherichia coli* gave lauric, myristic, palmitic, and (—)-3(D)-hydroxytetradecanoic acids as ether-soluble components [683], and D-glucosamine, ethanolamine, necrosamine (see p. 82), aspartic acid, and glycerophosphoric acid as water-soluble components [551]. By paper chromatographic analysis, Nowotny et al. [159] were able to detect all the series of normal chain saturated acids with even numbers of carbon atoms from C_{10} to C_{24} in the phospholipids A of several strains of gram-negative bacteria.

Hydrolysis of the phospholipid A of *Salmonella abortus equi* gave a hexosamine, aspartic,

TABLE 32. THE ISOLATION OF PHOSPHOLIPID A FROM THE LIPOPOLYSACCHARIDES
OF SALMONELLA ABORTUS EQUI (AFTER FROMME *et al.* [881])

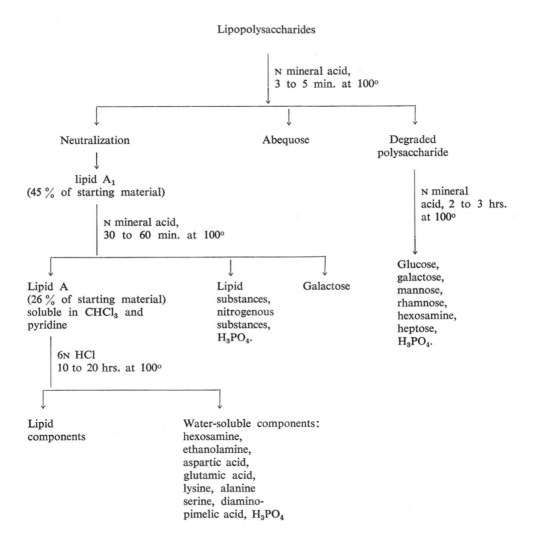

glutamic, and α,ε-diaminopimelic acids, lysine, alanine, serine, and ethanolamine, besides
the fatty acids already mentioned and phosphoric acid[881]. The structure of this phospholipid
A was thoroughly investigated by Nowotny[882] who from the identification of glucosamine

4-phosphate in the hydrolysis products, suggested structure [336] for the phospholipid A of *S. abortus equi* :

Peptide—Glucosamine—P—Glucosamine—P—Glucosamine—P—. . .

(Fatty acids)$_3$ (Fatty acids)$_3$ (Fatty acids)$_3$

[336] Glucosamine-P = 4-Phosphoglucosamine

Burton[534], obtained two fractions of phospholipid A from the lipopolysaccharide of *E. coli* (strain 0111:B4); the properties of these fractions (after chromatography on silicic acid and elution with chloroform-methanol 9:1) are given in Table 42 (p. 196). Both fractions are free of glycerol and amino-acids. Their basic structural unit contained 2 molecules glucosamine, one molecule of phosphoric acid, 4-6 molecules fatty acids, and 3-4 molecules of acetic acid. The results obtained did not allow a choice between structure [337] and [338], both of which contain a glucosamine 4-phosphate residue per structural unit. However, reduction studies favoured structure [337] (see also ref. 882$_a$).

VI. GLYCOLIPIDS

The term glycolipid designates the lipid fractions which contain sugars and remain soluble in organic solvents, in contrast to a lipopolysaccharide, also constituted of lipids and sugars, but water-soluble.

The bond between the lipid part and the sugar moiety can be either a glycosidic bond or an ester bond.

a) *Glycolipids of glycosidic nature*

— RHAMNOLIPIDS OF PSEUDOMONAS

From the culture medium of *Pseudomonas pyocyanea*, Bergström *et al.* [677, 883] isolated a very viscous colourless acidic oil, which they called pyolipic acid. Under the best culture conditions, the authors were able to obtain 1 gram of pyolipic acid per litre of culture medium. This acid is isolated by means of its lead salt; the free acid is soluble in ether and alcohol, and its alkali salts are very soluble in water. It does not reduce Fehling's solution.

Acid hydrolysis of pyolipic acid gives on the one hand (—)-3(D)-hydroxydecanoic acid accompanied by small quantities of 3-hydroxyoctanoic and 3-hydroxydodecanoic acids (see p. 111), and on the other hand L-rhamnose. This rhamnolipid is easily hydrolysed in acid medium and split in alkaline medium, probably by β-elimination.

Later, Jarvis and Johnson [678] isolated from the culture medium of *Pseudomonas aeruginosa*, with a yield approaching 2.5 g/l, a crystalline substance, m.p. 86° (small rectangular plates from dioxan or acetone diluted with water), $[\alpha]_D$ — 84°, molecular formula $C_{32}H_{58}O_{14}$. These crystals can be obtained directly by acidification (to pH 2) of the culture medium and standing in the refrigerator.

Acid hydrolysis of this substance gives (—)-3(D)-hydroxydecanoic acid as an ether-soluble constituent, accompanied by a compound (which has not been isolated in the pure state) which appears to be a hydroxydecanoate of hydroxydecanoic acid of molecular weight (titration) about 360, giving rise to 3-hydroxydecanoic acid by saponification. The water-soluble constituent is L-rhamnose (hydrated form m.p. 92—93°, anhydrous form m.p. 121—123°, $[\alpha]_D$ + 8.4° (water), phenylosazone m.p. 179—180°) [678].

The molecular weight of this glycolipid corresponds to two hydroxydecanoic acid residues and two rhamnose residues. From a study of its behaviour on periodic oxidation, the formula [339], containing a 1,2-linkage of the two rhamnose molecules, is considered the most probable [678].

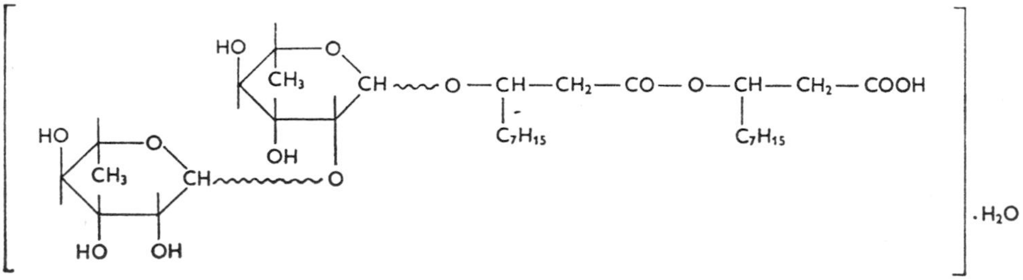

[339]

The biosynthesis of the components of the last rhamnolipid was studied by Hauser and Karnovsky [884, 885]: hydroxydecanoic acid appeared to be formed from acetate units according to the usual pathway, whereas the rhamnose moiety arose from two C_3 units supplied by glycerol.

The complete biosynthesis of this rhamnolipid was achieved by Burger *et al.*[886] with enzymic extracts of *Ps. aeruginosa;* two rhamnosyl transferases were obtained in a partially purified form. The synthesis has been shown to occur by the three following reactions[886]:

2(3-Hydroxydecanoyl-CoA) → 3-Hydroxydecanoyl-3-hydroxydecanoate + 2 CoA

TDP*-L-rhamnose + 3-Hydroxydecanoyl-3-hydroxydecanoate →

——→ TDP + L-rhamnosyl-3-hydroxydecanoyl-3-hydroxydecanoate

     TDP-L-rhamnose + L-Rhamnosyl-3-hydroxydecanoyl-3-hydroxydecanoate

——→ TDP + L-Rhamnosyl-L-rhamnosyl-3-hydroxydecanoyl-3-hydroxydecanoate.

— MYCOSIDES OF MYCOBACTERIA

In the course of their systematic study of the lipid extracts of Mycobacteria with infrared spectrography, Randall and Smith[251] observed the presence of several compounds specific to bacterial types. These compounds, designated G or J, were subsequently isolated[252]:

Compound G_A, present in photochromogenic strains of atypical mycobacteria.

Compound G_B, present in bovine strains (in particular BCG).

Compound J_{av}, present in avian strains and in *M. marianum*.

Compound J_a, present in scotochromogenic strains of atypical Mycobacteria.

It has been suggested that these compounds be named "mycosides", as "type-specific glycolipids of mycobacterial origin"[887]: compounds G_A, G_B, J_{av} are now called mycosides A, B, C. All these substances contain a lipid fraction and a sugar fraction, with glycosidic bonds. Moreover compounds J contain a peptide fraction, and this group of substances will be studied in paragraphe VIII (peptidoglycolipids) (page 191).

Mycoside A (compound G_A):

Mycoside A, m.p. 105°, $[\alpha]_D$ — 37°, has an IR spectrum which indicates a structural relationship between mycosides A and B; it contains in particular bands characteristic of a substituted benzene ring. The UV spectrum shows maxima at 222, 274 and 281 mμ (cyclohexane)[888, 518a]. Hydrolysis of mycoside A gives three sugars, identified as 2-*O*-methylfucose, 2-*O*-methylrhamnose and 2,4-di-*O*-methylrhamnose[252, 888]. This mycoside has been detected in particular in *M. kansasii*[890].

Mycoside B (compound G_B):

Noll[794] isolated from the wax C of the bovine strain Vallée a compound D_1, m.p. 27—32°, which has an IR spectrum identical with that of compound G_B of Smith *et al.*[252]. The IR spectra of these substances show three bands at 1 620, 1 590 and 1 515 cm^{-1}, characteristic of a substituted benzene ring; the UV spectra (λ_{max} 222, 274 and 281 mμ (cyclohexane)) support this conclusion.

---

* TDP = Thymidine diphosphate.

Demarteau-Ginsburg and Lederer [891] made a detailed study of the structure of mycoside B, isolated from BCG (m.p. 25°, $[\alpha]_D$ — 22°). Saponification gave one molecule of palmitic acid and one molecule of mycocerosic acid (see p. 102) together with "glycoside B", whereas acid hydrolysis gave "lipid B" and 2-O-methylrhamnose previously identified by MacLennan

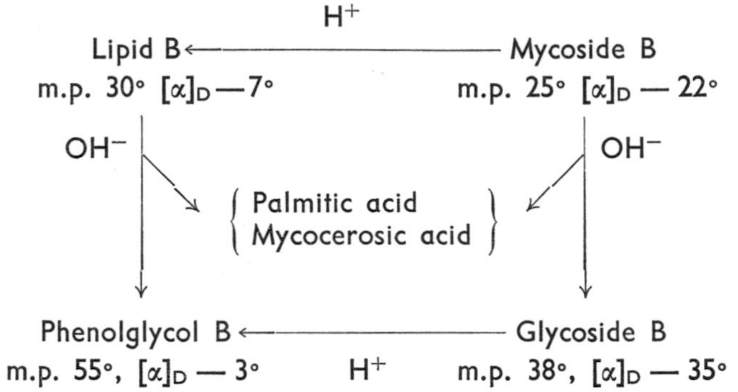

$$
\begin{array}{c}
\text{H}^+ \\
\text{Lipid B} \longleftarrow\!\!\!\!\!\!\!\!\!\longrightarrow \text{Mycoside B} \\
\text{m.p. } 30° \ [\alpha]_D - 7° \qquad\qquad \text{m.p. } 25° \ [\alpha]_D - 22° \\
\end{array}
$$

Lipid B ⟵———————————————— Mycoside B
m.p. 30° [α]_D —7°   m.p. 25° [α]_D — 22°

OH⁻ ↘   ↙ OH⁻

⎰ Palmitic acid ⎱
⎱ Mycocerosic acid ⎰

Phenolglycol B ⟵———————————————— Glycoside B
m.p. 55°, [α]_D — 3°   H⁺   m.p. 38°, [α]_D — 35°

et al. [888]. Acid hydrolysis of glycoside B or alkaline saponification of lipid B gave a new compound, called phenolglycol B, still containing the benzene ring (see p. 78). UV and mass spectrographic studies gave information about the structure of phenolglycol B, so that the formula [340] could be proposed for mycoside B [891]:

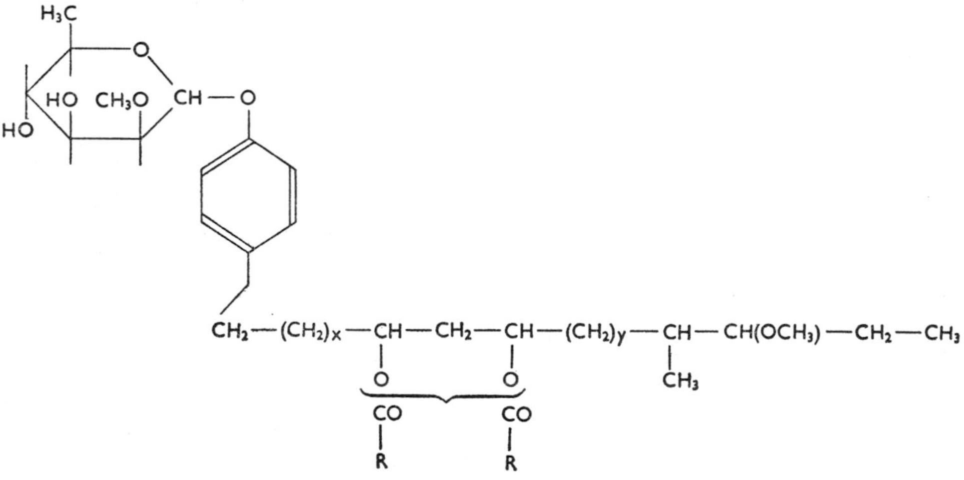

[340]

R—CO = Mycocerosoyl or palmitoyl residue,
x = 16   y = 4

The 2-O-methylrhamnose obtained by acid hydrolysis of mycoside B is the D-isomer, as it has a negative rotation [891, 784] whereas synthetic 2-O-methyl-L-rhamnose has a positive rotation [892].

Mycoside F

Mycoside F, isolated from *M. fortuitum*, contains only sugars and fatty acids. No information has been given about its properties except for its IR spectrum which is similar to that of cord factor [893]. It thus seems probable that it is a sugar ester rather than a glycoside, in spite of its name.

Mycoside G

From the lipids of *M. marinum (M. balnei)* has been isolated a specific glycolipid, called mycoside G. Its properties are similar to that of mycoside A, but the sugar components are different [893a].

b) Esters of fatty acids and sugars (microsides)

The work of Gubarev *et al.* [494, 642, 697, 797, 894] showed the existence of esters of fatty acids and polysaccharides containing galactose and mannose in the lipids of *Corynebacterium diphtheriae* : Gubarev proposed calling such esters "microsides". Likewise, Alimova [895] observed esters of hydroxy acids and mannose or trehalose. No such ester has yet been isolated except for a diester of trehalose described by Pudles *et al.* (see below).

Esters of trehalose

Anderson and Newman [896] isolated α-D-trehalose, m.p. 97—98° (octa-acetate m.p. 80—81°), as the water-soluble constituent of the fats of *M. tuberculosis* (human strain H_{37}); the same result was obtained in the case of several other human strains [897, 898]. More recently, Aebi *et al.* [65] isolated trehalose from the saponification products of the most strongly adsorbed (on alumina) fractions of the fat of the human strain Brévannes. Barbier [481] identified trehalose in the hydrolysis products of the fat of a strain of *M. phlei* (strain "Pasteur"). For a comparison of the properties, Willstaedt & Borggard [899] synthesized octa-octadecanoyl-trehalose, $C_{156}H_{298}O_{19}$, m.p. 65°, $[\alpha]_D + 81.8°$, and 2,3,4,2',3',4'-hexa-octadecanoyl-trehalose, $C_{120}H_{226}O_{17}$, m.p. 61°, $[\alpha]_D + 82.2°$.

However, the principal water-soluble constituent of the fats of the tubercle bacillus is glycerol, as shown by the work of Noll & Jackim [140] and Asselineau & Moron [139] in the case of human strains of *M. tuberculosis*, and of Asselineau & Toubiana [115] in the case of *M. phlei*.

Only one trehalose ester has been isolated to date from many strains of Mycobacteria : it is the "cord factor" or the 6,6'-dimycolate of D-trehalose. The name "cord factor" was originally attributed to it because of its isolation from cultures of tubercle bacilli characterized by the formation of "cords" under suitable conditions in vitro. This growth pattern is typical of virulent or attenuated strains (such as BCG) of *M. tuberculosis* [900]. The "cord factor" has toxic properties (see p. 274).

The presence of a toxic factor at the surface of virulent tubercle bacilli was shown by H. Bloch [901] in 1950. By washing the living bacilli with petroleum ether, he obtained a lipid fraction containing the toxic factor; the bacilli thus treated remain alive, but do not form more "cords" and their virulence is reduced [901].

The washing of the bacilli with petroleum ether gave too poor a yield of the toxic factor for the needs of a chemical study [902]. Testing of various lipid fractions extracted from the tubercle bacillus by the usual extraction procedure has led to the localization of the toxic factor principally in the wax C (see p. 239) [903, 904]. Purification of the "cord factor" was accomplished by successive chromatography of the wax C on magnesium silicate, then on silicic acid and on silica gel [253, 905]. The samples thus purified melted between 36 and 42°, $[\alpha]_D + 30°$, and their approximate molecular formula was $C_{95}H_{189}O_9N$.

An important result was obtained with the identification of mycolic acid and D-glucose in the saponification products of the "cord factor" [253]: the toxic factor therefore seemed to be a mycolate of a non-reducing glucoside containing a nitrogen fragment. Periodic oxidation of the "cord factor" shows a consumption of more than one molecule of oxidant, indicating the probable presence of two α-glycol groups [905].

Preparations of "cord factor" devoid of nitrogen could then be obtained. The determination of the glucose content of the glucoside obtained by saponification of the "cord factor" gave a value of 105 %, which led to its identification as trehalose, confirmed by the preparation of a crystalline octa-acetate (m.p. 81°). The "cord factor" therefore should be a trehalose dimycolate $C_{186}H_{366}O_{17}$ ($\pm$ 10 CH$_2$).

The position of the two mycolic acid residues on the hydroxyls of the trehalose moiety was determined by the usual method of methylating the free hydroxyls, and identifying the trimethyl-O-glucose obtained. The "cord factor" is a 6,6'-dimycolate of α-D-trehalose [341] [906].

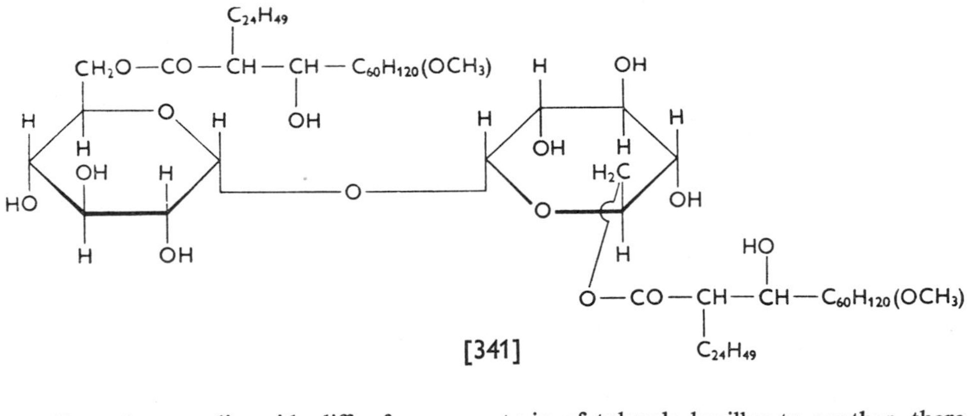

[341]

Since the mycolic acids differ from one strain of tubercle bacillus to another, there exist many "cord factors", differing in the nature of the mycolic acids they contain. This

TABLE 33. THE PROPERTIES OF "CORD FACTOR" PREPARATIONS, ISOLATED FROM VARIOUS
STRAINS OF MYCOBACTERIA, AND SYNTHETIC

Strain	M.p.	$[\alpha]_D$	Ref.
Human			
$H_{37}Rv$	41-42°	+30° ($\pm$ 1°)	253
Brévannes	38-42°	+30°	253
$H_{37}Rv$ s.r.	42-44°*	+30°	904
PN + DT + C	36-37°	+31°	253
Bovine			
Vallée	38-39°	+29°	253
Marmorek	42-44°	+26°	383
BCG.	43-45°	+40° ($\pm$ 5°)	905
Avian			
no. 802	41-43°	+17°	530
Saprophytic			
M. phlei	42-44°		909
M. smegmatis	41-43°		909
Synthetic product...........	40-42°	+32°	458
	42-44°	+28° ($\pm$ 4°)	462

* Acetyl derivative: m.p. 38-39°.

can in part explain slight variations in constants observed in samples of "cord factor" from diverse origins (see Table 33). Nojima [907] isolated "cord factor" from the wax D of BCG. In the case of the bovine strain Marmorek, Demarteau-Ginsburg [383] observed the presence, besides the 6,6'-dimycolate of trehalose, of a fraction m.p. 90—110°, $[\alpha]_D$ + 50°, which behaved as a trehalose monomycolate. Michel [908] isolated a trehalose dimycolate (for which no constant was given) from the lipids of *M. marianum :* its saponification gave the mycolic acids $C_{83}H_{166}O_3$, m.p. 57-58°, $C_{83}H_{166}O_4$, m.p. 56—57° and $C_{72}H_{142}O_6$, m.p. 60-61°. A sample of "cord factor" was isolated from an avian strain [530]: it contained a monocarboxylic and a dicarboxylic mycolic acid. Smith *et al.* [252] characterized the "cord factor" in a lipid extract from *M. phlei* by IR spectrography, and it was isolated by Toubiana [115]. Yamamura *et al.* [909, 910] isolated the " cord factor" from several strains of saprophytic Mycobacteria and of atypical Mycobacteria, and Lanéelle [563] isolated it from a strain of *M. paratuberculosis (M. johnei)*.

Bloch *et al.* [792] showed that the toxic factor obtained by Spitznagel & Dubos [911] by chlorobenzene extraction of BCG consisted of the 6,6'-dimycolate of trehalose mixed with large quantities of glycerides. From the bound lipids of a human strain of the tubercle bacillus,

TABLE 34. THE PROPERTIES OF GLUCOSE, GALACTOSE, GLUCOSYLAMINE, AND GLUCOSAMINE MYCOLATES (AFTER ASSELINEAU and LEDERER [459])

Name	Molecular Formula	Structural formula				M.p.	$[\alpha]_D$	Toxicity*	
		R_1	R_2	R_3	R_4			**	LD***
Esters of the 1-hydroxyl of the sugar [342]									
1) 1-(3',x-Dihydroxymycolanoyl)-β-D-galactose.	$C_{93}H_{184}O_9$	H	OH	H	H	49–53°		—	
2) 1-(3'-Acetoxy-x-methoxymycolanoyl)-β-D-glucose	$C_{96}H_{188}O_{10}$	OH	H	$CH_3\text{-}CO$	CH_3	47–52°		—	
Ester of the 2-hydroxyl of the sugar :									
3) Methyl 2-(3',acetoxy-x-methoxymycolanoyl)-α-D-glucoside	$C_{97}H_{190}O_{10}$					36–40°		—	
Esters of the 6-hydroxyl of the sugar [344]									
4) Methyl 6-(3'-x-sulphitomycolanoyl)-α-D-glucoside	$C_{94}H_{184}O_{10}S$	CH_3	OH	O—SO—O		43–45°		+	
5) Methyl 6-(3'-acetoxy-x-methoxymycolanoyl)-α-D-glucoside	$C_{97}H_{190}O_{10}$	CH_3	OH	$CH_3\text{-}CO$	CH_3	37–39°	+22°	+	0.1
6) Methyl 6-(3'-acetoxy-x-methoxymycolanoyl)-α-D-galactoside	$C_{97}H_{190}O_{10}$					35–37°		—	
7) 6-(3'-Acetoxy-x-methoxymycolanoyl)-N-acetyl-D-glucosamine.	$C_{98}H_{191}O_{10}N$	H	$CH_3\text{-}CO\text{-}NH$	$CH_3\text{-}CO$	CH_3	42–44°	+15°	+++	0.05

* The biological tests were made by Professor H. Bloch (University of Pittsburgh).

** Arbitrary scale.

*** LD_{50} = dose lethal to 50 % of the animals; approximate value.

Esters of the 6-hydroxyl of the sugar [344]

Name	Molecular Formula	R₁	R₂	R₃	R₄	M.p.	$[\alpha]_D$	**	LD***
8) 6-(3′,x-Sulphitomycolanoyl)-N-acetyl-D-glucosamine: *fraction I*	$C_{95}H_{185}O_{10}NS$	H	$CH_3\text{-CO-NH}$	$O\text{—}SO\text{—}O$		43-45°	−9°	—	
9) *fraction II*	$C_{95}H_{185}O_{10}NS$	H	$CH_3\text{-CO-NH}$	$O\text{—}SO\text{—}O$		47-51°	+ 2°	+	
10) 6-(3′,x-Dihydroxymycolanoyl)-N-acetyl-D-glucosamine: *fraction I*	$C_{95}H_{187}O_9N$	H	$CH_3\text{-CO-NH}$	OH	OH	44-46°	0	±	
11) *fraction II*	$C_{95}H_{187}O_9N$	H	$CH_3\text{-CO-NH}$	OH	OH	43-45°	0	++	
12) 6,x-Di-(3′,x′-dihydroxymycolanoyl)-N-acetyl-D-glucosamine	$C_{184}H_{363}O_{12}N$	H	$CH_3\text{-CO-NH}$	OH	OH	52-57°	+3°	—	
13) 6-(Mycola-2′,x-dienoyl)-N-acetyl-D-glucosamine	$C_{95}H_{183}O_7N$					50-53°		—	
14) 6-(3′-Acetoxy-2-tetradecyloctadecanoyl)-N-acetyl-D-glucosamine	$C_{42}H_{79}O_9N$					40°	+13°	—	
15) Methyl 6-(3′-acetoxy-x-methoxymycolanoyl)-N-acetyl-D-glucosaminide	$C_{99}H_{193}O_{10}N$	CH_3	$CH_3\text{-CO-NH}$	$CH_3\text{-CO}$	CH_3	43-45°	+9°	+	0.1
16) 6-(3′,x-Diacetoxymycolanoyl)-N-carbobenzoxy-D-glucosamine	$C_{105}H_{195}O_{12}N$	H	$C_6H_5\text{-}CH_2\text{-O-}CO\text{-NH-}$	$CH_3\text{-CO}$	$CH_3\text{-CO}$	42-44°		+	

* The biological tests were made by Professor H. Bloch (University of Pittsburgh).

** Arbitrary scale.

*** LD_{50} = dose lethal to 50 % of the animals; approximate value.

Azuma & Yamamura [912, 912a] isolated a toxic glycolipid m.p. 178—180°; its IR spectrum was similar to that of the "cord factor", but by hydrolysis it gave arabinose and an unidentified sugar (along with a lipid moiety which was probably mycolic acids). Several types of toxic glycolipid could occur in the lipids of Mycobacteria.

A glycolipid, which can be considered as a lower homologue of the "cord factor", was isolated from the lipids of *C. diphtheriae* by Pudles *et al.* [913]: this compound, m.p. 110—115°, $[\alpha]_D + 64°$, gave trehalose as the water-soluble constituent, and a mixture (about 1:1) of corynomycolic acid and corynomycolenic acid as the lipid moiety.

From the lipids of *M. fortuitum*, Vilkas & Rojas [1216] have isolated 6,6'-dipalmitoyl α-D-trehalose, m.p. 77—81°, $[\alpha]_D + 45°$.

As soon as the presence of mycolic acid and D-glucose in the molecule of "cord factor" had been shown, syntheses of mycolates of monosaccharides were undertaken by Asselineau & Lederer [459]. Numerous derivatives of D-glucosamine were prepared, because of the assumed existence of a nitrogen atom. Four different types of derivatives were synthesized:

— *Amides* of mycolic acid and D-glucosamine, e.g. *N*-(3'-hydroxy-x-methoxymyco-lanoyl) D-glucosamine [343], $C_{94}H_{187}O_8N$, m.p. 45—49°.

— *Esters* of mycolic acid with the 1-hydroxyl of D-glucose or of D-galactose (substance no. 1 and 2 of Table 34) [342].

— An *ester* of mycolic acid with the 2-hydroxyl of methyl α-D-glucoside (substance no. 3 of Table 34).

— *Esters* of mycolic acid with the 6-hydroxyl of methyl D-glucoside, methyl D-galacto-side, *N*-acetyl-D-glucosylamine and *N*-acyl-D-glucosamine (substances no. 4 to 16 of Table 34) [344].

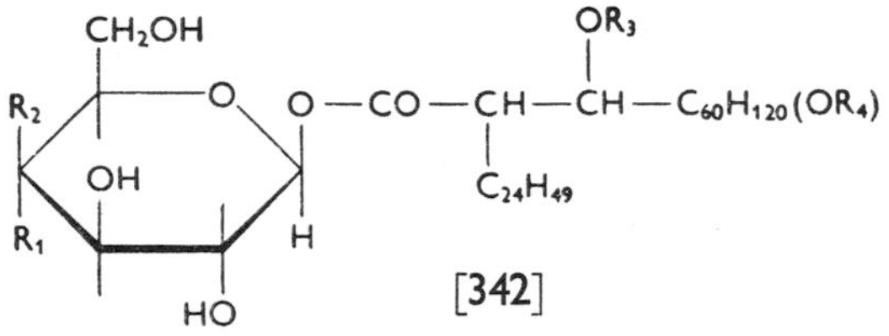

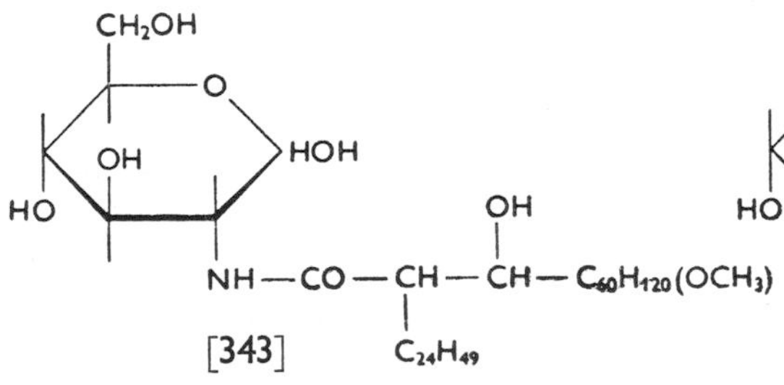

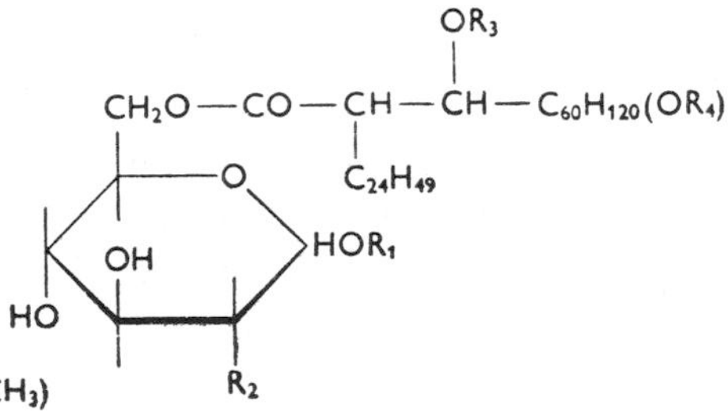

Only the esters having a bond with the 6-hydroxyl of the sugar showed toxic proper-ties [914]: this observation permitted some tentative conclusions about the ester nature of the "cord factor" and about the probability of a bond with the 6-hydroxyl of the glucoside residue. These experiments also showed that a non-nitrogenous substance (for example No. 5 of Table 34) could exhibit toxic properties. All these observations are in agreement with the "cord factor" structure [341]. These substances were moreover useful as "models" in the course of the study of the natural product, in particular as regards hydrolysis and periodic oxidation (see ref. 905).

The synthesis of 6,6'-dimycolates of trehalose was achieved by two methods:

(i) By reaction of two molecules of 3-acetoxy-x-methoxymycolanoyl chloride with one molecule of trehalose. One obtains a mixture of monomycolate of 6-trehalose, 6,6'-dimy- colate of trehalose and 2,6,6'-trimycolate of trehalose, having still an acetyl group on the 3-hydroxyl of the mycoloyl radical, separable by chromatography (see Table 35).

TABLE 35. THE PROPERTIES OF MONO-, DI-, AND TRIMYCOLATES OF TREHALOSE, SYNTHESIZED FROM 3-HYDROXY-X-METHOXYMYCOLANOIC ACID [1-Test] (AFTER GENDRE & LEDERER [458])

	Hydroxyl at C-3' of mycolic acid			
	Acetylated		Free	
	M.p.	$[\alpha]_D$	M.p.	$[\alpha]_D$
6-(3'-Hydroxy-x-methoxy-mycolanoyl)-α-D-trehalose. . . .	125°	+40°	122-123°	+51°
6,6'-Di-(3''-hydroxy-x-methoxy-mycolanoyl)-α-D-trehalose . . .	35-37°	+25°	40-42°	+32°
2,6,6'-Tri-(3''-hydroxy-x-methoxy-mycolanoyl)-α-D-trehalose . . .	37-38°	+24°		

(ii) By reaction of potassium mycolate with 6,6'-ditosyl-2,3,4,2',3',4'-hexa-acetyltrehalose, under the conditions developed by Polonsky et al. [461] giving a good yield of 6,6'-di-(3''-hydroxy-x-methoxymycolanoyl)-2,3,4,2',3',4'-hexa-acetyltrehalose, m.p. 38—39°, $[\alpha]_D + 44°$. This compound is deacetylated by hydroxylamine, and the 6,6'-di-(3''-hydroxy-x-methoxymycolanoyl)-trehalose, m.p. 39—40°, $[\alpha]_D + 33°$, is obtained [458].

This procedure was later improved by Brochere-Ferreol & Polonsky [462], by making the potassium mycolate react directly with the 6,6'-ditosyltrehalose. This method avoids the deacetylation of the intermediary hexa-acetate, which lowers considerably the yield because of the inevitable hydrolysis of part of the mycolic ester groups.

A homologue of the "cord factor" was prepared by Polonsky et al. [461], by condensing potassium 2-eicosyl-3-hydroxytetracosanoate with the ditosyl derivative of trehalose. In the same manner, 6,6'-di-(2''-tetradecyl-3''-hydroxyoctadecanoyl)-α-D-trehalose [345], m.p. 126—130°, $[\alpha]_D^{21} + 62°$, was prepared from the potassium salt of corynomycolic acid by Diara & Pudles [688], before the isolation by Pudles et al. [913] of a diester of corynomycolic and corynomycolenic acids, and trehalose.

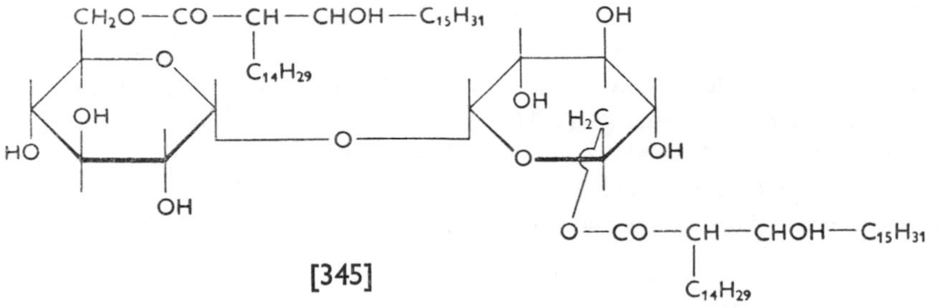

[345]

For reviews on the chemistry of the "cord factor", see ref. 916-918.

Esters of glycosylglycerol

Recently, glycosyl diglycerides have been detected in various strains of gram positive bacteria. A chromatographic technique has been devised for their separation from phospholipids [143a]. These glycolipids are akin to galactosyl-galactosyldiglycerides isolated by Benson[920] from plant chloroplasts.

Esters of mannosylglycerol

A glycolipid, $[\alpha]_D + 35°$ (soluble in ether, acetone, alcohol, chloroform), was isolated from the whole cells of *Micrococcus lysodeikticus* by MacFarlane[841]. The water-soluble saponification product was non-reducing; after acid hydrolysis, it gave a mixture (1:1) of glycerol and mannose. On periodic acid oxidation of the intact lipid, two moles of periodate per mole of sugar were consumed, indicating that the mannosylglycerol is not fully acylated. The fatty acids were mainly the anteiso- and iso-pentadecanoic acids.

Another sample of glycolipid was obtained from *M. lysodeikticus* by Lennarz[918a]; after chromatographic purification, it has $[\alpha]_D + 42.7°$. Chemical degradation gave results favouring structure [346 a]

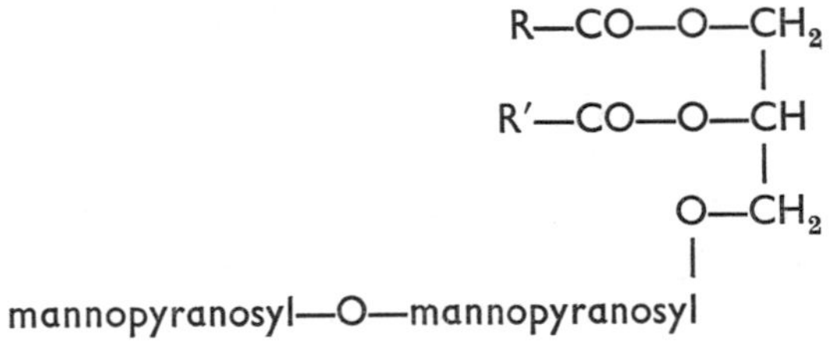

[346 a]

Esters of glucosylglycerol

A glycolipid, $[\alpha]_D - 19°$ (after chromatography on magnesium trisilicate), was isolated from the whole cells of *Staphylococcus aureus* Duncan (NCTC 9752), by MacFarlane [185]. The water-soluble product obtained by saponification was non-reducing; after acid hydrolysis, it gave a mixture of glycerol and glucose. This glycolipid is considered "presumptively a β-glucosylglyceride" [185].

Similar observations were made by Polonovsky *et al.*[919] in the case of the lipids of another strain of *S. aureus*.

From a study of the methylated derivatives of glucose obtained by methylation and hydrolysis of this lipid, it was concluded[919a] that it is a mixture of glucopyranosyl—1→6-glucopyranosyl-diglyceride and glucopyranosyl-1→3-glucopyranosyl-diglyceride.

The occurrence of glucosyl-glucosyl-diglycerides in the lipids of *Staphylococcus lactis*, *Staph. saprophyticus*, *B. subtilis* and *Streptococcus faecalis* was shown by Brundish *et al.*[919b].

From rough strains of *Pneumococcus* type I[920a] or type XIV[920b], a galactosyl-glucosyl-diglyceride has been isolated (ca. 1.5 % of the dry cells). The deacylation product, m.p. 165—167°, $[\alpha]_D + 176°$ (water), has been identified to 1-(O-α-D-galactopyranosyl-1→2-O-α-D-glucopyranosyl-1)-glycerol. The glycolipid has then the structure [346b]:

[346 b]

Esters of galactosylglycerol
From the lipids of an anaerobic bacteria (provisionally designated *Bacteroides symbiosus*), Reeves *et al.*[920c] have isolated a glycolipid containing only glycerol and galactose. The deacylation product is a sirup, $[\alpha]_D$—73° (water) (hexabenzoate m.p. 133—134°, $[\alpha]_D$—6° (CHCl₃)). From studies of periodic acid oxidation and measurements of hydrolysis rate, it was concluded that it is probably a α-galactofuranoside of diglyceride.

Esters of polysaccharides
At the beginning of this section, we have already mentioned that the work of Gubarev has shown the presence of fatty esters (hydroxylated or not) with polysaccharides containing mannose and galactose, in the lipids of *C. diphtheriae*.

Certain "waxes" of Mycobacteria contain esters of higher hydroxy acids with polysaccharides: these fractions constitute, on the one hand waxes D (for their isolation, see p. 239), and on the other, bound lipids.

Wax D of human strains of M. tuberculosis
According to the method used for their isolation, the wax D could be contaminated by phospholipids: by chromatography on silicic acid of their chloroform solution, the wax D is recovered in the chloroform eluate, whereas the phospholipids, more strongly adsorbed, are eluted only with a mixture of chloroform and methanol[143]. The samples thus purified still contain about 0.2 % of phosphorus, which cannot be eliminated.

Table 36 shows some properties of human strain wax D, i.e. of the fraction of waxes insoluble in boiling acetone. They occur in the form of a light yellow amorphous powder, soluble in ether, benzene and chloroform, insoluble in water, methanol and ethanol, and acetone even with boiling. A preparation of a glycolipid, called PmKo, obtained in an entirely different manner by Choucroun [921], exhibited the same chemical [922] and biological [921] properties as wax D.

Saponification splits wax D into an ether-soluble fraction composed of mycolic acids, and a water-soluble fraction (about 50 % each) containing a peptidopolysaccharide, the properties of which are given in Table 36.

The sugars of the polysaccharide are D-arabinose, D-mannose, and D-galactose (already discovered by Anderson [923, 924] in the hydrolysis products of "purified waxes"), glucosamine and galactosamine. Haworth *et al.* [925] studied the structure of a "polysaccharide bound to

TABLE 36. THE PROPERTIES OF SAMPLES OF WAX D ISOLATED FROM VARIOUS HUMAN STRAINS OF M. TUBERCULOSIS

Strain	Wax D				Polysaccharide obtained on saponification		Ref.
	M.p.	$[\alpha]_D$	N%	P%	$[\alpha]_D$ (water)	N%	
Test.	195-210°	+22°	1.59	0.15 0.16	+29°	1.98	
Brévannes.	195-210°		1.40	0.18	+26°	2.00	143
Canetti	195-210°	+22°	1.59 1.46	0.17	+30°	2.12	
H$_{37}$Ra	195-203°	+20°	1.65 1.50	0.28 0.20	+34°	2.08	
PB$_{15}$*	194-202°		0.72	0.22	+30°		922

* Glycolipid extracted by mineral oil and designated Pmko. [921]

lipids" ($[\alpha]_D$ + 25° (water)), probably identical with the polysaccharide of waxes D; after methylation and hydrolysis they obtained:

12.8 % Methyl 2,3,5-tri-*O*-methyl-D-arabofuranoside,
30.9 % Methyl 3,5-di-*O*-methyl-D-arabofuranoside,
33.8 % Methyl 2,3,6-tri-*O*-methyl-D-galactopyranoside,
14.4 % Methyl 3,4-di-*O*-methyl-D-mannopyranoside, and
8.0 % Methyl glucosaminide.

These results led Haworth *et al.* [925] to propose the structure [347] for this polysaccharide; according to these authors, the lipid part would be bound to the terminal residues of arabinose. An arabinose mycolate has been isolated from a wax D partial hydrolyzate by Azuma *et al.* [912a].

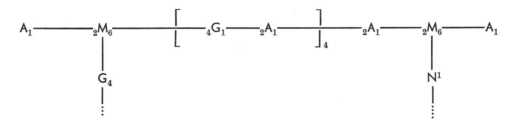

[347]   A: arabofuranose
        G: galactopyranose
        M: mannopyranose
        N: hexosamine

Asselineau [387] showed that the mycolic acids, which are hydroxy acids (see p. 123). are bound to the polysaccharide in the form of esters: this conclusion has been reached from a study of transesterification phenomena in methanol or benzyl alcohol [327], and of the hydrogenolysis of wax D by lithium aluminium hydride [64].

The nitrogen which is present in wax D comes either from hexosamines, or from ammonia or from amino-acids. In 1950, we showed that the acid hydrolysates of waxes D [926] and PmKo [922] contained three amino-acids: alanine, glutamic acid, and an amino acid, then unknown, identical with an unidentified substance observed by Work in extracts of *Corynebacterium diphtheriae* and later shown by the same author to be α,ε-diaminopimelic acid [927]. The determination of these amino-acids according to Moore & Stein shows that alanine, glutamic acid, and diaminopimelic acid are in a molecular ratio 3:2:2 in the case of the purified wax D isolated from several human strains [143]. The configuration of the amino-acids of the wax D Brévannes was determined: all the glutamic acid and a third of the alanine belong to the D series; the diaminopimelic acid is the meso isomer [143, 928].

From the results obtained by *N*-terminal (with dinitrofluorobenzene) and *C*-terminal (with carboxypeptidase) amino-acid analysis, from the determination of amino-nitrogen according to van Slyke by nitrous acid or by ninhydrin, and from the study of partial hydrolysates, it was concluded [143] that these amino-acids are bound to each other in the form of a peptide. According to recent work [929], the structure of this peptide moiety might be either [348] or [349]:

DAP—D-Ala—D-Glu—D-Glu—L-Ala—DAP—L-Ala   [348]

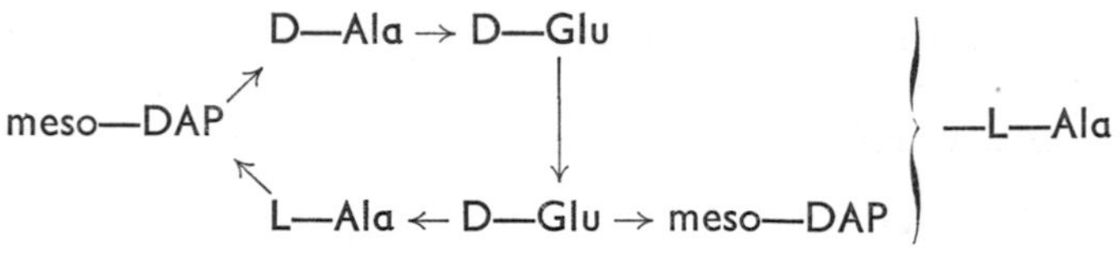

$$\text{meso—DAP} \overset{\nearrow}{\underset{\nwarrow}{\begin{matrix} \text{D—Ala} \rightarrow \text{D—Glu} \\ \downarrow \\ \text{L—Ala} \leftarrow \text{D—Glu} \rightarrow \text{meso—DAP} \end{matrix}}} \left.\begin{matrix} \\ \\ \\ \end{matrix}\right\} \text{—L—Ala} \qquad [349]$$

From the amino-acid contents, the mean minimum molecular weight was calculated and values of about 50 000 were obtained for the wax D.

The previous studies were done with samples of wax D that were "chromatographically homogeneous", but the value of this kind of homogeneity was very doubtful. For, as early as 1950, we observed that centrifugation at 15 000 r.p.m. of a solution of wax D in petroleum ether (or in ether) could easily separate waxes into 3 fractions which exhibited different contents of nitrogen and phosphorus [64, 922]. This fractionation was recently improved by Jollès et al. [930], by use of a Spinco centrifuge. 2g of wax D dissolved in 50 ml of ether were centrifuged at 50 000 g for 15, 35, 70, and 150 min. The properties of the fractions thus obtained are given in Table 37: fractions D_{15}, D_{35}, D_{70}, and D_{150} were the precipitates collected after 15,..., 150 min centrifugation; D_s was the fraction remaining in solution after 150 min centrifugation. D_{35v} was an intermediate viscous layer obtained after 35 min and separated by decantation. Fraction D_s contained sugars, hexosamines, but no amino-acids. In some fractions, one D-Glu residue was replaced by a Gly residue [930].

TABLE 37. THE PROPERTIES OF FRACTIONS OBTAINED BY ULTRACENTRIFUGATION OF WAX D
(HUMAN STRAIN CANETTI [930])

Fraction*	% Purified waxes D	M.p.	Elementary composition				Total amino sugars *	Peptide (% of wax D)
			C %	H %	N %	P %		
D_{15}	15.1	188-208°	60.54	9.47	1.97	0.3		6.34
D_{35}	11.4	188-208°	61.18	9.84	1.83	0.3	1.38	5.75
D_{35v}	28.2	188-208°	61.83	9.93	1.71	0.3		
D_{70}	6.1	188-208°	65.17	10.24	1.26	0.3		
D_{150}	9.8	180-200°	66.07	10.69	1.05	0.3		1.95
D_s	8.4	81-94°	74.28	11.75	0.31	0.58	0.10	0

* The significance of the fractions is explained in the text.

By combination of all these results [143, 930], the tentative structure [350] was proposed for the fractions of wax D. Minimum molecular weights of samples of wax D might be as high as 75 000 [930].

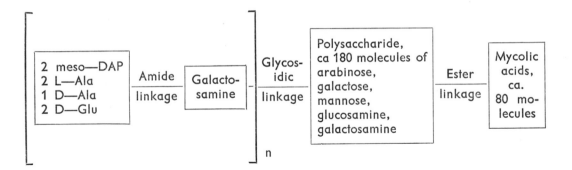

[350] : Tentative structure of wax D.

D_{15} and D_{35} n = 3 D_{70} n = 2 D_{150} n = 1

An interesting fractionation of wax D was achieved by Tanaka[931] by chromatography (on silicic acid) of the acetylated waxes: fractions free of amino-acids (less strongly adsorbed) are easily separated from fractions containing amino-acids. However, this procedure requires chemical transformations of the waxes and may produce artefacts. Acetylated wax D fractions (strain H_{37} Ra) exhibit molecular weights of only 16,000 to 20,000[931a].

The water-soluble part of the human strain waxes D shows a close relationship with the cell wall of the tubercle bacillus. The works of Kara & Keil[932], Cummins & Harris[933], Kitaura[934], Földes[935], and more recently of Takeya et al.[936], have demonstrated the existence in the cell wall of the tubercle bacillus of a glycopeptide which contains as principal sugars arabinose and galactose (and mannose according to Kara & Keil[932]) accompanied by glucosamine, the amino-acid being alanine, glutamic acid, and meso-α,ε-diaminopimelic acid. No information is given about the configuration of the alanine and glutamic acid residues; however, D-glutamic acid and D-alanine were found in the cell walls of certain gram-positive bacteria[937, 938], and D-glutamic acid was observed in hydrolysates of the whole bacterial cells of M. phlei, M. smegmatis, and M. ranae[939]. Moreover, muramic acid (which is a characteristic component of cell walls) has been detected in wax D[939a].

Wax D is very sensitive to enzymic hydrolysis: autolysis of cultures of tubercle bacilli lowers the yield of wax D and can even make them completely disappear[64]. The lack of high-melting waxes in the lipids of bacilli of strain H-37 grown in Long's medium in which the glycerol is replaced by glucose[13] is likely to be explained by such a phenomenon.

Wax D of bovine strains of M. tuberculosis

The fraction, insoluble in boiling acetone, of the waxes extracted by chloroform (see p. 239) from bovine strain bacilli was separated by chromatography on silicic acid into a fraction. with high melting point (first eluted) and a fraction with low melting point (see Table 38)[383].

TABLE 38. THE PROPERTIES OF WAX D ISOLATED FROM BOVINE STRAINS OF M. TUBERCULOSIS

Strain	Vallée		Marmorek		BCG	
% of dry bacilli . .	0.56		1.3		1.6	
M.p.	160-170°	44-49°	210-215°	42-45°	140-170°	38-41°
%N	0.2	0	0.1	—	0.3	0
On saponification						
Lipids %	55		55	66	63	
Sugars (and other watersoluble constituents)	Arabinose Galactose Mannose	Arabinose Galactose Mannose Glycerol	Arabinose Galactose Mannose	Arabinose Galactose Mannose Glycerol Ethyleneglycol		
References	383	383	383	383	64	383

The high-melting waxes had a composition quite similar to those of the wax D from human strains: saponification gave about 55 % mycolic acids and a polysaccharide containing the same three sugars: arabinose, galactose, and mannose [383]. However, they differ from the wax D of human strains by the low content (or the complete absence) of a peptide moiety [383].

Ultracentrifugation of solutions of wax D from bovine strains showed that they contain a high proportion of fraction D_s [940]. In the case of BCG, all the fractions were free from amino-acids (see below), and no DAP was observed in fractions obtained from bacilli of the strains Marmorek and Dupré (whereas Ala and Glu were present).

Wax D of other strains of Mycobacteria

Jollès et al. [940] studied the wax D from bacilli of *M. avium* (strain no. 802), *M. phlei*, *M. smegmatis*, and *M. kansasii* (photochromogenic atypical Mycobacteria). The waxes D of *M. kansasii* had only a low content of fraction D_s and its properties were similar to that of wax D of human strains. The samples of wax D of other origin had a rather high content of fraction D_s; "heavier" fractions contained Ala, Glu, DAP, accompanied by Gly and Asp [940].

In conclusion, as concerns wax D, human strains of *M. tuberculosis* and *M. kansasii* have a behaviour different from that of bovine, avian, and saprophytic strains. In the former case, the bacilli have a high content of wax D (crude fraction separated by its insolubility in boiling acetone) with high melting point and high content of "heavier" fractions (containing amino-acids), whereas in the latter case, the bacilli have a low content of wax D with a low melting point and a high content of "light" fractions (free from amino-acids).

Bound lipids of Mycobacteria

"Bound lipids" are the lipid fractions which, because of their linkage to proteins, cannot be directly extracted with neutral organic solvents. Weak acid or alkaline hydrolysis is required for their extraction.

Anderson and his collaborators discovered, in the bound lipids of tubercle bacilli of human strains (strains A-10 and A-12) [941], and avian strain [491], and a "leprosy bacillus" [492], esters of higher acids (principally mycolic acids) with polysaccharides.

The bound lipids of strain A-10 contain an "unfilterable" fraction (so called because it is retained by a porcelain candle during the filtration of a chloroform solution) composed of esters of mycolic acids and a polysaccharide. These esters showed properties very close to those of the wax D described above (Table 39). From the bound lipids of the human strain

TABLE 39. THE PROPERTIES OF GLYCOLIPIDS ISOLATED FROM THE BOUND LIPIDS
OF VARIOUS STRAINS OF MYCOBACTERIA
(compared with those of Brévannes wax D)

	M. tuberculosis var. hominis			M. avium	"Leprosy bacillus"
	Strain A-10	Strain Test	Strain Brévannes (waxes D)		
% of the dry weight of bacilli .	4.9	1.6	7.0	2.7	6.0
M.p.	∼200°	170-185°	195-210°	∼200°	175-185°
% N	0.4	0.2	1.4	0.5	0
% P	0.2	0	0.2	0.7	0
Saponification					
% Ether-soluble	50	50	50	50	66.4
% Mycolic acids	46	45	50	36	56.3
% Fatty acids	4	5	0	0	4.3
% Unsaponifiable.	0	0	0	14*	5.4*
% Water-soluble	50	52	50	50	40.5
% Polysaccharide.	50	52	50	50	40.5
$[\alpha]_D$ (water)	+30°	+28°	+26°		
N %	0.95	0.5	2.0	1.8	0
P %	0.38			1.0	0
% Arabinose**	38.7	+++	+++	20	41.4
% Galactose	12.2	++	++	+	2
% Mannose	6.6	+	+	27.3	
Other sugars	0	0	0		
% Glucosamine	traces	+	+	1.3	
Inositol.			0	+	
References	941	64	143	491	492,942

*Mixture of 2-eicosanol and 2-octadecanol.
** % of the polysaccharide.

Test, Asselineau [64] isolated a similar fraction differing from the waxes D of the same strain by the absence of amino-acids: they are therefore glycolipids (and not peptidoglycolipids).

By treating delipidated BCG cells by enzymes (lysozyme, L_{11} enzyme from a *Flavobacterium* sp.), Kotani *et al.* [942a] obtained a preparation of "bound wax D" which had the same properties as that of wax D from the human strain H_{37} Ra: m.p. 227—228°, N % 2.3 P % 0.5, mycolic acid % 48; presence of Ala, Glu and DAP.

The esters isolated from *M. avium* by Anderson *et al.* [491] were probably contaminated with phospholipids, because of the high phosphorus content of the polysaccharide (see Table 39). From the polysaccharide obtained by saponification, Anderson *et al.* [491] have also isolated a complex organo-phosphoric acid $C_9H_{20}O_{14}P_2$. In addition, the fractions isolated from *M. avium* or "leprosy bacillus" contain in the lipid part a small amount of higher alcohols which shows a contamination by true waxes.

We have mentioned above (see p. 178) that Azuma & Yamamura [912] have isolated, from the bound lipids of the human strain Aoyama B, a toxic glycolipid, the saponification of which gave arabinose, an unidentified sugar, and probably mycolic acids. From the same starting material, these authors [943] isolated also a glycolipid m.p. 154—155°, approximate molecular formula $C_{98}H_{192}O_{12}$. Saponification of this glycolipid (non-toxic) gave arabinose (claimed to be D-arabinose) and mycolic acid m.p. 53—55°, $C_{88}H_{176}O_4$ (one molecule of mycolic acid to two molecules of arabinose).

VII. PEPTIDOLIPIDS

The simplest representative of this group of lipids is serratamic acid, the amide of (—)-3(D)-hydroxydecanoic acid and L-(—)-serine [351]. This acid was isolated by Cartwright [944] from bacilli of a species of *Serratia*, by extraction with dilute aqueous sodium hydroxide. Serratamic acid, $C_{13}H_{25}O_5N$, was obtained as colourless crystals, m.p. 138° (dec.), $[\alpha]_D^{20} — 10.2°$ (ethanol); it could be extracted from ether solution by aqueous sodium hydrogen carbonate.

$$CH_3—(CH_2)_6—CHOH—CH_2—CO—HN—CH—COOH$$
$$| $$
$$[351] \qquad CH_2OH$$

Alkaline hydrolysis (30 min at 100° with 20 % aqueous potassium hydroxide) liberates L-serine and (—)-3(D)-hydroxydecanoic acid (see p. 110) [680, 944]. The structure of serratamic acid was confirmed by its synthesis from 3(D)-acetoxydecanoic acid and methyl L-serinate [680].

In fact, serratamic acid is a degradation product of a more complex substance, serratamolide m.p. 159—160°, $[\alpha]_D + 4.8°$ (ethanol), which was isolated from *Serratia marcescens* by Wasserman *et al.* [945]. Mild hydrolysis of serratamolide (N aqueous sodium hydroxide at room temperature) gave serratamic acid. From the properties of serratamolide, it was deduced that this product has the depsipeptide structure [352 a] [945].

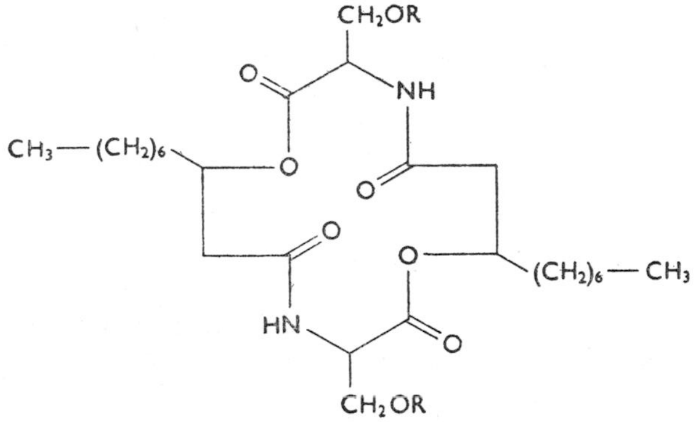

CH₂OR structure with CH₃—(CH₂)₆ and (CH₂)₆—CH₃ chains, NH, HN, O groups; CH₂OR

[352]   a R = H
        b R = CO—CH₃

Treatment of serratamolide with acetic anhydride in pyridine gave O,O'-diacetylserratamolide [352b], m.p. 222.5—223° (dec.) [945]. Synthesis of O,O'-diacetylserratamolide was recently achieved by Shemyakin et al. [946]: m.p. 222—223°, $[\alpha]_D^{20} + 20°$ (CHCl₃), which confirms the structure of serratamolide. It is then a rare example of a depsipeptide containing a β-hydroxy acid.

Viscosine, m.p. 270—273°, $[\alpha]_D^{29} - 168.3°$ (water), amide of (—)-3(D)-hydroxydecanoic acid and an hexapeptide produced by *Pseudomonas viscosa* [679], cannot be considered as a peptidolipid, since it is soluble in water.

Four peptidolipids were recently isolated from bacterial cells (see Table 40); all these compounds are insoluble in water and ether, and soluble in chloroform.

Esperine, m.p. 238°, $[\alpha]_D^{15} - 24°$ (methanol), $C_{39}H_{67}O_{11}N_5$, is produced by a species of *Bacillus mesentericus* [947]. The structure [353] was proposed by Ito and Ogawa [947]. Mild alkaline hydrolysis opened the lactone ring and gave esperinic acid, m.p. 195°, $[\alpha]_D^{15} + 12.5°$ (methanol). Complete hydrolysis gave five amino-acids (L-Glu, L-Asp, L-Val, L-Leu and D-Leu) and a β-hydroxy acid that was supposed to be 3-hydroxytridecanoic acid (it is likely to be a mixture of homologues, the mean elementary composition being in agreement with that of a C_{13} hydroxy acid).

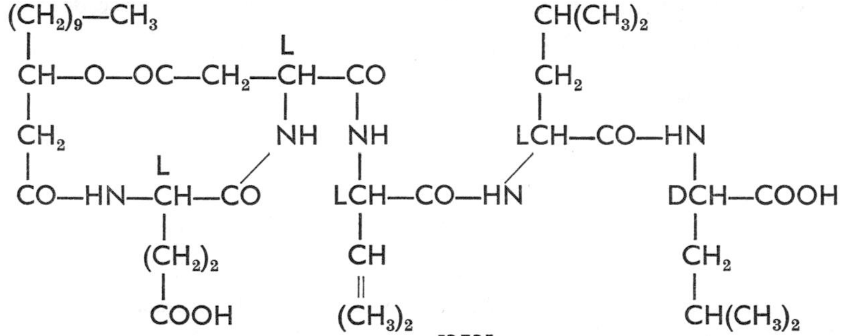

(CH₂)₉—CH₃ ... CH(CH₃)₂ structure [353]

[353]

TABLE 40. THE PROPERTIES OF BACTERIAL PEPTIDOLIPIDS

Name and approximate molecular formula	Origin	M.p.	$[\alpha]_D$	Amino-acids		Fatty acids	Ref.
Esperine $C_{39}H_{67}O_{11}N_5$	*Bacillus mesentericus*	238°	—24° MeOH	L-Asp L-Glu L-Val L-Leu	D-Leu	β-Hydroxy acid (C_{13}?)	947
Peptidolipid Na $C_{50}H_{89}O_{11}N_7$	*Nocardia asteroides*	232-233°	+42°	2 L-Thr L-Val L-Pro L-Ala	D-Ala D-allo-Ileu	β-Hydroxy acid C_{20}	948 949
Peptidolipid J $C_{54}H_{87}O_7N_5$	*Mycobacterium paratuberculosis*	138-139°	—87°	L-Phe L-Ala L-Leu L-Ileu	D-Phe	Straight chain acids; mainly C_{20}	951
Fortuitine $C_{72}H_{129}O_{15}N_9$ $C_{70}H_{125}O_{15}N_9$	*Mycobacterium fortuitum*	199-202°	—72°	3 L-Val 2 L-Thr 1 L-Ala 1 L-Pro 2 MeLeu		Straight chain acids; mainly C_{20}, C_{22}	343

A mixture of peptidolipids was isolated from *Nocardia asteroides* by Guinand *et al.*[948]. By counter-current distribution (with the mixture hexane/carbon tetrachloride/methanol/water 31:31:38:3), an homogeneous peptidolipid was obtained: m.p. 232—233°, $[\alpha]_D$ + 42° The configuration of the amino-acids was studied by Ikawa & Snell [950]. The structure [354] was proposed for this peptidolipid, from the results obtained by stepwise degradation by mild acid hydrolysis and mass spectrometry [949a].

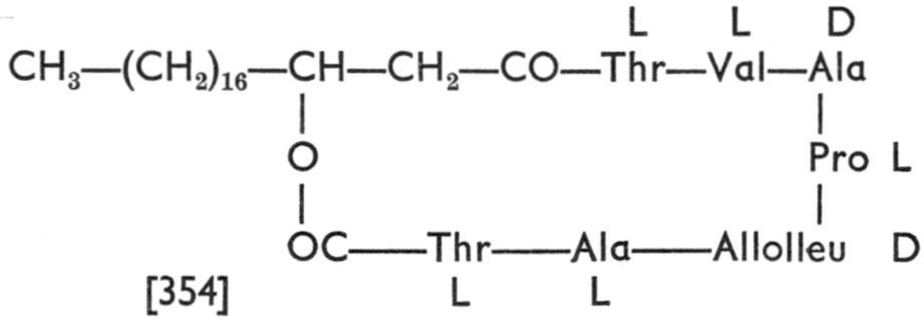

$$
\begin{array}{c}
 \text{L} \quad\ \text{L} \quad\ \text{D} \\
\text{CH}_3\text{---(CH}_2)_{16}\text{---CH---CH}_2\text{---CO---Thr---Val---Ala} \\
 | | \\
 \text{O} \text{Pro L} \\
 | | \\
 \text{OC---Thr---Ala---Allolleu} \quad \text{D} \\
\text{[354]} \text{L} \text{L}
\end{array}
$$

A mixture of closely related peptidolipids was isolated from *M. paratuberculosis (M. johnei)* by Lanéelle & Asselineau [951]. This fraction, m.p. 138—139°, $[\alpha]_D$ — 87°, approximate molecular formula $C_{54}H_{87}O_7N_5$, gave a mixture of fatty acids (mainly n-eicosanoic acid) and 4 amino-acids (Phe, Ala, Leu and Ileu) by hydrolysis [951]. It was shown that half of the phenylalanine had the D-configuration [950]. The main member of these peptidolipids has the structure [355] [951a]: the presence of a methyl ester grouping on the C-terminal-amino-acid was shown by comparison of the NMR spectrum of the natural product with that of methyl N-behenoyl phenylalaninate and of the product obtained from the natural peptidolipid by mild saponification (on alumina).

$$CH_3—(CH_2)_{18}—CO—NH—Phe—Ileu—Ileu—Phe—Ala—OCH_3 \qquad [355]$$

Fortuitine, m.p. 199—202°, $[\alpha]_D$ — 72°, was isolated from *Mycobacterium fortuitum (M. minetti)* by Vilkas et al. [343]. All the amino-acids had the L-configuration. Later, the presence of N-methyl leucine (MeLeu) was demonstrated by mass spectrometry and the structure [356] was established [313]:

$$CH_3—(CH_2)_n—CO—NH—Val—MeLeu—Val—Val—MeLeu—Thr—Thr—Ala—Pro—OCH_3$$

$$| \qquad |$$

$$Ac \qquad Ac$$

[356]   n : mainly 18 and 20

VIII. PEPTIDOGLYCOLIPIDS

The waxes D of human strains of *M. tuberculosis* and a part of the wax D of other strains of Mycobacteria, which were studied in Section VI, are in fact peptidoglycolipids. Because of their close structural relationship to the wax D of bovine strains and certain fractions of bound lipids which appear to be true glycolipids, these compounds were studied together.

The peptidoglycolipids contained in the wax D of Mycobacteria are built of a polysaccharide linked, on one hand to fatty acids (mycolic acids), and on the other hand to one or several molecules of a peptide.

Mycobacteria also contain another group of peptidoglycolipids which are glycosides of peptidolipids: in this case, the lipid moiety is directly linked to the peptide part, and sugars are linked to the peptidolipid by glycosidic bonds by means of hydroxyl groups contained in the peptide moiety. From this point of view, these glycosides of peptidolipids are more closely related to the peptidolipids (Section VII) than to the glycolipids.

These glycosides of peptidolipids are the mycosides C, first detected by Smith et al. [252] in the lipids of a strain of *M. avium*. Mycosides C (previously called "compound J_{av}") are characterized by the presence of a band at 8.1 μ in their IR spectrum [252].

Mycosides of avian strains

The first studies on the composition of mycoside C were performed simultaneously by Smith et al. [888, 952], MacLennan [953] and Gendre et al. [954].

Extraction of avian tubercle bacilli (strain n° 802, Pasteur Institute, Paris) by a mixture 1:1 of alcohol and ether gave a mixture of lipids from which crude mycoside C was isolated by means of its insolubility in ether.

Chromatography of mycoside C separated fractions having different optical rotation (— 31 to — 44°), carbon content (58.7 to 64.5 %), nitrogen content (3.8 to 4.5 %) and UV absorption [954]. Hydrolysis of these fractions gave eight sugars: glucose, arabinose, rhamnose, 3-O-methylrhamnose, 2,3-di-O-methylrhamnose, 3,4-di-O-methylrhamnose, 6-deoxytalose, and 3-O-methyl-6-deoxytalose [953].

The main fraction obtained by chromatography on silicic acid, called mycoside C_1, exhibited properties mentioned in Table 41. On hydrolysis, it gave an (or a mixture of) hydroxy acid, three sugars (3,4-di-O-methylrhamnose, 6-deoxytalose and 3-O-methyl-6-deoxytalose), amino-acids (identified as D-Phe, D-alloThr and D-Ala [928]), and two molecules of acetic acid [954]. The presence of acetate groupings explains the occurrence of the band at 8.1 μ characteristic of the IR spectra of mycosides C.

Studies of the products obtained by partial hydrolysis lead to the tentative structure [357]:

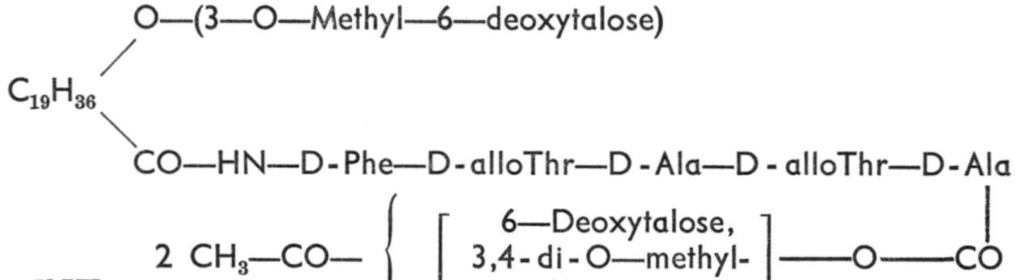

[357]

By combining chromatography on silicic acid and chromatography on magnesium trisilicate, Chaput et al. [955] isolated from the crude preparation of mycoside C three fractions, which were called mycosides C_2, C_3, and C_4 (see Table 41).

Results obtained by stepwise degradation of mycoside C_2 supported structure [358] [955].

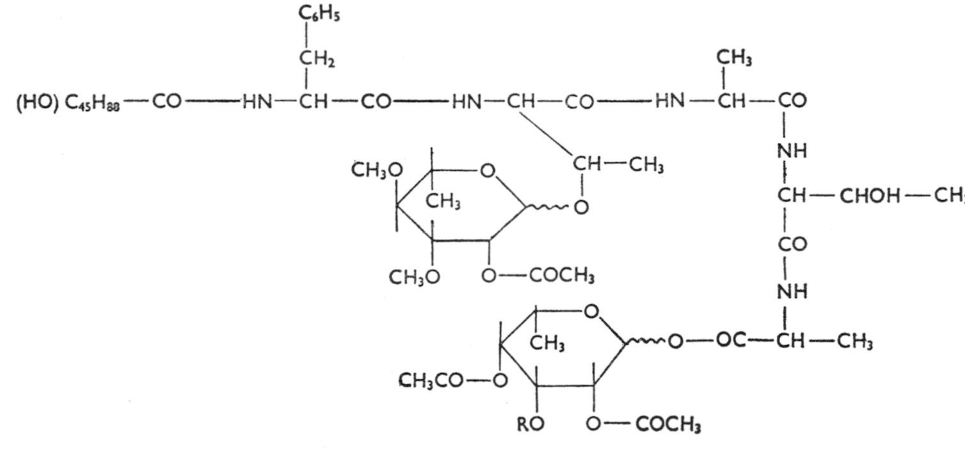

[358] R = H or CH$_3$

TABLE 41. THE PROPERTIES OF THE MAIN MEMBERS OF THE MYCOSIDE GROUP

Mycoside	Strain	M.p.	$[\alpha]_D$	Carbohydrates	Amino-acids	Fatty acids	Ref.
A	*M. kansasii*	105°	—37°	2-*O*-Methylfucose 2-*O*-Methylrhamnose 2,4-Di-*O*-methylrhamnose	None	Phenolglycol A	252 518*a* 888
B	*M. tuberculosis* var. *bovis*	25°	—22°	2-*O*-Methyl-D-rhamnose	None	Phenolglycol + palmitic and mycocerosic acids	252 891
C$_1$	*M. avium*	200-206°	—34°	3-*O*-Methyl-6-deoxytalose 6-Deoxytalose 3,4-Di-*O*-methylrhamnose	D-Phe 1 D-*allo*Thr 2 D-Ala 2	Acid $C_{20}H_{38}O_3$	954
C$_2$	*M. avium*	200°	—28°	3,4-Di-*O*-methyl-L-rhamnose 6-Deoxy-L-talose (or 3-*O*-methyl-6-deoxy-L-talose)	D-Phe 1 D-*allo*Thr 2 D-Ala 2	Acid $C_{43}H_{86}O_2$ or $C_{46}H_{90}O_3$	955
C$_3$ C$_4$		190-197° 194-198°	—21° —30°				955
C$_m$	*M. marianum*	198-200°	—31°	6-Deoxy-L-talose 3,4-Di-*O*-methyl-L-rhamnose	D-Phe 1 D-*allo*Thr 3 D-Ala 3	Acid $C_{50}H_{96}O_3$	956
C$_{1217}$	*non-photo-chromogenic mycobacteria*	207-212°	—33°	6-Deoxytalose 3,4-Di-*O*-methylrhamnose 2,3,4-Tri-*O*-methylrhamnose	Phe 1 *allo*Thr 2 Ala 2	Hydroxy-acid	1217

All the amino-acids have the D-configuration [928], and it is claimed that the sugars belong to the L-series [955].

Mycoside of M. marianum

From the lipids of *M. marianum*, Chaput *et al.* [956] isolated a peptidoglycolipid by its insolubility in ether. After purification by chromatography on magnesium trisilicate, this peptidoglycolipid, called mycoside C_m, exhibited properties given in Table 41.

Mycoside C_m contained only two different sugars, 6-deoxytalose (m.p. 112—120°, $[\alpha]_D$ — 15° (water)) and 3,4-di-*O*-methyl-L-rhamnose ($[\alpha]_D$ + 20° (water)), in the ratio 1:2 according to the colorimetric determination by the method of Dische & Shettles [957]. The amino-acids were identified as D-phenylalanine, D-allothreonine and D-alanine, in the molecular ratio 1:3:3 [956, 928]. 3 Acetyl groups were also present.

Stepwise degradation of mycoside C_m, with or without previous methylation of the free hydroxyl groups, gave results in agreement with the structure [359] [956].

Comparison of the formula [358] proposed for mycoside C_2 (from *M. avium*) with the formula [359] proposed for mycoside C_m (from *M. marianum*) shows that the main difference consists of the presence of one more grouping (D-Ala-D-alloThr)-sugar in the glycopeptide moiety of mycoside C_m. On the other hand, important differences exist between the structures of mycosides C_2 and C_m, and the structure of mycoside C_1. It is probable that further work will introduce homogeneity in the structures of these two groups of mycosides C.

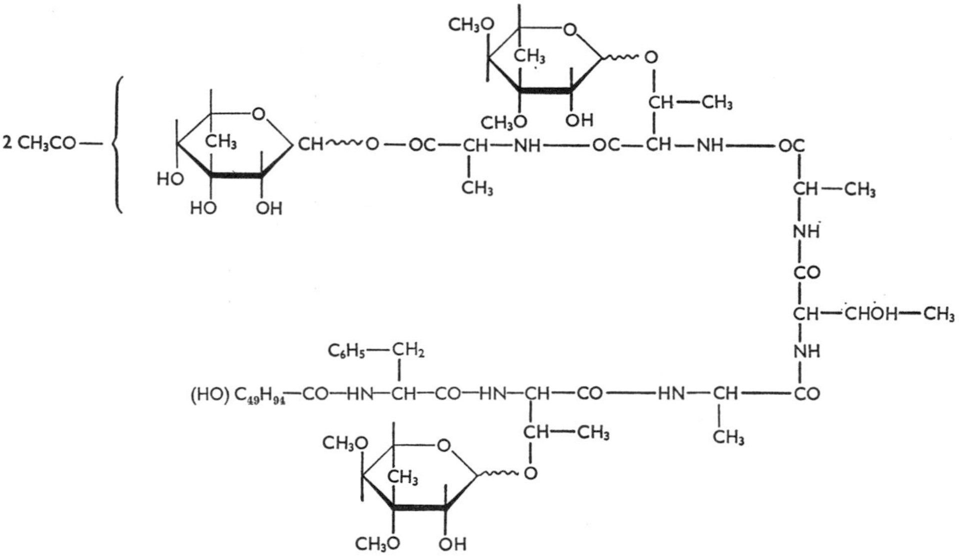

[359]

Mycoside of strain 1217

From a non-chromogenic strain of atypical mycobacteria, Lanéelle *et al.*[1217] isolated a mycoside, designated mycoside C_{1217}, the properties of which are given in table 41. This mycoside is split by saponification into "lipid C" and non identified fragments. Lipid C still contains the lipid moiety of the mycoside, Phe and Ala (still in the molecular ratio 1:2), and only 2 sugars (dimethyl- and trimethyl- rhamnose): it is completely free of allothreonine and 6-deoxytalose. The complete disappearance of allothreonine and deoxytalose may be explained by β-elimination. The rhamnose derivatives are probably linked to the lipid moiety[1217].

IX. LIPOPOLYSACCHARIDES

From gram-negative bacteria, it is possible to isolate complex substances having toxic and antigenic properties, which contain a polysaccharide part and a lipid part, as well as some amino-acids. These substances are called lipopolysaccharides, because they are soluble in water (giving opalescent solutions) and insoluble in the usual organic solvents (as opposed to glycolipids).

In 1933, Boivin *et al.*[958] isolated such a fraction from *Salmonella typhimurium* (Aertryck bacillus), and showed its lipopolysaccharide nature. Boivin[958, 959] isolated lipopolysaccharides from various bacilli, by extraction with 0.25N trichloroacetic acid. Raistrik & Topley[960] preferred to eliminate the bacterial proteins by trypsic digestion and to isolate the lipopolysaccharides from the hydrolysate by fractional precipitation with alcohol. Morgan[961, 962] used an extraction with diethyleneglycol, and Miles & Pirie[963], used phenol. This latter method was adopted by Westphal & Lüderitz in the course of an extensive study of the chemical and biological properties of these lipopolysaccharides[880]. Urea, in 2.5M aqueous solution, was also proposed as an extracting agent[964].

The isolation of these lipopolysaccharides may also be achieved by means of water at 80° for 30 min[965], or of water saturated with ethyl ether at room temperature[965a]. Nowotny *et al.*[966] have compared the results obtained with trichloracetic acid, aqueous phenol, water, and water saturated with ethyl ether as the extractive agents, as well as with two new solubilizing agents, hot pyridinium formiate aqueous solution or cetyltrimethylammonium bromide in 0.5 % solution. Large variations of yield were observed according to the technique used, and the chemical composition of the preparations, obtained from a same kind of bacilli, exhibited very important differences. I.R. spectrography may be a useful tool for testing the purification of a lipopolysaccharide sample[1065].

Data on the composition of lipopolysaccharides isolated from gram-negative bacteria are listed in Table 42: it must be stressed that different techniques of extraction were used and the results contained in the Table 42 cannot be directly compared.

Lipopolysaccharides were also isolated from *Pseudomonas aeruginosa*[840, 982], from *Salmonella paratyphi* B[983], and from *Vibrio fœtus*[984].

TABLE 42. THE PROPERTIES OF LIPOPOLYSACCHARIDES OF GRAM-NEGATIVE BACTERIA

	Lipopolysaccharide			Carbohydrates (% polysaccharide part)								% Lipopoly-saccharide	Lipid A				Ref.
	Extractants*	N %	P %	Hexosamine %	Galactose	Glucose	Mannose	Rhamnose	Xylose	Heptose	Abequose	Tyvelose		M.p.	N %	P %	Hexosamine %	
Brucella melitensis	PW	5.4	0.5-0.6										20—26		4.4-4.6	1.4-1.6		963, 970
Chromobacterium violaceum	PW	3.4	0.8	+	+	+							18					972
Escherichia coli**	PW	2.7	2.2	18									17—20	197-200°	1.6	1.8	20.4	534
	DEG	2.9	2.0	15									5—7	194-196°	1.7	1.9	19.2	534
E. coli 08 (Kröger) . .	PW	1.0	2.1	5.9	2.7	9.6		41.7	11.2	<1			13	195-196°	1.9	2.3	17.8	973
Neisseria gonorrhoeae. .	PW	3.3	3.8	13.8	+	+				+			28.4					974, 975
Pasteurella pestis. . .	TCA	1.6	2.2	+		+				+			50					972
Pasteurella tularense . .	WEE	8.0	1.5	22.6									9.0					969
Salmonella abortus equi .	PW	1.3	2.8	8.7	15.2	8.3	8.7	10.8			~8		26	192-196°	1.6	2.0	17.9	880
Salmonella typhosa. . .	PW			1.7	22.5	22.5	22.5	18				~9						880
	TCA	0.6-1.5	2.0	3.5-4.5				11.6 13.5		+			20—30					976
Serratia marcescens. . .	TCA	2.2	1.1	+		+							16		1.9	1.1		967, 977
Shigella flexneri. . . .	PyW	2.7	1.7	16.4		+		+		+			10		2.7	3.3		978, 979
Shigella sonnei	W	2.8	3.9	8.3	9	9				20			29		1.4	1.4		980, 981

* PW = aqueous phenol; DEG = diethyleneglycol; TCA = solution of trichloracetic acid; WEE = water saturated with ethyl ether; PyW = aqueous pyridine; W = water.

** Two fractions were obtained, one by extraction with phenol and the other by extraction with diethyleneglycol.

These lipopolysaccharides can have very high molecular weights: about 1 million for the one isolated from *Brucella melitensis* [963], and 10 millions for those from *Serratia marcescens* [967] and *Shigella dysenteriae* [969]. A low molecular weight crystalline lipopolysaccharide was isolated from the culture medium of a strain of *Pseudomonas pseudomallei*; in the centrifuge, it gives a single symmetrical peak [969 a].

We have mentioned above that the partial hydrolysis of these lipopolysaccharides gives a lipid fraction called "lipid A" (see p. 167). Another lipid fraction, called "lipid B", can be obtained from the crude "lipopolysaccharido-proteolipid" complex (also called "complete antigen"). Lipids B are easily extracted by simple heating with dilute acetic acid; as they do not seem to play a rôle in the biological properties of the initial complexes, their chemical composition was not studied.

According to the conditions used, the lipopolysaccharido-proteolipid complexes can be split either into a mixture of lipopolysaccharide, conjugated protein and lipid B, or into a mixture of phosphorylated polysaccharide, lipid A linked to the protein part, and lipid B. 0.1 N formic acid may be a useful reagent to make stepwise degradations of lipopolysaccharides [985].

Lipopolysaccharides frequently contain rare sugars such as heptoses (e. g. D-*glycero*-D-*mannoheptose* in the case of *Chromobacterium violaceum* [972]), 3,6-dideoxysugars (abequose [360], colitose [361], tyvelose [362], paratose [364], and ascarylose [363]) [986-990], or aminosugars (e.g. N-acetyl-D-fucosamine and viosamine from *C. violaceum* [972], [991]). It appears that, at least in the *Escherichia-Salmonella* group, the backbone of the polysaccharide moiety is made of a polymer of 2-keto-3-deoxyoctonoate, heptose and phosphoric acid [991 a].

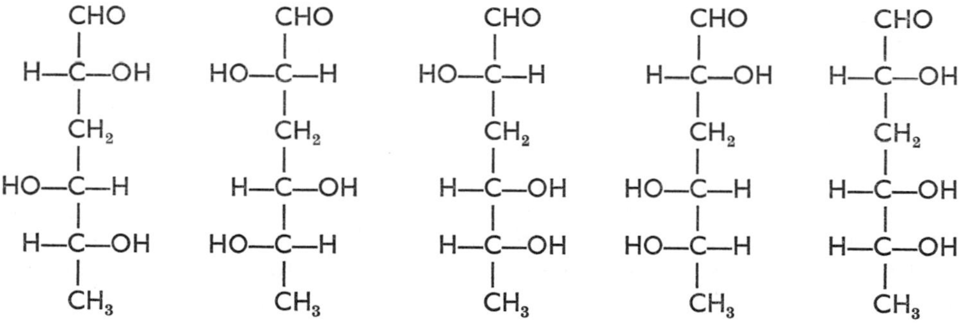

Abequose	Colitose	Tyvelose	Ascarylose	Paratose
$[\alpha]_D^*$—3.2°	+ 4.0°	+ 25°	− 26°	+ 8°
[360]	[361]	[362]	[363]	[364]

Reviews on the chemical and biological properties of the lipopolysaccharides of gram-negative bacteria have been published by Westphal & Lüderitz [880], [992], [992 a], and the papers of a symposium on bacterial endotoxins have been collected in a book [992 b].

---

* Water as solvent.

Attempts to isolate lipopolysaccharides from gram-positive bacteria gave negative results (see ref. 959). For example, the application to the tubercle bacillus of Boivin's technique (extraction with trichloracetic acid) gave only polysaccharides[993]. Nevertheless, Stacey et al.[994], by extraction of tubercle bacilli with urea or β-hydroxypropionamidine, obtained water-soluble preparations, almost homogeneous on electrophoresis, which contained 27 % ether-soluble lipids, 40 % non-saponifiable lipids (mycolic acids?), 16 % of a specific polysaccharide, 6 % deoxyribonucleic acid, and 4 % of a peptide component. The polysaccharide of this complex contained a pentose and an amino sugar. By phenol extraction of defatted BCG, Tsumita et al.[995] obtained a serologically active lipopolysaccharide (1.05 % P, 1.1 % N) containing 75 % hexoses (as glucose), 3.8 % pentoses (arabinose), 10.7 % protein, and 21 % lipids. By extraction of defatted and phenol extracted cells of a human strain of the tubercle bacillus by a borate buffer, Tsumita et al.[996] obtained a high molecular weight lipopolysaccharide (0.56 % P, 1.2 % N) containing 54 % mannose, 23.2 % arabinose, and 18.3 % lipids; a similar preparation has been obtained by Matsumoto[997] from BCG cells.

Kent[998] isolated from the culture medium of the tubercle bacillus a "polysaccharide II", $[\alpha]_D + 169°$ (water), which contained 1 part of lipids for 11 parts of sugars. The polysaccharide was composed principally of glucopyranose residues linked together by 1,2-bonds; a small amount of glucosamine was detected.

Sorkin et al.[999], from the culture medium of a virulent human strain of M. tuberculosis, prepared an "α-hemosensitine", essentially composed of a lipopolysaccharido-protein (or peptide). This complex, $[\alpha]_D + 72°$ (water), contained 1 % fatty acids (mycolic acids?) chemically bound to the polysaccharide. This latter was composed of 61 % arabinose, 25 % hexoses (galactose and mannose), and 1.3 % hexosamine. 4 % of protein (or peptide) was also present.

X. LOCALIZATION OF LIPIDS IN THE BACTERIAL CELL

Fractional centrifugation has enabled samples of several parts of the bacterial cell to be prepared in sufficient quantity for a preliminary study of their composition. The parts of the cell which are most easily accessible are the cell wall (which generally constitutes 20—30 % of the dry weight of the bacteria) and, to a lesser degree, the cytoplasmic membrane: it is, therefore, mainly these fractions which have been studied. In certain cases, information has been obtained about the cellular protoplasm and inclusions.

Cell wall

For the conclusions drawn from a study of the cell wall to be valuable, it is necessary that the purity of the material studied be controlled by examination with an electron microscope.

The systematic analysis of cell walls of various species of bacteria (1000-1005 a) showed a distinct difference of composition between the cell walls of gram-positive and gram-negative bacteria. The cell wall of gram-positive bacteria usually contains only a small amount of lipids; it consists essentially of a glycopeptide. The cell wall of gram-negative bacteria is rich in lipids and gives on hydrolysis a large number of amino-acids : it seems to be composed of lipoprotein and lipopolysaccharide complexes (see Table 43).

TABLE 43. THE COMPOSITION OF THE CELL WALL OF SOME BACTERIA
(% of the dry weight of the cell wall)

Species	N %	P %	Hexos-amines	Reducing substances	Lipids	Ref.
Gram-positive bacteria						
Bacillus subtilis	5.1	5.35	8.5	34.0	2.6	1000
Corynebacterium diphtheriae.					3.5	1006
					30.5	1007
Micrococcus halodenitrificans						
ultra-sound	4.4	0.4		0.5	6.0	1008
water	13.5	1.1			18.0	1018
Micrococcus lysodeikticus	8.7	0.09	16.1	44.9	1.2	1000
Mycobacterium tuberculosis (BCG) . .	3.0	0.36		21.2	61.1	934
Mycobacterium phlei	2.6		2.3	16	60.4	1008
Sarcina lutea	7.6	0.22	16.5	46.5	1.1	1000
Staphylococcus aureus	10.6	2.5		< 2	4.4	1009
					0.8	833
Streptococcus pyogenes	10.6	0.6	11.8	33.1		
Gram-negative bacteria						
Azotobacter vinelandii.					28	830
Escherichia coli 0113	9.5	1.2	4.9	8.7	35	1019
0111: B4	8.1	1.1	5.6	17	32	1019
Pseudomonas aeruginosa						
strain P 15	9.9	1.7	2.1	16.9	11.9	1012
strain McAlleese.	10.1	0.8	2.7	16.8	10.7	1012
Pseudomonas salinaria	11.0	1.0			11.0	1008
Salmonella gallinarum					22	1010
Salmonella pullorum.	6.4	0.9	4.8	46.0	19.0	1000
Vibrio costicolus						
ultra-sound	14.2	0.53		1.5	10.1	1008
water.	12.8			1.5	19.9	1008
Vibrio metchnikovii.					11.2	1010
Myxococcus xanthus	5			5	50	1011

According to the procedure used for the preparation of the cell walls, the composition of the material obtained can vary considerably. Table 43 contains two examples (relating to halophile bacteria: *Micrococcus halodenitrificans* and *Vibrio costicolus*) where the rupture of the cells was achieved either by an ultrasonic procedure or by action of a hypotonic medium : the nitrogen and lipid contents can vary in the proportion of 1:3 [1008]. In general, it is not possible to say whether these differences are caused by contamination of the preparation by material coming from another part of the cell or by the removal of a layer of the constituent of the cell wall by a more drastic procedure. On the other hand, Hill *et al.* [1016] have observed that the lipid content of the cell wall of *Staphylococcus aureus* may vary from 0.7 to 25.5 % of the dry weight of material according to the composition of the culture medium. Thus the figures listed in Table 43 have only a limited significance.

The cell wall is heterogeneous, and has been fractionated in the case of some gram-negative bacteria. For example, the cell wall of *E. coli* was separated by extraction with 90 % phenol into lipoprotein (soluble) and lipopolysaccharide (insoluble) fractions [1013].

The existence of lipids at the surface of *Salmonella* seems likely from the work of Colobert [1014, 1015], who observed that the cell wall of these bacteria can be attacked by lysozyme only after removal of lipids. Few studies have been devoted to the composition of the cell wall lipids, probably because of the very small quantities of material available. In one case *(M. halodenitrificans)*, "poly-β hydroxybutyrate" (see p. 108) was identified: lipid particles might have been carried along with the cell wall, without being a component of it [1008]. Nevertheless, Alimova [1006] was able to identify free fatty acids and esters of trehalose in the cell wall of *Corynebacterium diphtheriae*, besides a lipoglycoprotein complex. Marr and Kaneshiro [830] fractionated the lipids of the cell wall of *A. vinelandii*: 10—20 % neutral lipids and 70—75 % phospholipids were obtained. The neutral lipids were mainly free fatty acids, and the phospholipids mainly phosphatidyl ethanolamines. No particular features were found in the fatty acid composition of the cell wall lipids of 8 bacterial species [1008 a].

According to Knaysi *et al.* [1017], the cell wall of *M. avium* consists of a film about 230Å in thickness. Extraction of BCG by neutral organic solvents (alcohol + ether, then chloroform) left "apparently intact" and still acid-fast bacilli, from which the cell wall was isol-

TABLE 44. THE LIPID COMPOSITION OF THE SUBCELLULAR FRACTIONS OF THE BCG CELL
(after Kitaura [934])

	Whole cell	Cell wall	Particulate fraction	Soluble fraction (cytoplasm)
Lipids extracted by Anderson's method				
% Fats	3.1	2.8	5.6	3.9
% Phosphatides	3.5	7.9	4.2	0.3
% Wax A	0.5	4.7	2.7	Traces
% Wax B	1.5	8.4	1.1	0.8
% Wax C	4.0	3.4	0.8	1.1
% Wax D	2.3	9.0	0.6	0.4
Total free lipids	15.6	38.6	17.8	7.2
Bound lipids	12.1	22.5	5.9	2.0
Total lipids	27.7	61.1	23.7	9.2
Lipids extracted by ether from an acid hydrolysate	25.0	51.6	28.8	11.2

ated [933]. The cell wall isolated by Kitaura [934] from BCG contained 61 % lipids (see Table 44): it might be that free lipids were trapped within the cell wall without being true constituents, like the "poly-β-hydroxybutyrate" in the case of *M. halodenitrificans* (see above). The cell wall preparation, obtained by Takeya *et al.* [936] from *M. phlei*, contains 60.4 % lipids; after treatment of the walls with 0.5 % potassium hydroxide in methanol for 48 h at 37°, a "basal layer" has been obtained which contains only 7.7 % lipids. The basal layer has about the same composition as the walls from other species of gram-positive bacteria: 5.8 % N, 13.8 % amino-sugars, 51 % reducing sugars. The crude cell wall of Mycobacteria thus has a high content of lipids, which is in accord with the hydrophobic character of these bacteria, their staining properties (see acid-fastness, p. 255) and the localization in the cell wall of the factor inducing tuberculin hypersensitivity (see p. 277) [1020]. "Galactose, glucosamine, diaminopimelic acid and chloroform soluble lipids are almost exclusively localized in the cell wall fraction and are the peculiar components of the cell wall" [934]. The presence of the peptido-glycolipids of the waxes D (or of a related type of compounds) in the wall of Mycobacteria is therefore likely, as they play a rôle in the induction of tuberculin sensitivity (see p. 277).

A toxic lipid has been isolated from *Corynebacterium ovis* by washing the cells with petroleum ether: it may perhaps be localized on the surface of the bacteria.

Cytoplasmic membrane

By inhibition of the biosynthesis, or enzymatic hydrolysis, of the cell wall, bacilli are reduced to protoplasts, which are very sensitive to a hypotonic medium. Lysis of these protoplasts gives, on the one hand, a cytoplasmic membrane (or "ghost") which can be sedimented by centrifugation, and, on the other hand, soluble cytoplasm. General characteristics of the lipids of the cytoplasmic membrane of bacteria are included in a review of van Deenen [1020a].

The cytoplasmic membrane of *Bacillus M* represents about 15 % of the dry weight of the whole cells [804]; 55 to 75 % of the cell lipids are concentrated in this membrane. These lipids (3.2—4.0 % P) are principally phospholipids, and paper chromatography shows that they are essentially phosphatidic acids [804]. Ethanolamine and amino-acids were found in the lipids of the protoplast membrane of *B. megaterium* KM; no choline could be detected [1020]. Iso acids with 15, 16, and 18 carbon atoms and anteiso acids with 15, 16, and 17 carbon atoms were found in the lipids of the membrane of *B. megaterium* [544].

The lipids of the cytoplasmic membrane of *Micrococcus lysodeikticus* were isolated by MacQuillen [1021] and Gilby *et al.* [1022, 1023], and thoroughly investigated by MacFarlane [1024]: the phospholipids (27.6 % of the crude lipids) were separated by chromatography on silicic acid into diphosphatidylglycerol contaminated by a small amount of phosphatidic acids (68 % of the phospholipids), mannose-containing phospholipids (24 %) and phosphatidylinositol (5 %) [841, 1024]. The fatty acid composition was investigated by vapour phase chromatography: iso and anteiso acids were detected [544].

Lipids (28 %) were isolated from the membrane of *Streptococcus faecalis* (exponential phase cultures); it was observed that membranes of threonine-depleted or valine-depleted bacilli contained respectively 36 % and 40 % lipids. The phosphorus content of these lipids was relatively constant (2.8—3.0 %) and the nitrogen content was low (0.12—0.26 °/$_0$)[1026]. In the beginning of the stationary phase of growth, the dry cytoplasmic membrane contains ca. 21 % lipids (mainly a diphosphatidylglyceride, "fast moving" on thin-layer chromatography)[841b]. Membranes isolated from *Strept. faecalis* cells during the exponential phase of growth contain 94 % of the total cell lipids[1026a]. The major components of these lipids are: phosphatidylglycerol, amino acid esters (Lys, Gly, Ala) of phosphatidylglycerol, monoglucosyldiglyceride and a galactosyl-glucosyldiglyceride[1026a].

Because of its high content of phospholipids, it was suggested that the cytoplasmic membrane might play a rôle in the uptake of phosphate from the surrounding medium[1025]. More recently, Hill[879] has shown that phosphate is actively incorporated into the phospholipids of the spheroplast membrane of *E. coli*.

By fractional centrifugation of lysed bacterial cells, spherical particles, usually highly pigmented, are sometimes isolated. These particles seem to arise, at least in some cases, from the disintegration of the cytoplasmic membrane. For example, Yamamura *et al.*[1027] obtained, from *M. avium*, a red pigmented fraction composed of particles from 50 to 100 mμ in diameter, in which were concentrated the cellular phospholipids and phosphoproteins. Kitaura[934] isolated from BCG a "particular fraction" containing 23.7 % lipids, mainly composed of lipids extractable by a mixture of ether and alcohol (as the phospholipids). The "red fraction" isolated by Georgi *et al.*[1028] from *Bacillus stearothermophilus* contains 10.1 % lipids (4.8 % phospholipids), i.e. the major part of the lipids of the cell. This fraction is composed of 90 % of particles devoid of lipids, and a membrane of a lipid nature, soluble in a mixture of ether and alcohol. From *Staphylococcus aureus*, Few[833] obtained a fraction of "small particles", deep yellow, containing 22.3 % lipids (0.8 % N and 1.8 % P); the hydrolysis of these lipids gave ethanolamine and serine, but no choline.

A particulate fraction was isolated from the photosynthetic bacterium *Rhodopseudomonas spheroides*[1029]: the lipids of these particles gave 72—79 % octadecenoic acids by saponification. 90 % of the octadecenoic acids was vaccenic acid and 10 % was oleic, acid, when the bacteria were grown under aerobic conditions; anaerobically, the values were 97 and 3 % respectively. The fatty acids isolated from the anaerobically grown cell particles contained about 5 % linoleic acid: this point is most interesting in relation to the biosynthesis of unsaturated acids in bacteria.

Therefore, a general character of the cytoplasmic membrane is its pigmentation and its high content of phospholipids.

Cytoplasm

The cytoplasm is the part of the cell which is the most difficult to obtain free from contamination, and its chemical composition has often been neglected. Table 44 gives some data on the lipids occurring in the cytoplasm of BCG[934]. Fatty acids (24 %) were isolated by Milner *et al.*[1019] from the cytoplasm of *E. coli*.

More studies deal with the chemical composition of inclusion granules that can be separated from the cytoplasm: in almost every case, these inclusions consist of poly-β-hydroxybutyrate (*Bacillus megaterium*[1030, 1031, 661]; *Pseudomonas methanica*[1032]).

Composition of the lipids
of various bacterial species

In this fourth part, we will examine the composition of the lipids present in the different bacterial species studied so far. We have adopted the microbiological classification utilized in Bergey's Manual [5]. This classification, simplified to adapt it to our needs, can be summarized as follows:

Order	Family	Tribe	Genus
I. Pseudomonadales	Methanomonadaceae	. . . .	*Hydrogenomonas*
	Pseudomonadaceae		*Pseudomonas*
			Halobacterium
	Spirillaceae	. . . .	*Vibrio*
			Spirillum
II. Chlamydobacteriales	Chlamydobacteriaceae	. . . .	*Sphaerotilus*
IV. Eubacteriales	Azotobacteriaceae	. . . .	*Azotobacter*
	Rhizobiaceae	. . . .	*Rhizobium*
			Agrobacterium
	Achromobacteraceae	. . . .	*Alcaligenes*
			Achromobacter
	Enterobacteriaceae	Escherichieae	*Escherichia*
			Aerobacter
			Klebsiella
		Serratieae	*Serratia*
		Proteae	*Proteus*
		Salmonelleae	*Salmonella*
			Shigella
	Brucellaceae	. . . .	*Pasteurella*
			Brucella
			Bordetella
			Actinobacillus

Order	Family	Tribe	Genus
	Bacteroidaceae	. . . .	*Bacteroides*
			Streptobacillus
	Micrococcaceae	. . . .	*Micrococcus*
			Staphylococcus
			Gaffkya
			Sarcina
	Neisseriaceae	. . . .	*Neisseria*
	Lactobacillaceae	Streptococcaceae	*Streptococcus*
			Leuconostoc
		Lactobacilleae	*Lactobacillus*
	Corynebacteriaceae	. . . .	*Corynebacterium*
			Listeria
			Cellulomonas
	Bacillaceae	. . . .	*Bacillus*
			Clostridium
V. Actinomycetales	Mycobacteriaceae	. . . .	*Mycobacterium*
	Actinomycetaceae	. . . .	*Nocardia*
			Actinomyces
	Streptomycetaceae	. . . .	*Streptomyces*
			Micromonospora
VIII Myxobacteriales	Myxococcaceae	. . . .	*Myxococcus*

Some hypertrophy of the section relating to *Mycobacteriaceae* cannot be avoided, because of the much greater complexity of the lipids of Mycobacteria and the very large amount of research which has been devoted to them.

Nicolle & Alilaire [1033] studied the chemical composition of bacilli belonging to a dozen different species, grown on agar medium. Extraction of the bacilli with acetone gave a soluble fraction of which the percentage varied from 6.3 in the case of *Bacillus anthracis* to 15.7 in the case of *Pseudomonas pyocyanea* (calculated on the dry weight of the bacilli). No further study of the acetone extract was made, except to separate it into chloroform-soluble and insoluble parts.

For the purpose of characterizing in a sure and rapid manner a bacterial strain, O'Connor *et al.* [1034] examined the infrared spectra of the acetone extract from bacilli of different species. However, because of the high water content of the extraction solvent, the infrared spectra did not prove practicable for giving information about the presence of lipid compounds.

1. *Athiorhodaceae*

Rhodopseudomonas

The phospholipids of *R. spheroides* are mainly located in the cytoplasmic membrane; they consist of phosphatidylethanolamine (major component), phosphatidic acid, phosphatidylglycerol and phosphatidylcholine. The content of phospholipids in pigmented cells is higher than that in non-pigmented cells, and the concentration increases as organisms adapt from the non-pigmented to the pigmented state[1034a].

A lipid containing ornithine linked by amide bond has been isolated by Gorschein[875a] (see page 167); it is more abundant in the chromatophores.

2. *Methanomonadaceae*

Hydrogenomonas

Poly-β-hydroxybutyrate has been isolated from the cells of a *Hydrogenomonas* species[666] and its metabolism studied[668].

3. *Thiobacteriaceae*

Thiobacillus

T. thiooxydans excretes in the surrounding medium phospholipids (mainly phosphatidyl-glycerol)[841a] which may act as surfactants essential for metabolic attack at sulphur surfaces (sulphur being a metabolite indispensable for the respiration process of this chemilithotrophic bacteria).

4. *Pseudomonadaceae*

Pseudomonas

From the culture medium of *P. pyocyanea*, Bergström et al.[677] isolated a L-rhamnoside of D-3-hydroxydecanoic acid, which was studied on p. 170. A crystalline L-rhamnoside, m.p. 86°, was isolated by Jarvis & Johnson[678] from the culture medium of *P. aeruginosa* (see p. 170); it has haemolytic properties[646]. In the case of *P. fluorescens*, no rhamnolipid could be obtained[678].

James & Martin[178] analysed, by vapour-phase chromatography of the methyl esters, the fatty acids isolated from the culture medium of *P. aeruginosa*. About 29 acids were detected; the most abundant constituent was palmitic acid.

These acids were distributed in the following manner:
(i) *Straight-chain saturated acids:* C_6, C_7, C_{10}, C_{12}, C_{14}, C_{16}, C_{17}, and C_{18}.
(ii) *Straight-chain unsaturated acids:* C_5, C_6, C_7, C_8, C_9, C_{10}, C_{11}, C_{12}, C_{13}, and C_{14}.
(iii) *Branched-chain acids :* C_8, C_{10}, C_{12}, C_{13}, C_{14}, and C_{19};
in addition, two more branched acids, with 18 and 19 carbon atoms, were present. It is remarkable that no unsaturated acid higher than C_{14} was observed. On the other hand, it is not possible, according to this work, to conclude whether no acid higher than C_{19} exists, or if the technique which was employed did not permit its detection.

A phospholipid containing ethanolamine and a amino acid (mainly alanine) has been isolated from the lipids of *P. aeruginosa*[873a] (p. 166).

31 % Palmitoleic acid and 12 % vaccenic acid (as % of the total long-chain acids) were characterized in the lipids of a strain of *P. fluorescens*[754].

A lipopeptide containing D-3-hydroxydecanoic acid, *viscosine*, was isolated from the culture medium of *P. viscosa*[679] (see p. 189).

The whole cells of *P. salinaria* contained 4 % lipids [1008] and the cell walls 11 % (see p. 199). The cells walls of *P. denitrificans* contained 12.8 % lipids; these lipids showed a high phosphorus content (4.3 %) and a relatively low nitrogen content (1.1 %). Their hydrolysis gave ethanolamine and serine; choline was absent [833]. Newton [1012] studied the composition of the cell wall from two *P. aeruginosa* strains, one sensitive to polymyxine and the other one resistant. The lipid content was about the same (11.9 and 10.7 %, respectively), but the phosphorus content was higher in the lipids of the sensitive strain than in the lipids of the resistant one.

Poly-β-hydroxybutyrate (p. 107) has been isolated from *P. solanacerum, P. antimycetica,* from a particular group of *Pseudomonas* [653, 1035], from *P. pseudomallei* [1036] and *P. saccharo-phila* [1037].

Bongkrekic acid, $C_{29}H_{40}O_7$, has been isolated from *P. cocovenenans* [1038]. This acid $[\alpha]_D + 105°$ (ethanol), λ_{max} 238 and 267 mμ (ε = 41,000 and 45,000; ethanol), is unstable in acid medium. Partial formula [365] was suggested for its hydrogenation product, hydro-bongkrekic acid [1038].

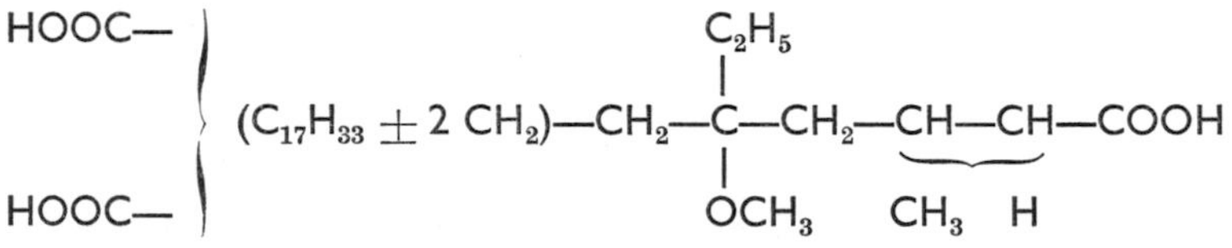

$$HOOC—$$
$$C_2H_5$$
$$\left.\begin{array}{c} HOOC— \\ \\ HOOC— \end{array}\right\} (C_{17}H_{33} \pm 2\ CH_2)—CH_2—\underset{\underset{OCH_3}{|}}{C}—CH_2—\underset{\underset{CH_3}{|}}{CH}—\underset{\underset{H}{|}}{CH}—COOH \qquad [365]$$

A toxic low molecular weight lipopolysaccharide has been isolated from the culture medium of *P. pseudomallei* [969a].

Halobacterium

The lipids of the red-pigmented extreme halophile *Halobacterium cutirubrum* were studied by Sehgal *et al.* [844]. Only 2 % total free lipids were isolated, of which 93 % were phospholipids. Most of the phosphatide fraction consist of a peculiar compound containing long-chain ether groupings. The structure of this phosphatide was studied by Faure *et al.* [845] and by Kates *et al.* [846a] (see p. 161). The long-chain alcohol, linked by an ether bond to the glycerophosphate residue, has been identified as dihydrophytol by examination of its NMR spectrum and by its oxidation to phytanic acid [846]. Kates *et al.* [846] have observed "the complete absence of normal straight-chain hydrocarbon groups. ... This halophile thus appears to lack the malonyl-CoA system for the synthesis of straight-chain hydrocarbon groups".

5. Spirillaceae

Vibrio

The lipids of *V. cholerae* constitute 9—10 % of the dry weight of the bacilli; 83—90 % of these lipids is soluble in acetone and consists almost entirely of free fatty acids. Hydrolysis of the phosphatides (about 6 % of the total lipids) gives ethanolamine, ornithine, and two unidentified substances reacting with ninhydrin. Neither choline nor inositol was detected in the hydrolysis products. A "wax" fraction (about 6 % of the total lipids) devoid of nitrogen, phosphorus, and carbohydrate, gave 48 % fatty acids after prolonged saponification. No study of the fatty acids was made [835].

V. costicolus contains 9.0 % lipids [1008]; on hydrolysis, the cell wall gave 10—20 % lipids, depending on the procedure utilized for their preparation. The cell walls of *V. metchnikovii* contain 11 % lipids [1010].

Saponification of the lipids of *V. comma* gives glycerol, glucose, arabinose, inositol and an unidentified heptose as hydrosoluble components. Straight-chain fatty acids have been characterized by paper chromatography; an unidentified acid has been detected [1010 a].

A toxic lipopolysaccharide, which is pyrogenic and antigenic, was isolated from *V. foetus* [984] by extraction of the bacilli with phenol according to the technique of Westphal & Lüderitz (see p. 195).

Spirillum

Several species of *Spirillum* synthesize important quantities of poly-β-hydroxybutyrate. After 38 hours of culture, *S. repens* contains 34 % poly-β-hydroxybutyrate; after 110 hours this falls to 7.5 % [1035]. The granules, observed by Lewis [1039] in the cells of *S. volutans*, probably consists of this polymer.

6. *Chlamydobacteriaceae*

Sphaerotilus

Sphaerotilus natans contains sudanophilic granules, which were isolated by Rouf & Stokes [660] and identified as poly-β-hydroxybutyrate. Depending on the composition of the culture medium, 11—22.5 % of poly-β-hydroxybutyrate was found. Mulder *et al.* [659] obtained similar results; a poly-β-hydroxybutyrate content of 30 % of the dry cell weight was observed.

Romano & Peloquin [1041] have studied the composition of the "sheath" that surrounds the cell; it contains 2.8 % free lipids and 2.4 % bound lipids. No details about the nature of these lipid fractions were given. It must be noted that muramic acid was not found in the sheath.

7. *Azotobacteraceae*

Azotobacter

Azotobacter chroococcum, grown for 18 to 21 days on a synthetic medium, contains 4.3 % fats soluble in acetone. From the unsaponifiable fraction of these fats, Sifferd & Anderson [808] isolated by precipitation with digitonin, a sterol, m.p. 156—158° $[\alpha]_D$ —16° (see p. 158). Nevertheless, K, Bloch (personal communication) was not able to find any sterol in the lipids of another batch of *A. chroococcum*.

On the other hand, Stapp [1040] isolated 9.4 % "glycerides" and 9.5 % of a fraction insoluble in ether and soluble in chloroform; this latter fraction probably corresponds to poly-β-hydroxybutyrate, previously characterized in these bacteria by Lemoigne & Girard [652].

More recently, the presence of poly-β-hydroxybutyrate has been demonstrated in
A. vinelandii and *A. agilis* [653]. A careful study of the lipids of *A. agilis* has been carried out
by Kaneshiro & Marr [825]. The lipid extracted with ethanol and methanol-chloroform was
10.4 % of the dry weight of bacteria. Further extraction with chloroform gave 0.05 % poly-
β-hydroxybutyrate. Ether-soluble lipids were shown to be a mixture of free fatty acids,
coenzyme Q, and phosphatidylethanolamine. Hydrolysis of the phospholipids gave myristic
acid (7 %), palmitic acid (35 %), palmitoleic acid (41 %), and octadecenoic acid (17 %) [825].
From the bound lipids of *A. agilis*, three hydroxy-acids were isolated: 3-hydroxydecanoic,
3-hydroxydodecanoic, and 2-hydroxydodecanoic acids [682] (see p. 112).

8. Rhizobiaceae

Rhizobium

Hopkins & Peterson [1042] isolated from *Rhizobium meliloti* 10—21.5 % of a waxy substance,
m.p. 172—173°, soluble in chloroform; the properties of this substance closely resemble those
of poly-β-hydroxybutyrate. Haywarth *et al.* [1035] has demonstrated the presence of poly-β-
hydroxybutyrate in cultures of various strains of *Rhizobium*, which may or may not fix
nitrogen. Poly-β-hydroxybutyrate has also been isolated from *R. trifolii* by Vincent *et al.* [657].
The principal lipid component of the bacilli of the genus *Rhizobium* is, therefore, poly-β-
hydroxybutyrate.

Agrobacterium

Crown galls on certain plants are induced by the bacterium *Agrobacterium tumefaciens*
(Phytomonas tumefaciens). The cellular modification produced is of a cancerous nature
and is transmissible by grafting, without re-intervention of the bacterium (see ref. 1043).

In 1935, Boivin *et al.* [1044], applying to *A. tumefaciens* their technique of isolating antigenic
lipopolysaccharides from gram-negative bacteria, obtained water-soluble a lipopolysaccharide complex containing 18 % fatty acids (and 40.8 % reducing sugars), able to induce
tumour formation in plants.

A little later, Chargaff & Levine [1045, 1046] undertook the systematic study of the lipids
of a strain of *A. tumefaciens* (strain 6N1S[6]) grown on broth in the dark for 14 days. The
results obtained are given in Table 45. Sterols, probably derived from the culture medium,
were isolated from the fats.

Geiger & Anderson [33] studied the lipids of two samples of *A. tumefaciens* grown on a
synthetic medium containing either glycerol or sucrose. The lipid contents observed are
shown in Table 45. The chloroform extracts contain a mixture of fats, phospholipids, and
an ether-insoluble substance. Hofmann & Tausig [591] obtained 7.5 % total free lipids from
A. tumefaciens grown on a sucrose medium. On saponification, these lipids gave 73.5 %
fatty acids and 11 % unsaponifiable fraction.

The fat (from bacilli grown on a sucrose medium) contained about 70 % free fatty acids.
The total fatty acids (obtained after saponification of the crude fat) contained a little palmitic
acid and a large proportion of unsaturated acids, which, after hydrogenation, gave chiefly,
stearic acid and a little palmitic acid. Liquid saturated acids were also present, in particular a

TABLE 45. THE LIPID FRACTIONS ISOLATED FROM A. TUMEFACIENS
(% of the dry bacilli)

	Bacilli grown on a broth medium	Bacilli grown on synthetic media	
		With glycerol	With sucrose
Fat.	5.7 Yellow viscous oil	0.9	2.2
Phosphatides	1.6 Waxy solid m.p. . . . 123° N 2.3 % P 3.2 %	0.9	3.9
Waxes extracted by chloroform	0.8		
Fraction insoluble in ether.		0.18	0.01
Total free lipids	8.1	2.0	6.4
Bound lipids			1.0 Brown oil
References	1046	33	33

$C_{20}H_{40}O_2$ acid. An unsaponifiable substance, $C_{12}H_{10}O$, m.p. 28°, identified as diphenyl ether, could not be found again during a study of the lipids from bacilli cultivated under slightly different conditions. The sugar-free water-soluble components consisted of a viscous liquid, giving a positive test for acrolein, but from which no crystalline tribenzoate could be prepared [1047].

On saponification, the phosphatides gave 61.2 % free fatty acids, glycerophosphoric acid, choline (isolated in the form of the chloroplatinate), and ethanolamine (characterized as its picrolonate). The phosphatides, therefore consist of a mixture of lecithins and cephalins [1047]. The presence of both phosphatidylethanolamine and phosphatidylcholine was recently confirmed by Kaneshiro & Marr [825] and the biosynthesis of phosphatidylcholine by means of a phosphatidylethanolamine N-methyl transferase, studied by the same authors [1038a]. An unidentified amino-acid has also been observed by Velick [826]. The phospholipid fraction contained a "liquid saturated acid", phytomonic acid, first studied by Velick [826, 310], and later identified with lactobacillic acid by Hofmann & Tausig [591] (see p. 94). The composition of the fatty acid mixture obtained by saponification of the phospholipid fraction was 1 % myristic, 15 % palmitic, 1 % hexadecenoic, 6 % methylene-hexadecanoic, 30 % octadecenoic and 47 % lactobacillic acids [825].

9. *Achromobacteraceae*

Alcaligenes

Saito & Akashi [823] isolated the lipids extractable by a mixture of alcohol and ether (1 : 1) from *Alcaligenes faecalis* grown on ordinary broth for 5 days. Lipids (2.5 %) were obtained in the form of a sticky, dark brown mass. These lipids were separated into an acetone-soluble fraction (47 %) and an acetone-insoluble fraction (39 %). Only the latter fraction has been studied to date by these authors. It was obtained as a light brown solid which, after elimination of an impurity insoluble in light petroleum, contained 3.75 % P and 1.5 % N. Electrophoresis on paper separated phosphatidic acids, and glycero-phosphatides (5.64 % P, 2.18 % N.). Hydrolysis of these latter gave fatty acids, glycerophosphoric acid, amino-acids (lysine, glutamic acid, serine, glycine), ethanolamine, and an unidentified nitrogen base; choline was absent. Partial alkaline hydrolysis of the purified glycerophosphatides gave ethanolamine-containing polypeptides [823]. Lauric, myristic, and palmitic acids, and C_{16} and C_{18} unsaturated acids have been characterized in the saponification products of the whole lipids [1049].

Alcaligenic acid, isolated from *Alcaligenes faecalis*, does not seem to contain lipids [1048] : it is essentially composed of nucleic acids, sugars, and a polypeptide fraction.

Achromobacter.

Information about the lipid composition of *Achromobacter* species appears to be limited to the results obtained by Surdy & Hartsell [1050] who found 12.6 % lipids in *A. hartlebii*, 11.4 % in *A. parvulus*, and 15.6 % in *A. guttatus*. The temperature of growth, 4° or 25°, had no influence on the lipid content of *A. guttatus* or on the iodine number, 236 and 231, respectively.

10. *Enterobacteriaceae*

Escherichia

Eckstein & Soule [1051] grew *E. coli* on a synthetic medium containing either alanine or cystine as source of nitrogen. The lipid content reached 7.8 % of the dry weight of the bacilli in the first case and only 3.6 % in the second.

A more extensive study of two species of *Escherichia* and of a species intermediate between *Escherichia* and *Aerobacter* was made by Williams *et al.* [800]. Four strains of *E. coli*, three strains of *E. communior*, and the *Escherichia-Aerobacter* strain were grown for 24 hours on a solid semi-synthetic medium. The bacteria harvested were lyophilized, ground, and extracted by Kumagawa's technique. The amounts of lipids obtained and their properties are summarized in Table 46. The phosphatide content is remarkably high, which is in accord with the results of Taylor [1052]. More recently, Vaczi & Incze [1053] observed very different lipid contents (see Table 45), probably because of different conditions of growth. Jones *et al.* [1054] found in the case of *E. coli* 45.3—48.0 μmole lipid phosphorus per gram dry bacilli (47.7 in the case of *Aerobacter aerogenes* and 67.0—68.0 in the case of *A. cloacae*). Williams *et al.* [800] concluded from their studies that sterols were absent and Schubert *et al.* [809 a] isolated a

TABLE 46. THE COMPOSITION OF THE LIPIDS FROM SEVERAL ESCHERICHIA SPECIES

	E. coli			Strain 0 : 111		E. communior			E. aerobacter
	214	214 PA-5	225	Sensitive**	Resistant**	234	239-I	248-I	
Total free lipids	7.36	7.91	4.45	3.23	4.43	6.88	4.66	6.44	5.44
Total fatty acids. . . .	4.21	4.27	2.51			4.60	2.62	4.41	3.43
Iodine number . . .	73	48	49			62	82	42	76
Fatty acids from neutral fats	1.57	0.43	0.00			1.68	0.00	1.14	0.17
Unsaponifiable	1.43	1.82	0.38			0.72	0.31	0.41	0.40
Phosphatides	4.36	5.66	4.07	1.05	2.35	4.48	4.35	4.89	4.87
Phosphorus*	4.40	2.77	3.41	2.10	3.81	3.11	4.66	3.51	3.45
Nitrogen*	0.0	1.84	2.89	2.06	3.26	2.03	1.28	1.74	2.33
Fatty acids	2.64	3.94	2.72			2.90	3.18	3.27	3.26
Phosphatidylethanolamine.				0.08	0.90				
References	800			1053		800			800

* Expressed as percentage of the phosphatides; all the other percentages are expressed relative to the dry weight of the bacilli.
** Strains that are sensitive or resistant to chloramphenicol.

mixture of sterols corresponding to 0.000 3 % of the dry cells (concerning the problem of sterols in E. coli, see p. 158). On the other hand, no relation between the composition of the lipids and the nature of the strain is evident from these studies.

The fatty acids from the saponification of the crude lipids of an E. coli strain have been examined by gas chromatography of the methyl esters [549] : the main constituent is palmitic acid, which was isolated. Satured straight-chain acids with C_{12}, C_{14}, and C_{18} are also present, as well as a $C_{17}H_{32}O_2$ acid containing a cyclopropane ring, 9 : 10-methylene-hexadecanoic acid (see p. 85). According to the conditions of growth, variations in the composition of the fatty acid mixture may be observed [7, 8b, 8c, 181, 550, 551] (see p. 19). Small amounts of a C_{19} cyclopropane fatty acid and 3-hydroxymyristic acid were also found. The unsaturated acids of E. coli B were identified as palmitoleic acid (7 % of the total fatty acids) and vaccenic acid (19 %) [754]. The influence of biotin-deficiency on the fatty acid composition has been studied [1048a,b]; 7,8-hexadecenoic and 7,8-octadecenoic acids were detected in the lipids of a biotin-requiring mutant of E. coli [1048a].

The phospholipid fraction consists mainly of phosphatidylethanolamine [825]. Small amounts of phosphatidylserine and phosphatidylglycerol were also observed: "pulse labelling" shows a high turnover rate of the last fraction in rapidly growing cultures [1055]. Phosphatidylserine and phosphatidylglycerol are synthesized by reaction of diglyceride cytidyl-diphosphate with L-serine or L-α-glycerophosphate respectively; phosphatidyl-ethanolamine arises from phosphatidylserine by decarboxylation [1055a]. Amino-acids are intimately associated with the phospholipid components of the spheroplast membrane fraction of *E. coli* strain 113/3 [879]. It was observed that the uptake of β-galactosides by *E. coli* cells is accompanied by an increase of the synthesis of glycerophospholipids; however, it may only reflect the relaxation of intracellular control mechanisms [1055a].

Preparations of water-soluble lipopolysaccharides were studied by Westphal *et al.* [973], Ikawa *et al.* [531, 683], and Burton[534] (see also ref. 882a). Hydrolysis of the phospholipid A isolated from these lipopolysaccharides gave lauric, myristic, palmitic, and 3(D)-hydroxytetradecanoic acids [683]. The composition of the phopholipid B isolated from a similar toxic lipopolysaccharide was studied by Kurokawa *et al.* [836] : of two fractions obtained, the ethanol-soluble one contained 7.0 % ethanolamine and 1.5 % serine and the ethanol-insoluble one, 2.0 % ethanolamine and 4.6 % serine; choline was absent. Some sugar-containing fractions were also prepared. A lipopolysaccharide was isolated from the culture medium of a strain of *E. coli* grown under lysine-limiting conditions; its chemical composition was different from that of the intracellular lipopolysaccharide [1057a].

The lipid content of *E. coli* strains B and Br has been studied as a function of the culture conditions [1052, 1057] : in the case of strain B, 9.1 % lipids were obtained by using a synthetic medium and 7.75 % with a broth medium [1052]. An increase in the lipid content of an *E. coli* strain by addition of sodium chloride to the culture medium has been observed [1058].

The composition of the cell walls of *E. coli* has been studied by Salton [1000] and by Smithies *et al.* [1008] (see Table 43, p. 199), and the fatty acid composition of the cytoplasmic membranes of *E. coli* B and of *E. alkalescens*, by Cho and Salton [1008a].

Aerobacter

Fats (15 %) containing 93 % glycerides with a high content of palmitic acid have been isolated from *A. cloacae* [1059]. The composition of the fatty acid mixture has been studied by Abel *et al.* [181].

O'Leary [592] has analysed by vapour phase chromatography the fatty acid mixture produced by a methionine auxotroph of *A. aerogenes* : the results obtained are given in Table 47.

Klebsiella

The fatty acid mixture isolated from a strain of *Klebsiella aerogenes (K. pneumoniae)* has been analysed by vapour phase chromatography : the elution pattern is similar to that given by the fatty acid mixture from *Escherichia* or *Aerobacter* species (which also belong to the family of Enterobacteriaceae) [181]. In particular, fatty acids with 17 and 19 carbon atoms were detected : they are very probably cyclopropane fatty acids.

Serratia

Chemical studies on *Serratia marcescens (Bacillus prodigiosus)* have for long been focussed mainly on its pigment prodigiosine.

Recently, the chemical composition of its lipids has been investigated; Kates & Adams [840a]

TABLE 47. THE COMPOSITION OF THE FATTY ACID MIXTURES ISOLATED FROM
AEROBACTER AEROGENES AND SERRATIA MARCESCENS
(% of the total fatty acids)

Number of carbon atoms	Aerobacter aerogenes	Serratia marcescens	
		Free lipids	Bound lipids
Saturated acids			
10	1.1	+	+
12	3.6	+	+
14	10.5	6.0	6.0
16	37.9	43.8	46.0
18	1.4	0.5	0.8
20	0.4		
Cyclopropane acids			
17	24.7*	32.4*	29.8*
19	5.7	3.1**	4.3**
Unsaturated acids			
16	4.1	2.3*	1.6*
18	8.9	10.5**	7.5**
Hydroxy acids			
3-Hydroxydecanoic acid . .		0.7	1.8
3-Hydroxydodecanoic acid		+	0.2
3-Hydroxydodec-5-cnoic acid		+	0.4
References	592	596	596

* Position 9,10.
** Position 11,12.

found 7—8 % lipids in a pigmented and an unpigmented strain of *S. marcescens*. The lipids
of pigmented cells had 35 % phosphatides and those of unpigmented cells 44 %. In both
types of cells the phosphatides were a mixture of phosphatidylethanolamine, lysophosphatidylethanolamine, phosphatidylserine, and polyglycerol phosphatide, in about the same
proportions.

The composition of the fatty acid mixture obtained from the free lipids and from the
bound lipids has been very carefully studied by Bishop & Still [8, 596, 681]. Palmitic acid and
9 :10-methylene-hexadecanoic acid accounted for about 75 % of the total fatty acids (see
Table 47). Three hydroxy acids were characterized : 3-hydroxydecanoic, 3-hydroxydode-
canoic, and 3-hydroxydodec-5-enoic acids [681]. The influence of temperature on fatty acid

composition of psychrophilic and mesophilic *Serratia* species was studied by Kates and Hagen [8a]: the psychrophilic species has lost its ability to synthesize cyclopropane acids.

From an unidentified strain of *Serratia*, Cartwright [680, 944] isolated *serratamic acid*, amide of 3(D)-hydroxydecanoic acid and L-serine (see p. 188), which may well occur in the bacterial cell as serratamolide, the depsipeptide formed from two molecules of serratamic acid [945] (see p. 189). The amide previously found by Castro *et al.* [1060] is in fact serratamolide.

From the filtrate of a culture of *Serratia marcescens*, Shear *et al.* [967, 1061] obtained a lipopolysaccharide capable of producing haemorrhages in tumours. The properties of this lipopolysaccharide, which contains 16 % lipids, have been noted in Table 42 (p. 196); its chemical structure has been studied by Nowotny [985]. From the work of Srivastava *et al.* [1062], the ability to cause regression of well-established tumours in mice appears to be linked with polysaccharide fractions.

Proteus

Strain P-18 of *Proteus morganii* contains 4—8 % lipids, and the L form derived from this strain 15—25 % lipids of which 50—70 % is phospholipids [1063, 1064].

Krembel *et al.* [812] have isolated the lipid fractions from L forms grown on a synthetic medium: they found 14 % fat, 1.9 % phospholipids, 2.9 % wax A, and 6.2 % chloroform-extractable waxes (with 25 % total free lipids); but no sterol was detected. Palmitoleic and oleic acids were characterized, and the presence of a C_{17} cyclopropane fatty acid was demonstrated [594, 1065]. The phospholipid fraction mainly contains phosphatidylethanolamine and polyglycerol-phosphatides [1065a].

Fatty acids with 11, 12, 14, 15, 16, 17, 18, 19 and 20 carbon atoms were found by vapour phase chromatography in the lipids of *Proteus vulgaris:* the main component was palmitic acid [181].

Some Proteus species possess antigens capable of giving cross reactions with the antibodies of sera from animals infected with *Rickettsia* (Weil-Felix reaction). Bendich & Chargaff [1066] isolated from Proteus OX-19, grown on a semi-synthetic medium for 24—36 hours at 37°, two antigenic fractions with distinctly different properties. Fraction I, of high molecular weight, contains 2.8 % lipids and reacts with the sera of animals infected with *Rickettsia prowaczki* or with Proteus; fraction II, of lower molecular weight, contains 11.1 % lipids and reacts only with the sera of animals which have received Proteus. The two fractions are phosphorus-containing lipopolysaccharidoproteins. The bacillary organism contains 3 to 5 times as much lipopolysaccharide as the L form, and the composition of the lipopolysaccharides isolated in each case is similar [1066a].

Salmonella

Lipids of several species of *Salmonella* have been systematically analysed by Čmelik [32, 43, 155, 790, 791, 818, 834]. Table 48 shows the content of various lipid fractions in the strains studied.

The fats are a mixture of free fatty acids and glycerides. The presence of glycerides was deduced from positive specific colour reactions obtained with the water-soluble material

TABLE 48. THE LIPIDS OF VARIOUS SPECIES OF SALMONELLA
(% of the dry weight of the bacilli)

	S. ballerup	S. gallinarum	S. paratyphi B		S. paratyphi C**	S. typhosa, strain				S. typhimurium
			Sensitive*	Resistant*		Vi Bhatnagar	Z-47	0-901	Vi Ty2	
Virulence	±	+			++	+++ +++	+++ +++			
1) Lipids soluble in acetone	1.01	9.48			2.85	1.29	5.01	3.96	2.48	0.8
Free fatty acids							3.37			
Sodium palmitate							0.93			
Unsaponifiable					0.2	0.09				
2) Phosphatides	1.07	0.57	1.4	2.1	0.81	0.21	0.14	2.79	2.68	4.8
% Fraction soluble in	Boiling acetone				Methanol			Methanol		
% Phosphorus***	0.17				0.5			1.4		
% Nitrogen***	0.13				3.91			3.40		
Insoluble fraction or whole phosphatides	2.47				2.23			2.68		
% Phosphorus ***	0.90				0.3	2.39	4.14	1.3		
% Nitrogen ***	3.87				4.32	4.43	2.5			
3) Waxy fractions	2.24				0.8				0.60	1.6
Total free lipids	2.08	10.05	4.42	5.45	3.9	1.50	5.24	6.75	6.11	5.6
Bound lipids							0.38			
References	155	818	1053		791	790, 818	834	43	1069	545

* To chloramphenicol.
** Hirschfeld strain.
*** As % of the lipid fraction.

after saponification [155, 790, 791]. Sugars could not be found. The unsaponifiable fraction did not contain sterols; on the other hand, friedelin a $C_{30}H_{50}O$ pentacyclic triterpene ketone, was isolated by chromatography of the unsaponifiable part of the fats from *S. typhosa*[790], *S. ballerup*[155], and *S.paratyphi* C[791]. With the strain Z-47 of *S. typhosa*, free sodium palmitate was characterized. The mixture of acids obtained on saponification of the fats was fractionated by the lead salt method. The characterization of the acids from each fraction was often insufficiently complete: remarkably enough, stearic acid was found to be the main component of the saturated acids of *S. typhosa* (strain Vi of Bhatnagar)[790] and of *S. ballerup*[155]. Palmitic acid was found in *S. paratyphi* C[791] and strain Z-47 of *S. typhosa*[834]. The principal unsaturated acid seemed to be oleic acid[155, 790, 791], except in the case of strain Z-47 of *S. typhosa*, where hydrogenation gave palmitic acid[834]. In the latter strain, a hydroxy acid, which might be an hydroxytetradecanoic acid, was observed.

The phosphatide content is generally low and, according to Čmelik[818], the greater the virulence of a strain, the lower its phosphatide content (see Table 48). The phosphatides of *S. ballerup* and *S. paratyphi* C do not contain sugar, inositol, choline, or ethanolamine. Glycerol was identified in the products of saponification, while paper chromatography of acid hydrolysates indicated the presence of 6 and 3 amino-acids, respectively, and an unidentified ninhydrin-positive substance[155, 791]. The phosphatide of *S. typhosa* strain Z-47 contained 8 amino-acids and ethanolamine[834].

The phosphatide of strain 0.901 of *S. typhosa*[154] was studied in greater detail; it was separated into 52% of a methanol-soluble fraction and 48% of a methanol-insoluble fraction. The methanol-soluble fraction contained 6—8 amino-acids and ethanolamine. The fraction insoluble in methanol was separated into:

(a) *Phosphatidic acids*, 7.6% P and 1.3% N. The nitrogen was ammoniacal in nature. Saponification gave 67% fatty acids and a mixture of glycerophosphoric and hexosephosphoric acids. Hydrolysis of these latter gave galactose and an unidentified sugar (R_f 0.47 in the system butanol/acetic acid/water (4:1:5).

(b) *Phosphatidylethanolamines*, 4.66% P and 1.96% N, containing glycerophosphoric acid, ethanolamine, and fatty acids in the ratio 1:1:2. The fatty acids consisted of lauric, myristic, and unidentified unsaturated acids.

(c) *Acetone-soluble fractions*, 1.72% P and 1.18% N, containing glycerophosphoric acid and ethanolamine. The fatty acids seem to have a high molecular weight and branched-chain acids may be present.

In the hydrolysis products from the phospholipids of another *S. typhosa* strain, Digeon[1067] observed the presence of ethanolamine, glucosamine, several amino-acids, and a substance having the same chromatographic behaviour as "necrosamine".

From *S. typhimurium* (Aertrycke Bacillus), Akasi[1068] obtained by ether extraction 4.9% lipids, m.p. 40—45°, $[\alpha]_D$ —2.6°, free of phosphorus and nitrogen. These lipids consisted almost entirely of free fatty acids, probably arising from an enzymic degradation of more complex lipids (see below). The main components were palmitic acid, oleic acid (*p*-phenylphenacylate m.p. 61°), and palmitoleic acid (dihydroxy derivative, m.p. 129°). None of the products identified is responsible for the laevorotation of the initial material;

this could be due either to a branched-chain acid or to a component of the unsaponifiable fraction (which represents 1.3 % of the total lipids and does not give a positive sterol colour reaction).

Examination of the lipids from another batch of *S. typhimurium* gave 0.8 % neutral lipids, containing diglycerides, and 4.8 % phospholipids [545], which confirms the lipolysis of the bacilli studied by Akasi. The phospholipid fraction consisted mainly of phosphatidylethanolamine, with a small amount of polyphosphatidylglycerol [545]. The composition of the fatty acid mixture isolated from the phospholipids was studied by Gray [595]: vapour phase chromatography showed the presence of myristic acid (3.3 % of the total fatty acids), palmitic acid (35.0 %), hexadecenoic acids (18.3 %), octadecenoic acids (21.0 %), and three cyclopropane acids — 9:10-methylene-hexadecanoic (16.0 %), lactobacillic (3.0 %), and dihydrosterculic acids (0.7 %).

The fatty acids present in whole cells and in endotoxin preparations of *S. choleraesuis* were analysed by paper chromatography [1070]: the presence of C_{18} acids with 1, 2, and 3 double bonds was claimed.

An antigenic lipopolysaccharide, containing 20—30 % lipids, has been prepared from *S. typhosa* [880, 976], and a lipopolysaccharide containing 14 % of lipids from *S. paratyphi* B [983]. Other preparations of lipopolysaccharides have been obtained from *S. abortus-equi* [880], *S. schottmülleri* [1071], *S. enteritidis* [965, 965 b, 965 c], and *S. typhimurium* [958] (see p. 195).

Salton [1000] isolated 19 % lipids from the cell wall of *S. pullorum* (see Table 43, p. 199).

Shigella

The lipids of *Shigella paradysenteriae* (Flexner's bacillus) were investigated by Williams *et al.* [800]. The strain 657 bacilli were grown on a semi-synthetic solid medium for 24 h at 37° and 5.36 % total free lipids was obtained. Most of these lipids consisted of phospholipids (4.4 % of the dry bacilli), containing 3.7 % P, 1.4 % N, and 61 % fatty acids (iodine number 86). The unsaponifiable part of the total lipids accounted for 0.4 % of the dry weight of bacilli; it was devoid of sterols.

For biological purposes, Neblett [1072] isolated lipids from strain no. 2308 (Dubos collection) of *Sh. dysenteriae* (Shiga's bacillus): only the IR spectrum of the crude lipids was recorded.

The somatic O antigen of *Sh. dysenteriae* is a phospholipido-polysaccharido-protein complex, studied by Davies *et al.* [968]. A phospholipid fraction (lipid B, soluble in ether) is removed by action of a strongly polar solvent (formamide). The remaining product, still antigenic, is split: (*a*) by dilute acetic acid at 100° into polysaccharide and lipoprotein; and (*b*) by aqueous phenol at 65°, which extracts the proteins; the aqueous layer contains a lipopolysaccharide, 0.8 % P, 2.04 % N, $[\alpha]_D$ + 95° (water), hydrolysis of which with hot dilute acetic acid gives 7 % phospholipid A, insoluble in ether and soluble in chloroform.

Similar lipopolysaccharide preparations were obtained by Westphal *et al.* [973] from *Sh. dysenteriae*. From *Sh. sonnei* phase II, a lipopolysaccharide, $[\alpha]_D$ +90° (water), was prepared by Jesaitis & Goebel [980]; on hydrolysis it gave 29 % phospholipid A (1.3 % P and 1.4 % N).

11. Brucellaceae

Pasteurella

The fats of *Pasteurella pestis* contain glycerides [177]. The fatty acids obtained by saponification of the crude fats have been analysed by vapour phase chromatography: the two principal components of the mixture were palmitic acid and a C_{17} cyclopropane acid [177], identified as 9:10-methylene-hexadecanoic acid [552]. Moreover, octadecenoic acid(s) and a C_{19} branched-chain acid probably containing a propane ring were present, as well as small amounts of C_{14} and C_{15} saturated and C_{16} unsaturated acids [177].

The fatty acids obtained from whole cells of *P. tularensis* were analysed by vapour phase chromatography: a pattern quite different from that of *P. pestis* was observed. The main fatty acid components had 22 and 24 carbon atoms; no C_{17} and C_{19} fatty acids were found; but unsaturated acids with 18, 20, 22, and 24 carbon atoms were characterized [181]. A preliminary analysis of the lipids of *P. pseudotuberculosis* was published: glycerol, glycerophosphoric acid, sugars, and fatty acids were obtained on hydrolysis, and the composition of the fatty acid mixture was studied by paper chromatography [1073].

A lipopolysaccharide, 2.2 % P, 1.6 % N, $[\alpha]_D$ +48° (water), was isolated from *P. pestis* by extraction with aqueous phenol [1074]. Hydrolysis with 1 % acetic acid for 4 h at 100° gave about 50 % phospholipid A, 2.2 % P, 1.7 % N, insoluble in ether, and soluble in chloroform. No study of the lipid moiety was made.

Lipopolysaccharides have been prepared from smooth and rough strains of *P. pseudotuberculosis* [1075].

Brucella

Brucella abortus, *Br. suis*, and *Br. melitensis* show a lipid content varying between 3 and 10 % of the dry weight, according to the species and to the age of the culture (see Table 49).

TABLE 49. THE COMPOSITION OF THE LIPIDS FROM BRUCELLA SPECIES
(% of the dry weight of the bacilli)

Species	Br. abortus					Br. suis				Br. melitensis			
Strain no.	1257			266	141	1538	1585			606	655		
Age of culture (days)	5	3	30					3	30			3	30
Alcohol-ether extract . . .	5.52			5.90	5.70	5.60	5.60			5.30	5.80		
Fats.	1.51			0.90	1.00	2.40	2.80			4.80	5.60		
Phosphatides	4.01			4.80	4.60	2.70	2.10			0.40	0.20		
Ether extract		0.98	2.23					2.06	5.69			0.86	4.78
Chloroform extract	0.26	2.15	6.56	0.40	0.30	0.20	0.40	3.07	2.12	0.10	0.10	3.58	6.21
Total free lipids	5.78	3.13	8.79	6.30	6.00	5.80	6.00	5.13	7.81	5.40	5.90	4.44	10.99
Bound lipids	0.33	0.95	1.69					0.54	2.23			0.43	0.52
References	1078	1079		1077		1077		1079		1077		1079	

The contents of fats and phosphatides may vary inversely in passing from *Br. abortus* to *Br. melitensis*.

The composition of the lipids from 5-day old cultures of *Br. abortus* was investigated by Stahl [1076]. The fat, a yellow-brown semi-solid mass, contained very little free fatty acids. On saponification, it gave 73.7 % solid fatty acids and 26.2 % liquid fatty acids, an unsaponifiable fraction devoid of sterols, and a water-soluble fraction obtained as a syrup and giving a positive test for acrolein. The fats, therefore, were considered to consist essentially of *glycerides*. These results were recently confirmed for strains 45/20 and B.-19 of *Br. abortus* [828].

The phosphatide fraction, 4.13 % P, 1.75 % N, softens at 135° and melts with decomposition at 190°. After hydrolysis with 5 % sulphuric acid for 20 hours, Stahl [1076] isolated glycerophosphoric acid (as the barium salt), ethanolamine (as the picrolonate, m.p. 222—224°), an unsaponifiable fraction (2.5 %), and fatty acids (51.5 %). Attempts to isolate choline gave negative results; nevertheless, the amino-nitrogen content (0.9 %) of the phosphatide was much lower than the total nitrogen content (1.75 %). Chromatography on silicic acid of the crude phosphatide from the strains 45/20 and B.19 afforded several fractions, which were analysed by thin-layer chromatography. Phosphatidylethanolamine, phosphatidylcholine, phosphatidylserine, and phosphatidylinositol were characterized; ornithine was found in one of the first fractions; and the presence of arabinose and glucose was also observed [828]. By a careful fractionation of the phospholipids of *Br. abortus*, more than 30 fractions were obtained [827].

Vapour phase chromatography of the fatty acid esters isolated either from the cell wall of *Br. abortus* or from the whole cell lipids of *Br. abortus* showed the presence of palmitic acid and a C_{19} cyclopropane acid as the main components [593, 828]. The same C_{19} acid was also found in the lipids of *Br. melitensis* [828].

The lipids extracted by chloroform consist essentially of a semi-solid substance, whose properties are similar to those of the fat; in particular, it contains glycerol. A small amount of crystals m.p. 118—119°, insoluble in ether and alcohol, soluble in chloroform and benzene, were isolated by recrystallization. Sulphur was found to be present, but no other information about their composition was obtained [1076]. The melting point and solubility characteristics suggest that they might simply be elementary sulphur m.p. 120°.

The saponification of bound lipids gave an ether-soluble fraction consisting of 73 % fatty acids (average molecular weight 289) and 27 % unsaponifiable matter; the water-soluble part gave a positive test for acrolein [1076].

Alimova *et al.* [1080], working with 30-day old cultures, obtained different results. The various lipid fractions obtained from *Br. abortus*, *Br. suis*, and *Br. melitensis* had a high acid number, which indicates a high content of *free fatty acids*. Furthermore, all the fractions studied contained sugars — especially pentoses. The lipids of *Br. suis* were studied more thoroughly: the lipids extracted by a mixture of benzene and ether gave, after saponification, a water-soluble fraction which, besides glycerol, contained glucose and arabinose [1081]. Recently, Gubarev *et al.* [1082] showed the presence in all the lipid fractions of a polysaccharide, which on hydrolysis gave a mixture of hexoses (glucose or galactose) and arabinose; a polypeptide (or a protein) was presumed also to be present in each fraction. The analysis of the fatty acid mixture, by reversed-phase paper chromatography, led to the identification of stearic and oleic acids, together with a C_{10} or C_{12} unsaturated acid. Lipoprotein fractions were observed [1083]; such fractions were found to occur in the cell wall of *Br. abortus* or *Br. melitensis* [828].

Dubrovskaya *et al.* [1084] found a strongly increased lipid content in *Brucella* infected with a phage; the excess of lipid was principally located in the neutral fats.

A great deal of work has been devoted to the lipopolysaccharide antigens of the three species of *Brucella* already mentioned. In 1937, Pennell & Huddleston [1085] isolated from these lipopolysaccharides 6—9 % of an acetone-soluble yellow oil and 5—9 % fatty acids. Damboviceanu *et al.* [1086] isolated by Boivin's technique [958, 959], 2.5—5.5 % of lipopolysaccharide antigens containing 8—20 % of fatty acids. The most detailed chemical study of these constituents was made by Miles & Pirie [963, 970, 1087] in the case of the antigens of *Br. melitensis*. Treatment of the antigen by a mixture of alcohol and ether containing 0.5 % hydrochloric acid removes phospholipid B, which constitutes about 20 % of the antigen. This phospholipid, 0.2—0.25 % P, is in fact a mixture of a fat soluble in acetone and at least two phospholipids. Subsequent treatment of the antigen with 0.1N hydrochloric acid at 100° liberates phospholipid A, 1.5 % P, 4.5 % N, insoluble in organic solvents, which constitutes 20—26 % of the dry weight of the antigen. Paterson *et al.* [1088] and Urbaschek [1089] have isolated similar, but not identical, lipopolysaccharide antigens from *Br. abortus* (see also [1090 *a*]).

A detailed review on the chemistry of the *Brucella* lipids was published by Pennell [788] in 1950, and a short one, limited to the toxic factors, by Roux [1090] in 1960.

Bordetella

Data in the literature are limited to a preliminary study of the chemical composition of *B. pertussis*, the causative agent of whooping cough. Utilizing Akasi's method of extraction [1091], Ida & Otani [1092] isolated 24 % free lipids, comprising 21.7 % fats and 2.37 % phosphatides. No information about the composition of these lipids was given.

A lipopolysaccharide, accounting for 20.4 % of the dry weight of the cell wall, has been isolated by Sutherland [1093]; it has no protective activity.

A review on the cellular components of *B. pertussis* has been published in Japanese [1094].

Actinobacillus

Actinobacillus mallei (Malleomyces mallei) is responsible for the disease of horses called glanders. The lipids of this bacillus were studied by Umezu [789].

The acetone-soluble fat represents 5.1—7.6 % of the dry weight of these bacilli. It is principally composed of free fatty acids, accompanied by a small proportion of glycerides (the glycerol was identified in the water-soluble part of the saponified material).

The phosphatide fraction was obtained as an amorphous, brownish substance m.p. 152—153°, $[\alpha]_D$ +11.1°; it contained 4.02 % P and 1.94 % N. The water-soluble part, obtained after saponification, gave on precipitation with basic lead acetate, a non-reducing syrup which contained sugars.

Chloroform-extracted waxes (0.54 % of the dry bacilli) were purified by precipitation from their chloroform solution with methanol; the precipitate consisted of a white amorphous solid, m.p. 169—172°, $[\alpha]_D$ —1.2°. According to Umezu[789], hydrolysis gave 49.8 % fatty acids and 12.2 % unsaponifiable fraction; by difference, the water-soluble fraction should therefore be 38 %. No substance was identified.

Morris & Roberts[656] remarked that the substance m.p. 169—172°, insoluble in ether and soluble in chloroform, might be poly-β-hydroxybutyrate (see p. 107). Kepes & Peaud-Lenoel[548] gave m. p. 179° for the most polymerised samples and the elementary composition published by Umezu (C 55.40—55.33 %, H 7.25—7.16 %) is in good accord with that required by the formula $(C_4H_6O_2)_n$ (C 55.80 % H 7.02 %).

Asselineau (unpublished results) obtained a chloroform extract from the bacillary residues of the manufacture of malleine. The principal constituent of this fraction was a colourless solid, m.p. 160—162°, $[\alpha]_D$ —2.2°; its IR spectrum was similar to that published by Blackwood & Epp[648] for poly-β-hydroxybutyrate and its elementary composition (C 55.6 %, H 7.22 %) was in agreement with that of this substance. Pyrolysis at 220—240° gave crotonic acid (m.p. 69—70°). These results showed that it was indeed poly-β-hydroxybutyric acid.

12. Bacteroidaceae

Bacteroides

The lipids of the ruminal bacterium *Bacteroides succinogenes* were studied by Wegner & Foster[762]. The phospholipids contain mainly phosphatidylethanolamine; also detected was a small amount of plasmologens hydrolysable by acetic acid for 18 hrs. at 38°.

B. succinogenes requires both a branched-chain volatile fatty acid (e.g. isobutyric acid) and a straight-chain acid (e.g. valeric acid) for growth. Wegner & Foster[762] have shown that isobutyric acid is incorporated primarily into iso-C_{14} and -C_{16} acids, and valeric acid into n-C_{13} and n-C_{15} acids. These acids are also used for the synthesis of aldehydes contained in the plasmalogen fraction.

A diglyceride galactofuranoside was isolated from a bacteria "provisionally designated *Bacteroides symbiosus*"[920 c] (page 181).

Streptobacillus

Information about the lipids of *Streptobacillus* species seems to be limited to the work of Smith & Rothblat[1095]: *S. moniliformis* contains 2.6 % lipids relative to the dry wetight of the bacilli. The unsaponifiable fraction represents 80 % of the crude free lipids; no serol has been detected. Suzuki[1095a] isolated from *S. moniliformis* a lipid antigen which reacts with syphilitic sera.

13. Micrococcaceae

Micrococcus

Several papers have been devoted to the lipids of *Micrococcus lysodeikticus;* however, this bacterial "species" seems to be only a variety of *Sarcina flava*[1096] and it will be discussed under the genus *Sarcina*. *M. tetragenus* has recently been classified as *Gaffkya tetragena*[5] and will be found under the genus *Gaffkya*.

The halophilic bacterium *M. halodenitrificans* contains refractive granules, produced during the exponential phase of growth. These inclusions are pure poly-β-hydroxybutyrate. The amount can vary from 1 % (of the dry weight of the bacilli) in a nitrogenous medium under vigorous aeration to 28 % with less vigorous aeration and to 40—60 % when glycerol, pyruvate, or acetate is added to the medium [655]. The metabolism of poly-β-hydroxybutyrate in *M. halodenitrificans* has been studied [667] (see p. 107).

Cells of *M. halodenitrificans* grown under different conditions in 1.0M sodium chloride contain about 11 % total free lipids. Half the lipids are phosphatides. The presence of phosphatidylethanolamine and phosphatidylglycerol was demonstrated; but no lecithin was detected. The amount of unsaponifiable fraction depends on the amount of sodium chloride in the medium. The main components of the fatty acid mixture were hexadecanoic, hexadecenoic, and octadecenoic acids; small amounts of branched-chain fatty acids with 13 and 17 carbon atoms were observed [832]. The major components of the fatty acid mixture isolated from *M. cryophilus* are hexadecanoic, hexadecenoic and octadecenoic acids [1096 a].

In the case of the lipids from *Micrococcus urae*, the main components of the fatty acid mixture are hexadecanoic acid and fatty acids with 19 and 20 carbon atoms. It is remarkable that the only unsaturated detected by vapour phase chromatography is a C_{15} monoene acid [181]; however, more data are required to give support to this tentative identification.

Staphylococcus

Staphylococcus aureus (Duncan, NCTC 9752) contains 0.4 % neutral lipids and 2.1 % phospholipids [545]. The phospholipids, 2.9 % P, 2.4 % N, were fractionated by chromatography on silicic acid and the main components identified as phosphatidylglycerol and diphosphatidylglycerol [545, 919]. The nitrogen found in the crude phosphatide is due to amino-acids linked to phosphatidylglycerol by ester bonds [871, 1097a].

The neutral lipids contain glucose and consist of diglyceride diglucoside [919, 919a].

The fatty acid composition of the lipids, in percentages of the total fatty acids, is: 45 % anteiso C_{15}, 13 % iso C_{15}, 12 % anteiso + iso C_{17}, 9 % palmitic acid, 9 % stearic acid and 3 % eicosanoic acid [545].

Vaczi & Farkas [1097] found 5.3 % lipid in a strain of *S. aureus* resistant to antibiotics, higher than the 3.6 % lipid in the sensitive strain; the increase in the lipids was mainly associated with the phospholipid fractions.

Costin-Podhorsky [1098] found an average lipid content of 6.2 % in a pathogenic strain of *Staphylococcus* and of 6.4 % in a non-pathogenic strain.

From the cell walls of *S. aureus* 0.8 % [833] or 4.4 % lipids [1009] was obtained, depending on the technique of isolation. "Lipid particles", which seem to play a rôle in the mechanism of action of penicillin, were described by Cooper [1099]; these particles are of lipoprotein nature and contain about 20 % lipids.

Several papers have been devoted to the carotenoid pigments of *S. aureus* and

S. citreus[1100-1104]. It was observed that the extractability of lipids from cells of *S. epidermidis* increased when the cells became gram negative through aging [1097 b].

Gaffkya

Analysis of the fatty acid mixture isolated from the crude lipids of *Gaffkya tetragena* by vapour phase chromatography has shown that the main components are a C_{20} saturated acid and a C_{15} unsaturated acid[181]; unsaturated acids with 17 and 19 carbon atoms were also detected, but one may wonder whether these acids were not actually branched-chain acids. In an unspecified strain of *Gaffkya*, saturated normal-chain acids with 14, 15, 16, 18 and 20 carbon atoms were found; an unsaturated C_{12} acid was the only unsaturated acid detected[1096 a].

Sarcina

Akashi & Saito [546] isolated 0.9 % fats and 1 % phospholipids from an unmentioned species of *Sarcina*, Saponification of the fats gave 53 % fatty acids and 40 % water-soluble material; this latter figure, unusually high, was given without comment.

The phospholipids consisted almost entirely of ammonium and magnesium salts of phosphatidic acids (4.6 % P, 1.7 % N). However, enzymic lysis may have occurred when drying the bacilli. Hydrolysis of these phosphatidic acids gave α-glycerophosphoric acid (isolated as its barium salt) and 66 % of an acid fraction which was mainly composed of a single, branched-chain acid, sarcinic acid, $C_{15}H_{30}O_2$. From its properties, Akashi & Saito [546] suggested that sarcinic acid is (+)-12-methyltetradecanoic acid (see p. 84).

Recently, the lipids of *S. lutea* were systematically investigated by Huston & Albro [785 a], [823 a], [1104 a]. The lipids consist of 2.1 % free fatty acids, 51.0 % glycerides and 22.7 % complex lipids. The complex lipids are a mixture of polyglycerol-phosphatides (17.0 %), lipo-amino acids (15.1 %), phosphatidylglycerol (13.8 %), phosphatidylinositol (5.5 %), phosphatidic acids (4.2 %), phosphatidylserine (2.0 %), and phosphatidylcholine (1.0 %). No phosphatidyl-ethanolamine could be detected, but an unidentified fraction (15.0%) was obtained. Moreover, an hydrocarbon fraction (containing more than 37 components) was isolated.

The lipids of *Micrococcus lysodeikticus*, which is a variety of *Sarcina flava* [1096], were investigated by MacFarlane [841]. By chromatography on silicic acid, a neutral ester of man-nosyl-glycerol with anteiso-pentadecanoic acid as the main acid component was isolated. The phospholipid fraction was a mixture of phosphatidylglycerol, diphosphatidylglycerol, and phosphatidylinositol. The fatty acids from the whole lipids consisted mainly of anteiso C_{15} acid. The mannose containing lipid is a dimannoside of a diglyceride mainly built of 12-methyltetradecanoic acid [918 a] (p. 180).

The cell walls *S. lutea* contain 1.1 % lipid [1000]. In *M. lysodeikticus*, most of the cell lipids are present in the protoplast membrane, either as phosphatidylglycerol or diphospha-tidylglycerol [1024]. The composition of the fatty acid mixture isolated from the lipids of the membrane was studied by Thorne & Kodicek [544]: iso and anteiso C_{15} acids account for 71.7 % of the total fatty acids.

The carotenoid pigments have been studied [1104-1110 a].

14. Neisseriaceae

Neisseria

The lipids of *Neisseria gonorrhoeae* were studied by Stokinger *et al.* [805]. Several strains, isolated recently (1 month) or a long time ago (32 years), were grown on a semi-synthetic medium for 3, 6, or 10 days. The lipid content increased from the third to the sixth day (10 to 13 % of the dry weight), whereas the phosphorus content decreased from the third to the tenth day (0.22 to 0.13 %).

The lipids were extracted with boiling benzene and methanol. A thorough fractionation of these lipids was carried out, but except for choline, which was characterized as its reineckate, no simple constituent was unequivocally identified. The presence of ethanolamine was deduced from the amino nitrogen content of a fraction with solubility characteristics similar to those attributed to phosphatidylethanolamines. The presence of sphingomyelins was deduced only from the value of the P/N ratio and the isolation from the hydrolysis products of choline and a $C_{22}H_{42}O_3$ fatty acid for which no criteria of homogeneity were given. About 0.8 % of the dry weight of the bacilli of free fatty acids were observed. Colour reactions for sterols were negative.

The fatty acid composition of the lipids of *N. meningitidis* (groups A, B, C and D), *N. flavescens*, *N. perflava*, *N. subflava*, *N. catarrhalis*, *N. hemolysans* and *N. gonorrhoeae* was studied by gas chromatography [1110 b]: the main fatty acids are palmitic acid and either hexadecenoic or octadecenoic acid. Small amounts of β-hydroxy- dodecanoic and -tetradecanoic acids were also detected.

In 1944, Boor & Miller [1111] isolated antigenic lipopolysaccharides from *N. gonorrhoeae* and *N. meningitidis;* the lipid part consisted of phospholipids, isolated in the form of an ether-soluble yellow oil. It was not possible to isolate such lipopolysaccharides from *N. catarrhalis* and *N. sicca*.

From *N. gonorrhoeae* Tauber *et al.* [974, 975] obtained a lipopolysaccharide containing 3.84 % P, 3.30 % N, and 28.4 % lipids.

The carotenoid-like pigments of *N. flava*, *N. perflava*, *N. subflava*, *N. flavescens*, *N. sicca*, and *N. catarrhalis* have been studied by chromatography and spectrophotometry by Ellinghausen & Pelczar [1112].

Veillonella

The fatty acid composition of the lipids of *V. alcalescens* was studied by gas chromatography [1096a]: saturated acids with 13, 15 and 16 carbon atoms were observed, along with a C_{18} monoenoic acid and an unidentified acid (either saturated C_{18} or unsaturated C_{17} acid).

15. Lactobacillaceae

Diplococcus

α-D-galactopyranosyl-1→2-α-D-glucopyranosyl-1→3-diglycerides were recently isolated from the lipids of *D. pneumoniae* type I [920a] and type XIV [920 b] (p. 180). The fatty acid composition of these glycolipids was: lauric acid (6.9 % of the total fatty acids), myristic acid (13.6 %), tetradecenoic acid (6.5 %), palmitic acid (33.8 %), hexadecenoic acid (25.9 %), stearic acid (2.9 %) and octadecenoic acid (10.4 °/₀) [920a].

Streptococcus

Hofmann & Tausig [556] obtained 4.5 % total lipids from a strain of *Streptococcus pyogenes* (type C; strain ATCC 10706) grown on Christensen's medium [1113]; the greater part of these lipids exists in the bound state in the bacterial cell. No study was made of the various lipid groups present in the mixture, but the free lipids, on the one hand, and the bound lipids on the other, were directly saponified and the fatty acids analysed. Table 50 shows the percentages of various acid groups which were separated.

The bound lipids contained 2.8 % dienoic acids and a negligible amount of tri- and tetra-enoic acids.

The straight-chain saturated acids consisted of lauric (m.p. 43.8—44.8°), myristic (m.p. 54.2—54.8°), palmitic (m.p. 63.0—63.5°; amide m.p. 105.0—106.1°), and stearic (m.p. 68.9—69.8°) acids.

The straight-chain unsaturated acids consisted of 9:10-hexadecenoic acid, accompanied by a little of the 11:12-isomer, and of cis-vaccenic acid (11:12-octadecenoic acid), accompanied by a little oleic acid (9:10-octadecenoic acid). These acids were characterized by analysis of the products formed on periodic acid oxidation of their dihydroxy derivatives.

No branched-chain acid was detected.

The lipid content in the cell wall of *S. pyogenes* was studied by Hill *et al.* [1016]: it is increased by addition of glycerol, sodium acetate, or sodium oleate to the growth medium. Two groups of naturally-occurring *S. pyogenes* strains had a particularly high cell-wall lipid content (15—25 % of the dry cell wall): tetracycline-resistant strains and strains isolated from impetigo lesions.

Cells of *S. lactis* var. maltigenes and *S. cremoris* yielded 5.3 and 5.5 %, respectively, of their dry weights as lipids by extraction of the ground bacteria [598, 1114]. Triglycerides, mono- or diglycerides and phospholipids were detected by thin-layer chromatography [598]; the phospholipids have been separated into six fractions, which were either ninhydrin-positive, or Dragendorf-positive [823 b]. The fatty acid composition of the crude lipids is given in Table 50; it is remarkable that both these strains contain a C_{19} cyclopropane acid, whereas it is absent from *S. pyogenes*.

The lipids of *S. faecalis* have been separated into acetone-soluble and acetone-insoluble fractions. On saponification, the acetone-soluble fraction gave 97 % (of the weight of the initial lipid fraction) of ether-soluble compounds and 25 % of unsaponifiable fraction; no glycerol was detected. No information was given as to the nature of the unsaponifiable fraction. These results would seem to indicate that the fat of *S. faecalis* is a mixture of cerides and free fatty acids. The composition of the phospholipid fraction, 3.2 % P, 1.4 % N, was studied more thoroughly. No choline, ethanolamine, or serine was found; instead, the bulk of the phospholipid consisted of a fraction containing L-lysine [865].

The lipid content of the protoplast membrane of *S. faecalis* was studied in relation to

TABLE 50. THE COMPOSITION OF THE FATTY ACID-MIXTURE ISOLATED FROM SEVERAL
SPECIES OF STREPTOCOCCUS
(% of the total fatty acids)

Acids (number of carbon atoms)	S. pyogenes		S. lactis var. maltigenes	S. cremoris
	Free lipids	Bound lipids		
10				
12		1.7	0.5	0.4
13 = or 14 br*	2.8		2.1	
14		5.0	16.6	15.0
15 = or 16 br			3.5	
16	17.9	32.1	34.5	27.5
16 =			2.7	2.3
18	17.7	37.2	0.7	0.4
18 =			16.8	4.8
19 cyclo*	—	—	19.3	44.7
References	556	556	598	598

* =: monoene; br: branched-chain; cyclo: cyclopropane.

the depletion of the cells in threonine and in valine; depletion of these amino acids signi-ficantly increased the lipid content [1026]. Working with bacteria collected during the exponen-tial phase of growth, Vorbeck & Marinetti [1026 a] found that the cytoplasmic membrane of *S. faecalis* (ATCC 9790) contained 94% of the total cell lipids. The major components were: phosphatidylglycerol, amino acid esters (Lys, Gly, Ala) of phosphatidylglycerol, mono-glucosyl-diglyceride and galactosido-glucosyldiglyceride. The main lipid component of the membrane of bacteria collected during the stationary phase of growth seems to be a diphos-phatidylglyceride [841 b].

The pigments of various strains of *S. pyogenes* have been studied [1115, 1116].

Leuconostoc

L. mesenteroides, grown on a lipid-free medium, contains 1% fats, 1.2% phosphatides, and 2.3% bound lipids.

Glycerol, glucose, and galactose were identified in the hydrolysis products of the fats. The phospholipid fraction, 1.8% P, 1.8% N, contained no choline, ethanolamine, serine, or inositol; on hydrolysis it yielded D-alanine as the principal ninhydrin-reacting substance [865]. Cis-vaccenic acid can make up to 75% of the total fatty acids [556a].

Lactobacillus

The lipids of four *Lactobacillus* species have been studied. Three species — *L. acidophilus*, *L. delbrückii*, and *L. casei* — produce L-(+)-lactic acid, while the fourth — *L. arabinosus*, or *L. plantarum* according to the latest rules of nomenclature [5] — produces DL-lactic acid.

In 1932, Crowder & Anderson [684, 787, 829] undertook a systematic study of the lipids of *L. acidophilus*, grown on a semi-synthetic medium. About 7 % total free lipids was obtained comprising 28 % free fatty acids, 35 % neutral fat, and 32 % phosphatides.

From the free fatty acids, Crowder & Anderson [684] isolated an optically active dihydroxyoctadecanoic acid, m.p. 106—107° (p. 112) ; this acid constituted 3.4 % of the total lipids. It was not found by Thorne & Kodicek [544] in the course of a recent investigation of the fatty acids from *L. acidophilus*.

The neutral fat gave on saponification 81.5 % fatty acids, 6.7 % unsaponifiable fraction, and 12.5 % crude glycerol [787]. The unsaponifiable fraction contained cholesterol, possibly arising from the culture medium containing skimed milk; part of the glycerides may also have the same origin. The fatty acids were separated by the lead salt method into straight-chain saturated acids (57.8 % of the total acids) and "liquid" acids. The saturated acids consisted of lauric, myristic, palmitic, and stearic acids. The liquid acids were converted by hydrogenation into stearic acid; however, small quantity of liquid saturated acids (branched-chain acids) was also observed [787]. This latter fraction probably consisted of the hydrogenolysis products of lactobacillic acid, which was later isolated from *L. acidophilus* by Thorne & Kodicek [544].

The phosphatide fraction, 1.42 % P and 1.21 % N, gave 55 % fatty acids on hydrolysis. From the water-soluble fraction, Crowder & Anderson [829] isolated choline (as the chloroplatinate), glycerophosphoric acid (as the barium salt), and D-galactose (m.p. 164—167°, $[\alpha]_D^{24}$ +82.3° (water)). Attempts to isolate ethanolamine gave negative results, so that the nature of a considerable part of the phosphatide nitrogen was unexplained (see below). The fatty acids were mainly palmitic and stearic acids (perhaps also a little of a C_{24} acid) and C_{16} and C_{18} unsaturated acids.

Saponification of the phosphatide gave a non-reducing, strongly acid, phosphorylated polysaccharide. After dephosphorylation with ammonia, a crystalline polysaccharide, m.p. 160—170°, $[\alpha]_D$ +69° → + 72° (water), was obtained. Hydrolysis gave D-galactose and a considerable amount of sugars which furnished glucosazone; because the reaction was positive for ketoses, Crowder & Anderson [829] assumed that they were dealing with a mixture of glucose and fructose. An oligosaccharide of the raffinose-stachyose type is excluded because the specific rotation is too low.

The lipids of *L. arabinosus*, *L. casei*, and *L. delbrückii* were isolated in Hofmann's laboratory. *L. arabinosus* contained 2.5 % total lipids (of which 80 % was bound) [122, 117] and *L. casei* 2.9 % total lipids (of which 79 % was bound) [554]. No study of these lipids was made: they were directly saponified and analysed. The presence of a small quantity of unsaponifiable material was noted, but no information was given as to its nature. The composition of the fatty acids present in each strain is summarized in Table 51; for the structure of lactobacillic acid [133], see p. 92. The unsaturated acids of *L. arabinosus* and *L. casei* consisted essentially of cis-11:12-octadecenoic acid (cis-vaccenic acid, p. 86). It is remarkable that in the case of these bacilli, oleic acid is replaced by its 11:12-unsaturated isomer. According to a spectrophotometric determination less than 1 % of the total fatty acids is is polyunsaturated acids. The acids of *L. delbrückii* were analysed by reversed-phase parti-tion chromatography and have not been isolated [153]. For this reason, the nature of the unsa-turated acids is not known. Small amounts of isopentadecanoic acid have been observed in the fatty acids from *L. arabinosus*, *L. casei*, and *L. acidophilus* [544] (see Table 51). Small amounts of C_{10}, C_{12} and C_{14} monoenoic acids are present: they were identified by O'Leary[1116a] with cis-3-decenoic, cis-5-dodecenoic and cis-7-tetradecenoic acids. They belong to the same series of monoenoic acids as cis-vaccenic acid, characterized by the grouping $CH_3—(CH_2)_5—CH=$.

TABLE 51. THE FATTY-ACID COMPOSITION OF THE TOTAL LIPIDS ISOLATED FROM SEVERAL SPECIES OF LACTOBACILLUS

(% of the total fatty acids)

Acids (number of carbon atoms)	*L. acidophilus*	*L. casei* Whole cells	*L. casei* Membranes	*L. arabinosus* (*L. plantarum*)	*L. delbrückii*
< 12	0.4	0.15	0.1	0.3	0.58
12	0.3	0.2	0.3	0.15	2.8
12 =*	0.2	0.2	0.2	0.3	
13			0.2		
14	4.3	0.7	2.2	0.7	2.5
14 br			0.5		
14 =			0.8		
15	0	0.3	0.9	0.4	
15 iso	1.0	0.3	0.4	0.5	
15 anteiso			0.5		
16	9.8	8.7	21.5	6.7	27.5
16 iso			0.5		
16 =	10.8	10.1	7.2	13.9	
17			1.6		
17 anteiso			1.1		
17 =	1.7	1.95	4.5	0.95	
18	0.9	1.4	6.8	1.3	10.8
18 iso			1.1		
18 =	40.3	26.1	21.7	26.4	
19 anteiso			3.0		
19 cyclo	28.3	49.4	16.6	48.1	6.4
21			8.3		
Total unsaturated acids					45.5
References.	544	544	544	544	153

* = monoene; br: branched-chain; 19 cyclo: lactobacillic acid.

Biotin deficiency in *L. plantarum* decreased the relative amounts of cis-vaccenic and lactobacillic acids, and increased palmitic acid[1048a].

The phospholipids of *L. arabinosus* (*L. plantarum*), 0.7 %, and *L. casei*, 2.5 %, were studied by Ikawa[865]. They contained respectively 2.4 and 1.4 % P and 1.8 and 1.1 % N. Paper chromatography of hydrolysates, or microbiological assays of lyophilized unextracted cells, showed the absence of ethanolamine, serine, choline, and inositol. L-lysine was detected in the phospholipids of *L. arabinosus* and *L. casei*[865]. However, Thorne[1116b] found diphosphatidylglycerol, phosphatidylethanolamine and phosphatidylcholine as the main components of the phospholipid fraction of *L. casei* (see also 1116c).

The fatty acids from the protoplast membranes of *L. casei* have been analysed by vapour phase chromatography[544] and the results are included in Table 51.

Camien *et al.*[1117] have isolated α-hydroxyisovaleric and α-hydroxyisocaproic acids from the cells of two strains of *L. casei:* whereas one strain produced principally DL-acids, the rest being L-acids, the other strain synthesized acids rich in the L-form.

16. *Corynebacteriaceae*

Corynebacterium

The lipids of three species of *Corynebacterium*, *C. diphtheriae*, *C. ovis*, and *C. parvum*, have been studied and the pigments of several other species have been investigated.

(1) *Corynebacterium diphtheriae*

C. diphtheriae, or the diphtheria bacillus (Lœffler's bacillus), is grown in large quantities for the production of toxoid; thus, large quantities of bacilli are easily available for chemical study. This is one of the reasons why, in spite of the low lipid content of the diphtheria bacillus, these lipids have been the subject of numerous studies. In almost all cases, the strain studied is Park-Williams no. 8, a good producer of diphtheria toxin (generally grown on Loiseau & Philippe's medium; see Table 1, p. 17).

The first investigations of the lipids were carried out by Chargaff[640, 1118] and by Macheboeuf & Cassagne[39, 1119]. The content of various lipid fractions observed by these authors is recorded in Table 52.

Chargaff[1118] showed that the fat contained a very large proportion of free fatty acids. The nature of the neutral fat could not be elucidated; after saponification, neither glycerol nor carbohydrates was detected in the water-soluble part. An unsaponifiable fraction, a soft brownish-red mass, highly unsaturated and free of sterols, was isolated. The fatty acids were composed of one-third saturated acids, consisting almost entirely of palmitic acid, and two-thirds unsaturated acids. The latter contained a C_{14} acid, palmitoleic acid, and diphtheric acid, m.p. 35—36°, $[\alpha]_D$ +2.6°, $C_{35}H_{68}O_2$ (see p. 106).

The phosphatide, 1.4 % P and 0.8 % N, was hydrolysed under acid conditions with the liberation of an unidentified aldohexose, an organic base precipitable by chloroplatinic acid, and fatty acids. From the fatty acids were isolated palmitic acid, unsaturated acids, and corynin (or corynolic acid), m.p. 70—71°, $C_{50}H_{100}O_4$ (see p. 118).

TABLE 52. THE LIPID CONTENT OF CORYNEBACTERIUM DIPHTHERIAE
(% of the weight of the dry bacilli)

Author	Chargaff	Macheboeuf-Cassagne	Gubarev	Čmelik	Pudles
References	1118	1119	642	31	1120
Fats	3.97	8.5		1.59	
Wax A	0.25			4.15	
Phosphatides	0.41			2.05	
Benzene extract		4.2	4.9		
Waxes extracted by chloroform. . . .	0.27		1.8	0.54	
Neutral lipids					2.4
Free acids.					5.6
Total free lipids	4.90	12.7	6.7	8.33	8.0
Bound lipids	5.1			0.73	

Macheboeuf & Cassagne [1119] showed that a part of the palmitic acid is present in the form of sodium palmitate; this observation was later confirmed [863].

The lipids of *C. diphtheriae* have been investigated by Pudles [1120] and more recently by Asselineau [863]. The major part of the fat is a mixture of free fatty acids, containing essentially palmitic, palmitoleic, corynomycolic, $C_{32}H_{64}O_3$, m.p. 70°, $[\alpha]_D$ +7.5°, and corynomycolenic, $C_{32}H_{62}O_3$, m.p. —15°, $[\alpha]_D$ +9.5°, acids. The structures of these latter acids were established by Pudles & Lederer [309, 412, 520, 686] (p. 113).

Gas chromatography enabled the detection, besides palmitic and palmitoleic acids, of small quantities of myristic, stearic, and oleic acids. The neutral fat contained glycerides, identified by their IR spectra and by the presence of glycerol in the saponification products; palmitic acid is the main fatty acid contained in these glycerides. Monoesters of ethyleneglycol and a small amount of glycolipids have also been detected [863]. From the lipid fraction insoluble in boiling acetone, Ioneda *et al.* [913] isolated a substance m.p. 110—115°, $[\alpha]_D$ +64°, which gave trehalose and corynomycolic and corynomycolenic acids on saponification. The unsaponifiable fraction of the fat contained palmitone, $C_{31}H_{62}O$, m.p. 80°, and cis-Δ^7-palmitenone, $C_{31}H_{60}O$, m.p. 40° (see p. 80) [686].

The phosphatide fraction, m.p. 185—195°, $[\alpha]_D$ +20°, 3.0 % P and 0.8 % N, gave glycerol, inositol, mannose (phenylhydrazone m.p. 191—193°), and 50 % fatty acids on acid hydrolysis [863].

Different results were obtained by Asano and Takahashi [482, 641, 699, 700, 1121]. Fatty acid esters of dihydroxyacetone, characterized by its 2,4-dinitrophenylhydrazone, were found in the fat. It was claimed that the fatty acids were a mixture of myristic, palmitic, heneicosanoic, behenic, lignoceric, myristoleic, palmitoleic, octacosenoic, and diphtheric acids. From the unsaponifiable fraction were isolated a sterol $C_{27}H_{46}O_2$, m.p. 137° (probably arising from the culture medium), and crystals of phthiocol (in spite of the acid character of this compound).

According to these authors [699], hydrolysis of the phosphatide gave palmitic and corynolic acids, besides dihydroxyacetone.

Saponification of the bound lipids [1121] gave C_{12}, C_{14}, C_{16}, C_{18}, and C_{26} saturated acids and palmitoleic acid as the principal acids. The water-soluble part contained dihydroxyacetone and glucosamine, as well as the amino-acids leucine and glutamic acid.

An extensive investigation of the lipids of the strain Park-Williams no. 8 was also performed in Gubarev's laboratory [157, 494, 797, 642, 696, 697, 704, 894, 895, 1006, 1122-1129]. Interesting results were obtained, but the characterization of the many new fatty acids that were described was often insufficient.

The bacilli were exhaustively extracted with benzene and with chloroform (see Table 52). A considerable proportion of free fatty acids was observed. The neutral fat was separated into two parts, by making use of the difference in solubility in ether [1123].

(a) The ether-soluble fraction, m.p. 18°, contained galactose in the form of an oligosaccharide.

(b) The ether-insoluble fraction, m.p. 115°, is likewise composed of sugar esters.

The unsaponifiable part, devoid of sterols, contained an unsaturated alcohol, $C_{35}H_{70}O$, m.p. 54°, called corinnic alcohol [797] (see p. 158).

A fraction soluble in ether and insoluble in acetone gave, on saponification, trehalose and α- and β-corinnic and α- and β-hydroxycorinnic acids [642] (p. 117). Esters of trehalose with branched-chain acids, hydroxylated or not, could therefore be present in the lipids of the diphtheria bacillus.

The chloroform extract consisted of a mixture of free fatty acids, esters of fatty acids and sugars (microsides), and true waxes [494]. The presence of trehalose, was demonstrated by the preparation of an octa-acetate (m.p. 73.5°) and by its hydrolysis to glucose (phenylosazone m.p. 210°). The unsaponifiable part contained an optically active alcohol, m.p. 58.5°, considered to be 3-hydroxyoctadecane [404] (p. 69).

The occurrence of esters of trehalose has also been noted by Kanchukh [1126] and Alimova [895]. This latter author also mentioned the presence of esters of mannose.

The homogeneity of the numerous fatty acids isolated in the course of these investigations was not always demonstrated and the molecular formulae proposed were only approximate. The following common fatty acids were mentioned: palmitic and arachidic acids, palmitoleic, octadecenoic, and eicosenoic acids [157], C_{19}, C_{21}, C_{22}, C_{24} and C_{26} fatty acids [894]. Branched-chain acids, hydroxylated or not, with 30—40 carbon atoms were frequently observed [157, 642, 696, 894, 1126].

Pustovalov [157] identified one of these hydroxy acids with the corynomycolic acid of Lederer & Pudles (p. 113). On the other hand, Kanchukh [1126] noted a $C_{50}H_{100}O_2$ acid and more recently Gubarev & Pustovalova [704] isolated, after a long series of fractionations, a hydroxy unsaturated acid called diphtherocorynnic acid, m.p. 29.0—29.6°, for which the molecular formula $C_{53}H_{104}O_3$ was proposed. This acid, the homogeneity of which seems established, could be related to corynolic acid (p. 118).

Whereas the lipids studied in Gubarev's laboratory have a rather high content of sugar derivatives (microsides), those studied in Paris contained mostly free acids and glycerides. This difference may be due either to the very large scale on which the Russian authors have worked (which permitted them to isolate fractions present in very small amounts) or to differences in the conditions of culture.

The bound lipids have been extensively investigated. Gubarev et al. [1124] showed that a prolonged extraction of the bacilli with chloroform (in the course of a year and a half) removed a significant part of the bound lipids; this observation could be explained as being due to the action of hydrochloric acid slowly liberated by the chloroform. Lubenets [1125] and Alimova [1127, 1128] isolated from the bound lipids very complex fractions containing sugars and numerous amino-acids; these preparations, moreover, contained phosphorus (which could arise from phospholipids; see Čmelik [32]). Orlova [1122] studied the fatty acids of the bound lipids.

From the bound lipids, Čmelik likewise obtained a fraction containing a protein. A higher hydroxy acid, m.p. 68°, having about 32 carbon atoms, was isolated; this acid was not identical with corynomycolic acid, since the mixed melting point was depressed. In addition, the influence of the composition of the culture medium on the nature of the bound lipids was studied [32].

The existence of lipids in the cell wall of C. diphtheriae was shown by Kitaura et al. [1007] (p. 199). Alimova [1129] isolated the surface lipids of the bacteria by means of a 2 % aqueous solution of sodium taurocholate; saponification of these lipids gave C_{14} to C_{20} fatty acids and sugars (arabinose, galactose, hexosamine, hexuronic acid, trehalose). The demonstration of two lipid antigens, one characteristic of the type, the other of the group, resulted from the work of Hoyle [1130; cf. 1131, 1132]. Lycopene was identified in the extracts of C. diphtheriae [1133], as well as a dihydrovitamine K_2 [1133a].

(2) Corynebacterium ovis

C. ovis (C. pseudotuberculosis) in sheep provokes a sickness called caseous lymphadenitis; the leucocytes of the sheep or guinea pigs having phagocytized C. ovis degenerate and die.

Carne et al. [1134] observed that the lipids obtained by washing the living bacilli with petroleum ether possess the leucotoxic action of the bacilli themselves. The light-petroleum extract contains a complex mixture of lipids, the chemical study of which was begun by Diara & Pudles [688]. A high content of alkaline salts of fatty acids was observed. Corynomycolic acid [201], m.p. 70°, $[\alpha]_D$ +7.5°, was isolated and identified by comparison of its IR spectrum with that of an authentic sample (isolated from C. diphtheriae) and by its degradation to palmitone.

Corynomycolenic acid is present only in small quantity. Saponification of the crude lipids of C. ovis gave myristic, palmitic, palmitoleic, and oleic acids. Several fractions containing polypeptides were detected [115].

(3) Corynebacterium parvum

This organism is obligatorily anaerobic, whereas C. diphtheriae and C. ovis are facultatively aerobic.

The fatty acid composition of the lipids of *C. parvum* is very different from that of the two other species of *Corynebacterium*. No corynomycolic acid was detected. On the contrary, the main acid was isopentadecanoic acid, m.p. 49—50.5°, while a small amount of isoheptadecanoic acid was also found [1135].

Triglycerides were characterized, but no information was given about other lipid fractions [1135].

(4) *Other species of Corynebacterium*

Organic solvents can extract 25—35 % lipids from the dry cells of the strictly aerobic species *C. rubrum* [1136]. Homologs of corynomycolic and corynomycolenic acids were characterized in the lipids of *Corynebacterium* 506, *C. rubrum* and C. 6083-9 [688 a]. The presence of such a type of β-hydroxy-acids appears to be a general feature of aerobic Corynebacteria.

C. hoffmannii possesses two lipid antigens, one specific for the species, the other for the genus [1130]. A lipid antigen is also present in *C. pseudodiphtheriticum* [1131].

Carotenoid pigments have been identified in *C. carotenum* [1137], *C. poinsettiae* [1138], and *C. michiganense* [1139].

Listeria

As monocytosis is induced in animals by chloroform-soluble lipids [1140], Girard & Murray [1141] extracted cultures of *L. monocytogenes* with chloroform and obtained 5.1 % lipids. No information was given about the chemical properties of these lipids.

Antigenic fractions were isolated from *L. monocytogenes* cells by Tubylewicz [1142]; palmitic, stearic, and oleic acids were characterized by paper chromatography.

17. *Bacillaceae*

Bacillus

Among the many species belonging to the genus *Bacillus*, the most studied, from a chemical point of view, are *B. megaterium*, *B. cereus*, *B. subtilis*, *B. albolactis*, *B. mycoides*, and *B. anthracis*.

The principal lipid component of these bacilli is often poly-β-hydroxybutyrate, the structure of which was discussed on p. 107. The distribution of poly-β-hydroxybutyrate in the genus *Bacillus* was particularly studied by Lemoigne *et al.* [647, 651]. This author found a correlation between the presence of intracellular globules, isolated by Weibull [1030] from *B. megaterium*, and the existence of poly-β-hydroxybutyrate [647]. When these globules are particularly numerous, significant quantities of poly-β-hydroxybutyrate can be isolated: this is the case with *B. megaterium*, *B. mycoides*, *B. cereus*, and *B. anthracis*. *B. subtilis*, which does not have any obvious globules, contains only very slight quantities of this lipid — 0.03 % of the dry weight.

The poly-β-hydroxybutyrate content of *B. megaterium* can reach 25 % of the dry weight in the case of cultures grown on an agar-sugar medium and it can exceed 50 % in the case of cultures agitated in a liquid sugar medium [649].

Milhaud *et al.* [649] sought the presence of other types of lipids, besides poly-β-hydroxy-

TABLE 53. THE COMPOSITION OF THE FATTY-ACID MIXTURE ISOLATED
FROM THREE SPECIES OF BACILLUS
(% of the total fatty acids)

Acid (number of carbon atoms)	B. subtilis whole cells	B. cereus whole cells	B. megaterium membranes
< 14		9.1	
14 iso	3	2	3
14	1	2.4	
15 iso	8.5	44.0	26.0
15 anteiso	42.5		28.9
15		0.3	
16 iso	10	4.4	1.3
16 anteiso			2.1
16	10	8.6	
17 iso	6.3	16.9	
17 anteiso	12.7		2.6
18 iso		0.9	0.7
18		0.7	
References	547	796	544

butyrate, in the case of *B. megaterium*. Table 2 (p. 20) shows that before sporulation, which occurs on the third day, the ether-soluble lipid content is only 6—9 % of the total lipids; these lipids contain neither glycerides nor sterols and give 40 % fatty acids on saponification. Williamson & Wilkinson [661] also found about 90 % poly-β-hydroxybutyrate in the lipid inclusions of certain species of *Bacillus* and 10 % ether-soluble lipids.

Esters of amino-acids, in particular arginine, with phosphatidylglycerols were characterized in the lipids of *B. megaterium* [873; cf. 872]. 5-Monoenoic acids were characterized in the C_{16} and C_{18} acid fractions [749 c]. The composition of the fatty acid mixture present in the membranes of *B. megaterium* was determined by Thorne & Kodicek [544] (see Table 53, p. 236); phosphatidylethanolamine, phosphatidylserine, and phosphatidylinositol were detected in these membranes [879]. The lipids of the protoplast membranes of *B. megaterium* KM were fractionated by Yudkin [1020]; neutral lipids accounted for 12.9 % of the dry membranes and phospholipids for 10.0 %.

Cells of *B. cereus*, grown on an alcohol-free medium, contained 2.6 % free lipids. About half these lipids were phosphatides, the components of which were phosphatidylethanolamine and phosphatidylglycerol. The neutral lipids consisted mainly of diglycerides. The fatty acid composition of the total lipids is given in Table 53. Hexadecanol and octadecanol were identified in the unsaponifiable fraction. Cells grown in the presence of alcohols (ethanol, propanol) usually had a higher phosphatide and a higher unsaponifiable matter content [796]. Ornithine esters of phosphatidylglycerol were also characterized [872; cf. 1143].

Extraction of *B. subtilis* cells, which contain little poly-β-hydroxybutyrate [647], gave 2.0% fats, 0.8% phosphatides, and 3.3% waxes [1091]. Akashi & Saito [546] characterized subtilopentadecanoic acid (13-methyltetradecanoic acid) and subtiloheptadecanoic acid (15-methylhexadecanoic acid) (p. 84) in the fatty acids of *B. subtilis* and *B. natto*. A careful analysis of the fatty acid components of the lipids of *B. subtilis* was recently achieved by Kaneda [547] (see Table 53).

Verna [1144] isolated 24% lipids from cells of *B. albolactis* grown on a synthetic medium containing glucose and 4.6% from cells grown on a medium containing lactose.

B. stearothermophilus contained 0.6% phospholipids in a total of only 1.5% lipids [1028, 1045]. Claims of the presence of sphingomyelins [1145] were not substantiated by further investigations [1146].

The main components of the phosphatide fraction of *B. polymyxa* are phosphatidylethanolamine and phosphatidylglycerol; small amounts of diphosphatidylglycerol, phosphatidic acids, lysophosphatidylethanolamine, -serine, and -choline, have also been detected. No difference in the composition of the phosphatide fraction was observed between vegetative cells and spores [1147].

Clostridium

In the phospholipid fraction of *Clostridium welchii* type A *(Cl. perfringens)*, MacFarlane [871] has characterized phosphatidic acids, phosphatidylglycerols, and esters of phosphatidylglycerols with amino-acids (mainly lysine and ornithine). The fatty acids isolated from the various lipid fractions were mainly saturated acids — 24% C_{14} and 30% C_{20} [871].

Goldfine [831] has fractionated the phospholipid fraction of *Cl. butyricum* by chromatography on silicic acid: just after the phosphatidylethanolamine peak a fraction containing phosphatidyl-N-methyl-ethanolamine emerged. The same author [847a] has found that most of these phospholipids occur as plasmalogens. By acid hydrolysis of these plasmalogens, the aldehydes were isolated (as their dimethylacetal derivatives) and analyzed by gas chromatography: the major components are palmitaldehyde, hexadecenal, and C_{17} and C_{19} cyclopropane fatty aldehydes [1147a]. The biosynthesis of these cyclopropane fatty aldehydes was studied by Chung and Goldfine [1147b]: they are formed by addition of a methyl group to an unsaturated aldehydogenic moiety of a plasmalogen.

Analysis of the fatty acids from *Cl. butyricum* was achieved by Goldfine & Bloch [597]: the saturated acids were a mixture of 0.5% C_{12}, 2.4% C_{14}, 0.4% C_{15}, 49.0% C_{16}, and 6.2% C_{18} acids; the unsaturated fraction contained 17% C_{16} and 7.9% C_{18} acids; moreover, 0.4% C_{13}, 1.5% C_{15}, 9.0% C_{17}, and 5.2% C_{19} cyclopropane acids were found. A cyclopropane synthetase was isolated from *Cl. butyricum* cells [770a]: it catalyzes the condensation of a C_1-compound (arising from the methyl of methionine) on the double bond of an unsaturated acid inside a phosphatidylethanolamine molecule.

The unsaturated acids of three species of *Clostridia* were investigated by Scheuerbrandt & Bloch [754]; the results are recorded in Table 54.

TABLE 54. THE NATURE OF THE UNSATURATED ACIDS OF THREE SPECIES OF CLOSTRIDIA [754]

Species	Acids					
	C_{14}		C_{16}		C_{18}	
	Isomer Δ	%*	Isomer Δ	%*	Isomer Δ	%*
Cl. butyricum	7	0.3	7 9	8 8	9 11	2 78
Cl. kluyveri			?	1	11	1
Cl. pasteurianum	7	1	9 11	3 1	11	2

*% of the total fatty acids.

18. Mycobacteriaceae

Mycobacterium

The species of the genus *Mycobacterium* constitute a very large group of bacteria, the study of which was stimulated by the correlation established quite early between their high content of lipids and certain aspects of the pathological manifestations they induce. In this review, the species are classified as follows:

(1) *M. tuberculosis* (a) var. *hominis*
                    (b) var. *bovis*
(2) *M. avium*
(3) *M. paratuberculosis (M. johnei)*
(4) Saprophytic *Mycobacterium* species
(5) "Atypical" *Mycobacterium* species
(6) *M. leprae*

The lipids of these various species of bacteria have usually been isolated by the extraction procedure devised by Anderson (see Fig. 1, p. 23). Table 55 shows an extension of this fractionation procedure, used by Asselineau *et al.* [64, 65]. It should be pointed out that "wax" is an inaccurate term, but it is retained here by reason of its long usage, particularly by Anderson. The letters A, B, C, and D applied to different wax fractions correspond to the order in which they were isolated.

(1) Mycobacterium tuberculosis

This species constitutes the tubercle bacillus (Koch's bacillus).

TABLE 55. THE WORK OF ASSELINEAU *et al.* [64,65] BASED ON ANDERSON'S PROCEDURE FOR THE EXTRACTION OF BACILLI

(see Fig. 1 p. 25)

Anderson's fractions	Solvent	Solubility characteristics	Final fractions
I. Alcohol-ether extract Crude fats	Aqueous solution of NaHCO₃	Soluble	Aromatic acids, phthiocol
	Solution of K₂CO₃	Soluble	Fatty acids
	Solution of KOH	Soluble	Fatty acids, phenols (?)
		Insoluble	Neutral fat
Crude phosphatide . .	Boiling acetone	Hot soluble, cold insoluble	Wax A
		Hot insoluble	Phosphatides
II. Chloroform extract Waxes soluble in methanol ("soft wax")	Ether-methanol (1:3)	Soluble	Wax B
Waxes insoluble in methanol ("purified wax")	Boiling acetone	Hot soluble, cold insoluble	Wax C
		Hot insoluble	Wax D

(a) *Human type* (var. *hominis*). The principal "human" strain studied by Anderson is the strain H_{37}; from it was isolated an avirulent variant (strain $H_{37}Ra$). The history of these strains has been described by Steenken & Gardner [1148]. The same authors have also written the history of strain R_1 [1149]. Strains L_{25} and L_{65} were isolated from lupous lesions by Dr. Canetti (see fig. 1, p. 23). All the other strains mentioned in Table 56 belong to the collection of the Pasteur Institute, Paris. The Test strain was isolated in 1904 from a case of testicular tuberculosis. The virulence of the Brévannes strain was studied by Desbordes *et al.* [1150] in 1954.

In Table 56 are listed the contents of various lipid fractions in the different strains which we have had the opportunity to examine. The significant proportion of lipids extracted by chloroform should be noted.

(i)   *Fats.* The fats — a pasty, odorous mass with a deep red colour — always have a high free fatty acid content (25—40 %). Demonstration of the presence of free fatty acids under conditions reducing to a minimum the onset of lipolysis was made by Fethke [47], using bacilli of the Vallée bovine strain grown for 4 weeks on Sauton's medium. The pigments are composed, on the one hand, of carotenoids (in particular leprotene $C_{40}H_{54}$ [1151], which will be described in the section on saprophytic *Mycobacteria*), and, on the other hand, of naphthaquinone derivatives (see phthiocol, vitamin K_x). These

TABLE 56. THE COMPOSITION OF THE LIPIDS OF HUMAN STRAINS OF M. TUBERCULOSIS
(as % of the dry weight of the bacilli; all strains grown in Sauton's medium, for 4 or 6 weeks)

Strain	Brévannes		Canetti	Test	R_1	$H_{37}Rv$	$H_{37}Rv$ s.r.	$H_{37}Ra$	L_{25}	L_{65}
	Batch I	Batch II								
Alcohol-ether extract										
Fats	7.6	6.6	6.4	7.3				6.8	5.6	
Wax A	0.15	5.3	3.1	4.2	11.2	12.7		2.0	2.2	
Phosphatides	1.7	2.2	1.9	0.8				1.2	1.8	
Chloroform extract. . .										
Wax B	0.7	0.2	0.3	0.5	2.0	0.6		1.1	0.5	0.8	1.0
Wax C	0.1	1.2	1.0	2.5	1.1	0.5		1.0	4.0	0.9	0.1
Wax D	6.9	8.3	8.2	6.2	2.1	7.3		8.3	2.0	4.5	1.3
Total free lipids	17.2	23.8	21.0	21.5	16.4	21.1		20.4	15.8		
Bound lipids	9.4			4.7				5.5			
References	65		731	64	710	724		76	710		

pigments form complex mixtures, as is shown by the great number of coloured zones on chromatographic columns.

Among the odorous fatty constituents, Kasuya [1152] characterized acetaldol, CH_3—CHOH—CH_2—CHO, by means of its derivative with dimedone. Goris & Sabetay [1153] showed the probable presence of phenylethyl alcohol, which was isolated by Asselineau [76] from the fats of strain H_{37}Ra and identified by its IR spectrum and its phenylurethan m.p. 75°. Phenylacetic acid, m.p. 76°, was isolated by Stendal [1154] from the fats of a tubercle bacillus strain of unspecified origin.

Other aromatic acids were isolated from fats of human strains, by extraction with a solution of sodium hydrogen carbonate :

Anisic acid, m.p. 181—183°, isolated from strains H_{37} [466], A-10, A-12 [897], H_{37}Ra [76], and Brévannes [65].

Phthalic acid, m.p. 210—215° (anhydride m.p. 129°), isolated from the Brévannes strain [65].

Salicylic acid, m.p. 158°, isolated from a strain of unspecified origin [1154].

A neutral phthalate of aliphatic octyl alcohol(s) $C_{24}H_{38}O_4$, n_D^{20} 1.4880, was isolated by Aebi et al. [65] from fats of the Brévannes strain. As butyl phthalate was obtained by washing plastic tubings with organic solvents [1155], phthalic esters might arise from contamination of the extracts, although direct contact of the extracts with plastic matter was always avoided (cf. ref. 1156).

In 1933, Anderson & Newman [896] found that "the acetone-soluble, neutral fats of acidfast bacteria are not glycerides, but esters of fatty acids with trehalose". This conclusion rested on the examination of the fats from bacilli of strains H_{37} [896], A-10, and A-12 [897].

Aebi *et al.* [65] isolated trehalose from certain fat fractions (of the Brévannes strain) that were strongly adsorbed on alumina. Nevertheless, recent studies, made on the fats from bacilli of the strains Canetti [139], $H_{37}RvS.$-r. [139], and Brévannes (grown in the U.S.A.) [140], have shown that the fats are composed essentially of glycerides (see p. 156). The discrepancy between the results of these recent studies and those of Anderson has not been explained.

The fats have a high content of unsaponifiable material: about 30 % neutral fats in those of the strain $H_{37}Ra$ [76]; it was isolated in the form of a highly unsaturated, deep brown, viscous mass. Fractionation of this material gave small quantities of branched-chain fatty acids (phthienoic acids [65], a C_{80} hydroxy acid [65, 139]), and hexacosanoic acid [65]. Poorly defined fractions, with tentative formulas $C_{26}H_{42}O_3$ and $C_{26}H_{42}O_5$ and containing respectively 4 and 5 double bonds and at least 5 C-CH_3 groups, were obtained by Aebi *et al.* [65]. Such substances could arise from the degradation of terpene compounds.

(ii) *Phosphatides.* These compounds have already been discussed in detail on p. 162 and will not be dealt with again here.

(iii) *Wax A.* Waxes A are essentially composed of the dimycocerosate of phthiocerol and related alcohols (p. 158); free mycolic acid is frequently present (see, e.g. ref. 64).

(iv) *Wax B.* Waxes B (Anderson's "soft wax") have a composition close to that of fats. The only detailed study of them dealt with the waxes B of strain H_{37} [923]. On saponification, they gave 69.5 % fatty acids, 13.6 % phthiocerol, 12.3 % "unsaponifiable waxes" (mycolic acids?), and glycerol, which constituted the sole water-soluble component.

(v) *Wax C.* The composition of waxes C is quite close to that of the waxes A: substances related to phthiocerol dimycoserate and, sometimes, free mycolic acid are found. Glycerides, in particular 1-glyceryl mycolate (p. 156), have also been identified [794]. Moreover, the waxes C constitute the best starting material for isolation of the "cord factor", the 6,6′-dimycolate of trehalose (p. 173).

(vi) *Wax D.* Waxes D of human strains are essentially composed of peptido-glycolipids, i.e. esters of mycolic acids with a polysaccharide containing D-galactose, D-arabinose, and D-mannose and glucosamine linked through galactosamine residues to peptides formed of alanine, glutamic acid, and α-ε-diaminopimelic acid; muramic acid has also been detected [939a]. The composition of these substances is discussed on p. 181.

(vii) *Bound lipids.* The bacterial residue after delipidation by neutral solvents is heated for 5 hours with a mixture of equal parts of alcohol and ether containing 1 % hydrochloric acid. The bacillary mass is next extracted with mixtures rich in ether and then by chloroform. The lipids thus obtained constitute the bound lipids.

Anderson *et al.* [941] studied the bound lipids of strain A-10, which represent 12.2 % of the dry weight of the whole bacilli. The chloroform solution of these lipids was filtered through a Chamberland filter: 60 % only of the lipids was recovered in the filtrate and constituted the filtrable fraction. The "unfiltrable part", composed essentially of esters of mycolic acids and polysaccharides containing galactose, arabinose, and mannose, has been discussed on p. 186 (see particularly Table 39, p. 187).

The filtrable fraction, m.p. 80—85°, gave on saponification 77 % ether-soluble material (consisting of mycolic acids and fatty acids in nearly equal proportions), 25.5 % polysaccharide, and 2 % glycerol.

The A-12 human strain gave irregular results: an unfiltrable fraction isolated from one batch could not be obtained from a second batch of bacilli [941].

From bacilli of the Test strain Asselineau [64] obtained 2.0 % of lipids extracted by a mixture of alcohol and ether and 2.7 % of lipids extracted by chloroform, i.e. 4.7 % of total bound lipids. Chromatography of the second fraction gave 60 % of esters of mycolic acids and a polysaccharide whose properties are given in Table 39 (p. 187). Several other fractions, some containing mycolic acids, were isolated during the fractionation of these lipids.

From the bound lipids of the human strain Aoyama B, Azuma & Yamamura [943, 912] have isolated a mycolate of arabinose and a toxic glycolipid [912 a].

(*viii*) *Fatty acids of various lipid fractions.* Saponification of these lipids gives mixtures of fatty acids which appear more and more complex as methods of investigation improve.

Among recent studies in this field, one was devoted to the analysis of the acids present in each lipid fraction (strain $H_{37}Ra$ [76]). All the other studies bear on the mixtures of acids which are obtained by saponification of the crude lipids from the alcohol-ether extract.

Cason and his collaborators achieved a very precise systematic analysis of this mixture by using fractional distillation, adsorption chromatography, and gas chromatography.

Strain H_{37} contains about one-third palmitic acid, one-third C_{18} and C_{19} acids, and one-third acids higher than C_{20} [560]. This observation was verified with other human strains [1157], including the avirulent strain $H_{37}Ra$ [561]. Table 57 shows the composition of the mixture of acids lower than C_{20}, from a virulent strain of the tubercle bacillus, as determined by gas chromatographic analysis [1158].

The acids present in the lipids of the tubercle bacillus can be classified into three groups:

α. Saturated acids with a straight chain. All the acids with even numbers of carbon atoms from C_{12} to C_{26} are present. The most important is palmitic acid. Hexacosanoic acid exists in relatively important quantities and constitutes essentially the longest straight-chain acid. However, very small amounts of octacosanoic acid can also be detected [145].

A preparation of acids considered to be a mixture of hexacosanoic acid with a little octacosanoic acid, isolated from $H_{37}Ra$ [76], was found to be a mixture of 9 % C_{24}, 4 % C_{25}, and 87 % C_{26} (Asselineau, Ställberg-Stenhagen, unpublished results). Gas chromatography made possible the detection of relatively significant amounts of acids with odd numbers of carbon atoms, in particular nonadecanoic acid (see Table 57, for example, and Fig. 3, p. 35).

β. Unsaturated acids with a straight chain. Goris & Sabetay [1153] isolated crotonic and isocrotonic acids from an unidentified strain of the tubercle bacillus. The higher unsaturated acids are mainly C_{18} acids. In 1920, Goris [1159] demonstrated the presence of oleic acid by isolating 9,10-dihydroxystearic acid, m.p. 134°, from the products of permanganate oxidation of liquid acids. Cason & Tavs [1160] examined the products from the ozonolysis of unsaturated C_{18} acids and concluded that oleic acid is the only octadecenoic acid of the tubercle bacillus.

Anderson & Chargaff [1161] isolated from the hydrogenation products of unsaturated acids prepared from an unspecified strain of tubercle bacillus (probably H_{37}) a hexacosanoic acid with m.p. 82—82.5°; according to these authors, the relatively low melting point could be ascribed either to a branch in the carbon chain or to contamination with homologues.

The alkaline isomerization method shows "the absence of appreciable quantities of poly-unsaturated acids" [560].

γ. Acids with branched chains; these acids belong essentially to four groups. C_{17}, C_{18}, or C_{19} acids, having a methyl substituent in the middle of the chain. The principal representative of this group, known since 1929, is tuberculostearic acid (10(D)-methylocta-decanoic acid) [105] which is discussed on p. 87; the work of Agre & Cason [1158] showed the existence of very small proportions (see Table 57) of a C_{18}-branched acid: 10-methyl-

TABLE 57. THE COMPOSITION OF THE FATTY-ACID MIXTURE WITH LESS THAN 20 CARBON ATOMS ISOLATED FROM THE LIPIDS OF THE TUBERCLE BACILLUS [1158]

Number of carbon atoms in the acid	% of total acids	Number of carbon atoms in the acid	% of total acids
14 straight-chain	0.35	17 branched-chain.	1.3
15 branched-chain.	0.06	17 straight-chain	4.8
15 straight-chain	2.2	18 branched-chain	1.3
16 branched-chain.	0.75	18 straight-chain	11.6
16 straight-chain	32.7	19 branched-chain	10.5
		19 straight-chain	11.6
Total: 77.16 %			

heptadecanoic acid and a C_{17} fraction containing 8- and 10-methyl-substituted acids. Labar-rère & Asselineau (unpublished results) observed, in the Canetti human strain, a C_{18}-branched acid which disappeared after bromination and which seems therefore to be unsaturated.

α,β-unsaturated acids having methyl substituents at positions 2,4 and 6 (mycolipenic or phthienoic acids). According to Cason & Fonken [202], there exist in the lipids of strain $H_{37}Rv$, at least 5 α-alkyl-α,β-unsaturated acids. The principal representatives of this group are C_{25}, C_{26}, C_{27}, and C_{29} acids. The acid studied in most detail is C_{27}-mycolipenic acid [149] (see p. 97). In the Test strain, the two principal representatives of this group are C_{25}- and C_{27}-phthienoic acids [128]. All these acids are strongly dextrorotatory; they are absent in the avirulent strains $H_{37}Ra$ [76, 573, 561] or attenuated BCG [561, 630]. Cason & Fonken [202] observed a branched α,β-unsaturated laevorotatory acid (strain $H_{37}Ra$) (see Table 58).

Saturated acids having methyl substituents in positions 2, 4, 6, and 8 (mycocerosic acids). As early as 1932, Anderson [600] demonstrated the existence of at least one laevorotatory acid higher than C_{30} (see also ref. 500), which was given the name mycocerosic acid (see p. 102). A recent study of mycocerosic acid by vapour phase chromatography and mass spectrometry [145] demonstrated a principal constituent, C_{32}-mycocerosic acid (2,4,6,8-tetra-methyloctacosanoic acid), accompanied by 2,4,6,8-tetramethyl-substituted C_{30} and C_{34}

TABLE 58. THE COMPOSITION OF THE FATTY ACID MIXTURES WITH MORE THAN 20 CARBON ATOMS ARISING FROM THE LIPIDS OF VIRULENT HUMAN STRAINS OF M. TUBERCULOSIS [202]

Methyl esters, approximate b. p./2 mm	Acids
210-230°	Unsaturated, non-conjugated and saturated laevorotatory
214°	C_{25}-Phthienoic acid
223°	C_{26}-Phthienoic acid
232°	C_{27}-Phthienoic acid
240°	C_{29}-Phthienoic acid
240-255°	Several saturated laevorotatory acids, unsaturated non-conjugated acids
244-255°	α-Methyl-α, β-unsaturated laevorotatory acids
258°	C_{32}-Mycocerosic acid

acids, and a 2,4,6-trimethyl-substituted C_{29} acid (human strains H_{37}, Test and Canetti). (See also ref. 1162.)

C_{42}-branched-chain acids were isolated from the lipids of the Canetti and Test strains (see p. 107).

Branched hydroxy acids. A hydroxy acid with the approximate formula $C_{27}H_{54}O_3$ was isolated from the lipids of the Test strain, and C_{60} hydroxy acids, from the unsaponifiable part of the fats of the strains Canetti and $H_{37}Rv$ S.r. [139].

Moreover, an important proportion of the lipids of the tubercle bacillus is composed of mycolic acids which were studied in detail on p. 122.

In conclusion, the tubercle bacillus contains a complete series of branched or straight-chain acids from C_{12} to C_{34} (Tables 57 and 58) and C_{42}, C_{60}, and C_{88} acids.

b) *Bovine type* (var. *bovis*). Among the bovine strains most commonly used for chemical studies, the Vallée strain occupies an important place; its virulence was studied by Boquet [1163]. The Marmorek strain, in the collection of the Pasteur Institute, Paris, has likewise been employed. On the other hand, BCG by reason of its innocuity and its commercial preparation on a large scale is a convenient material: the history of this strain is described in the work of Calmette (ref. 1164, in particular p. 909). The possibility of the heterogeneity of BCG has recently been discussed [1165].

Table 59 shows the lipid content of various fractions from bovine strains. These lipids were studied in detail by Anderson and his collaborators [1166, 1168, 1169, 501, 347] and by Demarteau-Ginsburg [383, 721, 722]. Their composition is very similar to that of the lipids of human strains. Nevertheless, a few remarks may be made:

(*i*) The fats are very much less pigmented than the fats from human strains (except for BCG).

(*ii*) The waxes of bovine bacilli are very much richer than the waxes of human bacilli in ketonic compounds: phthiodiolone and phthiocerolone (p. 78), mycolonic acids

TABLE 59. THE COMPOSITION OF THE LIPIDS FROM BOVINE STRAINS OF M. TUBERCULOSIS (as % of the dry weight of the bacilli; strains grown in Sauton's medium)

Strain	Vallée		Mar-morek	BCG				
Age of culture (days)	42	56*	42	12	28*	28	28**	42
Alcohol-ether extract								
Fats	3.3	7.5	3.4	7.47	9.7	10.14	3.96	10.9
Wax A	1.2	4.4	1.6	3.28	4.6	6.96	4.05	1.7
Phosphatides	1.5		0.6	0.57		3.62	4.24	0.5
Chloroform extract								
Wax B	1.4		3.5			0.05	0.36	2.1
Wax C	6.1	4.0	6.7	0.77	11.1	0.32	0.73	5.3
Wax D	0.8		2.8			0.06	1.19	1.6
Total free lipids	14.3	15.9	18.8	12.1	25.4	21.15	14.53	22.0
Bound lipids								11.2
References.	383	1166	383	819	1167	18	18	64

  * Cultured on Long's medium.
  ** Sauton's medium, in which the glycerol was replaced by glucose.

(p. 129), and C_{42}-oxo acid (p. 117). In particular, whereas all the bovine strains contain a mycolonic acid, such an acid has been found only once in a human strain (strain R_1).

(iii) The waxes A and C of bovine strains contain a characteristic substance, mycoside B (or compound G_B) [252]. This substance, discussed on p. 171, was observed in each of the bovine strains studied (including BCG).

(iv) The bovine bacilli have a low content of wax D, and this fraction is composed of a mixture of low melting and high melting waxes (Table 38, p. 186). The glycolipid fraction (high melting wax) is almost completely devoid of a peptide fraction.

The fats of BCG were studied by Aoyagi et al. [1172] and the phospholipids by Nojima [151] and Vilkas [856, 857, 860]. The waxes C of BCG were fractionated by Tsumita [793] and Bloch et al. [792]; the waxes C of the strain Vallée by Noll [794]; and the waxes D by Kondo [1171] and Jolles et al. [940]. A peptidoglycolipid similar to wax D from human strains was isolated from the cell wall of BCG by enzymatic treatments [942a]. The "cord factor", the 6,6'-dimycolate of trehalose, was isolated from BCG by Noll et al. [906]. The mycolic acids of the Vallée and Marmorek strains were analysed by Demarteau-Ginsburg [383, 721, 722] and those of BCG by Ginsburg & Lederer [723] and by Tsumita [1170].

From defatted cells of BCG, a lipopolysaccharide has been extracted with phenol: this compound contains 1.8 % N, 0.35 % P, 22.8 % lipids, and 58.6 % reducing sugars (calculated as glucose). Analysis of the carbohydrate moiety shows the presence of mannose, arabinose, and glucose [1173, 1175].

The composition of the mixture of fatty acids present in the Vallée strain seems very close to that of the mixtures isolated from human strains. Palmitic, stearic, and hexacosanoic acids are the principal straight-chain saturated acids. A "tetracosanoic" acid isolated from waxes by Cason & Anderson [347], was studied by Stallberg-Stenhagen & Stenhagen [720] in monomolecular layers: it was a mixture of homologous acids from C_{20} to C_{26}. The unsaturated acids were C_{18}-acids; their iodine number was higher than that of "liquid acids" from human strains, and it was thought that acids of the linoleic of linolenic type were present.

The branched-chain acids are represented by tuberculostearic acid [1168] and optically inactive higher fatty acids probably consisting of a mixture of phthienoic and mycocerosic acids (see below). In addition, a $C_{30}H_{60}O_2$ acid, m.p. 33—34°, $[\alpha]_D - 4°$, was isolated from waxes by Cason & Anderson [347]. A $C_{18}H_{36}O_2$ acid, m.p. 0°, optically inactive (p. 86) was also obtained [347]: it may correspond to the 10-methylheptadecanoic acid identified by Agre & Cason [1158] in the human strains.

The branched-chain acids from the alcohol-ether extract of BCG (American strain) have been analysed by Cason et al. [561]. α,β-Unsaturated dextrorotatory fractions were observed ($[\alpha]_D + 13$ to 15°, λ_{max} 218 mμ, $\varepsilon = 11\,000$), which differed from the phthienoic acids by a higher molecular weight (about C_{30}) and the probable existence of a further branch. Bennet & Asselineau [630], working on the acids isolated from the fats of the French strain of BCG, found a series of branched-chain acids with 9,13,15,17, and 19 carbon atoms. No acid of the phthienoic type was detected. The fraction of mycocerosic acids consisted mainly of 2,4,6-trimethylhexacosanoic and 2,4,6,8-tetrametyloctacosanoic acids, identified by their gas-chromatographic behaviour and by mass spectrometry.

Pyridine has been characterized in lipoprotein fractions isolated from BCG [1176].

(2) *Mycobacterium avium*

The composition of the lipids of *M. avium* was first investigated by Anderson et al. [348, 489, 491, 850, 852, 1177, 1179].

Table 60 shows the content of various lipid fractions present in two strains of *M. avium*. The fats contain relatively little free fatty acids. On saponification, they give 59 % fatty acids and 20 % unsaponifiable material. The nature of the water-soluble part was not elucidated. 7.2 % branched-chain acids ("liquid saturated" acids) were isolated [60].

The phosphatide, m.p. 210°, 2.18 % P and 0.48 % N, gave on acid hydrolysis 60 % of an ether-soluble fraction and 40 % of a water-soluble fraction (13.3 % mannose, 3 % inositol and at least one other unidentified sugar) [850, 1177]. From the saponification products of the phosphatide, du Mont & Anderson [852] isolated without previous dephosphorylation a polysaccharide whose properties are very close to those of manninositose. From another strain of *M. avium*, Paul & Vilkas [1180] isolated a phosphatide fraction, m.p. 208—210°, $[\alpha]_D + 29°$, 2.1 % P, 1 % N, and 30 % sugars. On hydrolysis it gave glycerol, inositol, mannose, glucose,

TABLE 60. THE LIPID CONTENTS OF M. AVIUM AND SAPROPHYTIC MYCOBACTERIA
(as % of the dry weight of the bacilli)

Strain	M. avium		M. phlei		M. smegmatis		M. marianum			"Seine" Bacillus	"Leprosy Bacillus"
Remarks	no. 531	no. 802	"Pasteur"	02145	Sauton's medium	glycerol broth	Batch I	Batch II			Different from M. leprae
Alcohol-ether extract											
Fats	2.2	9.9	3.0	2.7	6.5	7.1	14.4	14.7	7.8		6.47
Phosphatides		0.03	0.77		0.5		1.1	0.3	3.8	9.5	
Wax A	2.2	0.3	0.03	0.6	4.05	4.0	9.7	2.0	1.5		2.20
Chloroform extract											
Wax B		2.0	0.8		5.6		1.6	4.2		3.7	
Wax C	10.8	3.2	0.7	5.0	2.0	2.1	5.8	12.9	2.3	5.5	9.98
Wax D		0.3	1.4		4.5		0.5	0.6		1.2	
Total free lipids	15.2	15.8	6.7	8.3	23.15	13.2	33.1	34.7	15.4	20.0	18.7
Bound lipids	10.8		18.0		11.2						19.5
References	1179	530	481	1184	481	13	504		1203	64	1199

a mixture of fatty acids (myristic, palmitic, branched C_{17}, octadecenoic, nonadecanoic, and tuberculostearic acids), and ornithine. Incorporation of [^{32}P]-phosphate in the phospholipid fraction was studied by Tanaka [1178].

The branched-chain acids consisted of an acid probably identical with tuberculostearic acid, and a mixture of optically inactive higher acids which were not studied [60]. No α,β-unsaturated acid could be detected by UV spectrophotometry of the fats [530].

The waxes extracted by chloroform were separated into two fractions (by 40 precipitations from the ether solution with methanol), m.p. 54—55°, $[\alpha]_D$ + 38.6°, and m.p. 53—55°, $[\alpha]_D$ + 17.7°, respectively. Both these fractions gave on saponification at least 80 % mycolic acids, about 9 % unsaponifiable material, and trehalose as the sole identified water-soluble component (12.3 % and 5.5 %, respectively) [489].

From the waxes C, Miquel et al. [530] isolated glycerides, esters of ethyleneglycol, free mycolic acids, and a "cord factor" (m.p. 41—43°) containing only dicarboxylic mycolic acids. The waxes D had a low melting point (m.p. 42—45°) [530]; by ultracentrifugation of their ether solution, about 33 % of a peptido-glycolipid fraction (see p. 186) was obtained [940].

The lipids of avian strains contain a characteristic glycoside of peptidolipid, mycoside C (compound J), which was dealt with on page 191. This compound was detected in 11 out of 13 avian strains examined [252].

The bound lipids were isolated by Anderson et al. [491]; from their properties, it would seem that they were heavily contaminated by phospholipids (see p. 187).

Mycolic acids of the strain no. 802 had a high content of dicarboxylic acids [530], the properties of which are given on page 137.

(3) Mycobacterium paratuberculosis (M. johnei)

M. paratuberculosis is the agent of hypertrophic enteritis of cattle. This bacillus requires factors such as mycobactine (p. 250) for its growth.

Larsen & Merkal [1181] compared the yield of free lipids which could be extracted from a batch of bacteria with and without autoclaving. About the same yields of lipids were obtained by extraction of living bacilli and of bacilli autoclaved for 3 h (22—23% of the dry weight). After autoclaving for 48 or 112 h, the yields were respectively 41.4 % and 44.7 %; such an increase in the free lipid content may be explained by partial hydrolysis of the bound lipids.

The lipids of two strains of M. paratuberculosis adapted to grow on a synthetic medium were studied by Laneelle [709, 951, 951a]. Both these strains contained a characteristic peptidolipid (see p. 190). The fats of the strain 316 F (Weybridge) were mainly a mixture of free fatty acids and glycerides. Octadecanol-2 and eicosanol-2 were detected in the hydrolysis products of waxes A. A glyceryl monomycolate and a "cord factor" were isolated from waxes C [563].

Properties of the mycolic acids are given on page 123. The fatty acids obtained from the alcohol-ether extract are a mixture of saturated and unsaturated acids from C_{10} to C_{24}; tuberculostearic acid is present. No higher optically active acid of the phthienoic or mycocerosic type could be detected [563].

(4) *Saprophytic Mycobacteria*

In the group of saprophytic acid-fast bacilli are included many Mycobacteria isolated from very various sources and sometimes exhibiting very different biological properties. These bacteria are generally considered harmless, although their inoculation may provoke the formation of abscesses (see, e.g. ref. 1182 and 1183).

Taking advantage of the poor definition of this group of Mycobacteria, we have included *M. marianum* as well as the so-called "leprosy bacillus" studied by Anderson.

(a) *Mycobacterium phlei*

A certain confusion results from the fact that the strain of *M. phlei* studied by Anderson *et al.* [488, 707, 1184, 1187] is chemically very different from the strain of *M. phlei* in the Pasteur Institute collection studied by Barbier [481]. A strain of *M. phlei*, which we designate *M. phlei* "I.C.I." because the bacilli were grown by the Imperial Chemical Industries for the preparation of mycobactine [1188], gave results very close to those obtained by Anderson. The lipids of three strains of *M. phlei* have been therefore studied: *M. phlei* 02145 (Anderson), *M. phlei* "Pasteur", and *M. phlei* "I.C.I.".

The fats of *M. phlei* 02145 were liquid and fairly rich in free fatty acids. On saponification, they gave 74 % fatty acids, 22 % unsaponifiable fraction, and 4.8 % water-soluble fraction. The fatty acids consisted essentially of palmitic acid, a C_{16}-unsaturated acid (which gave palmitic acid on hydrogenation), and a liquid saturated acid $C_{18}H_{36}O_2$. In addition, a saturated hydroxy acid, m.p. 60—61°, $[\alpha]_D + 4.8°$ (acetate m.p. 48°), with molecular weight 488, was isolated [1185] ($C_{32}H_{64}O_3$ has mol. wt. 496.8). The unsaponifiable part, a brown oil with an iodine number of 126, did not give a sterol colour reaction. The water-soluble fraction did not contain glycerol and its nature was not elucidated [1185].

From the fats of *M. phlei* "Pasteur", Barbier [481] isolated 25 % free fatty acids, containing in particular palmitic acid. The neutral fractions contained esters of trehalose, which was isolated after saponification as a powder, m.p. 200—210°, $[\alpha]_D + 194°$ (water), octa-acetate m.p. 80°. n-Tetracosanoic acid, m.p. 80°, identified by its X-ray diffraction sprectum, was the highest straight-chain acid [150].

Glycerol was the only water-soluble constituent from the fat of *M. phlei* "I.C.I.", grown on peptone-glycerol medium [115]. Vapour phase chromatography of the fatty acids obtained by saponification showed the presence of myristic, palmitic, stearic, and tuberculostearic acids; the latter acid was isolated by inclusion of the normal chain acids in urea. Small amounts of C_{16} and C_{18} unsaturated acids, as well as a hydroxy acid having the approximate formula $C_{16}H_{30}O_3$, were detected [115]. A sample of the highest straight-chain acid was analysed by vapour phase chromatography: it contained 20 % docosanoic acid, 4 % tricosanoic acid, 70 % tetracosanoic acid, and 6 % hexacosanoic acid [493].

The phosphatide of *M. phlei* 02145 was obtained as an amorphous solid, m.p. 190°, 2.80 % P, and 0.22 % N. On hydrolysis it gave 40 % of a water-soluble fraction and 60 % of an ether-soluble fraction. 18 % (with respect to the initial phosphatide) "liquid saturated" acids were separated. 9.0 % mannose and 2.0 % inositol were detected, along with another unidentified sugar [1186].

From *M. phlei* "Pasteur" Barbier[481] obtained a preparation of phosphatide, m.p. 180—190°, $[\alpha]_D + 14°$, 1.1 % P, and 0.62 % N, which was devoid of choline and ethanolamine. Hydrolysis gave 60 % fatty acids, 5.5 % glycerol, mannose, glucose, and inositol; one or more amino-acids were also present (p. 165).

The phosphatide of *M. phlei* "I.C.I." was fractionated by chromatography on silicic acid[1189]: 4 fractions, melting between 200 and 220°, were obtained, in which the phosphorous content varied from 1.4 % (the least adsorbed fraction) to 3.9 % (the most strongly adsorbed fraction). All these fractions contained several amino-acids, particularly ornithine. A more recent investigation[1180] has shown that the main components of the phosphatide fraction are phosphatidylinositol, phosphatidylinositol monomannoside, and phosphatidylinositol dimannoside. The structure of a cardiolipin fraction has been established[842 b] (p. 161).

The "purified" waxes (mixture of waxes C and D of *M. phlei* 02145), a white amorphous solid with m.p. 45° and $[\alpha]_D + 15°$, gave on saponification 21.4 % mycolic acids, 12.6 % fatty acids, 6.5 % unsaponifiable fraction, 2.3 % trehalose (octa-acetate m.p. 78—80°), and 1.5 % glycerol (tribenzoate m.p. 75—76°)[488].

The mycolic acids, studied by Peck & Anderson[707] contain mainly a dicarboxylic acid. A similar acid was isolated from the waxes of *M. phlei* "I.C.I." and studied by Clermonte & Lederer[734] (see p. 137). The unsaponifiable fraction consisted of a mixture of 2-eicosanol and 2-octadecanol[488]; Asselineau et al.[493] isolated the same alcohols from the waxes A of *M. phlei* "I.C.I." (p. 158). The unsaponifiable fraction of the waxes of *M. phlei* "Pasteur" contained different alcohols, which could not be identified[481].

"Cord factor", which was detected by IR spectrography in the lipids of a strain of *M. phlei*, has recently been isolated[115, 909]. The main fraction of waxes D consisted of low melting glycolipids[940].

Several papers have been devoted to the carotenoid pigments of *M. phlei*[26, 1190-1197].

Francis et al.[1188] isolated from *M. phlei* "I.C.I." a complex substance, $C_{47}H_{75}O_{10}N_5$, which is a growth factor for *M. paratuberculosis*. Snow[553, 670, 672] showed that this substance, called *mycobactine* P, possesses the structure [366]; it contains in particular an octadec-2-enoic acid residue and 2-methyl-3-hydroxypentanoic acid. A review on the chemistry of mycobactine has been published by Rose & Snow[1198]. A closely related compound, mycobactine T, has been isolated[672 a].

(b) *Mycobacterium smegmatis*

The lipids of *M. smegmatis* were isolated for the first time by Chargaff[13] and studied more recently by Barbier[481] (see Table 60, p. 247).

Saponification of the fats gave 70 % fatty acids, glycerol and sugars. The principal fatty acid is palmitic acid. By partition chromatography, n-tetracosanoic acid, m.p. 80°, identified by X-ray diffraction, was obtained. Phthiocol, m.p. 168—171°, was isolated from the saponified fats[481].

The phosphatide fraction, m.p. 195—210°, $[\alpha]_D + 16°$, exhibited a low phosphorus content (1.1 %) and an abnormally high nitrogen content (4.18 %), although the preparation obtained by Chargaff[13] contained 2.36 % P and 0.39 % N. Saponification gave 73 % fatty

[366]

acids, 6.8 % glycerol, and sugars. Mannose and glucose were detected by paper chromatography of an acid hydrolysate; Scherrer's test for inositol was positive [481]. A recent examination of these phospholipids has shown that phosphatidylinositols are the main components [1180].

The waxes had a high content of free mycolic acids. The waxes D exhibited a low melting point and contained mainly glycolipids devoid of amino-acids [940] (p. 186). α-, β-, and γ-mycolic acids have been discussed on page 137. A toxic mycolic ester of sugars was isolated from the bound lipids by Azuma *et al.* [912a].

(c) *"Leprosy bacillus"*

Anderson *et al.* [490, 496, 942, 1199, 1200, 1204] studied the lipids of a bacillus isolated in 1909 from a case of human leprosy. This strain, no. 370, Hygienic Laboratory, Honolulu, grown in large quantities on Long's synthetic medium, does not belong to the species *M. leprae*, of which all attempts at culture have failed until now. It is probably a saprophytic Mycobacterium — it is well known that leprous lesions contain numerous saprophytic bacilli.

The fats of this bacillus gave on saponification 75.6 % fatty acids, 22 % unsaponifiable fraction, and 1 % of a water-soluble fraction which was identified as trehalose. C_6, C_{14}, C_{16}, C_{18}, C_{20}, C_{22}, and C_{24} straight-chain saturated acids are present; and here again the saturated acid with the longest straight-chain is tetracosanoic acid. C_{14}, C_{16}, C_{18}, C_{20}, C_{21}, C_{22}, and C_{25} unsaturated acids were characterized. Several optically active higher acids were observed, but no information was obtained about their composition [1200]. The unsaponifiable part of the fats contained two phenolic compounds, α- and β-leprosols [496, 497] (p. 69).

The phosphatide fraction, m.p. 231°, 1.75 % P, is practically devoid of nitrogen. Recovered unchanged after attempted hydrolysis with 5 % sulphuric acid, it was first saponified, which gave 66 % ether-soluble fraction; hydrolysis of the remaining polysaccharide gave 6 % (calculated on the initial phosphatide) of an organophosphoric acid, 10.8 % mannose, and 4.7 % inositol. Another sugar, not identified, was also present [1204].

The waxes A were studied by Anderson et al. [490] under the name leprosine. They ocurred in the form of a white powder, m.p. 50—51°, $[\alpha]_D + 4°$, which on saponification gave:

    63 % Mycolic acids (leprosinic acids);

    30 % Fatty acids (myristic, palmitic, stearic, and tetracosanoic acids);

     7 % Unsaponifiable fraction (mixture of 2-eicosanol and 2-octadecanol);

     6 % Glycerol.

The waxes extracted by chloroform do not appear to have been studied. The bound lipids were precipitated from their ethereal solution with methanol: the least soluble fraction (31 % of the bound lipids) contained a glycolipid, m.p. 175—186°, whose properties are noted in Table 39 (p. 187). A slightly more soluble fraction (21 % of the bound lipids) was next precipitated, m.p. 50—53°, whose properties are close to those of leprosine (waxes A). The ether-methanol mother-liquors, after evaporation to dryness gave 48 % of a pasty mass which has not been studied [492]. Two mycolic acids were isolated (see p. 123), and pyrolysis of one of the two gave n-tetracosanoic acid.

(d) Mycobacterium marianum

This bacillus was isolated in 1951 by Sister Marie-Suzanne et al. [1201] from a human leprous lesion and grown on Sauton's medium. Its microbiological characteristics were described by Penso & Sister Marie-Suzanne [1202]. Injection of M. marianum into the rat by different routes provokes the appearance of lesions having certain analogies with those observed in leprosy. Sister Marie-Suzanne et al. [1203] observed that M. marianum is "the first strain of Mycobacteria to be stained by the Sudan Black B method when grown on Sauton's medium".

The lipids of M. marianum were studied by Sister Marie-Suzanne et al. [1203] and by Michel [504, 908]. The lipid contents observed by these authors are mentioned in Table 60 (p. 247).

Sister Marie-Suzanne et al. [1203] have done important work on the fractionation, but have done little work on the fractions obtained. Saponification of the waxes A gave a neutral crystalline (needles) fraction, m.p. 56.5—59.5°, which is a mixture of 2-octadecanol and 2-eicosanol (isolated by Anderson from M. avium and M. phlei).

Michel [504] observed a high content of glycerides in the fats and in the waxes A and C. The glycerides of the waxes A were particularly studied [141] (see p. 157). The phosphatide fraction was separated by chromatography on silicic acid into seven fractions, of which three contained ethanolamine [838]. The most strongly adsorbed fraction, m.p. 197—200°, contained mannose, inositol, 6 % glycerol, ethanolamine, α,ε-diaminopimelic acid, lysine, and ornithine.

Several mycolic acids were isolated from various fractions of waxes and on pyrolysis gave n-tetracosanoic acid. n-Tetracosanoic acid is the longest straight-chain acid observed in the lipids of M. marianum [504].

A "cord factor" was isolated, which contained a monocarboxylic and a dicarboxylic mycolic acid (see p. 175).

Recently, Smith et al. [952] demonstrated the presence of the peptidoglycolipid mycoside C_m in *M. marianum*; this strain, therefore, could be related either to *M. avium* or to non-photochromogenic "atypical" bacteria. The structure of mycoside C_m was studied by Chaput et al. [956] and formula [359] was proposed.

(e) *Various bacilli*

Bruynoghe & Adant [1205] isolated from the pus of an abscess a saprophytic Mycobacterium whose lipids were studied by Asselineau (ref. 64 and unpublished results). 3.8 % Waxes was extracted by chloroform. On saponification they gave 17 % mycolic acids and a crystalline acid, m.p. 80—83°, which was identified as n-tetracosanoic acid by its X-ray diffraction spectrum ($d = 52.6$ Å). The mycolic acid fraction, after purification, melts at 53—55° and possesses the approximate formula $C_{83}H_{166}O_4$; its pyrolysis gave n-tetracosanoic acid, m.p. 79—82°, $d = 52.8$ Å.

A saprophytic Mycobacterium isolated from the waters of the Seine (Pasteur Institute Collection) was studied by Asselineau [64]. Its content of various lipid fractions is noted in Table 60 (p. 247). Saponification of the waxes C gave 12.5 % mycolic acids ($C_{83}H_{166}O_5$, m.p. 58—60°) and 69 % fatty acids (average molecular weight 330). The waxes D show the peculiarity of melting at 117—125°, i.e. considerably higher than the waxes D of other saprophytic Mycobacteria.

Several papers have been devoted to the carotenoid pigments of *M. lacticola* [1206, 1207], *M. lombardo-pellegrini*, *M. grassberger* [1208], *M. marianum*, and *M. battaglini* [1209, 1210]. A new pigment, mycoxanthine, was characterized [1210]. Leprotene, m.p. 197°, was isolated from four strains of Mycobacteria obtained from leprous lesions [1211]; it is identical with isoreniatene and is therefore a diaryl-carotenoide [1211a].

(5) *"Atypical" Mycobacteria*

These Mycobacteria are isolated from cases of human tuberculosis but are distinguished from *M. tuberculosis* by having a low pathogenic power towards the guinea-pig (although they kill the golden hamster). Their growth rate is usually more rapid than that of *M. tuberculosis*. They are differentiated from saprophytic Mycobacteria by their resistance to neo-tetrazolium [1212].

The "atypical" Mycobacteria have been classified in three groups according to their capacity to synthesize pigments [1213]:

(a) *Photochromogenic Mycobacteria*, non-pigmented in the dark, pigmented in light, e.g. *M. kansasii*;

(b) *Scotochromogenic Mycobacteria*, pigmented in the dark;

(c) *Non-photochromogenic Mycobacteria*, non-pigmented, e.g. *M. fortuitum* and strain no. 1217.

Smith et al. [252, 890, 952, 1218a] gave support to this arbitrary classification by showing that specific compounds are found in each group: mycoside A (p. 171) in *M. kansasii*, mycoside C (p. 191) in non-photochromogenic bacteria, and "compound Jat" (mycoside G) in scotochromogenic bacteria.

More information on the chemical composition of the lipids of a few strains has recently been obtained.

Mycoside A and "cord factor" were characterized in the lipids of M. kansasii [890, 952]. Jolles et al. [940] studied the wax D of M. kansasii : these have a content of peptidoglycolipids as high as that of wax D from human strains of M. tuberculosis. However, the difference with the latter strains is shown by the production of tetracosanoic acid on pyrolysis of mycolic acids from M. kansasii [312] whereas "human" mycolic acids give hexacosanoic acid (see p. 122), and by the absence of mycoside A in bacilli of human strains.

From the lipids of M. fortuitum (M. minetti), Fregnan et al. [890] isolated a compound that was called "mycoside F"; this compound had an IR spectrum similar to that of trehalose-6,6'-dimycolate ("cord factor") but possessed only a low level of toxicity for C57 mice [890]. Recently, Rojas & Vilkas [1216] isolated a diester of trehalose and palmitic acid, m.p. 77-81°, $[\alpha]_D + 45°$ from the lipids of another batch of M. fortuitum; it is likely that the compound obtained by Fregnan et al. is identical with trehalose dipalmitate and the term mycoside should no longer be used to designate it.

"Cord factor" (p. 173), m.p. 49—51°, $C_{186}H_{366}O_{17}$, has been obtained from the waxes C + D of M. fortuitum by Azuma & Yamamura [910]; hydrolysis gave a mycolic acid, $C_{88}H_{176}O_4$, m.p. 59—61°, and trehalose (characterized by paper chromatography).

Fortuitine, a peptidolipid, m.p. 199—202°, $[\alpha]_D — 72°$, was isolated from M. fortuitum by Vilkas et al. [343, 313] (see p. 191).

The lipids of a non-photochromogenic strain, no. 1217 of the International Centre for Information and Distribution of Type-Cultures, Lausanne, were studied by Lanéelle et al [1217]. Saponification of the fats gave 84 % fatty acids and 7 % unsaponifiable material; glycerol was the only water-soluble product detected. By chromatography on silicic acid, the phospholipids were separated into a fraction containing bound ornithine [875] (see p. 167) and nitrogen-free fractions having phosphatidylinositol-polymannosides as the main components. Waxes A were a mixture of triglycerides and mycoside C_{1217}; from waxes C were isolated mono-, di-, and triglycerides and "cord factor". Only a small amount of low melting wax D was obtained. Pyrolysis of the mycolic acids gave tetracosanoic acid. Branched-chain acids with 15, 17, and 19 carbon atoms were observed, but no acids of the phthienoic or mycocerosic type could be detected [1217].

Mycoside G was isolated from the lipids of M. marinum (M. balnei) [893a].

"Cord factor" has been isolated from several other strains of "atypical" Mycobacteria [909, 910].

(6) Mycobacterium leprae

It has not yet been possible to grow the leprosy bacillus in vitro because of its inability to utilize the usual sources of carbon [1218]. As a consequence, the only observations which it has been possible to make concern bacilli isolated from lesions. It is necessary to underline that such studies pertain to a heterogeneous bacterial population, as saprophytic Mycobacteria are frequently present in leprous lesions.

Dharmendra [1219] was able to isolate bacilli from a leprous nodule and submitted them to Anderson's procedure for the extraction of lipids. Glycerides, phosphatides, and waxes were obtained, but the author does not mention any properties of these various fractions. Chatterjee *et al.*[1220] applied cytochemical techniques to bacilli isolated from lesions and demonstrated the presence of lipids in the polar corpuscles, i.e. at the extremities of the bacteria).

Nakamura[54, 1221] isolated the bacilli of murine leprosy *(M. lepraemurium)* from the subcutaneous lesions of rats; these bacilli contained 34.5 % lipids, but no analysis was made.

All these studies have been hampered by the small quantities of material available.

(7) *Relation between acid-fastness and lipid content*

Acid-fastness (acido-résistance, Säure-festigkeit) is the property possessed by the majority of Mycobacteria, at a certain moment of their evolutionary cycle, of being stained with phenolic fuchsin and resisting decoloring with acids and alcohols.

This phenomenon is related to the presence of mycolic acids in the Mycobacteria[1222], these acids being likewise acid-fast. Nevertheless, we have insisted in 1950[64] on the necessity of making a sharp distinction between the two phenomena of acid-fastness of lipid fractions and acid-fastness of the entire bacillus.

(a) *Acid-fastness of lipid fractions*

Anderson[1222] showed in 1932 that mycolic acid is acid-fast, and the systematic examination of various lipid fractions led to the conclusion that this acid is the only bacterial constituent which possesses this property[636, 1223, 1224]. The acid-fastness of waxy fractions is explained either by the presence of free mycolic acids or by their liberation in the course of heating with phenolic fuchsin[1224].

In order to be acid-fast, the mycolic acid ought to possess a free carboxyl (neither methyl mycolate nor mycolic alcohol are acid-fast). The hydroxyl can be esterified (the acetate of mycolic acid is also acid-fast), but its elimination causes the property to be lost (anhydro-mycolic acid)[1222, 1223]. No difference in behaviour was observed between an α-mycolic acid, m.p. 55—56°, and a β-mycolic acid, m.p. 71—73°, of the Test human strain[64]. The mycolic acids of the avirulent strain $H_{37}Ra$ are equally acid fast.

Corynomycolic acid, (+)-2-tetradecyl-3-hydroxyoctadecanoic acid, [201], is acid-fast[1120], as are also the α-branched β-hydroxylated synthetic acids (mixtures of stereoisomers)[690]. The branch at α plays an ancillary rôle because DL-3-hydroxy-docosanoic and-tetracosanoic acids are likewise acid-fast. The β-hydroxy group is indispensable, since the non-hydroxylated higher fatty acids (docosanoic and hexacosanoic acids) or acids possessing a hydroxyl more remote from the carboxyl (9,10-dihydroxyoctadecanoic acid, aleuritic acid, cholic acid) are not acid-fast[1223, 1224].

That the acid-fastness of the mycolic acids (which are all β-hydroxy-acids) might be due to the formation of a complex salt with fuchsin[4] is supported by the experiments of Berg[1225, 1226], who demonstrated the formation between mycolic acids and crystal violet of a complex soluble in chloroform, absorbing specifically at about 350 mμ.

(b) *Acid-fastness of the entire bacillus*

The rôle of certain structural features in the bacillus in the phenomenon of acid-fastness is demonstrated by the disappearance of this property after mechanical treatments wich do not modify the mycolic acid molecule. For example, the tubercle bacilli are rendered non-acid-fast by simple grinding [1227, 1228], by ultra-sonic treatment [1229], or by heating with 0.1N hydrochloric acid for 10 min [1230].

The experiments of Sordelli & Arena [1231] and of Yegian & Vanderlinde [1232] show the rôle played by cellular permeability, and it is probable that the lipids intervene in this pheno-menon by reason of their existence, in a more or less complex form, in the cell wall (see p. 199). This explanation, proposed by Long [1233] in 1922, is in accord with the experiments on "artificial acid-fastness" [1234]: covering non-acid-fast bacilli in a fatty material such as butter (or the peptido-glycolipid PmKo [1235]) restores the acid-fastness. Nevertheless, artificial acid-fastness is only observed in the case of bacilli belonging to the genera *Mycobacterium*, *Actinomyces*, and *Corynebacterium* [1234]. On the other hand, surface active agents can cause the disappearance of acid-fastness at ordinary temperature at pH 7 [1236].

Lipids which play a part in the acid-fastness of the whole bacillus do not necessarily belong to the mycolic acid group. A relation between poly-β-hydroxybutyrate and the acid-fastness of spores of *Bacillus* species has been suggested [1237]. Cellular formations, apparently devoid of mycolic acids, can be acid-fast (eggs of *Toenia*, oocysts of *Eimeria cuniculi*, etc.). Likewise, the "ceroids", lipid granules produced in the animal by injection or by inhalation of oils rich in unsaturated fatty acids, are acid-fast (see, e.g. ref. 1238). On the other hand, bacteria can be devoid of acid-fastness and nevertheless contain an acid-fast mycolic acid, e.g. *C. diphtheriae*.

(8) *Relation between the lipid composition and the pathogenicity of Mycobacterial strains*

The *pathogenicity* of a bacillus represents its capacity for inducing in a given animal the various manifestations which constitute a disease [1239]. This property has been related, in a few cases, to the production by the bacillus of a definite chemical compound, e.g. the capsular polysaccharides of *Diplococcus pneumoniae* and the exogenous toxin of *Clostridum tetani*.

Owing to the importance of lipids in the case of the Mycobacteria, numerous authors have sought to demonstrate a lipid constituent capable of taking part in the pathogenicity of the tubercle bacillus. For this purpose, the lipid composition of bacilli of virulent, attenuated, or avirulent strains has been compared.

Martin [1240] ascertained that the $H_{37}Rv$ strain contained 24.5 % of total free lipids, whereas the $H_{37}Ra$ strain only contained 16.6 %. We had occasion to make similar observ-ations (Table 56, p. 240). Nevertheless, such differences have little significance and can at times be observed with the same strain in the course of successive analyses (Table 56, Brévannes strain). While some strains of saprophytic Mycobacteria show a relatively low content of lipids, others possess a lipid content similar to that of virulent strains of *M. tuberculosis* (Table 60, p. 247).

Seibert *et al.* [1241] noted that the lipids isolated from virulent S variants of human strains H_{37} and R_1 (and also a strain of *M. avium*) have an iodine number higher than that of the lipids from non-virulent R variants. On the other hand, Asselineau [76, 573] and Cason *et al.* [561] did not find any phthienoic acid in the avirulent H_{37}Ra strain, although the virulent H_{37}Rv, Brévannes, Canetti and Test strains contained it. This is, to our knowledge, the only qualitative difference which has been observed between the virulent and avirulent strains of *M. tuberculosis*. BCG, an attenuated strain, does not contain phthienoic acid, but a different dextrorotatory α,β-unsaturated acid [561, 630]. It would be important to examine the lipids of other avirulent strains. The systematic study of the mycolic acids of eight human strains of the tubercle bacillus showed no characteristic variation. Nevertheless, it should be noted that the virulent human strains generally have a low content of O_3-mycolic acids and that this acid is very strongly adsorbed on alumina columns, whereas the strains with little or no virulence are relatively rich in slightly adsorbed O_3-mycolic acids (see Table 26, p. 121).

The study of several human strains of *M. tuberculosis* showed that the wax D content varies in a manner approximately parallel with the virulence of the strain (see Table 56) [926, 1242]. It would be tempting to conclude from this that the waxes D are involved in the pathogenicity of the tubercle bacillus. Too few of the avirulent strains have as yet been examined. The wax D content of a strain can be reduced indirectly by phenomena which can escape direct observation. Dubos (ref. 1243, p. 110) made the remark that "it has been in our experience that, in general, attenuated and avirulent cultures die more rapidly and undergo autolytic changes sooner than do virulent cultures". Wax D are particularly sensitive to autolysis. Nevertheless, young cultures (a few days on Sauton's medium) of virulent bacilli have a diminished pathogenicity [1244] and a reduced content of wax D [38].

The toxic factor, "cord factor", could never be found in avirulent variants of tubercle bacilli [1245]. Nevertheless, it can easily be isolated from the attenuated strain of BCG [906], and "cord factors" have been characterized in the case of *M. phlei* [252], and *M. smegmatis* [909]. Yamamura *et al.* [1246] studied the rate of elimination of ^{32}P from the mouse after intravenous injection of bacilli labelled with ^{32}P, (some previously defatted with an alcohol-ether mixture and with chloroform and some not). These authors conclude that the virulent bacilli are more resistant to disintegration in vivo than the avirulent bacilli and that the lipid fraction extracted by chloroform (which contains the wax D and the "cord factor") play an important rôle in the phenomenon.

Dubos & Middlebrook [1247] observed in 1948 that suspensions of tubercle bacilli in a pH 8.9 buffer are coloured red by Neutral Red [367] when they are virulent bacilli and yellow when they are avirulent bacilli (for a review on this cytochemical test, see ref. 1248, p. 22). Neutral Red is a pH indicator, red in acid medium, and yellow in alkaline medium (zone of colour change: pH 6.8—8.0). Therefore, the red colour of the virulent bacilli points

[367]

TABLE 61. THE DISTRIBUTION OF VARIOUS SIMPLE LIPID COMPONENTS IN VARIOUS STRAINS OF MYCOBACTERIA

	M. tuberculosis var. hominis Virulent	M. tuberculosis var. hominis Avirulent	M. tuberculosis var. bovis Virulent	M. tuberculosis var. bovis BCG	M. avium	M. paratuberculosis	M. phlei "Pasteur"	M. phlei "I.C.1"	M. smegmatis	Bruynoghe-Adant	"Leprosy bacillus"	M. marianum	"Atypical" Photo-chromogenic	"Atypical" Non-photo-chromogenic	"Atypical" Scoto-chromogenic
Aromatic acids	+	+	+	+	+	+		+						+	
Tuberculostearic acid	+	+	+	−	−	−		−							
Phthienoic acids	+	−	+	+											
Mycocerosic acids	+	+	+	+											
Mycolic acids	+	+	+	+	+	+	+	+	+	+	+	+	+	+	+
Monocarboxylic	−	−	−	−	+	+	−	+	−		+	+			
Dicarboxylic															
Number of carbon atoms of the acid obtained by pyrolysis	26	26	26	26	24	24	24	24	24	24	24	24	24	24	
Mycolonic acid	±	−	+	+	26	+		22							
Fatty acid with the longest straight-chain	26	26	26	26	+	24	24	24	24	24	24	24		24	
Phthiocerol	+	+	+	+	−	−		−			−				
2-Eicosanol and 2-octadecanol	−	−	−	−	+	+		+			+	+	−	−	

to the formation of salts between the dye and the acid groups present on the surface of the bacilli. Asselineau & Lederer [926] ascertained that particles of wax D (of human strains) fix the dye and take on a red tint and particles of mycolic acid a rose tint. Simple fatty acids (stearic acid) are not coloured except after a prolonged time of contact. As the wax D seem to be more abundant in the case of virulent bacilli, they could play a rôle in the coloration of the bacilli. In support of this thesis, one can note that very young bacilli of virulent strains are coloured yellow [1249]; these bacilli have a relatively low content of wax D. On the other hand, Middlebrook *et al.* [341, 1250] isolated from a light petroleum washing of virulent bacilli a lipid fraction which fixes Neutral Red and which contains sulphur (1.1 % sulphur in the most pure preparations). From the IR spectrum, the sulphur is present in the form of a -SO_3H group. This sulpholipid could likewise take part in the colouration of the virulent bacilli. It may be added that Mankievicz [1251] observed that virulent bacilli, treated by an enzyme preparation (cerases) from the larvae of *Galleria mellonella* are coloured yellow by Neutral Red, as are avirulent bacilli.

Other colour reactions, using redox dyes, give results that depend on the virulence of the bacilli. In 1950, Bloch [1252] showed that suspensions of avirulent bacilli reduced methylene blue, whereas virulent bacilli did not. Wilson *et al.* [1253] made similar observations with dyes of the phenol-indophenol type: only avirulent (or saprophytic) strains produced a decoloration. This type of reaction could be explained by the existence, in the case of virulent bacilli, of a superficial pellicle of lipid nature which prevents the dehydrogenase present in all the bacilli from entering into contact with its substrate.

In conclusion, we can but quote a phrase of Dubos (ref. 1254, p. 13): "pathogenic behavior seems to depend upon a combination of minor and subtle peculiarities of the infective agents which permit them to survive, multiply and cause damage in specific in vivo environments".

(9) *Distribution of some lipid constituents among the various strains of Mycobacteria*

Tables 61 and 62 show the distribution of various constituents, more or less characteristic of the lipids of Mycobacteria, in different species. Too little data are still available concerning saprophytic and "atypical" Mycobacteria.

Among the simple constituents, phthiocerol and the mixture of 2-eicosanol and 2-octadecanol are distributed in a very distinct manner (in that one excludes the other): phthiocerol is characteristic of *M. tuberculosis* (*hominis* and *bovis* varieties), while the C_{18}–and C_{20}–alcohols are encountered in *M. avium*, *M. paratuberculosis*, and the saprophytic Mycobacteria. A similar type of distribution is found with the acids obtained by pyrolysis of mycolic acids (the results being intermediate in the case of *M. avium*) and with the acids having the longest straight-chain (hexacosanoic or tetracosanoic acids) that can be isolated from the saponification products.

Among the complex lipid constituents, two groups of substances could be utilized to differentiate certain species: the wax D with a high or a low melting point (according to their content of peptidoglycolipids) and the mycosides. In spite of important differences in properties, the wax D of all the Mycobacteria contain the same fundamental

TABLE 62. THE DISTRIBUTION OF COMPLEX LIPIDS IN VARIOUS STRAINS OF MYCOBACTERIA

	M. tuberculosis				M. avium	M. paratuberculosis	M. phlei		M. marianum	"Atypical Mycobacteria"		
	var. hominis		var. bovis				"Pasteur"	"I.C.I."		Photochromogenic (M. kansasii)	Non-photochromogenic	Scoto-chromogenic
	Virulent	Avirulent	Virulent	BCG								
Common glycerides	+	+	+	+	+	+		+	+	+	+	
Glyceryl mycolate	+			+	+							
Trehalose dimycolate ("cord factors")	+		+	+	+	+		+	+		+	
Phthiocerol dimycocerosate..	+	+	+	+								
Phosphatidylinositopolymannosides..........	+	+	+	+	+	+		+			+	
Wax D												
High melting waxes....	+	+	+	+						+		
Low melting waxes ...	—	—	+	+	+		+	+	+		+	
Mycoside A										+		
Mycoside B			+	+								
Mycoside C					+				+		+	
Compound J_{at}												+
Peptidolipids						+					+	

constituents: mycolic acids on the one hand, and arabinose, galactose, and mannose, on the other. The mycosides permit finer distinctions to be made among several bacterial groups.

Because of the quantity of material necessary and the time required for their execution, such analyses cannot be utilized for routine identifications.

19. Actinomycetaceae

Nocardia

Lipids of *Nocardia asteroides* were studied by Michel[504]: the bacteria contained 30.4% fats, 1.3% crude phosphatide fraction, 5.5% ether-insoluble fraction (from the alcohol-ether extract), 1.1% waxes B, 4.7% waxes C, and 0.32% waxes D. The total free lipids amounted to 43% of the dry weight of the bacilli, which is a very high value.

The fraction insoluble in ether was isolated in the form of a solid which collected at the ether-water interface when the ethereal solution of the lipids coming from the alcohol-ether extract was washed with water. This fraction consisted essentially of a peptidolipid, m.p. 215—217°, $[\alpha]_D$ + 44.5° ($CHCl_3$), which was dealt with on page 190[948, 949 a].

From the lipids of *N. asteroides*, Michel *et al.* [698] isolated nocardomycolic acid, an unsaturated hydroxy-acid, $C_{50}H_{96}O_3$ ($\pm$ 3 CH_2), oil, $[\alpha]_D$ + 5°, which was discussed on page 117. Identical or closely related nocardomycolic acids were isolated by Lanéelle *et al.*[1256 b] from two strains of *N. brasiliensis*, and from *N. pellegrino* and *N. rhodocrous*.

Saponification of the fats of *N. asteroides* gave 56 °/₀ unsaponifiable fraction (a very high value), from which was isolated a diunsaturated branched-chain alcohol, nocardol, $C_{49}H_{96}O$ ($\pm$ 3 CH_2), m.p. 55—59°, $[\alpha]_D$ + 0.5° (p. 79). In one strain (but not from another strain) of *N. brasiliensis*, a large part of the fats consists of esters of hentriacontanol-16 (p. 72) [1256a, 1256 b].

The composition of the mixtures of fatty acids obtained by saponification of the fats of *N. asteroides*, *N. brasiliensis*, *N. lurida*, and *N. rugosa* was studied by Bordet & Michel [1256] by means of vapour phase chromatography. Straight-chain saturated acids from C_{14} to C_{19} were found (palmitic acid was the major component of this group). Iso and anteiso acids with 15, 16, and 17 carbon atoms were detected, as well as iso-C_{18} and tuberculostearic acids. Hexadec-9- and 10-enoic, heptadec-9-enoic, and octadec-9-enoic acids were identified [1256].

The occurrence of nocardomycolic and tuberculostearic acids gives support to the classification of Nocardia and Mycobacteria in a same family.

Lipid inclusions were observed in the cells of *N. corallina* [1257] and *N. rubra* [1258].

From *N. acidophilus*, Johnson & Burdon [1259] isolated the antibiotic mycomycin, $C_{13}H_{10}O_2$, m.p. about 75° (with explosion), $[\alpha]_D^{25}$ — 120°. The work of Celmer & Solomons [1260] led to the formula [368] for mycomycin; the UV spectrum (in ether) shows maxima at 256, 267 and 281 mμ (ε = 35 000, 61 000 and 67 000).

$$HC{\equiv}C{-}C{\equiv}C{-}CH{=}C{=}CH{-}\ CH{=}CH{-}CH{=}CH{-}CH_2{-}COOH \qquad [368]$$

Actinomyces

The lipids of four strains of *A. israelii* have been isolated: they account for 2.8—3.3 % of the weight of dry bacilli; their phosphorus content was 0.2—0.4 %. The main fatty acids obtained on saponification were identified as palmitic, stearic, and oleic acids [1261].

MacLennan [1262] detected 6-deoxy-L-talose in the cell wall of *A. bovis*, but he was unable to isolated glycolipids containing this deoxy-sugar from the lipids of the same strain.

20. *Streptomycetaceae*

Streptomyces

The cultures of *Streptomyces* are composed of an undivided mycelium. Nevertheless, these micro-organisms are considered as bacteria [5]. The validity of this classification is supported by the absence of sterols [806, 1263].

While a great number of strains of *Streptomyces* have been isolated and grown in order to seek the possible presence of antibiotics in the culture medium (see, e.g. ref. 1264), the chemical composition of the mycelium has been poorly studied.

Str. griseus contains 2.7 % lipids; the fatty acids obtained on saponification have a mean molecular weight of 380 [1263]. Palmitic, stearic, and oleic acids were detected, as well as an unidentified acid [1265]. 0.56 % lipids was obtained from a culture of *Str. pheochromogenus* [1263]. Recently, careful studies of the fatty acid composition of several strains of *Streptomyces* was achieved. Ballio *et al.* [544b] observed that C_{14}, C_{15} and C_{16} iso acids and C_{15} anteiso acid are the most prominent acids of the lipids of *Str. aureofaciens*, *Str. coelicolor*, *Str. flavovirens*, *Str. gelaticus*, *Str. griseus* and *Str. viridochromogenes*. Simultaneously, Hofheinz and Grisebach [563a] obtained similar results on *Str. erythreus and Str. halstedii*; small amounts of tuberculostearic acid (10-methyloctadecanoic acid) were also characterized. It must be stressed that, in spite of the use of propionic acid for building macrolide aglycones, these latter strains does not produce branched-chain fatty acids of the mycocerosic acid type. (+)-12-Methyl-tetradec-3-enoic and 13-methyltetradec-3-enoic acids were found in the antibiotic aspartocin, produced by *S. griseus* var. *spiralis* [1265a].

Waxy fractions were isolated from *Str. noursei;* the high nitrogen content of one of these (10.6 %) indicates the probable presence of peptidolipids [1266].

Dodecyl 5-oxo-octadecanoate was obtained from the culture of a strain of *Str. flavus*, and called actinomycin J_2 [1267]. From the antibiotic glumamycine (produced by a species of *Streptomyces*), an optically active fatty acid suggested to be x-methyltridec-4-enoic acid, b.p. 139°/1 mm, $[\alpha]_D + 4°$ (ethanol) has been isolated [1268].

Several strains of *Streptomyces* synthesize macrolide antibiotics, which result from the glycosidic linkage of one or two peculiar sugars with macrocyclic lactones. These lactones come from hydroxy-acids with methyl branches, the locations of which are similar to those in phthienoic and mycocerosic acids (p. 95). The hydroxy-acids derived from the lactones of some macrolides are listed below:

$$\underset{\substack{| \\ OH}}{CH_3-CH_2-CH} \underset{\substack{| \\ CH_3}}{-C} \underset{\substack{| \\ OH}}{-CH} =CH-CO- \underset{\substack{| \\ CH_3}}{CH} -CH_2- \underset{\substack{| \\ CH_3}}{CH} - \underset{\substack{| \\ OH}}{CH} - \underset{\substack{| \\ CH_3}}{CH} -COOH \qquad [369]$$

derived from methymycine, synthesized by a species of *Streptomyces* [1269].

$$\underset{\substack{| \\ OH}}{CH_3-CH} - \underset{\substack{| \\ CH_3}}{CH} - \underset{\substack{| \\ OH}}{CH} - \underset{\substack{| \\ CH_3}}{CH} -CH-CO- \underset{\substack{|| \\ CH_2}}{C} -CH_2- \underset{\substack{| \\ CH_3}}{CH} - \underset{\substack{| \\ OH}}{CH} - \underset{\substack{| \\ CH_3}}{CH} - \underset{\substack{| \\ OH}}{CH} - \underset{\substack{| \\ CH_3}}{CH} -COOH \qquad [370]$$

derived from oleandomycine (synthesized by *Str. antibioticus*) [1270].

$$\underset{\substack{| \\ OH}}{CH_3-CH_2-CH} - \underset{\substack{| \\ CH_3}}{C} --- \underset{\substack{| \\ OH}}{CH} - \underset{\substack{| \\ CH_3}}{CH} -CO- \underset{\substack{| \\ CH_3}}{CH} -CH_2- \underset{\substack{| \\ CH_3}}{C} --- \underset{\substack{| \\ OH}}{CH} - \underset{\substack{| \\ CH_3}}{CH} - \underset{\substack{| \\ OH}}{CH} - \underset{\substack{| \\ CH_3}}{CH} -COOH$$
$$[371]$$

derived from erythromycine A (synthesized by *Str. erythreus*) [1271].

In the formulae [369]-[371], the OH written in bold face is linked to the carboxy group in the macrocyclic natural lactone.

The biosynthesis of the aglycone part of erythromycine and methymycine has been considered on p. 147.

Bacteria isolated from animal digestive tracts

We have assembled here work carried out on the lipids of bacteria which live in the digestive tract of man and ruminants. Such bacterial preparations often contain mixtures of species, more or less identified, and they may also be contaminated with protozoa.

In 1955, Garton & Oxford [1272] extracted the lipids from bacteria obtained from the rumen of sheep fed on hay. About 9 % lipids were obtained, containing in particular 38 % neutral fat and 39 % phospholipids.

The neutral fat, on saponification, gave glycerol (identified by its tribenzoate m.p. 73—74°), fatty acids (higher than C_{10}), and 21 % of an unsaponifiable fraction which contained carotenoids and a sterol $C_{27}H_{48}O_2$, m.p. 130—132°, $[\alpha]_D \pm 0°$. Linoleic and linoleic acids, as well as *trans*-unsaturated acids, could not be detected in the total fatty acids.

The fatty acids of these bacteria were particularly investigated by Allison *et al.* [1273], and Wegner & Foster [762]. Analyses of the fatty acid mixtures obtained from the whole bacterial content of the rumen of a cow (maintained on a normal hay and grain ration) are listed in Table 63; for comparison, the results obtained in the case of the protozoal population, and of *Ruminococcus flavefaciens*, have been added. *R. flavefaciens* is a bacterial species not recognized in the seventh edition of Bergey's manual [5]; it was isolated from the rumen by Sijpesteijn [1274]. Aldehydes (mainly normal-C_{16} and branched-C_{15}) were detected in the product of acid hydrolysis of lipids of mixed rumen bacteria [1274a].

Elsden & Lewis [1275] studied by chromatographic techniques the volatile fatty acids synthesized by a gram-negative *coccus* isolated from the rumen of sheep.

Sammons *et al.* [1276] grew bacteria isolated from human faeces; lipids collected at the surface of the medium and a few of their characteristics were described. It could be a species close to *Streptococcus faecalis*.

Small micro-organisms

Pleuropneumonia-like organisms (PPLO) are small spherical organisms which, in spite of some similarities with the L-forms of bacteria, have been shown by filtration and electron microscopy to be fundamentally different (see, e.g. ref. 1277). The name of *Mycoplasmataceae* has been proposed for the PPLO group.

Data on the lipid composition of several strains of PPLO [1278, 1279, 1280a] and of *Mycoplasma gallisepticum* [1280] have recently been published. Sterols are growth factors for strains of PPLO, but these organisms seem unable to synthesize them [814]. A small book has been devoted to the psittacosis group of organisms [1282a]; it was stated that "lipids are surprisingly high, comparable in level to that of the mycobacteria".

O'Leary [1281] obtained 190 mg fatty acids from 55 litres of cultures of the PPLO strain 07. By vapour phase chromatography, palmitic and stearic acids were found to be the major

TABLE 63. THE COMPOSITION OF THE FATTY ACID MIXTURES ISOLATED FROM BACTERIA AND PROTOZOA OF THE RUMEN OF A COW [1274]

(as % of the total fatty acids)

Acid: number of carbon atoms	Bacteria			Rumino-coccus flave-faciens	Protozoa		
	Neutral lipids	Free fatty acids	Polar lipids		Neutral lipids	Free fatty acids	Polar lipids
12	0.6		1.5	0.7			
13 branched. .			1.2	1.5			
13			0.7	—			0.7
14 branched. .	0.7		1.3	2.0			
14	2.0	0.9	3.8	2.5	1.0		1.6
15 branched. .	6.7	1.9	20.3	43.7	0.5		3.7
15	4.5	1.2	8.2	4.3	1.1	0.6	2.0
16 branched. .	2.9		1.6	9.3	2.2		1.1
16	26.1	16.9	30.6	19.0	26.5	14.2	37.5
16 = *	1.5	0.8	1.3	3.4	0.7		1.2
17 branched. .	1.5	0.5	1.2		1.2	0.6	2.8
17	0.4	1.9	0.8	1.8		1.3	0.8
18	10.7	58.9	6.5	4.1	12.3	68.3	10.3
18 = ...	16.2	12.5	10.2	6.9	17.1	10.0	20.3
18 2= . . .	18.1	4.3	10.7	0.8	27.5	4.9	14.6
18 4= or . . 20 = ...	7.9				9.7		3.2

* Double bond.

components of the mixture (56.5 and 15.5 %, respectively, of the total fatty acids). Fatty acids with 15 and 17 carbon atoms (2.4 and 5.3 %) were also observed: they may be cyclopropane acids. Moreover, a fraction was eluted between the C_{14}-and the branched C_{15}-acids: its chromatographic behaviour was similar to that of a cyclopropene acid [1281].

Some information on the lipids of an antigenic fraction of *Rickettsia prowazeki* was given by Cohen & Chargaff [1282]. The incorporation of palmitate, oleate and linoleate in the phospholipids (phosphatidic acid, cardiolipin, phosphatidylethanolamine and choline) of *Wolbachia persica*, a rickettsia-like microorganism, was shown by Neptune *et al.* [1282b].

Influence of antibiotic resistance on the composition of the lipids of bacterial species

We shall consider in this section only the studies of variations in lipid composition that a bacterial species can exhibit according to its resistance or sensitivity to a given antibiotic. The work carried out on the rôle of lipids in the action mechanism of an antibiotic (e.g. ref. 833, 1294, 1283) will be left aside, because of the scarcity of data currently available.

(1) *M. tuberculosis*

(a) *Streptomycin:* Table 56 (p. 240) shows the content of various lipid fractions in a strain $H_{37}Rv$ and a $H_{37}Rv$ strain resistant to 200 µg/ml of streptomycin in culture medium (designated $H_{37}Rv$ S.r.). No significant difference was observed in the mycolic acids of either of the two strains [724]. Beljanski & Grumbach [1284] studied a strain $H_{37}Ra$ and a $H_{37}Ra$ strain resistant to streptomycin (2,000 µg/ml): on the 15th day of culture, the two strains had the same lipid content, whereas on the 30th day the resistant strain was distinctly less rich in lipids.

It is surprising that Chandrasekar *et al.* [1285] found, in the case of a variant of $H_{37}Rv$ resistant to 100 µg/ml of streptomycin, twice the quantity of lipids as in a sensitive strain. By spectrophotometric determination, the same authors obtained higher values for the α,β-unsaturated content in the resistant strain and lower values for the C_{27}-phthienoic acid (no information was given about the method of determining the C_{27}-phthienoic acid in the presence of the other α,β-unsaturated acids).

Motomiya *et al.* [1286, 1287] grew a streptomycin-sensitive avian strain for 72 h on Sauton's medium. The bacilli were harvested and "submerged" in Sauton's medium with or without dihydrostreptomycin (100 µg/ml) and kept at 37° for 6 h with occasional shaking. The streptomycin-treated bacilli had a higher content of phospholipids and a higher arabinose content of the lipids extracted with methanol-chloroform 3:1 and insoluble in acetone.

(b) *Isonicotinic hydrazide (isoniazide):* Russe & Barclay [1288] grew bacilli of strain R_1Rv with or without addition of isonicotinic hydrazide (10 mg/ml): the controls contained 16.5 % total lipids and the bacilli grown in the presence of isoniazide 11.6 %. No significant difference was found between the phospholipid content of bacilli sensitive or resistant to isoniazide [1289]. The content of "cord factor" was about the same in the isoniazide-resistant and sensitive bacilli [1290]. Unusual pigments are produced when BCG is grown in the presence of isoniazide [1291].

Isoniazide-treated Mycobacteria show a decreased ability to incorporate [1—^{14}C]-acetate into their fatty acids [1292]. However, Winder *et al.* [1289] observed no inhibitory effect of isoniazide on the incorporation of acetate into lipids in presence of cell-free extracts of BCG or *M. smegmatis.*

(2) *Other bacterial species*

The lipid content of chloramphenicol-resistant strains of *Salmonella typhosa, S. paratyphi* B, *S. typhimurium,* and *Escherichia coli* (0:111) was found to be higher than that of the respective sensitive strains [1293]. In particular, the ether-extractable lipid content increased in proportion to the development of resistance to chloramphenicol in *S. paratyphi* B. It should be noted that this resistance is not specific, and the bacilli adapted to chloramphenicol also become resistant to terramycin and penicillin (but not streptomycin) [1293]. The lipid content of a poly-resistant strain of *Staphylococcus aureus* (resistant to 6 antibiotics) was higher than that of a sensitive strain (5.3 % instead of 3.6 %); the phospholipid fraction particularly was increased. No characteristic differences in the fatty acid composition were observed [1097].

A correlation between the phospholipid content of bacteria (two *Pseudomonas species,* and *Sta. aureus)* and their resistance to basic polypeptide antibiotics (polymyxins) was observed as early as 1956 by Newton [1012].

Hill *et al.* [1016] found an unusually high lipid content in the cell wall of tetracyclin-resistant strains of *Streptococcus pyogenes;* however, cell walls of *Str. pyogenes* isolated from impetigo lesions also has a high lipid content in spite of the sensitivity of these strains to tetracyclins.

Biological properties
of bacterial lipids

Because of the high lipid content exhibited by Mycobacteria and the rôle that certain of them can play in the pathogenicity of these bacilli, the biological properties of the lipids of Mycobacteria have been studied much more intensively than those of other bacterial lipids. "The whole tubercle bacillus is a rich packet of biological activities, all theoretically residing in substances capable of chemical definition" [1440].

Reviews of the biological properties of the lipids from Mycobacteria have been published by Sabin [1295], Roulet & Brenner [1296], Cattaneo [1297], Negre [1298], Raffel [1299], Popp [1300], Asselineau [1242] and Lederer [1306]. In addition, considerable information can be found in the books by Rich [1301], Canetti [1302], Drea & Andrejew [1303], Negre [1304], and Long [1305].

A review, including the properties of lipids from other bacterial species, has been written by Asselineau & Lederer [63].

I. TISSUE REACTIONS

1. LIPIDS OF MYCOBACTERIA

The first experiments on the biological properties of tubercle bacillus lipids demonstrated the production of granulomas by subcutaneous or intraperitoneal injection of some lipid fractions. During the decade 1930-1940, this problem stimulated numerous researches.

It became evident from these investigations that the most active lipid fraction in the formation of granulomas was the phosphatide fraction [1307]: the transformation of monocytes into epithelioid cells and the formation of giant cells by atypical mitosis of a single cell were described minutely. Nevertheless, up to 12 daily injections of 80 mg of material are necessary to produce an intense reaction. The activity of phosphatide preparations varies according to the species of bacteria from which they are obtained: in rabbits a decreasing activity was observed in the order: *M. tuberculosis* var. *hominis*, *M. avium*, *M. tuberculosis* var. *bovis*, and *M. phlei* (ref. 1308; see also ref. 1309). However, none of these experiments were done with well defined fractions.

Sabin [1295] concluded that "phthioic" acids, i.e. acids of the phthienoic type, are responsible for the activity of the phosphatides. The activity of numerous branched-chain fatty acids, synthetic or isolated from the tubercle bacillus, was then tested [1310-1318]. Some results, obtained after intraperitoneal injection of alcoholic saline suspensions into the guinea-pig, are assembled in Table 64. They show that synthetic acids can be as active as the natural (phthienoic) acids, and that it is difficult to determine what conditions are required to endow a compound with the maximum inducing activity. 10-methyltetracosanoic acid, for example, "has proved to cause intraperitoneal lesions rather closely related to tubercles" [1319], while tuberculostearic acid (10-methyloctadecanoic acid) is devoid of activity [1307].

The conclusion of these investigations is somewhat deceiving, since in 1955 Ungar [1318] wrote: "I regard the lesion produced by synthetic fatty acids as 'foreign body reaction' and

TABLE 64. THE PRODUCTION OF TISSUE REACTIONS BY THE INJECTION OF BRANCHED-CHAIN FATTY ACIDS (and amines)

Substance	Dose necessary to induce the formation of a granuloma (mg)	Ref.
ACIDS		
Mycocerosic	5—10	200
2,4-Dimethyldocosanoic	10	1318
Phthienoic	20	200
2-Methyloctadec-2-enoic	25	1318
3,12,15-Trimethyldocosanoic	25	1316
2,4,6-Trimethyltetracos-2-enoic (mixture of stereoisomers corresponding to phthienoic acid)	50	1318
4,13,16-Trimethyltricosanoic	50	1316
3,13-Dimethyltricosanoic	50	1316
2,12,15-Trimethyldocosanoic	50	1316
3,12,15-Trimethyldocos-12-enoic	100	1316
3,13,19-Trimethyltricosanoic	100	1316
3,13-19-Trimethyltricosa-13,19-dienoic	100	1316
2,4-Dimethyldocos-2-enoic	100	1318
"Crude dextrorotatory acids from human strain of tubercle bacilli"	100	1316
2,13,17,21-Tetramethyldocosanoic	Inactive at 200	1316
2,13-Dimethylpentacosanoic	200	1316
AMINES (hydrochlorides)		
2,4-Dimethyldocosylamine	2—5	1318
2,4-Dimethyldocos-2-enylamine	2—5	1318
N,N, Dimethyl-2,4-dimethyldocosylamine	2—5	1318
N,N-Dimethyl-2,4-dimethyldocos-2-enylamine	Inactive	1318

any resemblance to a specific granulomata at certain stages of development of the lesion should be interpreted accordingly".

Even with the natural acid, the results are no more convincing: "phthienoic acid is strikingly active in stimulating the production of lesions which have much resemblance to some of those seen in tuberculosis, although the similarity has to do chiefly with the non-specific aspects of tuberculosis pathology"[1317].

Rich[1301], among others, insisted on the disproportion that existed between the quantities of substance necessary to provoke a granuloma (80 mg of phosphatides[1307]; about 1 mg of C_{27}-phthienoic acid[1317]) and those which living bacilli could contain.

First of all, the tuberculin hypersensitivity which develops in the host in the course of an infection should be taken into consideration. Catel & Schmidt[1320] discovered that only 0.0001 mg of phthioic acid provoked a tissue reaction in the infected animal. On the other hand, it is difficult to compare the action of a definite quantity of material with that of bacilli capable of multiplying and of synthesizing in a slow and continuous manner the materials concerned.

Other types of lipids can take part in the formation of a granuloma. Thomas & Dessau[1321] described the foreign body reaction after injection of phthiocerol, as did Sabin et al.[1322], after injection of "unsaponifiable waxes" (essentially composed of mycolic acids).

Gerstl et al.[1323] observed, after injection of mycolic acids isolated by Anderson from bacilli of human, bovine, and avian strains and from "leprosy bacillus" (see p. 122), a necrotic reaction particularly persistant with the acids from human and bovine strains, besides the formation of giant cells. According to Gerstl et al.[1323] the mycolic acids can contribute to the persistance of lesions induced by the tubercle bacillus. However, a careful study of Kracht & Gusek[1323a] showed that the granulomata induced by mycolic acids was of a non-specific type, and tubercle structures could not be observed. Similar cellular modifications were observed by Delaunay et al.[1324] on injection into guinea-pigs of waxes D of a human strain (peptidoglycolipids) and a bovine strain (glycolipids) in physiological serum suspension. Likewise, in vitro, Frederic & Racadot[1325] were able to obtain in the cultures of fibroblasts and myoblasts the formation of epithelioid cells and giant cells by the action of an aqueous suspension of PmKo (peptidoglycolipid, p. 182). Moreover, White[1326] observed after injection of 40 μg of waxes D, in a water-in-oil emulsion into the sole of a guinea-pig's foot, a proliferation of cells that "look like the epithelioid cells of a tuberculous granuloma". Similar cellular modifications are also produced in the popliteal lymphatic ganglions, and after injection of 200 μg of waxes D, even in the lungs. The activity of these waxes was confirmed by the work of Takeda & Ogata[1327]. Waxes C, although they contain derivatives of mycolic acids (in particular the "cord factor"), do not produce similar modifications[1326]. In the same way, Kradolfer[1328], employing synthetic glucosamine mycolates (p. 178), was able to dissociate the formation of granulomas and the toxic activity of these compounds.

In conclusion, numerous substances are able to induce in vivo more or less specific cellular modifications. These substances are of two types:

(i) simple aliphatic compounds (acids or amines) having one or several suitably disposed methyl substituents (see Table 64, p. 270); and (*ii*) complex substances (phosphatides, waxes D), which can contain in their molecule active simple compounds such as phthienoic, mycolic acids. Their activity is not solely attributable to a simple active compound, since related chemical substances (6,6-′ dimycoloyltrehalose, for example) are inactive.

We should cite here the formation of cavities in the lung of a rabbit by injection of lipoprotein fractions isolated from an extract of tubercle bacilli by paraffin oil [1329, 1330], fractions which contain mycolic acid and "cord factor". Similar phenomena could be reproduced by Endo [1331] by means of mycolic acid-azoprotein (prepared from ovalbumin or the proteins of tubercle bacillus).

2. LIPIDS OF OTHER BACTERIAL SPECIES

Granulomas have been obtained after injection of lipids isolated from colon bacilli [1332], streptococci [1333], and *Listeria monocytogenes* [1141, 1334]. But the authors conclude that the cellular reaction is non-specific, and is essentially a case of "foreign body" type lesions.

Motida *et al.* [1335] observed, after injection of phosphatides from *Actinobacillus mallei* into a mouse, the same pathological effects in the liver that are produced by the injection of live bacilli.

The action of lipids from *Salmonella typhosa* on the rabbit was studied in detail by Dennis [1069]. Intraperitoneal (or intrapleural) injection of fats or phosphatides provoked a reaction which seemed to be chiefly of the inflammatory type, the reaction being obtained more rapidly with the phosphatides than with the fats.

Boivin *et al.* [1044] isolated a lipopolysaccharide from *Agrobacterium tumefaciens* (p. 210) capable of inducing the formation of tumoral tissue in a plant *(Helianthus annuus)*. Levine & Chargaff [1336] observed that the phosphatide fraction provoked a cellular hyperplasia in the plant: in this fraction is located a branched-chain fatty acid 11:12-methyleneoctadecanoic acid (phytomonic or lactobacillic acid) (p. 92). No recent study of the ability of branched-chain acids to induce cellular proliferation in plants seems to have been made, attention being held by deoxyribonucleic acids, and their rôle as transforming factor in the case of *A. tumefaciens* (see e.g., ref. 1337).

II. ENZYME INHIBITION

Jobling & Petersen [1338] discovered that the activity of trypsin and of a leucocyte protease is inhibited by the salts of unsaturated fatty acids. These authors [1339] suggested that this phenomenon could intervene in the casefication of the tubercle, because of the high content of free fatty acids in the lipids of the tubercle bacillus.

Furthermore, Gerstl & Tennant [1340] noted that a lecithinase is inhibited by fatty acids obtained on hydrolysis of tubercle bacillus phosphatide; variations in the degree of inhibition are related to the origin of the enzyme preparations (according to the animal species and the organ chosen).

Unsaturation of the acids is not indispensable in bringing about inhibition, since Peck [1341] has shown that potassium tuberculostearate is as active as the oleate. Potassium phthioate (mixture of salts of branched α,β-unsaturated acids having an average of 27 carbon atoms) is more active than salts of C_{18}- and C_{19}-acids. There is no simple relation between the surface-activity of a fatty acid and its inhibitory power [1342]; moreover, the configuration and molecular weight of the acid play a rôle.

Nevertheless, it does not seem that casefication can be explained by the simple intervention of fatty acid salts, because Sabin [1295] obtained practically no casefication after injection of very high doses of phthioic acid (which is one of the most potent inhibitors of this type). The phosphatide of the tubercle bacillus (Anderson's sample) exerts an inhibitory activity on cellular cathepsins which lead to cellular lesions [1343]. The degree of inhibition by phosphatides seems more important for the cathepsins of tuberculous tissue than for those of identical tissues removed from a healthy animal (rabbit). The polysaccharide of chloroform-extracted waxes (p. 182) very strongly inhibits the protease activity of tuberculous tissue [1343].

Kato *et al.* [1344-1346] showed that intraperitoneal injection of "cord factor" into mice (minimum effective dose: 5 µg) brings about a decrease in the activity of succinic, malic, lactic, and α-glycerophosphoric dehydrogenases present in the liver of the animal, about 24 hours after the injection. At least three of these enzymes have diphosphopyridine-nucleotide as co-factor. Nevertheless, other dehydrogenases of similar structure (in particular the dehydrogenase of glutamic acid) are not affected by the injection of "cord factor". Martin *et al.* [1347] observed a decrease in succinic dehydrogenase activity in the kidney of tubercular guinea-pigs. On the other hand, injection of "cord factor" into the mouse produces a marked increase in the NADase activity of the liver, lung, and spleen [1347a].

Yamamura *et al.* [1348] prepared N-mycoloyl-alanine, -valine, and -leucine: these substances are devoid of toxic activity, but they provoke a significant decrease in the activity of succinic dehydrogenase of mouse liver 24 h after intraperitoneal injection of a 0.1 mg dose. Such an effect was not observed after injection of N-mycoloyl-phenylalanine.

III. ACTION ON LEUCOCYTES

Because of the important rôle played by leucocytes during microbial infection, the action of certain bacterial lipids on their behaviour has been studied.

1. LIPIDS OF THE TUBERCLE BACILLUS

Leucocytes show positive chemotactism for starch granules. In 1938, Fethke [47] observed that after contact for 20 to 30 min at 37° with emulsions of acetone extracts of tubercle bacilli, the number of leucocytes (horse) attracted by starch granules was greatly diminished. Fethke [47] established that it was the free fatty acids that were responsible for this phenomenon and, more precisely, the acids higher than C_{10}. In accord with these results, Husseini & Elberg [1317] noted an inhibition of the migration of leucocytes after the action of C_{27}-phthienoic acid.

According to Nasta *et al.* [1349], leucocytes of animals treated with BCG have an increased resistance to the toxic effects of acetone-soluble lipids from tubercle bacillus. Phagocytosis of phosphatide (Anderson's sample) brings about the death of leucocytes [1350].

In 1949, Allgower & Bloch [1351] showed that the phagocytosis of virulent tubercle bacilli (dead or alive) strongly inhibited the migration of polynuclear leucocytes, while bacilli of avirulent strains are without action. This observation was confirmed and extended by Martin *et al.* [1352]. Light petroleum extracts of virulent bacilli (strains $H_{37}Rv$ and Vallée) likewise inhibit the migration of leucocytes, whereas the extracts from avirulent bacilli ($H_{37}Ra$, *M. smegmatis*) are without action [901]. Oiwa [1353] showed that virulent bacilli washed with light petroleum still inhibit the migration of leucocytes; this is simply because of the inefficacy of the light petroleum washing in removing all the active lipids (a fact already observed during the isolation of the "cord factor").

Choucroun *et al.* [1354] observed that the chemotactism of leucocytes for starch granules is inhibited by prior contact with fine emulsions of Pmko (peptidoglycolipid p. 182). Utilizing other experimental conditions, Meier and Schär [1355] found almost no effect by the wax D of tubercle bacillus on the migration of leucocytes.

According to Suter & White [1356, 1357], monocytes obtained from guinea-pigs which have been treated with wax D (which do not confer on them an appreciable degree of tuberculin hypersensitivity), showed inhibiting properties towards the intracellular multiplication of phagocytized tubercle bacilli (strain R_1Rv): wax D induces "a systemic proliferative cell reaction of the reticulo-endothelial system" [1356].

2. LIPIDS OF OTHER BACTERIAL SPECIES

Girard & Murray [1141] studied the properties of a "monocyte producing agent" (M.P.A.) present in the lipids extracted by chloroform from *Listeria monocytogenes* and already discovered by Stanley [1140]. This non-toxic and non-antigenic factor provokes in the rabbit a monocytosis which persists for more than 20 days.

Lipids of *Shigella dysenteriae* stimulate the phagocytic activity of rabbit leucocytes; those of *E. coli* have a much weaker activity [1072]. However, stimulation of the phagocytic activity of the reticulo-endothelial system can be observed in the mouse by injection of glycerol trioleate [1357a].

Washing *Corynebacterium ovis* with light petroleum gives a complex mixture of lipids capable of provoking the degeneration and death of leucocytes of sheep and guinea pig in vitro [1134].

Water-soluble lipopolysaccharides isolated from gram-negative bacilli stimulate in vitro leucocyte migration. Lipid A, which is present in these lipopolysaccharides, seems to be the factor responsible for the action on the leucocytes; the polysaccharide fraction acts only as a solubilizing agent and can be replaced by other inert substances, such as casein [1358].

IV. TOXICITY

1. LIPIDS OF MYCOBACTERIA

So far only a single toxic factor has been demonstrated in the tubercle bacillus; it is the "cord factor", discovered by H. Bloch in 1950 [901], and identified in 1956 as 6,6'-dimycoloyltrehalose [341] [906], (see p. 173). The toxic lipid of Spitznagel & Dubos [911] is only an impure preparation of "cord factor" [792].

The following comments are pertinent to the toxicity of "cord factor":

(i) The lethal dose for the mouse (LD_{50}) is 15 µg, but several small doses (3 doses of 5 µg spaced 2-3 days apart) are more effective than one large dose (20 µg)[1359].

(ii) The cord factor seems to act selectively on the capillaries, haemorrhagic phenomena being visible in the lungs of animals killed by this substance.

(iii) A single injection of "cord factor" into a tubercular animal aggravates its condition, the effect being quantitative and specific (other microbial infections are not influenced by analogous doses of "cord factor").

(iv) Tubercular infections aggravated by injection of "cord factor" do not respond further to the action of isoniazide. The effect seems to be competitive, since the therapeutic action of a dose of isoniazide is neutralized by a corresponding dose of "cord factor". and vice-versa. This influence occurs only in vivo[1359, 1360].

Complete acetylation of the "cord factor" renders it inactive, whereas acetylation of the 3- hydroxyl only of mycolic acid residues (synthetic substances) only slightly modifies its activity.

Table 34 shows the activity of some synthetic monose monomycolates. These substances possess "delayed" toxicity, characteristic of the "cord factor", but are without action on the state of a tubercular animal.

The 6,6'-dimycolate of trehalose seems a little more active than the 6-mono or the 2,6,6'-trimycolate. A 6,6'-diester of trehalose with 3'-hydroxy-2'-eicosyltetracosanoic acid [372] only possesses about half the activity of a dimycolate; the stereochemistry oi the asymmetric centres at 2' and 3' of the hydroxy-acid might intervene. The 6,6'-diester of trehalose with the unsaturated acid [373], arising from the dehydration of the hydroxy-acid [372], is inactive at a dose of 100 µg.

$$
\begin{array}{cc}
\overset{\displaystyle OH}{\underset{\displaystyle C_{20}H_{41}}{C_{21}H_{43}-\overset{|}{C}H-\overset{|}{C}H-COOH}} & C_{21}H_{43}-CH=\underset{\displaystyle C_{20}H_{41}}{\overset{|}{C}}-COOH \\
[372] & [373]
\end{array}
$$

With higher doses (higher than 100 µg), even the 6,6'-didocosanoate of trehalose (diester of trehalose and behenic acid $C_{21}H_{43}COOH$) is active (H. Bloch, unpublished tests). "Cord factor" alone, injected into a rabbit, does not give rise to specific antibodies, but specific precipitating antibodies are obtained after injection of "cord factor" along with swine serum. The anti-cord factor serum thus prepared diminishes the toxicity of a dose of "cord factor" injected simultaneously into the mouse[1361]. According to Yamamura et al.[1362], the "cord factor" intervenes in the course of an experimental tuberculosis by protecting the tubercle bacilli from disintegration and elimination from the body of the host (mouse).

Do other toxic factors exist in the tubercle bacillus? Spitznagel & Dubos remarked that "weight for weight, suspensions of the avirulent culture $H_{37}Ra$ were fully as toxic as suspensions of the highly virulent M. V. culture" [911]. According to Bloch [1360] the avirulent bacilli contain little or no "cord factor". Fractions soluble (or dispersible) in water, capable of producing in the animal a chronic intoxication leading to cachexia and death, were obtained by Pinner & Woldrich [1363] from autolysed old cultures. Furthermore, Negre (ref. 1298 p. 28) observed similar phenomena in the rabbit after several spaced intravenous injections of an acetone extract of tubercle bacilli, whereas an acetone extract of *M. phlei* prepared and utilized under the same conditions did not show any activity. Toxic fractions were also isolated from a preparation of "antigène méthylique" [1364].

In the latter case at least, toxicity could be caused by the presence of "cord factor", because Demarteau-Ginsburg, Moron & Asselineau (unpublished results) isolated from methanol extracts (made at 55°) of BCG a fraction containing esters of mycolic acids which gave on saponification several polyhydroxy constituents, especially trehalose. The toxicity of acetone extracts might arise from the high content of strongly haemolytic fatty acids (see ref. 1365) which are not present, at least not in appreciable quantities, in the corresponding extracts of *M. phlei*.

The existence of toxic lipid factors other than "cord factor" in tubercle bacilli is thus rather doubtful.

2. LIPIDS OF OTHER BACTERIAL SPECIES

We have already mentioned the presence of fatty acid esters of trehalose in *C. diphtheriae* (see p. 233); intradermal injection of these esters induces toxic phenomena in the skin of guinea-pigs and rabbits [1366].

On the other hand, the lipids of *C. ovis* contain a factor toxic to the leucocytes of sheep and guinea-pig (see p. 234). The presence of this toxic factor in the lipids obtained by a light petroleum wahing of *C. ovis* suggested an analogy with the "cord factor" of Mycobacteria. From corynomycolic acid, which is a constituent of the lipids of *C. ovis*, Diara & Pudles [573] synthesized a 6,6'-dicorynomycolate of trehalose, which was devoid of leucotoxic action.

The toxicity of water-soluble lipopolysaccharides isolated from gram-negative bacteria has long been known (see for example ref. 959). Recent works of Westphal *et al.* [992, 1367] tend to show that lipid A is the factor responsible for the toxicity of these lipopolysaccharide complexes: "lipid A, in colloidal aqueous solution, itself exerts an endotoxic action". Purified lipid A, arising from a lipopolysaccharide isolated from *E. coli* 08, has an LD_{50} of 50 mg/kg, i.e. about 10 times greater than that of the initial lipopolysaccharide. The lipid shows a pyrogenic action at a dose of 0.02 µg/kg in the rabbit and of 0.004 µg/kg in the horse [1367].

The rôle of lipid A in the toxicity of lipopolysaccharides is confirmed by the studies of Takeda *et al.* [983] and of Kasai [1368]. Moreover, from a study on the endotoxin inactivating-principle of the guinea-pig liver, Corwin & Farrar [1368a] concluded that the inactivation process is linked to enzymic systems involved in fatty acid activation and oxidation Such a finding suggests that the lipid moiety of lipopolysaccharides is required for toxicity [1368 a].

On the other hand, Howard *et al.* [1369] observed only a slight toxicity in the case of the mouse for a preparation of lipid A injected intravenously. Ribi *et al.* [965-965c] devised a new method for isolating lipopolysaccharides from gram-negative bacteria: the samples thus obtained had a low lipid content and a toxicity as high as that of other types of preparations. Fukushi *et al.* [965c] conclude that "no correlation was evident between potency and content of nitrogen, fatty acids and hexosamine".

According to Suter *et al.* [1370], the LD_{50} of a lipopolysaccharide isolated from *E. coli* decreases from 355 μg in the case of normal animals to 6-7 μg in the case of animals previously vaccinated with BCG or treated with "cord factor".

Levine *et al.* [1371] observed a toxic effect on injecting a chloroform extract of *Pseudomonas pseudomallei* into animals and Redfearn [969a] isolated a toxic and hemolytic lipopolysaccharide from the culture medium of *Ps. pseudomallei*.

V. "DELAYED" HYPERSENSITIVITY

The tubercle bacillus induces in the animal the establishment of a particular type of hypersensitivity, called "tuberculin hypersensitivity" or "delayed hypersensitivity".

A detailed discussion of the characteristics of "delayed hypersensitivity" is beyond the scope of this review and in any case this problem has been fully discussed particularly by Rich [1301], Raffel [1299, 1372, 1385], and Bendixen [1375].

In 1939, Choucroun [1373] was able to induce in the healthy guinea-pig a genuine state of delayed hypersensitivity by injecting a nitrogenous fraction, poorly defined chemically, isolated from the extract of tubercle bacilli by mineral oil.

In 1948, the same author [1235, 1374] discovered that the establishment of tuberculin hypersensitivity results from the simultaneous action of a glycolipid component (Pmko, p.182) and a nitrogenous substance probably of protein nature. More recently, Choucroun [1376] obtained similar results in humans by injection of 0.2 ml of paraffin oil containing 250μg of Pmko and 250μg of a protein fraction.

Since 1946, Raffel [1377, 1380] has made a systematic study of this phenomenon : delayed hypersensitivity vis-à-vis antigens as different as ovalbumin and picryl chloride can be induced in animals by the simultaneous injection of Anderson's "purified waxes" (mixture of waxes C and D) and the chosen antigen. These results were confirmed by Kanai [1381]. Myrvik & Weiser [1382] obtained animals showing the tuberculin hypersensitive state by injecting only "purified waxes" : although no analysis of the samples of purified waxes employed by these authors was given, it is probable that they were contaminated by a protein impurity, since the treatment of the waxes by papain destroyed their activity.

The work of Raffel [1299] next underlined the importance of waxes D as a lipid factor necessary to the establishment of tuberculin hypersensitivity. Waxes D represent the most active bacterial constituents in this phenomenon: neither free mycolic acids nor the polysaccharide obtained on saponification of the waxes D, possess activity, isolated or in a mixture [1299]. Waxes D isolated from bovine strains of *M. tuberculosis* (i.e. glycolipids) are as active as those which arise from human strains (peptidoglycolipids). The active factor therefore consists essentially of esters of mycolic acids and a polysaccharide [1384]. More simple esters (synthetic or not) such as the mycolates of 2,3,4,6-tetraacetyl-D-galactose [1383] or "cord factor" (trehalose 6,6′-dimycolate) are equally active: these results show that the nature of the sugar and of the sugar hydroxyl involved in the ester bond are of little importance [1384]. Among the numerous substances tested, only the esters of mycolic acids possessed this property. According to Raffel [1385], the waxes D allowed the antigen to enter into certain cells of the animal organism, where normally it does not have access.

In agreement with the results of Raffel, Forney [1386] established, in the case of the guinea-pig, a delayed hypersensitivity against the bacterial cells belonging to the species *Micrococcus pyrogenes* var. *aureus*, by simultaneous injection of bacilli with waxes extracted by chloroform from *M. tuberculosis* or *M. smegmatis* (waxes B + C + D).

Pound [1387], using a preparation of "waxes", m.p., 45—49°, 1.85 % P, could not with such a different material reproduce Raffel's results; no chemical investigation was made and no conclusions can be drawn.

Let us now consider the reverse problem, i.e. what substances are capable of giving a positive reaction after intradermal injection into the tuberculin hypersensitive animal, e.g. a tubercular one. The usual agent is tuberculin, and in the complex mixture which constitutes tuberculin it is essentially the proteins which possess the ability to react with the sensitized animal. More recently, it has been shown that a crystalline polypeptide arising from the degradation of a tuberculoprotein [1388] and a glycopeptide, in which the peptide part comprises alanine, glutamic acid, and α,ε-diaminopimelic acid [932], as in the waxes D of human strains, give a positive reaction in a sensitized animal.

Akabori *et al.* [1389] obtained positive reactions with crotonaldehyde, CH_3-CH = CH-CHO which these authors isolated from the culture medium of tubercle bacilli. The existence of a volatile product, which could be present in the acetone extracts of bacilli, would explain the tuberculin reactions shown by those who handle large quantities of tubercle bacilli, or who often manipulate large amounts of acetone extracts.

The occurrence of positive reactions by intradermal injection of synthetic branched-chain fatty acids, announced in 1945 by Paraf & Desbordes, could not be repeated, even by the same authors [1390].

More recently, Choucroun *et al.* [1391] noted that tubercular individuals capable of reacting to tuberculin (3 units of tuberculin IP-48) gave a reaction, sometimes very strong, with a suspension of Pmko (5 μg of peptidoglycolipid). The differences in the degree of reaction vis-à-vis tuberculin or vis-à-vis Pmko seemed to depend on the manner in which the tuberculosis was evolving; "the aptitude of the organism to develop a stronger allergy to the lipopolysaccharide Pmko than to tuberculin seemed bound to the defensive means of the organism" [1391]. Whatever the case may be, it is interesting to discover that the tuberculin hypersensitivity, which can be conferred by the simultaneous injection of glycolipids (waxes D or Pmko) and protein, can be detected by reaction both with the lipid component and with the protein.

In White's experiments [1326, 1417, 1418], the establishment of delayed hypersensitivity always goes parallel with adjuvant activity, so that these two properties (as well as the production of granuloma) might be different aspects of the same biological action.

VI. ANTIGENICITY

1. LIPIDS OF THE TUBERCLE BACILLUS

In their review on the antigens of *M. tuberculosis*, Boyden & Sorkin [1392] underlined the difficulty of knowing if the antibodies are formed against a lipid molecule, as the tubercle bacillus lipids often contain a polysaccharide component and sometimes even protein.

The antigenicity of phospholipids has been studied for a long time, and more particularly after the preparation by Negre and Boquet [1393], about 1920, of the "antigène méthylique", a methanol extract from tubercle bacilli previously defatted by acetone (see ref. 1304). This preparation possesses antigenic properties and is capable of fixing the complement of tuberculous serums; it has a high content of phospholipids.

Machebœuf *et al.* [1394] isolated from the phosphatide fraction of the tubercle bacillus, phosphatidic acids which were only haptens: they did not induce the formation of antibodies in rabbits in vivo.

According to Chargaff & Schaefer [1395], the phosphatide of BCG "is a true antigen because it not only gives a fixation reaction, but it also produces antiphosphatide antibodies in rabbits immunized by six intravenous injections of one milligram".

Takahashi *et al.* [1396, 1397] showed that the erythrocytes of sheep sensitized by the phosphatide fraction of tubercle bacillus, are agglutinated by the serum of tubercular rabbits.

Pangborn [1398] obtained an antigenic preparation by extraction of bacilli with a mixture of water, alcohol, and ether (5: 5: 3); after concentration and precipitation by acetone, the insoluble fraction was extracted with pyridine. The pyridine solution gave an antigen, consisting of a mixture of phospholipids, in a yield of 5—7 % of the dry weight of the bacilli. More recently, two active phospholipopolysaccharides were isolated from it, [862] of which the one containing 1.7 % P, 10.5 % inositol, and 50 % mannose is probably a pentamannoside of phosphatidylinositol.

Saprophytic mycobacteria and diphtheria bacilli have antigens in common with the tubercle bacillus, because the methanol extracts of these two groups of germs (previously defatted with acetone) on injection into animals produce antibodies which fix the complement with both the corresponding antigens and with the methanol extract of tubercle bacilli (ref. 1304, p. 45; see also ref. 1399).

Takeda and his collaborators observed that, among the various fractions of "waxes", only waxes D show antigenic properties. In 1943, Takeda *et al.* [1400] demonstrated the antigenicity of Anderson's "purified waxes" (mixture of waxes C and D), and confirmed these results in 1954 [1401]: the waxes C + D provoke the formation in the rabbit of antibodies which agglutinate erythrocytes treated by Seibert's polysaccharide I. Six injections of 2 µg waxes D give a serum that is very active in agglutinating sensitized erythrocytes [1402]. In accord with Choucroun [921], the glycolipid Pmko was found to be antigenic by the same test. From the serological point of view, no difference was observed between polysaccharide I and the polysaccharide isolated from waxes D [1401]. The immunochemical relationship of these two polysaccharides was confirmed by Burtin [1403] with the aid of immuno-electrophoresis. The wax D polysaccharide permitted Choucroun [1404], in the case of serums of tuberculous and leprous people, and Takeda et al. [1402], in the case of rabbit immune sera, to detect antibodies by a precipitation reaction. Waxes B and C are devoid of antigenic activity [1402].

Nevertheless, as waxes D (isolated from human strain bacilli) have adjuvant properties, the observed antigenicity could be due to impurities present in the preparations of waxes D, whose activity would be enhanced by the waxes D themselves.

The lipoproteins active in the formation of cavities [1329, 1330] have antigenic properties. Other constituents of tubercle bacilli, such as phthienoic and mycolic acids [1405] and "cord factor" [1406], seem able to act as haptens.

On the other hand, Stacey et al. [994] extracted antigenic lipopolysaccharide complexes from tubercle bacilli with urea or β-hydroxypropionamidine. Elimination of a part of the lipids of these complexes by ether extraction caused the disappearance of their agglutinating activity tested against collodion particles.

2. Lipids of other bacterial species

Hoyle [1130] showed in 1942 that alcohol-soluble lipids isolated from *Corynebacterium diphtheriae* and *C. hofmannii* possessed the property of fixing the complement of rabbit immune sera. Three different antigens seem to exist: an antigen common to *C. diphtheriae* and to *C. hofmannii*; an antigen specific to *C. hofmannii*; and an antigen existing essentially in the mitis variety of *C. diphtheriae*. The work of Learned & Metcalf [1131] pointed to the probability of the phospholipid nature of these antigens. The antigens of *C. diphtheriae* (var. gravis) and of *C. pseudodiphtheriticum* produced agglutination of the red blood cells of chickens.

Lipid preparations of the cardiolipid type were obtained by Hara [1407] from *C. diphtheriae* and by Suzuki [1408] from *Streptobacillus monoliformis:* they react with the syphilitic serum, as well as phosphatide preparations from *M. tuberculosis* [1398].

Two phosphatide fractions isolated from *Salmonella typhosa* by Dennis [1069] were found to be immunologically active in the course of tests vis-à-vis the sera of rabbits infected by the bacilli.

Urbaschek, Thiele et al. [1409-1411] have observed that the Schultz-Dale reaction of an isolated uterus from guinea-pig, sensitized by the injection of killed *Brucella* bacilli, is completely inhibited by a crude lipid extract of the same bacilli. Fractionation of the lipids has shown that the inhibiting fraction is a phospholipid.

Chemical treatments are able to transform lipopolysaccharides (from gram-negative bacteria) into "endotoxoids", which are antigenic and almost devoid of toxicity [1411a].

VII. ADJUVANT EFFECT

The work of Coulaud [1412] and Saenz [1413] showed that paraffin oil enhanced certain properties of dead tubercle bacilli. Proceeding from these observations, Freund *et al.* [1414] noted that "paraffin oil added to killed tubercle bacilli had a remarkable effect... on antibody formation" [1415], which led to the discovery of a general method for obtaining higher antibody titre in immune sera. The injection into the animal of an aqueous solution of antigen emulsified in paraffin oil containg dead tubercle bacilli [1416] induces the formation of a quantity of antibodies much higher than that produced by injecting the antigen alone. The suspension of tubercle bacilli (of human, bovine, avian, or saprophytic strains, or *Nocardia asteroides*) in paraffin oil constitutes an adjuvant commonly called "Freund's adjuvant". The oil plays an indispensable rôle, and the injection of an aqueous solution of antigen emulsified in the oil without bacilli (incomplete adjuvant) itself brings about the formation of a quantity of antibodies higher than that produced by the aqueous solution of antigen (but notably inferior to that obtained with the complete adjuvant). A review on the mode of action of immunological adjuvants was published by Freund [1415] in 1956.

Raffel *et al.* [1380], as well as White *et al.* [1417], showed that Anderson's "purified waxes" (waxes C + D) could replace the tubercle bacilli in the complete adjuvant. The waxes D are the active fraction of the "purified waxes". White *et al.* [1418] discovered that a solution of ovalbumin emulsified in paraffin oil with the addition of 40µg of waxes D of human strains of *M. tuberculosis* (Test, Canetti and $H_{37}Rv$ strains) produced in the guinea-pig a strong increase in the antibody titre against ovalbumin in comparison with that of animals treated with ovalbumin without adjuvant. Other lipid fractions obtained from human strains as well as the waxes D of bovine, avian, and saprophytic strains are inactive [1418]. Nevertheless, Freund *et al.* [1420] observed adjuvant effects with an alcohol-ether extract of tubercle bacilli (whereas waxes D are isolated from the chloroform extract), in the production in rabbits of specific agglutinins of *Salmonella typhosa*.

Pound [1421] obtained an adjuvant effect in the production of antibodies against ovalbumin by using a lipid preparation (close to Anderson's "purified waxes") isolated from tubercle bacilli.

The difference in behaviour between waxes D from human and from bovine strains of *M. tuberculosis* was explained by the presence of a peptide fraction in the waxes D of human strains, which is almost completely absent in the waxes D of bovine strain [1418]. These conclusions have received support from the recent work of White *et al.* [1419], performed with fractions of waxes D of various strains prepared by ultracentrifugation (see p. 184). The sedimentable fractions, which contain a peptide moiety whatever the species of Mycobacteria may be, are active as adjuvant, while the more soluble fractions (devoid of a peptide moiety) are inactive (see also 942 *a*). The importance of the amino sugar components in the adjuvant activity was underlined [1419 *a*, 1419 *b*]. The bacillary residues (Mycobacteria) obtained after removal of the free lipids are still active, but elimination of the bound lipids causes them to lose this property [1418].

If ovalbumin is injected along with waxes D in the form of aqueous emulsions (devoid of oil), the establishment of a delayed hypersensitivity vis-à-vis ovalbumin is observed, but there is no significant increase of the anti-ovalbumin antibody content (with respect to that of control animals treated with ovalbumin alone) [1380].

The adjuvant effect intervenes in the production of allergic encephalomyelitis and allergic aspermatogenesis. Here again, waxes D of human strains of *M. tuberculosis* can replace killed bacilli for the production of allergic encephalomyelitis [1422-1425] and aspermatogenesis [1425].

Freund & Stone [1425] noted that to cause these allergic effects ten times more by weight of waxes than dead bacilli were required. There exists, therefore, in the bacilli, a factor more active than in the waxes D. The preparations of waxes D which give positive results are composed of a glycolipid bound to a peptide fraction; on the other hand, the bound lipids (which contain similar glycolipids) seem likely to take part in this phenomenon. The linkage of such glycolipids with proteins or polypeptides of high molecular weight, forming almost insoluble combinations — such as those which exist in the cell wall — might be advantageous.

In a similar manner, White [1424] provoked allergic thyroidosis by injecting a homogenate of thyroid along with waxes D (human strain) in a water-in-oil emulsion.

By injecting Freund's adjuvant (without the addition of antigen) or waxes D (human strain), Pearson [1426] was able to produce experimental arthritis in the rat. "Most of the results do strongly suggest that the arthritis and the other observed lesions are the result of some form of allergic or hypersensitivity response". It is remarkable that such phenomena are not manifested when Freund's adjuvant is administered with an antigen.

A lipid fraction, isolated from enzymatically digested cell walls of *Corynebacterium diphtheriae* (according to a procedure similar to that used to obtain "bound wax D" from BCG. cell walls [942a]), had an adjuvant activity [1425a]. On the other hand, cells of *Corynebacterium parvum* have a high adjuvant activity [1426a], whereas they are devoid of corynomycolic acid [1135] (at least in their free lipids). It must be added that no definite lipid component responsible of adjuvant activity has been as yet isolated from *N. asteroides* cells.

Acute polyarthritis was also observed after injection of lipopolysaccharide (from *Salmonella abortus-equi*) into rats [1427].

The adjuvant effect has been observed by using lipopolysaccharides of gram-negative bacteria, e.g. lipopolysaccharide, or lipid A, of *Bordetella pertussis* has an adjuvant effect in antibody production [1428]. However, this action is linked with the properdin system and is of very short duration, whereas the action of Freund's adjuvant can last for several months [1429, 1430].

VIII. IMMUNIZATION

1. M. TUBERCULOSIS

Research on immunization against tubercular infections is hampered by the difficulty of determining in animals, which can have variations of susceptibility from one individual to another, more or less increased degrees of resistance. Moreover, numerous secondary factors, such as the mode of introduction of the substance, the nature of the vehicle employed, the animal species employed, etc., can intervene in the results. These difficulties are particularly illustrated by the results obtained on injecting dead tubercle bacilli: protection of the animal against an experimental infection can be "of the same order as that produced by BCG"[1431] in the mouse, whereas "guinea-pigs prepared by heat-killed bacilli... were not protected"[1356]. Usually, it is admitted that dead tubercle bacilli confer some resistance on the animal, which remains inferior to that induced by living BCG (e.g. ref. 1432).

The fact that dead bacilli can increase the resistance of the animal has led to the speculation that chemical constituents of these bacilli could possess this property.

Polysaccharides and proteins tested separately seem almost devoid of activity. On the contrary, several lipid fractions have given encouraging results. Two groups of lipids appear capable of increasing the resistance of the animal: on the one hand, phosphatide fractions, present in the "antigène méthylique", and, on the other hand, wax fractions. Crowle[1433] has recently discussed this question in detail.

In 1927, Negre & Boquet[1434] showed that the injection of a methanol extract of bacilli defatted by acetone ("antigène méthylique") conferred a certain degree of protection with regard to a test infection. Since then, the "antigène méthylique" has been made the subject of extensive clinical study. It seems advantageous to use it together with BCG for preventive treatment and with streptomycin for curative treatment. Its mode of administration and discussions on its mechanism of action are set forth in a recent book by Nègre[1304]. The activity of the "antigène méthylique" constitutes an argument in favour of the dissociation of tuberculosis resistance and hypersensitivity[1435].

Weiss & Dubos[1436] confirmed the protective effect furnished by methanol extracts of bacilli (killed by phenol), previously washed with acetone, in using either BCG or strain $H_{37}Ra$. These authors ascertained that the methanol extraction of bacilli should be carried out at 55° in order to isolate the maximum active substance. The employment of adjuvants such as the lipopolysaccharide of *Salmonella typhosa*, the *Hemophilus pertussis* commercial vaccine, or a mixture of arlacel and mineral oil increases and extends the immunizing effect[1437, 1438]. Dubos and Schaedler[1439] observed that the employment of lipopolysaccharides from gram-negative bacteria as adjuvants leads to an immunity which does not seem to be specific and which is, moreover, obtained with the lipopolysaccharides alone.

More recently, Williams & Dubos[1440] fractionated the methanol extract (prepared at 60°) of bacilli of strain $H_{37}Rv$. Two fractions, containing phosphorus and sugars, show a distinct activity: "the levels of resistance elicited by these preparations are equivalent to those following vaccination with BCG (Phipps)" in a mouse. On the other hand, the mixture of these two fractions shows an enhanced activity: 0.05 mg (per mouse) of each fraction leads to an easily detectable degree of resistance. It is interesting to note the lack of sensitivity of these fractions to oxidation, since they are obtained by evaporation of the initial methanol solution at 45—50°, "while a jet of air is directed on the surface of the solution"[1440]. The dimannoside of phosphatidylinositol does not possess any immunizing activity whereas some related fractions are able to induce a state of resistance similar to that obtained with BCG[1440a].

Choucroun [1374] observed a certain level of resistance to infection in animals that had received the glycolipid Pmko. Nevertheless, Bloch & Raffel (unpublished experiments) were not able to establish any immunizing activity when using waxes D, which are glycolipids of chemical structure close to that of Pmko.

On the other hand, according to Hoyt *et al.* [1441-1443], fractions of waxes obtained from Anderson's "purified waxes" possessed a certain immunizing activity. These authors underlined the importance for these experiments of eliminating bacillary residues and in their last work[1443] they used low-speed centrifugation and filtration on 450 and 300 mμ Millipore filters: "the filtered fractions retained their definite power to immunize mice against experimental tuberculosis". Moreover, Hoyt *et al.* [1443] observed that when heptane solutions of the "purified wax" were centrifuged at high speed, 5 fractions could be separated: the 5th fraction, which contained material that could not be sedimented, was immunologically inert, whereas, the other fractions significantly immunized mice against tuberculosis. The behaviour of these last fractions is thus similar to that of waxes D.

Robson & Smith [1444] found that two injections of 50 μg of Pmko provoke a small reduction in the size of lesions in the cornea of mice: the activity of Pmko in this test was lower than that of BCG, when the two materials were compared on a weight for weight basis.

However, the situation is not so simple, for Crowle [1445] has found that two lipid fractions are capable of eliciting statistically significant immunity against an experimental tuberculosis: Pmko and waxes B. The chemical structure of these fractions is rather different, and Pmko is chemically very similar to waxes D, which are inert according to Crowle. It thus appears that the immunogenic active component is a small fraction which, according to the fractionation procedure, is associated with one or another group of lipids. On the other hand, residues of mycobacteria exhaustively extracted with neutral organic solvents are still able to produce a level of resistance against tuberculosis comparable to that produced by BCG[1443 a]. Bound lipids are thus likely to intervene in this phenomenon.

2. OTHER BACTERIAL SPECIES

Antigenic lipopolysaccharides isolated from gram-negative bacteria (see p. 195) are able to produce in the animal a non-specific increase in the resistance to bacterial infections [1439, 1446, 1447]. Lipid A may be the factor responsible for this action [1367, 1448]. With doses up to 30 μg, lipid A produces in the mouse a significant increase in the non-specific resistance to infection [1367].

CONCLUSION

The question now arises of determining if there exist specific characteristics common to the lipids of different bacterial species.

The sole property which seems to be general and which distinctly distinguishes bacterial lipids from those of other living species, is the total absence of sterols (see p. 158). Whereas lower organisms such as *Aspergillus* or yeasts contain significant quantities of sterols, bacteria contain only traces (see Table 65). The question of determining whether these traces are significant or whether they arise from contaminations of various origins is still under discussion.

TABLE 65. THE STEROL CONTENT OF VARIOUS MICRO-ORGANISMS

Species	Sterols (% of the dry weight)	References
FUNGI		
Aspergillus niger	1.4	1449
Aspergillus sydowi	5.4	1450
Penicillium aurantio-brunneum	1.9	1451
Blastomyces dermatitidis	4.0	1452
Candida albicans.	7.0	1453
BACTERIA		
Streptomyces griseus	0	806
Streptomyces natans	0	806
Rhodospirillum rubrum	< 0.001	806
Micromonospora sp.	~ 0.001*	806
Mycobacterium tuberculosis	< 0.001	803
Escherichia coli	0.005	1454
VIRUS		
Influenza virus.	5.0—7.0	1455-1457

* % of the weight of wet bacilli.

TABLE 66. THE DISTRIBUTION OF SOME LIPID COMPONENTS IN VARIOUS BACTERIAL SPECIES

| | Fatty acids | | | | | Phospholipids containing: | | | Glycolipids |
	Hydroxy acids			Cyclo-propane acids	Other types of branched-chain acids	Choline	Ethanolamine	Amino-acids (other than serine)*	
	Poly-β-hydroxy-butyrate	Straight-chain β-hydroxy-acid	Branched-chain β-hydroxy-acid						
PSEUDOMONADALES									
Pseudomonas	+	+			+		+	+	+
Spirillum	+								
EUBACTERIALES									
Azotobacter	+	+					+		
Rhizobium	+								
Agrobacterium tumefaciens				C_{19}		+	+		
Alcaligenes faecalis							+	+	
Escherichia coli		+		C_{17}			+		
Aerobacter aerogenes				C_{17}					
Serratia marcescens		+		C_{17}					
Proteus P-18				C_{17}					
Salmonella				C_{17}**			+	+	
Pasteurella pestis				C_{17}					
Brucella				C_{19}		+	+	+	
Actinobacillus mallei	+								
Micrococcus halodenitrificans	+								
Staphylococcus aureus							+	+	+
Sarcina					+	+			+
Streptococcus				C_{19}***					+
Lactobacillus				C_{19}			+	+	
Corynebacterium			+						+
Bacillus	++				+		+		
Clostridium				C_{19}			+		
ACTINOMYCETALES									
Mycobacterium			++		+		+	+	++
Nocardia			+		+		+		

* Whatever may be the type of linkage.
** Isolated from *Salmonella typhimurium*; no information is available about its occurrence in other species.
*** Isolated from *Str. cremoris* and *Str. lactis*, but not from *Str. pyogenes*.

Sphingomyelins likewise seem to be absent from bacterial lipids; in the only two cases where their presence has been mentioned *(Neisseria gonorrhoeae* and *Bacillus stearothermophilus)*, the conclusion was based solely on the results of the nitrogen/phosphorus/choline ratios. Little knowledge exists about the distribution of sphingosine lipids in lower fungi; however, phytosphingosine (2-amino-1,3,4-trihydroxy-n-eicosane) [1458] has been isolated from *Saccharomyces cerevisiae* [1459], an analogous base $C_{20}H_{43}O_3N$ has been obtained from the mycelium of *Aspergillus sydowi* [1460], and a base $C_{18}H_{39}O_3N$ from a strain of *Penicillium* [1461]. Neither sphingosine nor related substances has been isolated from bacterial lipids.

Bacterial phospholipids are frequently devoid of the usual nitrogen bases choline and ethanolamine (see Table 66) (the occurrence of choline is particularly rare); they often consist of phosphatidic acids or of esters of phosphatidic acids with sugar constituents. Such compounds are also encountered in higher plants [1462]. Amino-acids other than serine are often observed in the hydrolysis products of bacterial phospholipids, as esters of phosphatidylglycerol or as contaminating peptidolipids.

The glycolipids are often encountered in the lipids of gram-positive bacteria (particularly Mycobacteria and Corynebacteria), but one cannot consider their presence as a characteristic of bacterial lipids. The occurrence of complex molecules such as the biologically active lipopolysaccharides of gram-negative bacteria seems to be more specific to the bacteria.

Anaerobic bacteria (and facultative aerobic, and even some aerobic bacteria) synthesize their monoenoic fatty acids through a pathway which is different from that used by animal cells. On the other hand, every species of bacteria are practically devoid of polyunsaturated acids (which are encountered in other unicellular micro-organisms such as yeasts, algae or protozoa).

Among the other properties sometimes considered specific to bacterial lipids is the presence of branched-chain fatty acids. Table 66 shows that, except for cyclopropane fatty acids, branched-chain acids have only been observed in a restricted number of bacterial species. However, in many cases, a reinvestigation of the fatty acid composition is needed, with the finer methods available today. A great deal of work has been done during the last few years, and the comparison of Table 66 of this book with Table 62 of the French edition (1962) is quite demonstrative. The wide-spread occurrence of cyclopropane fatty acids in bacterial species may be emphasized; moreover, the branched-chain fatty acids of the tuberculostearic acid type, which have a similar way of biosynthesis, must be borne in mind. These acids have not (so far) been found in other types of living organisms, as sterculic acid [1463] and malvalic acid [1464] contain a cyclopropene ring. Nothing is known about the rôle of the cyclopropane fatty acids in bacteria.

A review of the recent literature shows an increased interest in bacterial lipids during the last few years and some of the many gaps that occur in this field are likely to be filled very soon.

SUBJECT INDEX

abequose: 197.
acetaldol: 240.
Acetobacter suboxydans: 19.
acetol esters: 38.
acetone-soluble fractions: 218-222-227-240.
Achromobacter: 205-212.
Achromobacteriaceae: 205-212.
Achromobacter guttatus: 212.
Achromobacter hartlebii: 212.
Achromobacter parvulus: 212.
acids, characteristic, bacterial acids: 82 to 143.
acid-fast bacteria: 19-200-201-238 to 261.
acid phthalates, use, of: 37.
Actinobacillus: 205-222.
Actinobacillus mallei: 108-156-**222**-272-286.
Actinomyces: 206-256-261.
Actinomyces israelii: 261.
Actinomycetaceae: 206-260.
Actinomycetales: 206-**238**-286.
actinomycin J_2: 262.
acute polyarthritis: 282.
acyl-CoA: 143.
Adachi test: 55.
adjuvant effect: 281.
adsorption chromatography: 32-33.
Aerobacter: 205-214.
Aerobacter aerogenes: 95-146-**214**-215-286.
Aerobacter cloacae: 212-214.

aerobic bacteria: 144-145-202-234-235.
Aertrycke bacillus: 195-218.
agglutination: 280.
agglutining activity: 280.
Agrobacterium: 205-210.
Agrobacterium tumefaciens: 13-19-49-87-94-
    95-146-156-160-**210**-272-286.
Agrobacterium radiobacter: 160.
Agrobacterium rhizogenes: 160.
Akasi's method: 222.
alanine:166-168-183-185-190-191-192-193-194-
    195-212-228-241-273-278.
Alcaligenes: 205-212.
Alcaligenes faecalis: 160-165-**212**-286.
alcaligenic acid: 212.
aleuritic acid: 255.
α-kansamycolic acid: 138.
allergic aspermatogenesis: 282.
allergic encephalomyelitis: 282.
allergic thyroidosis: 288.
allothreonine: 194-195.
amino-acid: 165-166-167-183-185-186-188-
    189-190-191-192-194-195-199-201-202 - 207 -
    211-212-214-218-224-228-233-234-236 - 237 -
    250-286-287.
amino compounds: 82.
amino-sugars: 168-178-182-185-187-197-198-
    201-277.

AUTHORS INDEX

—, 167, 254 [875]
—, 174, 175 [904]
—, 174, 175, 179 [905]
—, 174, 245, 257, 274 [906]
—, 178 [914]
—, 182, 183, 184 [922]
—, 183, 257, 259 [926]
—, 190, 191, 248 [951]
—, 191, 248 [951 a]
—, 138, 167, 193, 195, 254 [1217]
—, 255 [1224]
—, 257, 269 [1242]
—, 72, 87, 157, 261 [1256 b]
—, 271 [1324]
—, 278 [1383]
—, 278 [1384]
ASTVATSATUR' YAN, A. T., 209 [1010 a]
—, 220 [1073]
AXELROD, B., 167 [878]
AYLWARD, F., 28 [105]
AYRES, J. C., 237 [1147]
AZUMA, I., 175, 250, 254 [909]
—, 175, 254 [910]
—, 178, 188, 242 [912]
—, 178, 183, 242, 251 [912 a]
—, 188, 242 [943]

BADDILEY, J., 181 [919 b]
—, 181, 226, 227 [920 a]
BADER, A.-M., 159 [811]
—, 216 [1064]
BADER, A. R., 60 [418]
BAER, E., 47 [286]
—, 47 [287]
—, 64 [452]
—, 64 [454]
—, 64 [457]
—, 64 [457 a]
BAILEY, A. S., 63 [433]
—, 98, 99 [618]
BAILEY, P. S., 60 [407]
BAILEY, W. J., 32 [127]
—, 32 [131]
BAKAY, B., 202, 228 [1026]
BAKER, M. J., 55 [360]
BALDESCHWILLER, J. D., 52 [338]
BALL, E. G., 68 [475]
—, 68 [476]
BALLANCE, P. E., 34 [158]
BALLIO, A., 84, 85, 262 [544 b]

BALLOU, C. E., 161, 250 [842 b]
—, 163, 165, 245 [860]
—, 163 [861 a]
—, 163 [861 b]
—, 163, 165 [861 c]
BANASZAK, L. J., 37 [183]
BARATOVA, L. A., 82, 83 [537 a]
BARBER, C., 222 [1086]
BARBER, M., 49, 138, 254 [312]
—, 49, 191, 254 [313]
—, 190, 260 [949 a]
BARBEZAT, S., 48 [303]
—, 49, 113, 115 [309]
BARBIER, M., 18 [20]
—, 33, 123, 128, 137, 151, 249 [150]
—, 68, 165, 173, 247, 249, 250, 251 [481]
—, 165 [866]
BARBIER-WIELAND, 83
BARCELLONA, S., 84, 85, 262 [544 b]
BARCLAY, W. R., 265 [1288]
BARNARD, D., 44 [257]
BARONOWSKI, P., 143 [749]
—, 144 [751]
BARRETT, C. B., 34 [164]
BARTHA, R. von, 108 [654]
BARTHLEY, W., 202 [1029]
BASSLER, G. C., 44 [261 a]
BATEMAN, L., 44 [257]
BATES, D. S., 143 [745]
BATES, R. B., 60 [417]
BAUDART, P., 60 [410]
BAUER, W. H., 44 [271]
BAUERLE, H., 280 [1409]
BAUGH, C. L., 143 [745]
BAUMANN, C. A., 235 [1137]
BAUMANN, N. A., 162, 237 [847 a]
BAYKUT, F., 55 [381]
BAYLEY, S. T., 199, 200, 208, 209, 214 [1008]
BAZIN, S., 274 [1354]
BEARD, J. W., 285 [1455]
BECKMANN, 79, 118
BEGEMANN, P. H., 36 [176]
BEHRING, H. von, 158 [798]
BEILBY, A. L., 216 [1060]
BEKIERKUNST, A., 273 [1347 a]
BELJANSKI, M., 265 [1284]
BELL, P. H., 82, 83 [536]
BELLAMY, L. J., 44 [258]
BENDICH, A., 216 [1066]
BENDIXEN, G., 277 [1375]
BENGEN, F., 26 [94]

CLAUS, G. W., 143 [745]
CLÉMENT, R., 115 [692]
CLEMO, G. R., 13 [3]
CLERMONTÉ, R., 123, 137, 250 [734]
ČMELIK, S., 19, 114, 232 [31]
—, 19, 216, 234 [32]
—, 19, 20, 216, 217, 273 [43]
—, 34, 160, 162, 165, 218 [154]
—, 34, 156, 165, 216, 217, 218 [155]
—, 156, 158, 159, 216, 217, 218 [790]
—, 156, 158, 159, 165, 216, 217, 218 [791]
—, 159, 216, 217, 218 [818]
—, 160, 216, 217, 218 [834]
COHEN, S. S., 264 [1282]
COLE, A. R. H., 44 [260]
COLEMAN, C. M., 52, 259 [341]
—, 259 [1250]
COLEMAN, J. E., 26, 28 [99]
COLLINS, F. D., 26 [92 a]
COLOBERT, L., 200 [1014]
—, 200 [1015]
—, 223, 225 [1096]
COLOMBI, L., 41 [231]
COLOVER, J., 282 [1423]
COMEAU, L., 60 [409]
CONNOLLY, J. M., 279, 281 [1417]
CONOVER, M. J., 202, 228 [1026]
CONROY, H., 52 [337]
CONSTABLE, B. J., 231 [1116 c]
CONTOPOULO, R., 108, 109 [658]
COONS, A. H., 279, 281 [1417]
COOPER, C. D., 273 [1347]
COOPER, P. D., 264 [1294]
CORCORAN, J. W., 147 [774]
—, 147 [776 a]
CORPE, W. A., 19 [30 a]
CORWIN, A. H., 216 [1060]
CORWIN, L. M., 276 [1368 a]
COSENZA, B. J., 224, 225, 226 [1096 a]
COSTIL, L., 22 [59]
COSTIN-PODHORSKY, E., 224 [1098]
COUGHLIN, C. A., 285 [1454]
COULAUD, E., 281 [1412]
COULTER, C. B., 234 [1133]
COULTHARD, C. E., 270 [1316]
CRAIG, L. C., 25 [82]
—, 26 [85]
—, 82 [535]
CRAM, D. J., 77 [516]
CRAMER, F., 26 [93]
CRANDALL, D. I., 42, 43 [249]

CRAVEN, B., 93 [583]
CREACH, O., 200 [1015]
CREECH, H. J., 216 [1062]
CREIGHTON, M. M., 18 [16]
—, 20, 21 [48]
—, 53, 122, 246 [348]
—, 56, 162, 163 [384]
—, 67 [471]
—, 69, 122, 187, 188, 246, 248 [491]
—, 91 [576]
—, 162 [853]
—, 173 [898]
—, 187, 251 [942]
CRIEGEE, R., 59 [405]
CRISTOL, S. J., 62 [429]
CROMBIE, L., 40 [226]
—, 41 [238]
CROMBIE, W. M., 34 [158]
CROOM, A. J., 213, 231 [1048 a]
CROOM, J. A., 19 [44]
CROSON, M., 19, 20 [42]
—, 108, 159, 235 [649]
—, 108, 235 [651]
CROSS, A. D., 44 [262]
CROWDER, J. A., 69 [470]
—, 69, 70, 71, 122, 123, 248, 251, 252 [490]
—, 69, 72, 251 [496]
—, 112, 229 [684]
—, 156, 158, 229, [787]
—, 158, 285 [803]
—, 160, 162, 229 [829]
—, 173, 240 [897]
—, 251 [1200]
CROWE, M. O'L., 68 [474]
CROWLE, A. J., 235 [1136]
—, 283 [1433]
—, 284 [1445]
CRUMPTON, M. I., 196, 197 [972]
CULLEN, J., 18, 213 [8 b]
CUMMINGS, M. M., 143 [743]
CUMMINS, C. S., 185, 201 [933]

DAGLEY, S., 19 [35]
DALLAS, M. S., 34 [164]
DAMBOVICEANU, A., 198 [993]
—, 222 [1086]
DANIHER, F. A., 197 [991]
DARZENS, G., 58 [397]
DAT-XUONG, N., 90, 91 [571]
DAUBEN, W. G., 59 [398]

DUTTON, H. J., 25 [83]
—, 26 [87]
—, 26 [90]
DYER, D. L., 237 [1145]

EBERHAGEN, D., 37 [184]
EBERHARDT, F. M., 24, 160 [68]
EBINA, T., 265 [1292]
ECKLUND, C. M., 224 [1099]
ECKSTEIN, F., 64 [454]
ECKSTEIN, H. C., 212 [1051]
EDELBERG, E. A., 285 [1454]
EDENS, C. O., 91 [576]
—, 173 [898]
EDLEY, T. H., 64 [465]
EDMONSON, P. R., 44 [275]
EDWARDS, J. R., 110, 170, 207 [678]
EGAMI, F., 160, 195 [840]
—, 195 [982]
EICHENBERGER, E., 196, 214, 219 [973]
—, 197, 276 [992]
—, 274 [1358]
—, 276, 284 [1367]
EISNER, U., 42, 43 [246]
—, 139 [735]
ELBERG, S., 28 [114]
—, 87, 91, 242, 243 [560]
—, 270, 271, 273 [1317]
ELLINGHAUSEN, H. C., 226 [1112]
ELLIS, D. S., 225 [1110 a]
ELLIS, M. E., 160 [874]
ELS, H., 262 [1270]
ELSDEN, S. R., 263 [1275]
ELVIDGE, J. A., 42, 43 [246]
ENDO, K., 272, 280 [1329]
—, 272 [1331]
ENGLISH, J. P., 82, 83 [536]
ENTSCHEL, R., 55 [366]
EPP, A., 108, 223 [648]
ERLENMEYER, H., 174 [902]
ETÉMADI, A., 52 [342]
ETÉMADI, A. H., 49, 138, 254 [312]
—, 114, 116, 235 [688 a]
—, 118 [698 a]
—, 128 [720 a]
—, 149 [781 a]
—, 155 [781 b]
—, 235, 282 [1135]
—, 240 [1155]
EUGSTER, C. H., 55 [366]

EVANS, L. K., 39, 41, 42 [211]
—, 40 [219]

FABRICANT, C., 200 [1017]
FARKAS, L., 224, 265 [1097]
FARRAR, W. E., 276 [1368 a]
FARTHING, J. R., 282 [1428]
FAURE, M., 38 [207]
—, 159, 163 [822]
—, 161 [842]
—, 161, 208 [845]
—, 279 [1394]
FELLOWS, C. E., 82, 83 [536]
FERRARI, R. A., 180 [920]
FERRÉOL, G., 64, 179 [461]
FESSEDEN, J. S., 59, 85 [401]
FETHKE, N., 20, 239 [47]
—, 22 [57]
—, 255 [1223]
FEW, A. V., 160, 199, 202, 208, 224, 264 [833]
—, 201 [1022]
—, 201 [1023]
FIEDMAN, S. M., 147 [776 a]
FIERTEL, A., 158, 261, 285 [806]
FIESER, L. F., 44 [216]
—, 69 [487]
FIKER, S., 34 [160]
FINCHLER, A., 64 [463]
FINNER, L. L., 18 [12]
FIRTH, W. C., 62 [429]
FISCHMEISTER, I., 44 [274]
FISH, C. H., 259 [1253]
FLITTER, D., 28 [102]
FLOYD, D. E., 62 [430]
FLYNN, E. H., 262 [1271]
FÖLDES, J., 185 [935]
FOLKERS, K., 80, 158 [525]
—, 110 [674]
—, 110 [675]
—, 110 [676]
FONKEN, G. J., 38, 99, 102, 103, 243, 244 [202]
—, 87, 102, 242, 243, 246, 257 [561]
FORBES, W. F., 40, 41, 44 [215]
FORKNER, C. E., 269, 270, 271 [1307]
FORNEY, J. E., 278 [1386]
FORSYTH, W. G. G., 108, 208, 210 [653]
—, 208, 209, 210 [1035]
FOSTER, E. M., 146, 162, 223, 263 [762]
FOSTER, J. W., 240 [1156]
FOUQUEY, C., 197 [986]
—, 197 [989]

MacCloskey, A., 146 [771 a]
MacCluer, R. H., 26 [92]
MacClung, J., 261 [1258]
MacCombie, J. T., 40 [220]
MacDermott, K., 281 [1416]
MacDonald, H. J., 37 [183]
MacElroy, O. E., 27 [108]
MacFarlane, M. G., 37, 180 [185]
—, 85, 157, 160, 217, 219, 224 [545]
—, 161, 165, 180, 201, 225 [841]
—, 166, 224, 237 [871]
—, 201, 225 [1024]
Machebœuf, M. A., 25 [57]
—, 159, 163 [822]
—, 231, 232 [1119]
—, 279 [1394]
MacKay, A. F., 44 [268]
—, 44 [269]
—, 44 [270]
MacKeon, J. E., 188, 189, 216 [945]
MacLafferty, F. W., 49 [317]
—, 49 [318]
—, 49 [319]
MacLaughin, J., 27 [108]
MacLennan, A.-P., 171 [887]
—, 171, 172, 191, 193 [888]
—, 191, 253, 254 [952]
—, 191, 192 [953]
—, 261 [1262]
MacLeod, D. L., 270 [1319]
MacLeod, P., 160, 227 [823 b]
—, 227 [1114]
MacLeod, P., 90, 95, 227, 228 [598]
MacNeill, J. J., 19 [44]
—, 213, 231 [1048 a]
MacPherson, I. A., 196, 197 [972]
MacQuillen, K., 201 [1021]
—, 201 [1022]
Macrae, R. M., 109 [665]
MacTurk, H. M., 155 [785]
—, 249, 250 [1188]
MacTurk, M. M., 68 [484]
Madinaveitia, J., 67 [472]
—, 68 [484]
—, 155 [785]
—, 249, 250 [1188]
Maeda, H., 246 [1176]
Magat, M., 41 [229]
Mahapatra, S. N., 72 [497 a]
Maher, G. G., 173 [892]

Mahoney, M. J., 47 [283]
Majer, J., 147 [773]
Makino, T., 115 [694]
Makita, M., 160, 214 [836]
Malani, C., 135, 136, 151 [733]
Malkin, T., 48 [294]
—, 64 [441]
—, 64 [451]
Malmgren, B., 199, 202 [1019]
Mandel, P., 159 [811]
—, 159 [813]
—, 216 [1064]
—, 216 [1065 a]
Mangold, H. K., 34, 38 [163]
—, 39 [212]
Mangouri, H. A., El, 37 [191]
Mankievicz, L., 259 [1251]
Marbe, M., 210, 272 [1044]
Marchessault, R. H., 108 [661 b]
Marco, G. J., 92 [579]
Marechal, J., 161 [842]
—, 161, 208 [845]
Marie-Suzanne, sœur, 252 [1201]
—, 252 [1202]
—, 247, 252 [1203]
Marinetti, G. V., 32 [136]
—, 32 [143 a]
—, 44, 47 [256]
—, 202, 220 [1026 a]
Marinov, I., 222 [1086]
Markley, K. S., 48 [296]
—, 62 [427 a]
Marks, G. S., 55, 103 [378]
Marr, A. G., 18, 213 [7]
—, 86, 94, 95, 167, 213 [551]
—, 110, 111, 210 [682]
—, 160, 210, 211, 213 [825]
—, 160, 199, 200 [830]
Marschner, R. F., 28 [103]
Marshall, A. H. E., 282 [1424]
Martin, A. J. P., 36, 207 [178]
Martin, D. B., 36 [174]
Martin, G. J., 256 [1240]
Martin, J. B., 64 [447]
Martin, J. H., 262 [1265 a]
Martin, S. P., 273 [1347]
—, 274 [1352]
Mason, D. J., 199 [1011]
Mastrangelo, S. V., 44 [265]
Matches, J. R., 237 [1147]
Mathieu, J., 57 [394]

SCHMIDT, W., 271 [1320]
SCHNAITMAM, C., 108 [661 b]
SCHNEIDER, A. K., 96 [606]
SCHOENFELD, R., 24 [71]
—, 31 [119]
SCHOENHEIMER, R., 158, 285 [803]
SCHOGT, J. C. M., 36 [176]
SCHOLES, P., B., 81, 234 [1133 a]
SCHOLFIELD, C. R., 26 [87]
—, 26 [91]
—, 60 [417]
SCHÖNHOLZER, G., 276, 284 [1367]
SCHREIBER, K., 49 [314]
SCHROEPFER, G. J., 144 [750]
SCHUBERT, K., 159, 212 [809 a]
SCHUETTE, H. A., 44 [273]
SCHWARTZMAN, L. H., 40 [224]
SCHWARZ, H. P., 44 [265]
SCOTT, A. I., 39 [210]
SEGAL, W., 21 [51]
—, 21 [52]
—, 283 [1432]
SEHER, A., 38 [195]
SEHGAL, S. N., 19 [36]
—, 160, 161, 224 [832]
—, 161, 208 [844]
SEIBERT, F. B., 256 [1241]
SEIJO, E., 270 [1312]
SEKIKAWA, I., 275 [1361]
—, 280 [1406]
SELLERS, W., 214 [1058]
SELYE, H., 282 [1427]
SEN, Y., 279 [1400]
SENSENBRENNER, M., 159 [811]
—, 216 [1064]
—, 216 [1065 a]
SENTI, F. R., 108 [662]
SEPHTON, H. H., 27 [106]
SERK-HANSSEN, K., 63, 99 [436]
—, 63, 69, 70, 71 [437]
—, 63, 110 [438]
—, 63 [439]
—, 115, 116, 255 [690]
SHANK, R. S., 94 [587]
SHAPIRO, B. L., 262 [1270]
SHAPIRO, S. K., 146 [764 a]
SHAW, M. K., 213 [8 c]
SHAW, N., 181 [919 b]
—, 181, 226, 227 [920 a]
SHCHELOKOV, V. I., 189 [946]

SHEAR, M. J., 196, 197, 216 [967]
—, 216 [1061]
SHEARER, G., 48 [295]
SHECHTER, H., 94 [587]
SHEEHAN, H. L., 21 [49]
SHELTON, B., 164 [861]
SHEMYAKIN, M. M., 189 [946]
SHENKER, F., 72 [497 a]
SHENSTONE, F. S., 287 [1464]
SHEPHARD, B. R., 96 [613]
SHEPHERD, R. G., 82, 83 [536]
SHEPPARD, N., 44 [257]
—, 46 [279]
SHERMAN, H., 256 [1227]
SHETTLES, L. B., 194 [957]
SHIBATA, M., 262 [1268]
SHILTON, R., 40, 41, 43 [215]
SHIMMYO, Y., 275 [1361]
—, 280 [1406]
SHINA, D. B., 166, 207 [873 a]
SHINOHARA, C., 265 [1287]
SHIPMAN, J. S., 272 [1332]
SHIRLEY, D. A., 90 [570]
—, 91 [574]
SHKROB, A. M., 189 [946]
SHOCKMAN, G. D., 202, 228 [1026]
SHOJIMA, K., 278 [1388]
SHREVE, O. D., 44, 47 [267]
SHTUL'BAUM, F. I., 233, 234 [1124]
SHUNK, C. H., 110 [676]
SIERRA, G., 108, 109, 224 [655]
—, 109, 224 [667]
SIFFERD, R. H., 158, 209 [808]
SIFFERLEN, J., 114, 116 [688 a]
SIGAL, M. V., 262 [1271]
SIJPESTEIJN, A. K., 263, 264 [1274]
SILAEV, A. B., 82, 83 [573 a]
SILK, M. H., 27 [106]
—, 33 [152]
SILVERSTEIN, R. M., 44 [261 a]
SIMMONS, H. E., 93 [586]
SINCLAIR, R. G., 44 [268]
—, 44 [269]
—, 44 [270]
SKEGGS, H. R., 110 [675]
SLAGLE, F. B., 48 [291]
SLEPECKY, R. A., 108 [663]
SLIFER, E. D., 26 [92]
SLOBODIN, M., 55 [372]
SMAKULA, E., 43 [247]

THALLER, V., 42 [250]
THEORELL, H., 110, 111, 170, 207 [677]
—, 170 [883]
THEUS, V., 41 [231]
THIELE, O. W., 95, 221 [593]
—, 160, 221 [827]
—, 280 [1409]
—, 280 [1410]
—, 280 [1411]
THOMAS, R. M., 271 [1321]
—, 271 [1322]
THOMAS, S., 195 [966]
THOMPSON, M. A., 284 [1442]
—, 284 [1443]
THOMPSON, P. J., 147 [776]
THOMSON, K. J., 281 [1420]
THORNE, C. B., 185 [938]
THORNE, K. J. I., 19 [27]
—, 19 [28]
—, 19 [29]
—, 84, 85, 95, 201, 225, 229, 230, 231, 236 [544]
—, 155, 158 [783]
—, 231 [1116 b]
—, 231 [1116 c]
TIGAUD, J., 185 [938]
—, 259 [1249]
TIMMONS, C. J., 40 [225]
—, 40 [228]
TINELLI, R., 197 [986]
TOBBACK, P., 108 [655 a]
TOCANNE, J.-F., 109 [671]
TOENNIES, G., 202, 228 [1026]
TOKI, K., 110, 189, 207 [679]
TOPLEY, W. W. C., 195 [960]
TÖRÓ, I., 143, 248 [740]
TOUBIANA, R., 28, 43, 102, 123, 155 157, 158,
     173, 175, 234, 249, 250 [115]
—, 41 [230]
—, 41 [234]
—, 42 [242]
—, 62 [428]
—, 179 [451]
—, 64 [461]
—, 69, 249, 250 [493]
—, 86, 94, 147, 220 [552]
—, 119 [701]
—, 120 [702]
—, 120, 135, 139, 140, 141 [703]
TOURTELLOTTE, M. E., 159 [815]
—, 263 [1280]
TOVE, S. B., 213, 231 [1048 a]

TRENNER, N. R., 80, 158 [525]
TREVELYAN, W. E., 21 [55 a]
TRILLAT, J. J., 48 [292]
—, 48 [303]
—, 49, 113, 115 [309]
TROESTLER, J., 161, 208 [845]
TRUTER, E. V., 26 [96]
—, 27, 28 [100]
—, 34 [162]
TSUCHITANI, T., 199, 234 [1007]
TSUJIMOTO, M., 25 [78]
TSUMITA, T., 156, 245 [793]
—, 198 [995]
—, 198 [996]
—, 245 [1170]
—, 246 [1175]
TUBYLEWICZ, H., 235 [1142]
TULASNE, R., 216 [1063]
TÜMMLER, R., 49 [314]
—, 159, 212 [809 a]
TUNICLIFF, D. D., 40 [227]
TUREK, W. N., 32 [131]
TURIAN, G., 250 [1195]
—, 250 [1196]
TURNER, D. A., 36 [181 a]
TURNER, F. C., 216 [1061]
TURULA, P., 287 [1459]
TWITCHELL, E., 25 [74]
TYRELL, D. A. J., 285 [1457]

UETA, N., 226 [1110 b]
ULLMAN, G. E., 277 [1370]
UMBREIT, L., 21 [50]
UMBREIT, W. W., 165 [864]
—, 213 [1048 b]
UMEZU, L. L., 47 [288]
UMEZU, M., 73 [502]
—, 156, 222, 223 [789]
—, 272 [1335]
UNGAR, J., 270 [1316]
—, 270 [1318]
URBASCHEK, B., 160, 221 [827]
—, 222 [1089]
—, 280 [1409]
—, 280 [1410]
—, 280 [1411]
URSCHULER, H.-R., 39, 49, 101 [179]
—, 95 [598 a]
UYEI, N., 247, 251 [1199]
—, 251, 252 [1204]

REFERENCES

1. A. J. Kluyver, C. B. van Niel, "The microbe's contribution to biology", Harvard University Press, Cambridge, U. S. A. (1956).
2. O. Rahn, "Microbes of merit", Ronald Press Co., New York (1945).
3. G. R. Clemo, *J. chem. Soc.* **1955** 2057.
4. J. Asselineau & E. Lederer, *Progr. Chem. org. nat. Prod.* **10** 170 (1953).
5. R. S. Breed, E. G. D. Murray & N. R. Smith, "Bergeys' manual of determinative bacteriology", 7th ed., Baillière, Tindall & Cox Ltd, London (1957).
5a. M. Kates, *Adv. lipid Research*, **2** 17 (1964).
5b. W. M. O'Leary, *Bact. Rev.* **26** 421 (1962).
6. E. F. Terroine & R. Bonnet, *Bull. Soc. Chim. biol.* **9** 588 (1927).
7. A. G. Marr & J. L. Ingraham, *J. Bact.* **84** 1260 (1962).
8. D. G. Bishop & J. L. Still, *J. lipid Res.* **4** 87 (1963).
8a. M. Kates & P. O. Hagen, *Can. J. Biochem.* **42** 481 (1964).
8b. V. A. Knivett & J. Cullen, *Biochem. J.* **94** 36P (1965).
8c. M. K. Shaw & J. L. Ingraham, *J. Bact.* **90** 141 (1965).
9. E. R. L. Gaughran, *J. Bact.* **53** 506 (1947).
10. A. Frouin, *C. r. Séanc. Soc. Biol.* **84** 606 (1921).
11. A. Frouin & M. Guillaumie, *Bull. Soc. Chim. biol.* **8** 1151 (1926).
12. E. R. Long & L. L. Finner, *Amer. Rev. Tuberc. pulm. Dis.* **16** 523 (1927).
13. E. Chargaff, *Z. physiol. Chem.* **201** 198 (1931).
14. E. Chargaff & J. Dieryck, *Biochem. Z.* **255** 319 (1932).
15. E. F. Terroine & J. E. Lobstein, *Bull. Soc. Chim. biol.* **5** 182 (1923).
16. M. M. Creighton, L. H. Chang & R. J. Anderson, *J. biol. Chem.* **154** 569 (1944).
17. E. Lederer, "Chimie et biochimie des lipides des Mycobactéries", Symposium sur le métabolisme microbien, 2nd Inter. Congr. Biochem., Paris (1952).
18. V. Portelance & M. Panisset, *Rev. Can. Biol.* **16** 112 (1957).

19. M. Stephenson & M. D. Whetham, *Proc. Roy. Soc.* **93**B 262 (1922); *ibid.*, **95** 200 (1924).
20. M. Barbier & E. Lederer, 6th Inter. Congr. Microbiol., abstr. commun. p. 49 Rome (1953).
21. B. Sauton, *Cr. hebd. Séanc. Acad. Sci., Paris* **155** 860 (1912).
22. E. R. Long, *Amer. Rev. Tuberc. pulm. Dis.* **13** 393 (1926).
23. G. Lockemann, *Z. Hyg. Infektionskr.* **124** 373 (1942).
24. R. J. Dubos & G. Middlebrook, *Amer. Rev. Tuberc. pulm. Dis.* **56** 334 (1947).
25. G. Loiseau & M. Philippe, *Annales Inst. Pasteur, Paris* **62** 469 (1939).
26. T. W. Goodwin & M. Jamikorn, *Biochem. J.* **62** 275 (1956).
27. K. J. I. Thorne & E. Kodicek, *Biochim. biophys. Acta* **59** 273 (1962).
28. K. J. I. Thorne & E. Kodicek, *Biochim. biophys. Acta* **59** 280 (1962).
29. K. J. I. Thorne & E. Kodicek, *Biochem. J.* **89** 24P (1963).
30. V. H. Cheldelin, "Metabolic pathways in microörganisms", p. 2, Wiley & Sons, New York (1961).
30a. K. Y. Cho, W. A. Corpe & M. R. J. Salton, *Biochem. J.* **93** 26C (1964).
31. S. Čmelik, *Schweiz. allg. Path. Bakt.* **17** 289 (1954).
32. S. Čmelik, *Z. physiol. Chem.* **300** 167 (1955).
33. W. B. Geiger & R. J. Anderson, *J. biol. Chem.* **129** 519 (1939).
34. L. W. Larson & W. P. Larson, *J. inf. Dis.* **31** 407 (1922).
35. S. Dagley & A. R. Johnson, *Biochim. biophys. Acta* **11** 158 (1953).
35a. K. Hofmann, D. B. Henis & C. Panos, *J. Biol. Chem.* **228** 349 (1957).
36. M. Kates, S. N. Sehgal & N. E. Gibbons, *Can. J. Microbiol.* **7** 427 (1961).
37. A. Frouin & M. Guillaumie, *Annales Inst. Pasteur, Paris* **46** 667 (1928).
38. J. Asselineau, *Annales Inst. Pasteur, Paris* **81** 306 (1951).
39. H. Cassagne, *C. r. Séanc. Soc. Biol.* **131** 693 (1939).
40. J. K. Spitznagel & R. J. Dubos, *J. exp. Med.* **101** 291 (1955).
41. A. Andrejew, *Annales Inst. Pasteur, Paris* **81** 550 (1951).
42. M. Lemoigne, G. Milhaud & M. Croson, *Bull. Soc. Chim. biol.* **31** 1587 (1949).
43. S. Čmelik, *Naturwiss.* **46** 489 (1955).
44. J. A. Croom & J. J. McNeill, *Bact. Proc., Abstr. 61st annual meeting* 1961, p. 170, *Amer. bact. Soc.*, Baltimore (1961).
45. A. T. Norris, unpublished results, quoted in (46).
46. W. J. Lennarz, G. Scheuerbrandt & K. Bloch, *J. biol. Chem.* **237** 664 (1962).
47. N. Fethke, "Substances lipoïdiques du bacille tuberculeux", Hermann, Paris (1938).
48. R. J. Anderson, R. E. Reeves, M. M. Creighton & W. C. Lothrop, *Amer. Rev. Tuberc. pulm. Dis.* **48** 65 (1943).
49. H. L. Sheehan & F. Whitwell, *J. Bact. Path.* **61** 269 (1949).
50. S. Raffel, W. Hanns, R. Guy, L. Umbreit, unpublished results quoted in S. Raffel "Immunity", p. 338, Appleton-Century-Crofts Inc., New York (1953).
51. W. Segal & H. Bloch, *J. Bact.* **72** 132 (1956).
52. W. Segal & H. Bloch, *Amer. Rev. Tuberc. pulm. Dis.* **75** 495 (1957).
53. J. S. Youngner & H. Noll, *Virology* **6** 157 (1958).
54. M. Nakamura, *Igaku to Seibutsugaku*, **39** 41 (1956); *Chem. Abstr.* **52** 7426 (1958).
55. H. Smith & J. Keppie, "Mechanisms of microbial pathogenicity"; 5th Symp. Soc. Gen. Microbiol., p. 126, Cambridge Univ. Press (1955).
55a. J. S. Harrison & W. E. Trevelyan, *Nature, Lond.* **200** 1189 (1963).
56. D. J. Hanahan, "Lipid Chemistry", Wiley & Sons Inc., New York (1960).
57. M. A. Macheboeuf & N. Fethke, *Bull. Soc. Chim. biol.* **16** 229 (1934).
58. K. Bloch, *Z. physiol. Chem.* **244** 1 (1936).
59. A. Saenz, L. Costil & M. Sadettin, *C. r. Séanc. Soc. Biol.* **115** 1175 (1934).
60. R. J. Anderson, *Progr. Chem. org. nat. Prod.* **3** 145 (1939).
61. H. Aronson, *Berl. klin. Wschr.* **35** 484 (1898).
62. Q. Myrvik & R. S. Weiser, *J. Immun.* **68** 413 (1952).

63. J. Asselineau & E. Lederer, "Chemistry and metabolism of bacterial lipids", *in* "Metabolism of lipids", ed. by K. Bloch, p. 337, Wiley & Sons Inc., New York (1960).
64. J. Asselineau, Thesis Dr. Sci., Univ. Paris 1950, Ed. Arnette (1951).
65. A. Aebi, J. Asselineau & E. Lederer, *Bull. Soc. Chim. biol.* **35** 661 (1953).
66. D. J. Hanahan, *J. biol. Chem.* **195** 199 (1952).
67. M. Kates, *Nature, Lond.* **172** 814 (1955); *Can. J. Biochem. Physiol.* **35** 127 (1957).
68. M. Kates & F. M. Eberhardt, *Can. J. Bot.* **35** 895 (1957).
69. J. A. Lovern, *in* "Essential fatty acids", p. 246, Butterworths Sci. Publ., London (1958).
70. C. M. Grossman, *Biochim. biophys. Acta* **36** 541 (1959).
71. K. E. Murray & R. Schoenfeld, *J. Amer. oil Chem. Soc.* **28** 461 (1951).
72. C. A. Gusserow, *Arch. Pharm. Berl.* **27** 153 (1828).
73. F. Varrentrapp, *Liebigs Annln* **35** 196 (1840).
74. E. Twitchell, *Ind. eng. Chem.* **13** 807 (1921).
75. T. P. Hilditch, "The chemical constitution of natural fats", Chapman & Hall, London (1949).
76. J. Asselineau, *Bull. Soc. Chim. biol.* **38** 1397 (1956).
77. J. Cason & G. Sumrell, *J. org. Chem.* **16** 1193 (1951).
78. M. Tsujimoto, *J. Chem. Ind., Japan* **23** 1007 (1920).
79. S. F. Velick, *J. biol. Chem.* **159** 175 (1954).
80. J. B. Brown, *Chem. Rev.* **29** 333 (1941).
81. J. B. Brown & D. K. Kolb, *Progr. Chem. Fats Lipids* **3** 57 (1955).
82. L. C. Craig, *Fortschr. chem. Forsch.* **1** 292 (1949).
83. H. J. Dutton, *Progr. Chem. Fats Lipids* **2** 292 (1954).
84. E. H. Ahrens, *in* "Biochemical problems of Lipids, p. 30, Butterworths Sci. Publ., London (1956).
85. E. H. Ahrens & L. C. Craig, *J. biol. Chem.* **195** 299 (1952).
86. D. H. S. Horn, F. W. Hougen, E. von Rudloff & D. A. Sutton, *J. chem. Soc.* **1954** 177.
87. C. R. Scholfield, J. Nowakowska & H. J. Dutton, *J. Amer. oil. Chem. Soc.* **37** 27 (1960).
88. C. R. Smith, T. L. Wilson, E. H. Melvin & I. A. Wolff, *J. Amer. Chem. Soc.* **82** 1417 (1960).
89. J. Olley, *Chem. Ind.* **1956** 1120.
90. H. J. Dutton & J. A. Cannon, *J. Amer. oil Chem. Soc.* **33** 46 (1956).
91. C. R. Scholfield & M. A. Hicks, *J. Amer. oil Chem. Soc.* **34** 77 (1957).
92. H. E. Carter, R. H. McCluer & E. D. Slifer, *J. Amer. Chem. Soc.* **87** 3735 (1956).
92a. F. D. Collins, *Biochem. J.* **89** 177 (1963).
93. F. Cramer, "Einschlussverbindungen", Springer, Heidelberg (1954).
94. F. Bengen, *Angew. Chem.* **63** 207 (1951).
95. W. Schlenk, *Fortschr. chem. Forsch.* **2** 92 (1951).
96. E. V. Truter, *Research* **6** 320 (1943).
97. H. Schlenk, *Progr. Chem. Fats Lipids* **2** 243 (1954).
98. W. Schlenk, *Angew. Chem.* **72** 26 (1960).
98a. C. Asselineau & J. Asselineau, *Ann. Chimie* **9** 461 (1964).
99. H. B. Knight, L. P. Witnauer, J. E. Coleman, W. R. Noble & D. Swern, *Analyt. Chem.* **24** 1331 (1952).
100. E. V. Truter, *J. Chem. Soc.* **1951** 2416.
101. A. W. Weitkamp & N. J. Bowman, U. S. Patents 2,594,481 and 2,598,953 (1952).
102. R. W. Schiessler & D. Flitter, *J. Amer. chem. Soc.* **74** 1720 (1952).
103. W. J. Zimmerschied, R. A. Dinerstein, A. W. Weitkamp & R. F. Marschner, *Ind. eng. Chem.* **42** 1300 (1950).
104. E. M. Meade, 12th Int. Congr. pure appl. Chem., New York (1951).
105. F. Aylward & P. D. S. Wood, *Nature, Lond.* **177** 146 (1955).
106. M. H. Silk, H. H. Sephton & H. H. Hahn, *Biochem. J.* **57** 574 (1954).
107. A. M. Abu-Nasr, W. M. Potts & R. T. Holman, *J. Amer. oil Chem. Soc.* **31** 16 (1954).

108. O. E. McElroy, W. Jordon, J. McLaughin & M. E. Freeman, *J. Amer. oil Chem. Soc.* **32** 286 (1955).
109. W. E. Parker, R. E. Koos & D. Swern, *Biochem. prep.* **4** 86 (1955).
110. O. Redlich, C. M. Gable, A. K. Dunlop & R. W. Millar, *J. Amer. chem. Soc.* **72** 4153 (1950).
111. D. Swern, L. P. Witnauer & H. B. Knight, *J. Amer. chem. Soc.* **74** 1655 (1952).
112. N. Nicolaides & F. Laves, *J. Amer. chem. Soc.* **80** 5752 (1958).
113. W. Schlenk, *Experientia* **8** 337 (1952).
114. J. Cason, G. Sumrell, C. F. Allen, G. A. Gillies & S. Elberg, *J. biol. Chem.* **205** 435 (1953).
115. J. Asselineau & R. Toubiana, unpublished results.
116. D. E. Pearson, *J. chem. Educ.* **28** 60 (1951).
117. J. Cason, N. L. Allinger, G. Sumrell & D. E. Williams, *J. org. Chem.* **16** 1170 (1951).
118. H. Stage, *Fette u. Seif.* **55** 217 (1953).
119. K. E. Murray & R. Schoenfeld, *J. Amer. oil. Chem. Soc.* **30** 25 (1953).
120. F. A. Norris & D. E. Terry, *Oil & Soap* **26** 41 (1945).
121. J. Cason & G. Sumrell, *J. biol. Chem.* **195** 405 (1952).
122. K. Hofmann, R. A. Lucas & M. Sax, *J. biol. Chem.* **195** 473 (1952).
123. K. E. Murray, *Progr. Chem. Fats Lipids* **3** 244 (1955).
124. A. W. Weitkamp, *J. Amer. chem. Soc.* **67** 447 (1945).
125. A. W. Weitkamp, *J. Amer. oil Chem. Soc.* **24** 236 (1947).
126. J. Asselineau & E. Lederer, *Biochim. biophys. Acta* **7** 126 (1951).
127. W. J. Bailey & W. F. Hale, *J. Amer. chem. Soc.* **81** 647 (1959).
128. L. Ahlquist, C. Asselineau, J. Asselineau, S. Ställberg-Stenhagen & E. Stenhagen, *Ark. Kemi* **13** 543 (1959).
129. F. Krafft, *Ber. dt. chem. Ges.* **16** 3024 (1883).
130. G. G. Smith & W. H. Wetzel, *J. Amer. chem. Soc.* **79** 875 (1957).
131. W. J. Bailey & W. N. Turek, *J. Amer. oil. Chem. Soc.* **33** 317 (1956).
132. H. H. Hatt, *J. & Proc. Aust. chem. Inst.* **15** 322 (1948).
133. F. A. Norris, I. I. Rusoff, E. S. Miller & G. O. Burr, *J. biol. Chem.* **147** 273 (1943).
134. J. Asselineau, *in* "Chromatographie en chimie organique et biologique", vol. I, p. 441, Masson, Paris (1959); *ibid.*, vol. II p. 251 (1960).
135. L. J. Morris, *in* "Chromatography", p. 428, Reinhold Publ. Corp., New York (1961).
136. G. V. Marinetti, *J. lipid Res.* **3** 1 (1962).
137. J. J. Wren, *Chromat. Rev.* **3** 111 (1961).
137a. G. B. Ansell & J. N. Hawthorne, Phospholipids, BBA Library, Elsevier, Amsterdam (1964).
138. K. K. Carroll, *J. lipid Res.* **2** 135 (1961).
139. J. Asselineau & J. Moron, *Bull. Soc. Chim. biol.* **40** 899 (1958).
140. H. Noll & E. Jackim, *J. biol. Chem.* **232** 903 (1958).
141. G. Michel, *C. r. hebd. Séanc. Acad. Sci., Paris* **244** 2429 (1957).
142. E. Vilkas & E. Lederer, *Bull. Soc. Chim. biol.* **38** 111 (1956).
143. J. Asselineau, H. Buc, P. Jolles & E. Lederer, *Bull. Soc. Chim. biol.* **40** 1953 (1958).
143a. M. L. Vorbeck & G. V. Marinetti, *J. lipid Res.* **6** 3 (1965).
144. O. Renkonen, *J. lipid Res.* **3** 181 (1962).
145. C. Asselineau, J. Asselineau, R. Ryhage, S. Ställberg-Stenhagen & E. Stenhagen, *Acta chem. scand.* **13** 822 (1959).
146. J. Cason & G. A. Gillies, *J. org. Chem.* **20** 419 (1955).
147. B. de Vries, *Chem. & Ind.* **1962** 1049. *J. Amer. oil Chem. Soc.* **40** 184 (1963).
148. L. L. Ramsey & W. I. Patterson, *J. Ass. off. agric. Chem.* **31** 441 (1948).
149. J. Asselineau & E. Lederer, *Bull. Soc. chim. Fr.* **1953** 335.
150. M. Barbier & E. Lederer, *Biochim. biophys. Acta* **14** 246 (1954).
151. S. Nojima, *J. Biochem., Tokyo* **46** 607 (1959).
152. M. H. Silk & H. H. Hahn, *Biochem. J.* **56** 406 (1954).

153. K. Hofmann, C.-Y. Hsiao, D. B. Henis & C. Panos, *J. biol. Chem.* **217** 49 (1955).
154. S. Čmelik, *Z. physiol. Chem.* **302** 20 (1955).
155. S. Čmelik, *Z. physiol. Chem.* **293** 222 (1953).
156. J. Pokorny, *Rozhl. Tuberk.* **15** 119 (1955); *ibid.* **16** 484 (1956).
157. V. L. Pustovalov, *Biokhimiya* **20** 730 (1955); *ibid.*, **21** 38 (1956).
158. P. E. Ballance & W. M. Crombie, *Biochem. J.* **69** 632 (1958).
159. A. Nowotny, O. Lüderitz & O. Westphal, *Biochem. Z.* **330** 47 (1958).
160. S. Fiker & V. Hajek, *Chem. Listy* **52** 549 (1958); *Chem. Abstr.* **53** 2647 (1959).
160a. V. Wollrab & M. Streibel, *Colln. Trav. chim. Tchécosl.* **28** 1895 (1963).
161. E. Stahl, "Dünnschichtchromatographie", Springer, Berlin (1962).
161a. K. Randerath, Chromatographie sur couches minces, Gauthier-Villars, Paris (1964).
162. E. V. Truter, "Thin film chromatography", Cleaver-Hume Press, London (1963).
163. H. K. Mangold, *J. Amer. oil chem. Soc.* **38** 708 (1961).
164. C. B. Barrett, M. S. Dallas & F. B. Padley, *Chem. & Ind.* **1962** 1050.
165. B. de Vries & G. Jurriens, *Fette, Seifen, Anstrichmitt.* **65** 725 (1963).
165 a. H. Wagner, J.-D. Goetschel & P. Lesch, *Helv. chim. Acta* **46** 2986 (1963).
165b. Y. Kishimoto & N. S. Radin, *J. lipid Res.* **4** 437 (1963).
166. A. T. James, *Methods biochem. Analysis* **8** 1 (1960).
166a. E. C. Horning, A. Karmen & G. C. Sweeley, *Progr. Chem. Fats Lipids* **7** part 2 167 (1964).
167. M. A. Khan & B. T. Witham, *J. appl. Chem.* **8** 549 (1958).
168. M. J. E. Golay, "Gas chromatography", Academic Press, New York (1958).
169. S. R. Lipsky, J. E. Lovelock & R. A. Landowne, *J. Amer. chem. Soc.* **81** 1010 (1959); *Analyt. Chem.* **31** 852 (1959).
169a. G. Odham, *Ark. Kemi* **22** 417 (1964).
170. S. R. Lipsky & R. A. Landowne, *Ann. N. Y. Acad. Sci.* **72** 666 (1959); C. H. Orr & J. E. Callen, *Ann. N. Y. Acad. Sci.* **72** 649 (1959); A. T. James, *J. Chromat.* **2** 552 (1959); *Analyst, Lond.* **88** 572 (1963).
171. R. A. Landowne & S. R. Lipsky, *Biochim. biophys. Acta* **47** 589 (1961).
172. H. Schlenk, J. L. Gellerman & D. M. Sand, *Analyt. Chem.* **34** 1529 (1962).
173. F. P. Woodford & C. M. van Gent, *J. lipid Res.* **1** 188 (1960).
174. P. R. Vagelos, D. B. Martin, A. Karmen & M. G. Horning, "Biosynthesis of lipids", 5th Inter. Congr. Biochem., Moscow, 1961, p. 104, Pergamon Press (1963).
175. J. Cason, P. Tavs & A. Weiss, *Tetrahedron* **18** 437 (1962).
176. W. Sonneveld, P. H. Begemann, G. I. van Beers, R. Keuning & J. C. M. Schogt, *J. lipid. Res.* **3** 351 (1962).
177. J. Asselineau, *Annls Inst. Pasteur, Paris* **100** 109 (1961).
178. A. T. James & A. J. P. Martin, *Biochem. J.* **63** 144 (1956).
179. J. Cason, H-.R. Urscheler & C. F. Allen, *J. org. Chem.* **22** 1284 (1957).
180. H. Demarteau-Ginsburg, E. Lederer, R. Ryhage, S. Ställberg-Stenhagen & E. Stenhagen, *Nature, Lond.* **183** 1117 (1959).
181. K. Abel, H. de Schmertzing & J. Peterson, *J. Bact.* **85** 1039 (1963).
181a. E. C. Horning, E. H. Ahrens, S. R. Lipsky, F. H. Mattson, J. F. Mead, D. A. Turner & W. H. Goldwater, *J. lipid Res.* **5** 20 (1964).
181b. M. Pascaud, *Adv. lipid Res.* **1** 253 (1963).
182. J. Cason, G. Sumrell & R. S. Mitchell, *J. org. Chem.* **15** 850 (1950).
183. L. J. Banaszak & H. J. McDonald, *Biochim. biophys. Acta* **53** 404 (1961).
184. D. Eberhagen & H. Betzing, *J. lipid Res.* **3** 382 (1962).
185. M. G. Macfarlane, *Biochem. J.* **82** 40P (1962).
186. A. Haller, *C. r. hebd. Séanc. Acad. Sci., Paris* **122** 865 (1896).
187. A. C. Chibnall, S. H. Piper, A. Pollard, J. A. B. Smith & E. F. Williams, *Biochem. J.* **25** 2095 (1931).

188. G. Sandulesco & A. Girard, *C. r. hebd. Séanc. Acad. Sci., Paris* **207** 874 (1938).
189. B. Gastambide, Thesis Dr. Sci., Univ. Paris 1954, p. 40, Masson.
190. M. Anchel & H. Waelsch, *J. biol. Chem.* **145** 605 (1942).
191. H. A. El Mangouri, *Biochem. J.* **31** 1978 (1937).
192. A. Girard & G. Sandulesco, *Helv. chim. Acta* **19** 1095 (1936).
193. C. Asselineau, *Chim. analyt.* **36** 257 (1954).
194. O. H. Wheeler, *Chem. Rev.* **62** 205 (1962).
195. A. Seher, *Liebigs Annln* **589** 222 (1954).
196. N. Polgar, *J. Chem. Soc.* **1954** 1008.
197. S. Berschandy, Thesis Dr. Sci., Univ. Strasbourg, p. 23 and 31 (1953).
198. M. Brini, *Bull. Soc. chim. Fr.* **1955** 339.
199. H. Demarteau-Ginsburg, A. Ginsburg & E. Lederer, *Biochim. biophys. Acta* **12** 587 (1953).
200. J. D. Chanley & N. Polgar, *J. chem. Soc.* **1954** 1003.
201. J. Cason, N. L. Allinger & E. D. Williams, *J. org. Chem.* **18** 842 (1953).
202. J. Cason & G. J. Fonken, *J. biol. Chem.* **220** 391 (1965).
203. N. Polgar, *Biochem. J.* **42** 206 (1948).
204. E. Jantzen & H. Andreas, *Chem. Ber.* **92** 1427 (1959).
205. H. B. White & F. W. Quackenbush, *J. Amer. oil Chem. Soc.* **39** 511 (1962).
206. R. F. Paschke & D. H. Wheeler, *J. Amer. oil Chem. Soc.* **31** 81 (1954).
207. M. Faure, *in* "Techniques de Laboratoire", vol. II, p. 1247, Masson, Paris (1963).
208. R. T. O'Connor, *J. Amer. oil Chem. Soc.* **32** 616 (1955).
209. G. A. Pitt & R. A. Morton, *Progr. Chem. Fats Lipids* **4** 228 (1957).
210. A. I. Scott, "The interpretation of ultraviolet spectra of natural products", Pergamon Press, Oxford (1962).
210a. C. N. R. Rao, Ultraviolet and visible spectroscopy, Butterworths, London (1961).
211. L. K. Evans & A. E. Gillam, *J. Chem. Soc.* **1945** 432.
212. H. Schlenk, H. K. Mangold, J. L. Gellerman, W. E. Link, R. A. Morisette, R. T. Holman & H. Hayes, *J. Amer. oil Chem. Soc.* **37** 547 (1960).
213. C. Asselineau & J. Asselineau, *Bull. Soc. chim. Fr.* **1960** 1776.
214. R. B. Woodward, *J. Amer. chem. Soc.* **63** 1123 (1941); *ibid.*, **64** 72, 76 (1942).
215. W. F. Forbes & R. Shilton, *J. org. Chem.* **24** 436 (1959).
216. L. F. Fieser, *J. org. Chem.* **15** 930 (1950).
217. K. Hirayama, *J. Amer. chem. Soc.* **77** 373 (1955).
218. A. T. Nielsen, *J. org. Chem.* **22** 1539 (1957).
219. H. Booker, L. K. Evans & A. E. Gillam, *J. chem. Soc.* **1940** 1453.
220. I. Heilbron, E. R. H. Jones, J. T. McCombie & B. C. L. Weedon, *J. chem. Soc.* **1945** 84.
221. P. L. Nichols, S. F. Herb & R. W. Riemenschneider, *J. Amer. chem. Soc.* **73** 247 (1951).
222. R. R. Allen, *J. org. Chem.* **21** 143 (1956).
223. H. K. Black & B. C. L. Weedon, *J. chem. Soc.* **1953** 1785.
224. G. F. Woods & L. H. Schwartzman, *J. Amer. chem. Soc.* **70** 3394 (1948).
225. E. A. Braude & C. J. Timmons, *J. chem. Soc.* **1950** 2006.
226. L. Crombie & A. G. Jacklin, *Chem. & Ind.* **1955** 1186.
227. H. F. Gray, R. S. Rasmussen & D. D. Tunicliff, *J. Amer. chem. Soc.* **69** 1630 (1947).
228. E. A. Braude & C. J. Timmons, *J. chem. Soc.* **1953** 3144.
229. M. Magat & N. Meier, "Spectres d'absorption des liquides, solutions et solides", Tables annuelles de constantes et données numériques, Hermann, Paris (1943).
230. R. Toubiana, *C. r. hebd. Séanc. Acad. Sci., Paris* **248** 247 (1959).
231. V. Theus, W. Surber, L. Colombi & H. Schinz, *Helv. chim. Acta* **38** 239 (1955).
232. J. Szmuskovicz, *J. org. Chem.* **19** 1424 (1954).
233. J. Nichols & E. Schiffer, *J. Amer. chem. Soc.* **80** 5705 (1958).
234. R. Toubiana & J. Asselineau, *C. r. hebd. Séanc. Acad. Sci., Paris* **245** 1577 (1957).

235. E. L. Pippen & M. Monaka, *J. org. Chem.* **23** 1580 (1958).
236. H. H. Inhoffen & G. von der Bey, *Liebigs Annln* **583** 100 (1953).
237. S. G. Powell & W. J. Wasserman, *J. Amer. chem. Soc.* **79** 1934 (1957).
238. L. Crombie, *Quart. Rev. Chem. Soc., Lond.* **6** 101 (1952).
239. J. Cason & G. Sumrell, *J. org. Chem.* **16** 1177 (1951).
240. J. L. H. Allan, E. R. H. Jones & M. C. Whitting, *J. chem. Soc.* **1955** 1862.
241. G. S. Myers, *J. Amer. chem. Soc.* **73** 2100 (1951).
242. R. Toubiana & J. Asselineau, *C. r. hebd. Séanc. Acad. Sci., Paris* **247** 2054 (1958).
243. J. Cason & G. Sumrell, *J. org. Chem.* **16** 1181 (1951).
244. R. F. Rekker, J. P. Brombacher, H. Hamann & W. T. Nauta, *Rec. Trav. chim.* **73** 410 (1954).
245. R. E. Bowman & W. D. Ames, *J. chem. Soc.* **1952** 3945.
246. U. Eisner, J. A. Elvidge & R. P. Linstead, *J. chem. Soc.* **1953** 1372.
247. E. Smakula, *Angew. Chem.* **47** 657 (1934).
248. F. Korte & D. Scharf, *Chem. Ber.* **95** 443 (1962).
249. C. T. Kisker & D. I. Crandall, *Tetrahedron* **19** 701 (1963).
250. E. E. Boehm, V. Thaller & M. C. Whiting, *J. chem. Soc.* **1963** 2535.
251. H. M. Randall & D. W. Smith, *J. optic. Soc. Amer.* **43** 1086 (1953).
252. D. W. Smith, H. M. Randall, M. Gastambide-Odier & A. L. Koevoet, *Ann. N. Y. Acad. Sci.* **69** 145 (1957).
253. H. Noll & H. Bloch, *J. biol. Chem.* **214** 251 (1955).
254. N. K. Freeman, *J. Amer. chem. Soc.* **74** 2523 (1952).
255. N. K. Freeman, *J. Amer. chem. Soc.* **75** 1859 (1953).
256. G. Marinetti & E. Stotz, *J. Amer. chem. Soc.* **76** 1347 (1954).
257. D. Barnard, L. Bateman, A. J. Harding, H. P. Koch, N. Sheppard & G. B. B. M. Sutherland, *J. chem. Soc.* **1950** 915.
258. L. J. Bellamy, "The infrared spectra of complex molecules", Methuen & Co., London (1959).
259. R. C. Gore, *in* "Determination of organic structures by physical methods", p. 195, ed. by E. A. Braude & F. C. Nachod, Academic Press Inc., New York (1955).
260. A. R. H. Cole, *Progr. Chem. org. nat. Prod.* **13** 1 (1956).
261. K. Nakanishi, "Infrared absorption spectroscopy—pratical", Holden-Day Inc., San Francisco (1962).
261a. R. M. Silverstein & G. C. Bassler, Spectrometric identification of organic compounds, Wiley, New York (1963).
262. A. D. Cross, "Introduction to practical infrared spectroscopy", Butterworths, London (1960).
263. D. H. Wheeler, *Progr. Chem. Fats Lipids* **2** 268 (1954).
264. R. T. O'Connor, *J. Amer. oil Chem. Soc.* **32** 624 (1955); *ibid.,* **33** 1 (1956); *ibid.,* **38** 648 (1961).
265. H. P. Schwarz, L. Dreisbach, R. Childs & S. V. Mastrangelo, *Ann. N. Y. Acad. Sci.* **69** 116 (1957).
266. N. K. Freeman, *Ann. N. Y. Acad. Sci.* **69** 131 (1957).
267. O. D. Shreve, M. R. Heether, H. B. Knight & D. Swern, *Analyt. Chem.* **22** 1498 (1950).
268. R. G. Sinclair, A. F. MacKay, G. S. Myers & R. N. Jones, *J. Amer. chem. Soc.* **74** 2570 (1952).
269. R. N. Jones, A. F. MacKay & R. G. Sinclair, *J. Amer. chem. Soc.* **74** 2575 (1952).
270. R. G. Sinclair, A. F. MacKay, G. S. Myers & R. N. Jones, *J. Amer. chem. Soc.* **74** 2578 (1952).
271. D. L. Guertin, S. E. Wiberley, W. H. Bauer & J. Goldenson, *Analyt. Chem.* **28** 1194 (1956).
272. W. Fuchs, *Fette, Seifen. Anstrichmitt.* **58** 3 (1956).
273. R. A. Meikeljohn, R. J. Meyer, S. M. Aronovic, H. A. Schuette & V. W. Meloch, *Analyt. Chem.* **29** 329 (1957).
274. I. Fischmeister, *Ark. Kemi* **20** 353, 385, 399 (1963).
275. R. T. Holman & P. R. Edmondson, *Analyt. Chem.* **28** 1533 (1956).
276. O. H. Wheeler, *Chem. Rev.* **59** 629 (1959); R. F. Goddu & D. A. Delker, *Analyt. Chem.* **32** 140 (1960).
277. R. T. O'Connor, *J. Amer. oil Chem. Soc.* **38** 641 (1961).

278. H. Primas & H. H. Gunthard, *Helv. chim. Acta* **36** 1659 (1953).
279. S. Ställberg-Stenhagen, E. Stenhagen, N. Sheppard, G. B. B. M. Sutherland & A. Walsh, *Nature, Lond.* **160** 580 (1947).
280. H. Sobotka & F. E. Stynler, *J. Amer. chem. Soc.* **72** 5139 (1950).
281. D. Chapman, *J. chem. Soc.* **1957** 4489.
282. C. F. H. Allen, T. J. Davis, W. J. Humphlett & D. W. Stewart, *J. org. Chem.* **22** 1291 (1957).
283. W. H. Washburn & M. J. Mahoney, *J. Amer. chem. Soc.* **80** 504 (1958).
284. H. Weitkamp, U. Hasserodt & F. Korte, *Chem. Ber.* **95** 2280 (1962).
285. D. Chapman, *J. chem. Soc.*, **1958** 3186, 4680.
286. E. Baer, *J. Amer. chem. Soc.* **74** 152 (1952).
287. E. Baer, *J. Amer. chem. Soc.* **75** 621 (1953).
288. L. L. Umezu, *Archs. Biochem. Biophys.* **45** 149 (1953).
289. N. K. Freeman, F. T. Lindgren. Y. C. Ng & A. V. Nichols, *J. biol. Chem.* **203** (1953).
290. S. H. Piper, A. C. Chibnall, S. J. Hopkins, A. Pollard, J. A. B. Smith & E. F. Williams, *Biochem. J.* **25** 2072 (1931).
291. F. B. Slagle & E. Ott, *J. Amer. chem. Soc.* **55** 4396 (1933).
292. J. J. Trillat & T. von Hirsch, *J. Phys. Radium* [7] **4** 38 (1933).
293. D. R. Kreger & C. Schamhart, *Biochim. biophys. Acta* **19** 22 (1956).
294. T. Malkin, *Progr. Chem. Fats Lipids* **1** 1 (1952).
295. W. B. Saville & G. Shearer, *J. chem. Soc.* **127** 591 (1925).
296. K. S. Markley, S. B. Hendricks & C. E. Sando, *J. biol. Chem.* **98** 103 (1932).
297. S. F. Velick, *J. biol. Chem.* **154** 497 (1944).
298. S. Abrahamsson, *Ark. Kemi* **14** 65 (1959).
299. E. Stenhagen, *Acta chem. Scand.* **5** 805 (1951).
300. F. Francis & S. H. Piper, *J. Amer. chem. Soc.* **61** 577 (1939).
301. E. von Sydow, *Ark. Kemi* **9** 231 (1956).
302. S. C. Nyburg, "X-Ray analysis of organic structures", Academic Press, New York (1961).
303. J. J. Trillat & S. Barbezat, *Bull. Soc. Chim. biol.* **33** 1012 (1951).
304. E. Stenhagen & S. Ställberg, *J. biol. Chem.* **139** 345 (1941).
305. S. Ställberg-Stenhagen & E. Stenhagen, *J. biol. Chem.* **159** 255 (1945).
306. M. Spiegel-Adolf & G. C. Henny, *J. biol. Chem.* **140** CXXII (1941).
307. S. Ställberg-Stenhagen & E. Stenhagen, *J. biol. Chem.* **173** 383 (1948).
308. R. Ryhage, E. Stenhagen & E. von Sydow, *Acta chem. scand.* **10** 158 (1956).
309. E. Lederer, J. Pudles, S. Barbezat & J. J. Trillat, *Bull. Soc. chim. Fr.* **19** 93 (1952).
310. S. F. Velick, *J. biol. Chem.* **156** 101 (1944).
311. R. Ryhage, *Ark. Kemi* **13** 475 (1959); **16** 19 (1960); **20** 185 (1963).
312 A. H. Etemadi, A.-M. Miquel, E. Lederer & M. Barber, *Bull. Soc. Chim. Fr.* **1964** 3274.
313 M. Barber, P. Jollès, E. Vilkas & E. Lederer, *Biochem. biophys. Research Comm.* **18** 469 (1965).
314. M. von Ardenne, K. Steinfelder, R. Tümmler & K. Schreiber, *Experientia* **19** 178 (1963).
315. R. Ryhage & E. Stenhagen, *J. Lipid Res.* **1** 361 (1960).
316. R. Ryhage, S. Ställberg-Stenhagen & E. Stenhagen, *Ark. Kemi* **18** 179 (1962).
317. F. W. McLafferty, *Analyt. Chem.* **28** 306 (1956).
318. F. W. LcLafferty, *Appl. Spectrosc.* **11** 148 (1957).
319. F. W. McLafferty, "Mass spectrometry of organic ions", Academic Press, New York (1963).
320. E. Stenhagen, 9ende Nordiske Kemikermöde i Aarhus, p. 59 (1956).
321. E. Stenhagen, *Z. analyt. Chem.* **181** 462 (1961).
322. H. Budzikiewicz, C. Djerassi & D. H. Williams, "Interpretation of mass spectra of organic compounds", Holden-Day Inc., San Francisco (1964).
323. K. Biemann, *Angew. Chem.* **74** 102 (1962).
324. K. Biemann, "Mass spectrometry, organic chemical applications", McGraw-Hill Book Co., New York (1962).

324a. R. I. Reed, *Adv. org. Chem.* **3** 1 (1963).
325. B. Hallgren, E. Stenhagen & R. Ryhage, *Acta chem. scand.* **11** 1064 (1957).
326. R. Ryhage & E. Stenhagen, *Ark. Kemi* **15** 291, 333, 545 (1960).
327. B. Hallgren, E. Stenhagen & R. Ryhage, *Acta chem. scand.* **12** 1351 (1958); *ibid.*, **13** 845 (1959).
328. Nguyen Dinh Nguyen, R. Ryhage & S. Ställberg-Stenhagen, *Ark. Kemi* **15** 433 (1960).
329. J. Asselineau, R. Ryhage & E. Stenhagen, *Acta chem. scand.* **11** 196 (1957).
330. R. Ryhage, S. Ställberg-Stenhagen & E. Stenhagen, *Ark. Kemi* **18** 179 (1962).
331. R. Ryhage, E. Stenhagen & E. von Sydow, *Acta chem. scand.* **11** 180 (1957).
332. J. D. Roberts, "Nuclear magnetic resonance, applications to organic chemistry", McGraw-Hill Book Co., New York (1959).
333. L. M. Jackman, "Applications of nuclear magnetic resonance spectroscopy in organic chemistry", Pergamon Press, London (1959).
334. Nuclear magnetic resonance, *Ann. N. Y. Acad. Sci.* **70** 763 (1958); *Proc. chem. Soc.* **1958** 127.
335. S. Brownstein, *Chem. Rev.* **59** 463 (1959).
336. N. F. Chamberlain, *Analyt. Chem.* **31** 56 (1958).
337. H. Conroy, *Adv. org. Chem.* **2** 265 (1960).
338. J. D. Baldeschwiller & E. W. Randall, *Chem. Rev.* **63** 81 (1963).
339. C. Y. Hopkins, *J. Amer. oil Chem. Soc.* **38** 664 (1961).
340. D. Chapman, *J. chem. Soc.* **1963** 131.
341. G. Middlebrook, C. M. Coleman & W. B. Schaefer, *Proc. nat. Acad. Sci. U. S.* **45** 1801 (1959).
342. A. Etemadi, R. Okuda & E. Lederer, *Bull. Soc. chim. Fr.* **1964** 868.
343. E. Vilkas, A.-M. Miquel & E. Lederer, *Biochim. biophys. Acta* **70** 217 (1963).
343a. J. Cason & G. L. Lange, *J. Org. Chem.* **29** 2107 (1964).
344. D. G. Dervichian, *Progr. Chem. Fats Lipids* **2** 193 (1954).
345. E. Stenhagen, in "Determination of organic structures by physical methods" p. 325, ed. by E. A. Braude & F. C. Nachod, Academic Press Inc., New York (1955).
346. S. Ställberg-Stenhagen & E. Stenhagen, *J. biol. Chem.* **173** 171 (1942).
347. J. Cason & R. J. Anderson, *J. biol. Chem.* **126** 527 (1938).
348. R. J. Anderson & M. M. Creighton, *J. biol. Chem.* **129** 57 (1939).
349. S. Ställberg-Stenhagen, *J. biol. Chem.* **165** 599 (1947).
350. S. Ställberg-Stenhagen & E. Stenhagen, *Acta chem. scand.* **3** 1035 (1949).
351. J. Cason & F. S. Prout, *J. Amer. chem. Soc.* **70** 879 (1948).
352. C. Djerassi, "Optical rotatory dispersion; applications to organic chemistry", McGraw-Hill Book Co., New York (1960).
353. W. Klyne, *Adv. org. Chem.* **1** 239 (1960).
354. J. Cason & W. R. Winans, *J. org. Chem.* **15** 148 (1950).
355. F. Percheron, *in* "Mises au point de chimie analytique pure et appliquée et d'analyse bromatologique", p. 119, Masson, Paris (1960).
356. R. Kuhn & H. Roth, *Chem. Ber.* **66** 1274 (1933).
357. J. Cason & G. Sumrell, *J. biol. Chem.* **192** 405 (1951).
358. W. Kirsten & E. Stenhagen, *Acta chem. scand.* **6** 682 (1952).
359. A. D. Campbell & J. E. Morton, *J. chem. Soc.* **1952** 1693.
360. V. H. Tashinian, M. J. Baker & C. W. Koch, *Analyt. Chem.* **28** 1304 (1956).
361. L. G. Ginger, *J. biol. Chem.* **156** 453 (1944).
362. A. D. Campbell & V. J. Chettleburgh, *J. chem. Soc.* **1953** 1942.
363. L. Henry & G. Ourisson, *Bull. Soc. chim. Fr.* **1955** 99.
364. C. F. Garbers, H. Schmid & P. Karrer, *Helv. chim. Acta* **37** 1336 (1954).
365. H. Bickel, H. Schmid & P. Karrer, *Helv. chim. Acta*, **38** 649 (1955).
366. R. Entschel, C. H. Eugster & P. Karrer, *Helv. chim. Acta* **39** 1263 (1956).
367. H. Demarteau-Ginsburg, *C. r. hebd. Séanc. Acad. Sci., Paris*, **243** 2169 (1956).

368. J. Cason & H. J. Wolfhagen, *J. org. Chem.* **14** 155 (1949).
369. J. Cason, C. Gastaldo, D. L. Glusker, J. Allinger & L. B. Ash, *J. org. Chem.* **18** 1129 (1953).
370. M. S. Newman, "Steric effects in organic chemistry", p. 206, Wiley & Sons, Inc., New York (1956).
371. H. P. Kaufmann, *Chem. Ber.* **75** 1201 (1942).
372. M. Slobodin, *J. gen. Chem. U. S. S. R.* **16** 1698 (1946); *Chem. Abstr.* **41** 5851 (1947).
373. L. H. Briggs & B. F. Cain, *J. chem. Soc.* **1954** 4182.
374. M. Pesez & P. Poirier, "Méthodes et réactions de l'analyse organique", vol. III, p. 56, Masson, Paris (1954).
375. C. Asselineau, unpublished observations.
376. J. Adachi, *Analyt. Chem.* **23** 1491 (1951).
377. A. Kirmann & S. Geiger-Berschandy, *Bull. Soc. chim. Fr.* **1955** 991.
378. G. S. Marks & N. Polgar, *J. chem. Soc.* **1955** 3851.
379. W. R. Churchward, N. A. Gibson, R. J. Meakins & J. W. Mulley, *J. chem. Soc.* **1950** 959.
380. J. Hansley, *J. Amer. Chem. Soc.* **57** 2303 (1935).
381. F. Baykut & S. Özeris, *Rev. Fac. Sci. Univ. Istanbul* **23**C 86 (1958).
382. R. J. Anderson, *J. biol. Chem.* **83** 505 (1929).
383. H. Demarteau-Ginsburg, Thesis Ing.-Dr., Paris (1958).
384. R. J. Anderson, W. C. Lothrop & M. M. Creighton, *J. biol. Chem.* **125** 299 (1938).
385. W. D. Celmer & H. E. Carter, *Physiol. Rev.* **32** 167 (1952).
386. P. Stoffyn & A. Stoffyn, *Biochim. biophys. Acta* **70** 107 (1963).
387. J. Asselineau, *C. r. hebd. Séanc. Acad. Sci., Paris* **229** 791 (1949).
388. R. J. Anderson, *J. biol. Chem.* **74** 537 (1927).
389. N. Stendal, *C. r. hebd. Séanc. Acad. Sci., Paris* **198** 1549 (1934).
390. N. Polgar, *J. chem. Soc.* **1954** 1011.
391. G. D. Hunter & G. Popják, *Biochem. J.* **50** 163 (1951).
392. N. P. Buu-Hoi, *Bull. Soc. chim. Fr.* **13** 147 (1946).
393. H. K. Black & B. C. L. Weedon, *Chemy Ind.* **1953** 40.
394. A. Allais, J. Mathieu, A. Petit, P. Poirier & L. Velluz, "Substances naturelles de synthèse", vol. VII, Masson, Paris (1953).
395. C. Meystre & K. Miescher, *Helv. chim. Acta* **28** 1252, 1497 (1945).
396. S. Wilkinson, *Nature, Lond.* **164** 622 (1949).
397. G. Darzens & C. Mentzer, *C. r. hebd. Séanc. Acad. Sci., Paris* **213** 268 (1941).
398. W. G. Dauben, E. Hoerger & J. W. Petersen, *J. Amer. chem. Soc.* **75** 2347 (1953).
399. W. P. Gibble, E. B. Kurtz & A. Kelley, *J. Amer. oil Chem. Soc.* **33** 66 (1956).
400. M. A. Spielman, *J. biol. Chem.* **106** 87 (1934).
401. J. Cason, J. S. Fessenden & C. L. Agre, *Tetrahedron* **7** 289 (1959).
402. C. L. Agre & J. Cason, *J. biol. Chem.* **234** 2555 (1959).
403. K. E. Murray, *Aust. J. Chem.* **12** 657 (1959).
404. E. L. Jackson, *Org. Reactions* **2** 341 (1944).
405. R. Criegee, "Newer methods of organic preparative chemistry", p. 1, New York (1948).
406. F. D. Gunstone, *J. chem. Soc.* **1954** 1611.
407. P. S. Bailey, *Chem. Rev.* **58** 925 (1958).
408. O. S. Privett & C. Nickell, *J. Amer. oil Chem. Soc.* **39** 414 (1962).
408a, O. S. Privett, M. L. Blank & O. Romanus, *J. lipid Res.* **4** 260 (1963).
408b. R. G. Kadesch, *Progr. Chem. Fats Lipids* **6** 291 (1963).
409. F. L. Benton, A. A. Kiess & H. J. Harwood, *J. Amer. oil Chem. Soc.* **36** 457 (1959); J. Pasero, L. Comeau & M. Naudet, *Bull. Soc. chim. Fr.* **1963** 1794.
410. P. Baudart, *Bull. Soc. chim. Fr.* **9** 919 (1942).
411. N. A. Abraham, *Annly Chim.* **5** 979 (1960).
412. J. Pudles & E. Lederer, *Bull. Soc. Chim. biol.* **36** 759 (1954).

413. R. U. Lemieux & E. von Rudloff, *Can. J. Chem.* **33** 1701 (1955).
414. E. von Rudloff, *J. Amer. oil. Chem. Soc.* **33** 126 (1956).
415. E. von Rudloff, *Can. J. Chem.* **34** 1413 (1956).
416. E. P. Jones & J. A. Stolp, *J. Amer. oil Chem. Soc.* **35** 71 (1958).
417. C. R. Smith, T. L. Wilson, R. B. Bates & C. R. Scholfield, *J. org. Chem.* **27** 3112 (1962).
418. A. R. Bader, *J. Amer. chem. Soc.* **70** 3938 (1948).
419. C. Prevost, *in* "Traité de Chimie organique", vol. V, p. 662, ed. by V. Grignard, G. Dupont & R. Locquin, Masson, Paris (1937).
420. J. P. Riley, *J. chem. Soc.* **1951** 1346.
421. F. D. Gunstone, *J. chem. Soc.* **1952** 1274.
422. J. Asselineau, *Bull. Soc. chim. Fr.* **1960** 135.
423. C. H. Hassal, *Org. Reactions* **9** 73 (1957).
424. W. J. Gensler, *Chem. Rev.* **57** 191 (1957).
425. F. D. Gunstone, *Progr. Chem. Fats Lipids* **4** 1 (1957).
426. D. G. M. Diaper & A. Kuksis, *Chem. Rev.* **59** 89 (1959).
427. S. Abrahamsson, S. Ställberg-Stenhagen & E. Stenhagen, *Progr. Chem. Fats Lipids* **7** 1 (1963).
427a. K. S. Markley, Fatty acids, Wiley, New York (1964), vol. 3, p. 1769.
428. R. Toubiana, *Annls Chim.* **7** 567 (1962) .
429. R. G. Johnson & R. K. Ingham, *Chem. Rev.* **56** 219 (1956); C. V. Wilson, *Org. Reactions* **9** 332 (1957); S. J. Cristol & W. C. Firth, *J. org. Chem.* **26** 280 (1961).
430. D. E. Floyd & S. E. Miller, *Org. Syntheses* **34** 13 (1954).
431. S. Ställberg-Stenhagen, *Ark. Kemi Miner. Geol.* **25**A no. 10 (1947).
432. R. P. Linstead, J. C. Lunt & B. C. Weedon, *J. chem. Soc.* **1951** 1130.
433. A. S. Bailey, V. D. Brice, M. G. Horne & N. Polgar, *J. chem. Soc.* **1959** 661.
434. G. I. Fray & N. Polgar, *J. chem. Soc.* **1956** 2036.
435. G. Ställberg, *Acta chem. scand.* **11** 1430 (1957).
436. L. Ahlquist, J. Asselineau, C. Asselineau, K. Serck-Hanssen, S. Ställberg-Stenhagen & E. Stenhagen, *Ark. Kemi* **14** 171 (1959).
437. K. Serck-Hanssen, S. Ställberg-Stenhagen & E. Stenhagen, *Ark. Kemi* **5** 203 (1953).
438. K. Serck-Hanssen & E. Stenhagen, *Acta chem. scand.* **9** 866 (1955).
439. K. Serck-Hanssen, *Ark. Kemi* **10** 135 (1956).
440. R. Brettle & F. S. Holland, *J. chem. Soc.* **1962** 4836.
441. T. Malkin & T. H. Bevan, *Progr. Chem. Fats Lipids* **4** 63 (1957).
442. P. E. Verkade, *Festschrift A. Stoll*, p. 395 (1957).
443. L. Hartman, *Chem. Rev.* **58** 845 (1958).
444. F. H. Mattson & R. A. Volpenhein, *J. lipid Res.* **3** 281 (1962).
445. M. Renoll & M. S. Newman, *Org. Syntheses*, coll. vol. III p. 502 (1955).
446. H. Hilbart & N. M. Carter, *J. Amer. chem. Soc.* **51** 1601 (1929).
447. J. B. Martin, *J. Amer. chem. Soc.* **75** 5482 (1953).
448. L. Hartmann, *Nature, Lond.* **176** 1024 (1955).
449. G. I. Fray & N. Polgar, *J. Chem. Soc.* **1955** 1802.
450. J. Defaye & E. Lederer, *Bull. Soc. Chim. biol.* **38** 1301 (1956).
451. T. Malkin & T. H. Bevan, *Progr. Chem. Fats Lipids* **4** 97 (1957).
452. E. Baer, *Progr. Chem. Fats Lipids* **6** 33 (1963).
453. P. E. Verkade, *Bull. Soc. Chim. Fr.* **1963** 1993.
454. E. Baer & F. Eckstein, *J. biol. Chem.* **237** 1449 (1962).
455. E. Baer & A. Kindler, *Biochemistry* **1** 518 (1962).
456. F. Kögl, G. H. de Haas & L. L. M. van Deenen, *Rec. Trav. chim.* **79** 661 (1960).
457. E. Baer, Y. Suzuki & J. Blackwell, *Biochemistry* **2** 1227 (1963).
457a. E. Baer & K. V. J. Rao, *J. Amer. Chem. Soc.* **87** 135 (1965).
458. T. Gendre & E. Lederer, *Bull. Soc. chim. Fr.* **1956** 1478.

459. J. Asselineau & E. Lederer, *Bull. Soc. chim. Fr.* **1955** 1232.
460. J. Asselineau, *Bull. Soc. chim. Fr.* **1955** 937.
461. J. Polonsky, G. Ferreol, R. Toubiana & E. Lederer, *Bull. Soc. chim. Fr.* **1956** 1471.
462. G. Brochere-Ferreol & J. Polonsky, *Bull. Soc. chim. Fr.* **1958** 714.
463. W. C. York, A. Finchler, L. Osipow & F. D. Snell, *J. Amer. oil Chem. Soc.* **33** 424 (1956).
464. H. B. Haas, *Mfg. Chem.* **29** 152 (1958).
465. T. H. Edley, Brit. Pat. 804, 197, Nov. 1958; *Chem. Abstr.* **53** 6657 (1959).
466. R. J. Anderson & M. S. Newman, *J. biol. Chem.* **101** 773 (1933).
467. R. J. Anderson & M. S. Newman, *J. biol. Chem.* **103** 197 (1933).
468. R. J. Anderson & M. S. Newman, *J. biol. Chem.* **103** 405 (1933).
469. C. Kuroda, *J. Sci. Res. Inst., Tokyo* **45** 166 (1951); *Chem. Abstr.* **46** 6115 (1952).
470. M. S. Newman, J. A. Crowder & R. J. Anderson, *J. biol. Chem.* **105** 279 (1934).
471. R. J. Anderson & M. M. Creighton, *J. biol. Chem.* **130** 429 (1939).
472. J. Madinaveitia, *An R. Soc. esp. Fas. Quim.* **31** 750 (1933).
473. R. J. Anderson & R. E. Reeves, *J. biol. Chem.* **119** 543 (1937).
474. M. O'L. Crowe, *J. biol. Chem.* **115** 479 (1936).
475. E. G. Ball, *J. biol. Chem.* **106** 515 (1934).
476. E. G. Ball, *J. Amer. chem. Soc.* **59** 2071 (1937).
477. E. S. Hill, *Proc. Soc. exp. Biol. Med.* **35** 363 (1936).
478. J. W. H. Lugg, A. K. Macbeth & F. L. Winzor, *J. chem. Soc.* **1936** 1457.
479. H. J. Almquist & A. A. Klose, *J. Amer. chem. Soc.* **61** 1611, 1923 (1939).
480. F. A. Cajori, T. T. Otani & M. A. Hamilton, *J. biol. Chem.* **208** 107 (1954).
481. M. Barbier, Thesis, Univ. Paris (1954).
482. M. Asano & H. Takahashi, *J. pharm. Soc., Japan* **65** 17 (1945); *Chem. Abstr.* **45** 3906 (1951).
483. A. N. Parshin, *Biokhimiya* **11** 53 (1946).
484. J. Francis, J. Madinaveitia, M. M. MacTurk & G. A. Snow, *Nature, Lond.* **163** 365 (1949).
485. J. Asselineau & E. Lederer, *Experientia* **7** 281 (1951).
486. G. A. Snow, 2nd Inter. Congr. Biochem., Paris 1952, abstr. comm. p. 95.
487. L. F. Fieser, W. P. Campbell & E. M. Fry, *J. Amer. chem. Soc.* **61** 2206 (1939).
488. M. C. Pangborn & R. J. Anderson, *J. Amer. chem. Soc.* **58** 10 (1936).
489. R. E. Reeves & R. J. Anderson, *J. Amer. chem. Soc.* **59** 858 (1937).
490. R. J. Anderson, J. A. Crowder, M. S. Newman & F. H. Stodola, *J. biol. Chem.* **113** 637 (1936).
491. R. J. Anderson, R. L. Peck & M. M. Creighton, *J. biol. Chem.* **133** 675 (1940).
492. W. B. Geiger & R. J. Anderson, *J. biol. Chem.* **131** 539 (1939).
493. J. Asselineau & R. Toubiana, unpublished results.
494. A. A. Kanchukh, *Ukr. Biokhim. Zh.* **26** 186 (1954); *Chem. Abstr.* **49** 1142 (1955).
495. R. H. Pickard & J. Kenyon, *J. chem. Soc.* **103** 1953 (1913).
496. J. A. Crowder, F. H. Stodola & R. J. Anderson, *J. biol. Chem.* **114** 431 (1936).
497. A. Butenandt & F. H. Stodola, *Liebigs Annln* **539** 40 (1939).
497a. E. Wenkert, E.-M. Loeser, S. N. Mahapatra, F. Shenker & E. M. Wilson, *J. org. Chem.* **29** 435 (1964).
498. F. H. Stodola & R. J. Anderson, *J. biol. Chem.* **114** 467 (1936).
499. R. E. Reeves & R. J. Anderson, *J. biol. Chem.* **119** 535 (1937).
500. C. W. Wieghard & R. J. Anderson, *J. biol. Chem.* **126** 515 (1938).
501. J. Cason & R. J. Anderson, *J. biol. Chem.* **119** 549 (1937).
502. M. Umezu & T. Wagner-Jauregg, *Biochem. Z.* **298** 115 (1938).
503. J. A. Hall, J. W. Lewis & N. Polgar, *J. chem. Soc.* **1955** 3971.
504. G. Michel, Thesis Dr. Sci. Univ., Paris (1958).
505. L. G. Ginger & R. J. Anderson, *J. biol. Chem.* **157** 213 (1945).
506. E. Stenhagen, *J. biol. Chem.* **148** 695 (1943).
507. H. Demarteau-Ginsburg & E. Lederer, *C. r. hebd. Séanc. Acad. Sci. Paris* **240** 815 (1955).

508. S. Ställberg-Stenhagen & E. Stenhagen, *J. biol. Chem.* **183** 223 (1950).

509. J. A. Hall & N. Polgar, *Chem. & Ind.* **1954** 1293.

510. L. Ahlquist, R. Ryhage, E. Stenhagen & E. von Sydow, *Ark. Kemi* **14** 211 (1959).

511. R. Ryhage, S. Ställberg-Stenhagen & E. Stenhagen, *Ark. Kemi* **14** 247 (1959).

512. J. W. Lewis & N. Polgar, *J. chem. Soc.* **1958** 102.

513. F. K. Drayson, J. W. Lewis & N. Polgar, *J. chem. Soc.* **1958** 430.

514. F. K. Drayson & N. Polgar, *J. chem. Soc.* **1959** 3652.

515. R. Ryhage, S. Ställberg-Stenhagen & E. Stenhagen, *Ark. Kemi* **14** 259 (1959).

516. D. J. Cram & F. A. Abd Elhafez, *J. Amer. chem. Soc.* **74** 5828 (1952).

517. M. Gastambide-Odier, J.-M. Delaumeny & E. Lederer, *Chem. & Ind.* **1963** 1285.

518. H. Demarteau-Ginsburg & E. Lederer, *Biochim. biophys. Acta* **70** 442 (1963).

518a. M. Gastambide-Odier, P. Sarda & E. Lederer, *Tetrahedron Let.* **1965** 3135.

519. G. Michel & E. Lederer, *Bull. Soc. chim. Fr.* **1962** 651.

520. J. Pudles & E. Lederer, *Bull. Soc. chim. Fr.* **1954** 919.

521. H. Noll, *J. biol. Chem.* **232** 919 (1958).

522. H. Noll, R. Ruegg, U. Gloor, G. Ryser & O. Isler, *Helv. chim. Acta* **43** 433 (1960).

523. A. F. Brodie, B. R. Davis & L. F. Fieser, *J. Amer. chem. Soc.* **80** 6454 (1958).

524. E. R. Kashket & A. F. Brodie, *Biochim. biophys. Acta* **40** 550 (1960).

525. P. H. Gale, B. H. Arison, N. R. Trenner, A. C. Page, K. Folkers & A. F. Brodie, *Biochemistry* **2** 200 (1963).

526. D. H. L. Bishop, K. P. Pandya & H. K. King, *Biochem. J.* **83** 606 (1962).

527. D. H. L. Bishop & H. K. King, *Biochem. J.* **85** 550 (1962).

528. J. Asselineau, *Bull. Soc. chim. Fr.* **1954** 108.

529. J. Asselineau, *C. r. hebd. Séanc. Acad. Sci., Paris* **239** 1561 (1954).

530. A.-M. Miquel, H. Ginsburg & J. Asselineau, *Bull. Soc. Chim. biol.* **45** 715 (1963).

531. M. Ikawa, J. B. Koepfli, S. G. Mudd & C. Niemann, *J. Amer. chem. Soc.* **75** 3439 (1953).

532. M. Ikawa & C. Niemann, *J. Amer. chem. Soc.* **75** 6314 (1953).

533. P. Alaupović & M. Proštenik, *Croat. chem. Acta* **28** 211 (1956).

534. A. J. Burton, Thesis, Univ. Illinois, U. S. A. 1961 (*Univ. Microfilms* no. 61-4266); A. J. Burton & H. E. Carter, *Biochemistry* **3** 411 (1964).

535. W. Hausmann & L. C. Craig, *J. Amer. chem. Soc.* **76** 4892 (1954).

535a. S. Wilkinson & L. A. Lowe, *Nature, Lond.* **200** 1008 (1963).

536. P. H. Bell, J. F. Bone, J. P. English, C. E. Fellows, K. S. Howard, L. M. Rogers, R. G. Shepherd & R. Winterbottom, *Ann. N. Y. Acad. Sci.* **51** 897 (1948).

537. J. R. Catch, T. S. G. Jones & S. Wilkinson, *Ann. N. Y. Acad. Sci.* **51** 917 (1948).

537a. A. B. Silaev, E. P. Yulikova & L. A. Baratova, *Zh. Obshch. Khim.* **32** 818 (1962).

538. T. Oda & F. Ueda, *J. pharm. Soc., Japan* **74** 1246 (1954).

539. R. C. Gore & E. M. Petersen, *Ann. N. Y. Acad. Sci.* **51** 924 (1948).

540. L. Crombie & S. H. Harper, *J. chem. Soc.* **1950** 2685.

541. K. Vogler & L. H. Chopard-Dit-Jean, *Helv. chim. Acta* **43** 279 (1960).

542. W. Klyne, *Biochem. J.* **53** 378 (1953).

543. K. Saito, *J. Biochem., Tokyo* **47** 710 (1960).

544. K. J. I. Thorne & E. Kodicek, *Biochim. biophys. Acta* **59** 306 (1962).

544a. M.-A. Lanéelle & J. Asselineau, unpublished results.

544b. A. Ballio, S. Barcellona & L. Boniforti, *Biochem. J.* **94** 11C (1965).

545. M. G. MacFarlane, *Biochem. J.* **82** 40P (1962).

546. S. Akashi & K. Saito, *J. Biochem., Tokyo* **47** 222 (1960).

547. T. Kaneda, *J. biol. Chem.* **238** 1222 (1963).

547a. A. J. Fulco, R. Levy & K. Bloch, *J. biol. Chem.* **239** 998 (1964).

548. J. Cason & W. T. Miller, *J. biol. Chem.* **238** 883 (1963).

549. S. Dauchy & J. Asselineau, *C. r. hebd. Séanc. Acad. Sci., Paris* **250** 2635 (1960).

550. K. J. I. Chalk & E. Kodicek, *Biochim. biophys. Acta* **50** 579 (1961).
551. T. Kaneshiro & A. G. Marr, *J. biol. Chem.* **236** 2615 (1961).
552. R. Toubiana & J. Asselineau, *C. r. hebd. Séanc. Acad. Sci., Paris* **254** 369 (1962).
553. G. A. Snow, *J. chem. Soc.* **1954** 2588.
554. K. Hofmann & S. M. Sax, *J. biol. Chem.* **205** 55 (1953).
555. K. Hofmann & F. Tausig, *J. biol. Chem.* **213** 425 (1955).
556. K. Hofmann & F. Tausig, *J. biol. Chem.* **213** 415 (1955).
556a. M. Ikawa, *Biochim. biophys. Acta.* **84** 208 (1964).
557. D. G. Bounds, R. P. Linstead & B. C. L. Weedon, *J. chem. Soc.* **1954** 4219.
558. K. Ahmad, F. M. Bumpus & F. M. Strong, *J. Amer. chem. Soc.* **70** 3391 (1948).
559. R. J. Anderson & E. Chargaff, *J. biol. Chem.* **85** 77 (1929).
560. J. Cason, G. Sumrell, C. F. Allen, G. A. Gillies & S. Elberg, *J. biol. Chem.* **205** 435 (1953).
561. J. Cason, C. F. Allen, W. de Acetis, & G. J. Fonken, *J. biol. Chem.* **220** 893 (1956).
562. A.-M. Miquel & J. Asselineau, unpublished results.
563. G. Laneelle, unpublished results.
563a. W. Hofheinz & H. Grisebach, *Z. Naturforsch.* **20**b 43 (1965).
564. F. S. Prout, J. Cason & A. W. Ingersoll, *J. Amer. chem. Soc.* **69** 1233 (1947).
565. F. S. Prout, J. Cason & A. W. Ingersoll, *J. Amer. chem. Soc.* **70** 298 (1948).
566. S. Ställberg-Stenhagen. *Ark. Kemi Miner. Geol.* **26**A no. 12 (1948).
567. R. P. Linstead, J. C. Lunt & B. C. L. Weedon, *J. Chem. Soc.* **1950** 3331.
568. M. Asano, Y. Kameda & J. Ohta, *J. pharm. Soc., Japan* **64** 29 (1944); *Chem. Abstr.* **45** 4302 (1951).
569. M. Asano & J. Ohta, *J. pharm. Soc., Japan* **65** 10 (1945); *Chem. Abstr.* **45** 4302 (1951).
570. G. A. Schmidt & D. A. Shirley, *J. Amer. chem. Soc.* **71** 3804 (1949).
571. M. Sy, N. P. Buu-Hoi & N. Dat-Xuong, *C. r. hebd. Séanc. Acad. Sci., Paris* **239** 1813 (1954).
572. S. Hünig & M. Salzwedel, *Angew. Chem.* **71** 339 (1959).
573. J. Asselineau, *C. r. hebd. Séanc. Acad. Sci., Paris* **267** 1804 (1953).
574. D. A. Shirley & G. A. Schmidt, *J. Amer. chem. Soc.* **73** 867 (1951).
575. F. M. L. Pattison & R. G. Woolford, *J. Amer. chem. Soc.* **79** 2306 (1957).
576. C. O. Edens, M. M. Creighton & R. J. Anderson, *J. biol. Chem.* **154** 587 (1944).
577. K. Hofmann & R. A. Lucas, *J. Amer. chem. Soc.* **72** 4328 (1950).
578. E. Klenk & W. Bongard, *Z. physiol. Chem.* **290** 181 (1952).
579. K. Hofmann, G. J. Marco & G. A. Jeffrey, *J. Amer. chem. Soc.* **80** 5717 (1958).
580. K. Hofmann, O. Jucker, W. R. Miller, A. C. Young & F. Tausig, *J. Amer. chem. Soc.* **76** 1799 (1954).
581. S. Ställberg-Stenhagen, *Ark. Kemi Miner. Geol.* **22**A no. 19 (1946).
582. K. Hofmann, S. F. Orochena & C. W. Yoho, *J. Amer. chem. Soc.* **79** 3608 (1957).
583. B. Craven & G. A. Jeffrey, *J. Amer. chem. Soc.* **82** 3858 (1960).
584. K. Hofmann, S. F. Orochena, S. M. Sax & G. A. Jeffrey, *J. Amer. chem. Soc.* **81** 992 (1959).
585. K. Hofmann & C. W. Yoho, *J. Amer. chem. Soc.* **81** 3356 (1959).
586. H. E. Simmons & R. D. Smith, *J. Amer. chem. Soc.* **81** 4256 (1959).
587. R. S. Shank & H. Shechter, *J. org. Chem.* **24** 1825 (1959).
588. E. Chargaff & M. Levine, *J. biol. Chem.* **124** 195 (1938).
589. S. F. Velick & R. J. Anderson, *J. biol. Chem.* **152** 523 (1944).
590. R. Cavanna & S. Ställberg-Stenhagen, *Atti Acad. naz. Lincei* **347** 33 (1950).
591. K. Hofmann & F. Tausig, *J. biol. Chem.* **213** 425 (1955).
592. W. M. O'Leary, *J. Bact.* **84** 967 (1962).
593. J. Asselineau, C. Lacave & O. W. Thiele, *Bull. Soc. Chim. biol.* **46** 168 (1964).
594. J. Krembel & S. Pinson, *Path. Microbiol.* **26** 592 (1963); *Bull. Soc. chim. biol.* **46** 503 (1964).
595. G. M. Gray, *Biochim. biophys. Acta* **65** 135 (1962).
596. D. G. Bishop & J. L. Still, *J. lipid Res.* **4** 81 (1963).

597. H. Goldfine & K. Bloch, *J. biol. Chem.* **236** 2615 (1961).
598. P. McLeod & J. P. Brown, *J. Bact.* **85** 1056 (1963).
598*a.* J. Cason, G. L. Lange & H.-R. Urscheler, *Tetrahedron* **20** 1955 (1964).
599. R. J. Anderson, *J. biol. Chem.* **83** 169 (1929).
600. R. J. Anderson, *J. biol. Chem.* **97** 639 (1932).
601. E. Chargaff, *Chem. Ber.* **65** 745 (1932).
602. M. A. Spielman & R. J. Anderson, *J. biol. Chem.* **112** 759 (1935).
603. T. Wagner-Jauregg, *Z. physiol. Chem.* **247** 135 (1937).
604. C. V. Wilson, *J. Amer. chem. Soc.* **67** 2161 (1945).
605. N. Polgar & R. Robinson, *J. chem. Soc.* **1945** 389.
606. A. K. Schneider & M. A. Spielman, *J. biol. Chem.* **142** 345 (1942).
607. N. P. Buu-Hoi & P. Cagniant, *Chem. Ber.* **76** 689 (1943).
608. N. P. Buu-Hoi & P. Cagniant, *Z. physiol. Chem.* **279** 76 (1943).
609. N. Polgar & R. Robinson, *J. chem. Soc.* **1943** 615.
610. M. Asano, Y. Kameda & T. Wada, *J. pharm. Soc., Japan* **63** 538 (1943); *Chem. Abstr.* **44** 7229 (1950).
611. M. Asano, Y. Kameda & T. Wada, *J. pharm. Soc., Japan* **64** 25 (1944); *Chem. Abstr.* **45** 4302 (1951).
612. M. Asano, Y. Kameda & T. Wada, *J. pharm. Soc., Japan* **65** 15 (1945); *Chem. Abstr.* **45** 4302 (1951).
613. R. P. Linstead, J. C. Lunt, B. R. Shephard & B. C. L. Weedon, *J. Chem. Soc.* **1953** 1538.
614. L. G. Ginger & R. J. Anderson, *J. biol. Chem.* **156** 443 (1944).
615. J. D. Chanley & N. Polgar, *Nature, Lond.* **166** 693 (1950).
616. J. Cason & G. Sumrell, *J. Amer. chem. Soc.* **72** 4837 (1950).
617. N. Polgar & R. Robinson, *Chem. & Ind.* **1951** 685.
618. A. S. Bailey, N. Polgar & R. Robinson, *J. chem. Soc.* **1953** 3031.
619. S. Ställberg-Stenhagen, *Ark. Kemi* **6** 537 (1954).
620. P. C. Jocelyn & N. Polgar, *J. chem. Soc.* **1953** 132.
621. C. Asselineau, J. Asselineau, S. Ställberg-Stenhagen & E. Stenhagen, *Acta chem. scand.* **10** 478, 1035 (1956).
622. G. I. Fray & N. Polgar, *Chem. & Ind.* **1956** 22.
623. D. J. Millin & N. Polgar, *J. chem. Soc.* **1958** 1902.
624. J. Cason, N. K. Freeman & G. Sumrell, *J. biol. Chem.* **192** 415 (1951).
625. J. Cason & C. F. Allen, *J. biol. Chem.* **205** 449 (1953).
626. J. Cason & M. J. Kalm, *J. org. Chem.* **19** 1947 (1954).
627. J. Cason & M. J. Kalm, *J. org. Chem.* **19** 1836 (1954).
628. J. Cason & K. L. Rinehart, *J. org. Chem.* **20** 1591 (1955).
629. K. E. Murray, personal communication.
630. P. Bennet & J. Asselineau, *Bull. Soc. Chim. biol.* **45** 1379 (1963).
631. L. G. Ginger & R. J. Anderson, *J. biol. Chem.* **157** 203 (1945).
631*a.* I. Hedlund-Stoltz & E. Stenhagen, *Acta chem. scand.* **11** 405 (1957).
632. N. Polgar, *Chem. & Ind.* **1953** 353.
633. S. Ställberg-Stenhagen & E. Stenhagen, *Ark. Kemi Miner. Geol.* **24 B** no. 9 (1947).
634. N. Polgar & W. Smith, *J. chem. Soc.* **1963** 3081.
635. N. Polgar & W. Smith, *J. chem. Soc.* **1963** 3085.
636. F. J. Philpot & A. Q. Wells, *Amer. Rev. Tuberc. pulm. Dis.* **66** 28 (1952).
637. H. Noll, *J. biol. Chem.* **224** 149 (1957).
638. K. E. Murray, *Aust. J. Chem.* **15** 510 (1962).
639. G. Odham, *Ark. Kemi* **21** 379 (1963).
640. E. Chargaff, *Z. physiol. Chem.* **218** 223 (1933).
641. M. Asano & H. Takahashi, *J. pharm. Soc., Japan* **68** 188 (1948); *Chem. Abstr.* **47** 8825 (1953).

642. E. M. Gubarev, E. K. Lubenets, A. A. Kanchukh & Yu. V. Galaev, *Biokhimiya* **16** 139 (1951).

643. C. Asselineau, J.-C. Promé & J. Asselineau, unpublished results.

644. M. Lemoigne, *C. r. hebd. Séanc. Acad. Sci., Paris* **180** 1539 (1925).

645. J. H. Ottaway, *Biochem. J.* **84** 11 (1962).

646. P. A. Levene & H. L. Haller, *J. biol. Chem.* **67** 329 (1926); *ibid.,* **76** 415 (1928).

647. M. Lemoigne, *Helv. chim. Acta* **29** 1303 (1946).

648. A. C. Blackwood & A. Epp, *J. Bact.* **74** 266 (1957).

649. M. Lemoigne, G. Milhaud & M. Croson, *Bull. Soc. Chim. biol.* **31** 1587 (1949).

650. A. Kepes & C. Peaud-Lenoel, *Bull. Soc. Chim. biol.* **34** 563 (1952).

651. M. Lemoigne, B. Delaporte & M. Croson, *Annls Inst. Pasteur, Paris* **70** 224 (1944).

652. M. Lemoigne & H. Girard, *C. r. hebd. Séanc. Acad. Sci., Paris* **217** 557 (1943).

653. W. G. G. Forsyth, A. C. Hayward & J. B. Roberts, *Nature, Lond.* **182** 800 (1958).

654. H. G. Schlegel, G. Gottschalk & R. von Bartha, *Nature, Lond* **191** 643 (1961).

655. G. Sierra & N. E. Gibbons, *Can. J. Microbiol.* **8** 249 (1962).

655a. P. Tobback & H. Laudelout, *Biochim. biophys. Acta* **97** 589 (1965).

656. M. B. Morris & J. B. Roberts, *Nature, Lond.* **183** 1538 (1959).

657. J. M. Vincent, B. Humphrey & R. J. North, *J. gen. Microbiol.* **29** 551 (1962).

658. R. Y. Stanier, M. Doudoroff, R. Kunisawa & R. Contopoulou, *Proc. nat. Acad. Sci. U. S.* **45** 1246 (1959).

658a. J. M. Merrick & M. Doudoroff, *J. Bacteriol.* **88** 60 (1964).

659. E. G. Mulder, M. H. Deinema, W. L. van Veen & L. P. T. M. Zevenhuizen, *Rec.Trav. Chim.* **81** 797 (1962).

660. M. A. Rouf & J. L. Stokes, *J. Bact.* **83** 343 (1962).

661. D. H. Williamson & J. F. Wilkinson, *J. gen. Microbiol.* **19** 198 (1958).

661a. J. M. Merrick, D. G. Lundgren & R. M. Pfister, *J. Bacteriol,* **89** 234 (1965).

661b. D. G. Lundgren, R. Alper, C. Schnaitmam & R. H. Marchessault, *J. Bacteriol.* **89** 245 (1965).

662. W. C. Haynes, E. H. Melvin, J. M. Locke, C. A. Glass & F. R. Senti, *Appl. Microbiol.* **6** 298 (1958).

663. R. A. Slepecky & J. H. Law, *Analyt. Chem.* **32** 1697 (1960); J. H. Law & R. B. Slepecky, *J. Bact.* **82** 33 (1961).

663a. D. G. Lundgren, R.-M. Pfister & J. M. Merrick, *J. gen. Microbiol.* **34** 441 (1964).

664. R. E. Kallio & A. A. Harrington, *J. Bact.* **80** 321 (1960).

665. R. M. Macrae & J. F. Wilkinson, *J. gen. Microbiol.* **19** 210 (1958).

666. P. Hirsch, G. Georgiev & H. G. Schlegel, *Nature, Lond.* **197** 313 (1963).

666a. G. Gottschalk & H. G. Schlegel, *Nature (Lond.)* **205** 308 (1965).

667. G. Sierra & N. E. Gibbons, *Can. J. Microbiol.* **8** 255 (1962).

668. J. Schindler & H. G. Schlegel, *Biochem. Z.* **339** 154 (1963).

669. H. G. Schlegel & G. Gottschalk, *Angew. Chem.* **74** 342 (1962).

669a. E. A. Dawes & D. W. Ribbons, *Bacteriol. Revs* **28** 126 (1964).

670. G. A. Snow, *J. chem. Soc.* **1954** 4080.

671. J.-F. Tocanne & C. Asselineau, unpublished results.

672. G. A. Snow, *Biochem. J.* **94** 160 (1965).

672a. G. A. Snow, *Biochem. J.* **97** 166 (1965).

673. G. Tamura, *Bull. agric. chem. Soc., Japan* **21** 202 (1957).

674. G. Tamura & K. Folkers, *J. org. Chem.* **23** 772 (1958).

675. D. E. Wolf, C. H. Aldrich, H. R. Skeggs, L. D. Wright & K. Folkers, *J. Amer. chem. Soc.* **78** 4499, 5273 (1956).

676. C. H. Hoffman, A. F. Wagner, A. N. Wilson, E. Walton, C. H. Shunk, D. E. Wolf, F. W. Holly & K. Folkers, *J. Amer. chem. Soc.* **79** 2316 (1957).

677. S. Bergström, H. Theorell & H. Davide, *Archs. Biochem.* **10** 165 (1946).

678. F. G. Jarvis & M. Johnson, *J. Amer. chem. Soc.* **71** 4124 (1949); J. R. Edwards & J. A. Hayashi, *Archs Biochem. biophys.* **111** 415 (1965).

679. K. Toki & T. Ohno, *Nippon Nogei-Kagaku Kaishi* **29** 370 (1955); *Chem. Abstr.* **53** 243 (1959); *J. agric. chem. Soc., Japan* **29** 370 (1955).
680. N. J. Cartwright, *Biochem. J.* **67** 663 (1957).
681. D. G. Bishop & J. L. Still, *Biochem. biophys. Res. Commun* **7** 337 (1962).
682. T. Kaneshiro & A. G. Marr, *Biochim. biophys. Acta* **70** 271 (1963).
683. M. Ikawa, J. B. Koepfli, S. G. Mudd & C. Niemann, *J. Amer. chem. Soc.* **75** 1035 (1953).
683a. N. Polgar & W. Smith, *J. chem. Soc.* **1962** 4262.
684. J. A. Crowder & R. J. Anderson, *J. biol. Chem.* **97** 393 (1932).
685. D. Swern, *Progr. Chem. Fats Lipids* **3** 214 (1955).
686. E. Lederer & J. Pudles, *Bull. Soc. Chim. biol.* **33** 1003 (1951).
687. V. L. Pustovalov, *Biokhimiya* **21** 38 (1956).
688. A. Diara & J. Pudles, *Bull. Soc. Chim. biol.* **41** 481 (1959).
688a. A. H. Etémadi, J. Gasche & J. Sifferlen, *Bull. Soc. Chim. biol.*, **47** 631 (1965).
689. C. Asselineau & J. Asselineau, *Bull. Soc. chim. Fr.* **1966.**
690. E. Lederer, V. Portelance & K. Serck-Hanssen, *Bull. Soc. chim. Fr.* **1952** 413.
691. V. L. Hansley, U. S. Pat 2,218,026, 15 Oct. 1940.
692. R. Clement, *C. r. hebd. Séanc. Acad. Sci., Paris* **238** 718 (1953).
693. J. Polonsky & E. Lederer, *Bull. Soc. chim. Fr.* **1954** 504.
694. H. Oura & T. Makino, *Chem. pharm. Bull., Tokyo* **6** 451 (1958); *Yakugaku Zasshi* **78** 141 (1958).
695. J. Pudles & E. Lederer, *Bull. Soc. chim. Fr.* **1954** 919.
696. E. M. Gubarev, *Biokhimiya* **11** 517 (1946).
697. E. M. Gubarev, *Usp. sovrem. Biol. U. S. S. R.* **31** 108 (1951).
698. G. Michel, C. Bordet & E. Lederer, *C. r. hebd. Seanc. Acad. Sci., Paris* **250** 3518 (1960).
698a. C. Bordet, A. H. Etémadi, G. Michel & E. Lederer, *Bull. Soc. Chim. Fr.* **1965** 234.
699. M. Asano & H. Takahashi, *J. pharm. Soc. Japan* **65** 81 (1945); *Chem. Abstr.* **45** 4303 (1951).
700. H. Takahashi, *J. pharm. Soc. Japan* **68** 292 (1948); *Chem. Abstr.* **45** 9482 (1951).
701. R. Toubiana & J. Asselineau, *C. r. hebd. Séanc. Acad. Sci., Paris* **251** 884 (1960).
702. R. Toubiana & J. Asselineau, *C. r. hebd. Séanc. Acad. Sci., Paris* **253** 1965 (1961).
703. R. Toubiana & J. Asselineau, *Annls Chim.* **7** 593 (1962).
704. E. M. Gubarev & L. M. Pustovalova, *Biokhimiya* **30** 569 (1958).
705. F. H. Stodola, A. Lesuk & R. J. Anderson, *J. biol. Chem.* **126** 505 (1938).
706. R. J. Anderson, *J. biol. Chem.* **85** 351 (1929).
707. R. L. Peck & R. J. Anderson, *J. biol. Chem.* **140** 89 (1941).
708. J. Asselineau & E. Lederer, *C. r. hebd. Séanc. Acad. Sci., Paris* **228** 1892 (1949).
709. G. Laneelle, *C. r. hebd. Séanc. Acad. Sci., Paris* **257** 781 (1963).
710. J. Asselineau, *Biochim. biophys. Acta* **10** 453 (1953).
711. J. Asselineau & E. Lederer, "A Ciba Foundation Colloquium on experimental tuberculosis", p. 14 Churchill, London (1955).
712. A. Lesuk & R. J. Anderson, *J. biol. Chem.* **136** 603 (1940).
713. J. Asselineau, *C. r. hebd. Séanc. Acad. Sci., Paris* **230** 1620 (1950).
714. E. J. Jones, *Liebigs Annln* **226** 287 (1884).
715. O. Wallach, *Liebigs Annln* **365** 255 (1909).
716. M. D. Ivanoff & N. I. Nicoloff, *Bull. Soc. chim. Fr.* **51** 1337 (1932).
717. M. Stoll, *Helv. Chim. Acta* **34** 678 (1951).
718. A. Horeau & J. Jacques, *Bull. Soc. chim. Fr.* **1952** 527.
719. A. Horeau & A. Ormancey, *C. r. hebd. Séanc. Acad. Sci., Paris* **236** 826 (1953).
720. S. Ställberg-Stenhagen & E. Stenhagen, *J. biol. Chem.* **165** 599 (1946).
720a. A. H. Etémadi, *Bull. Soc. Chim. Fr.*, **1964** 1537.
721. H. Demarteau, *C. r. hebd. Séanc. Acad. Sci., Paris*, **232** 2494 (1951).
722. H. Demarteau & E. Lederer, *C. r. hebd. Séanc. Acad. Sci., Paris* **235** 265 (1952).
723. A. Ginsburg & E. Lederer, *Biochim. biophys. Acta* **9** 328 (1952).

724. J. Asselineau & T. Gendre, *Bull. Soc. chim. Fr.* **1954** 1226.

725. J. Asselineau, E. Ganz & E. Lederer, *C. r. hebd. Séanc. Acad. Sci. Paris* **232** 2050 (1951).

725a. M. Gastambide-Odier, J.-M. Delaumény & E. Lederer, *C. r. hebd. Séanc. Acad. Sci. Paris* **259** 3404 (1964).

726. R. Toubiana & J. Asselineau, *C. r. hebd. Séanc. Acac. Sci., Paris* **253** 1965 (1961).

727. J. Asselineau, *Bull. Soc. chim. Fr.* **1952** 557.

728. J. Asselineau & A. Ginsburg, *Bull. Soc. chim. Fr.* **1955** 1241.

729. J. Asselineau, *Bull. Soc. chim. Fr.* **1953** 427.

730. A. Aebi, E. Vilkas & E. Lederer, *Bull. Soc. chim. Fr.* **1954** 79.

731. G. Tener, J. Asselineau & E. Lederer, unpublished results.

732. E. D. Morgan & N. Polgar, *J. chem. Soc.* **1957** 3779.

733. C. Malani & N. Polgar, *J. chem. Soc.* **1963** 3092.

734. R. Clermonte & E. Lederer, *C. r. hebd. Séanc. Acad. Sci., Paris* **242** 2600 (1956).

734a. G. Lanéelle, unpublished results.

735. U. Eisner, J. Polonsky & E. Lederer, *Bull. Soc. chim. Fr.* **1955** 212.

736. E. D. Morgan & N. Polgar, *J. chem. Soc.* **1958** 4077.

737. H. Oura, *Chem. pharm. Bull., Tokyo* **6** 456 (1958).

738. H. Oura, *Chem. pharm. Bull., Tokyo* **6** 462 (1958).

739. E. S. J. King, *J. Path. Bact.* **70** 459 (1955).

740. Z. Pósalaky & I. Töró, *Nature, Lond.* **179** 150 (1957).

741. J. W. Berg. *A. M. A. Archs. Path.* **57** 115 (1954).

742. S. E. Nethercott & W. G. Strawbridge, *Lancet* **1956** 1132.

743. M. M. Cummings & P. C. Hudgins, *Amer. J. med. Sci.* **236** 311 (1958).

744. M. Kusunose, E. Kusunose, Y. Kowa & Y. Yamamura, *J. Biochem., Japan* **46** 525 (1959); *ibid.,* **47** 689 (1960).

745. C. L. Baugh, D. S. Bates, G. W. Claus & C. H. Werkman, *Iowa State J. Sci.* **37** 23 (1962).

746. A. Piérard & D. S. Goldman, *Archs Biochem. Biophys.* **100** 56 (1963).

747. P. Goldman, A. W. Alberts & P. R. Vagelos, *J. biol. Chem.* **238** 1255, 3579 (1963).

748. W. J. Lennarz, *Biochim. biophys. Acta* **73** 335 (1963).

749. K. Bloch, P. Baronowski, H. Goldfine, W. J. Lennarz, R. Light, A. T. Norris & G. Scheuer-brandt, *Feder. Proc.* **20** 921 (1961).

749a. A. J. Fulco & K. Bloch, *Biochim. biophys. Acta* **63** 545 (1962).

749b. K. Bloch, in "The control of lipid metabolism", p. 1, ed. by J. K. Grant, Academic Press, New York (1963).

749c. A. J. Fulco, R. Levy & K. Bloch, *J. biol. Chem.* **239** 998 (1964).

750. G. J. Schroepfer & K. Bloch. *J. Amer. chem. Soc.* **85** 3310 (1693); *J. biol. Chem.* **240** 54 (1965).

751. G. Scheuerbrandt, H. Goldfine, P. E. Baronowski & K. Bloch, *J. biol. Chem.* **236** PC 70 (1961).

752. K. Hofmann, W. M. O'Leary, C. W. Yoho & T.-Y. Liu, *J. biol. Chem.* **234** 1672 (1959).

753. A. T. Norris & K. Bloch, *J. biol. Chem.* **238** PC 3133 (1963); A. T. Norris, S. Matsumura & K. Bloch, *J. biol. Chem.* **239** 3653 (1964).

754. G. Scheuerbrandt & K. Bloch, *J. biol. Chem.* **237** 2064 (1962).

755. T. H. Haines, S. Aaronson, J. L. Gellerman & H. Schlenk, *Nature, Lond.* **194** 1282 (1962).

756. F. Davidoff & E. D. Korn, *J. biol. Chem.* **238** 3199 (1963).

757. E. D. Korn, *J. biol. Chem.* **238** 3584 (1963).

758. T. von Brand, *Rev. Inst. Med. trop., Saõ-Paulo* **4** 53 (1962).

759. E. Lederer, Proc. 5th Inter. Congr. Biochem., vol. VII, p. 90, Pergamon Press, London (1963); *Biochem. J.* **93** 449 (1964).

760. J. Asselineau & P. Bennet, in "Lipids of physiological significance", ed. by D. N. Rhodes and R. M. C. Dawson, Wiley & Sons, New York (1964), p. 111.

761. M. J. Allison, M. P. Bryant, I. Katz & M. Keeney, *J. Bact.* **83** 1084 (1962).

762. G. H. Wegner & E. M. Foster, *J. Bact.* **85** 53 (1963).

763. R. Kaneda, *J. biol. Chem.* **238** 1229 (1963).
764. K. Hofmann, "Fatty acid metabolism in microörganisms", Wiley & Sons, New York (1963).
764*a*. W. M. O'Leary, *in* "Transmethylation and methionine biosynthesis", ed. by S. K. Shapiro & F. Schlenk, University of Chicago Press (1965) p. 94.
765. T.-Y. Liu & K. Hofmann, *Biochemistry* **1** 189 (1962).
766. W. M. O'Leary, *J. Bact.* **77** 367 (1959); *ibid.*, **78** 709 (1959).
767. J. H. Law, H. Zalkin & T. Kaneshiro, *Biochim. biophys. Acta* **70** 143 (1963).
768. H. Zalkin, J. H. Law & H. Goldfine, *J. biol. Chem.* **238** 1242 (1963).
769. W. M. O'Leary, *J. Bact.* **84** 967 (1962).
770. S. Pohl, J. H. Law & R. Ryhage, *Biochim. biophys. Acta* **70** 583 (1963).
770*a*. J. G. Hildebrand & J. H. Law, *Biochemistry* **3** 1304 (1964).
771. J. L. Karlsson, *J. Bact.* **72** 813 (1956).
771*a*. G. Jaureguiberry, J. H. Law, J. A. McCloskey & E. Lederer, *C. r. hebd. Séanc. Acad. Sci., Paris* **258** 3587 (1964); *Biochemistry* **4** 347 (1965).
772. R. B. Woodward, *Angew. Chem.* **68** 13 (1956).
773. Z. Vanek, P. Puza, J. Majer & L. Dolezilova, *Folia microbiol.* **6** 408 (1961).
774. T. Kaneda, J. C. Butte, S. B. Taubman & J. W. Corcoran, *J. biol. Chem.* **237** 322 (1962).
775. H. Grisebach, H. Achenbach & W. Hofheinz, *Z. Naturforsch.* **15b** 560 (1960).
776. A. J. Birch, E. Pride, R. W. Pickards, P. J. Thomson, J. D. Dutcher, D. Perlman, C. Djerassi, *Chem. & Ind.* **1960** 1245.
776*a*. S. M. Fiedman, T. Kaneda & J. W. Corcoran, *J. biol. Chem.* **239** 2386 (1964).
777. M. Gastambide-Odier, J.-M. Delaumeny & E. Lederer, *Biochim. biophys. Acta* **70** 670 (1963).
778. R. E. Noble, R. L. Stjernholm, D. Mercier & E. Lederer, *Nature, Lond.* **199** 600 (1963).
779. R. L. Stjernholm, R. E. Noble & D. Koch-Weser, *Biochim. biophys. Acta* **64** 174 (1962).
780. H. Grisebach, W. Hofheinz & H. Achenbach, *Z. Naturforsch* **17b** 63 (1962).
781. M. Gastambide-Odier & E. Lederer, *Nature, Lond.* **184** 1763 (1959); *Biochem. Z.* **333** 285 (1960).
781*a*. A. H. Etémadi & E. Lederer, *Bull. Soc. Chim. biol.* **47** 107 (1965).
781*b*. A. H. Etémadi & Lederer, *Biochim, biophys. Acta* **98** 160 (1965).
782. E. Kodicek, "A Ciba Foundation Symposium on the biosynthesis of terpenes and sterols", p. 173, London (1959).
783. K. J. I. Thorne & E. Kodicek, *Biochim. biophys. Acta* **59** 295 (1962).
784. P. Bennet & J. Asselineau, unpublished results.
784*a*. Y. Kanemasa & D. S. Goldman, *Biochim. biophys. Acta* **98** 476 (1965).
785. J. Francis, H. M. MacTurk, J. Madinaveitia & G. A. Snow, *Biochem. J.* **55** 596 (1953).
785*a*. P. W. Albro & C. K. Huston, *J. Bacteriol.* **88** 981 (1964).
786. A. Diara & J. Asselineau. unpublished results.
787. J. A. Crowder & R. J. Anderson, *J. biol. Chem.* **104** 399 (1934).
788. R. B. Pennell, The chemistry of Brucella organisms, in "Brucellosis", p. 37 Washington (1950).
789. M. Umezu, *Rep. Inst. sci. Res., Manchoukuo* **4** 273 (1940).
790. S. Čmelik, *Z. physiol. Chem.* **290** 146 (1952).
791. S. Čmelik, *Z. physiol. Chem.* **296** 67 (1954).
792. H. Bloch, J. Defaye, E. Lederer & H. Noll, *Biochim. biophys. Acta* **23** 312 (1957).
793. T. Tsumita, *Japan. J. med. Sci. Biol.* **9** 205 (1956); *Chem. Abstr.* **51** 8876 (1957).
794. H. Noll, *J. biol. Chem.* **224** 149 (1957).
795. B. Borgström, *Acta physiol. scand.* **30** 231 (1954).
796. M. Kates, D. J. Kushner & A. T. James, *Can. J. Biochem. Physiol.* **40** 83 (1962).
797. E. M. Gubarev & I. L. Vakulenko, *Biokhimiya* **10** 285 (1945).
798. H. von Behring, *Z. physiol. Chem.* **192** 112 (1930).
799. E. Hecht, *Z. physiol. Chem.* **231** 279 (1935).
800. C. H. Williams, W. R. Bloor & L. A. Sandholzer, *J. Bacteriol.* **37** 301 (1939).
801. A. R. Taylor, *J. biol. Chem.* **165** 271 (1946).

802. E. Hecht, *Z. physiol. Chem.* **231** 29 (1935).
803. R. J. Anderson, R. Schoenheimer, J. A. Crowder & F. H. Stodola, *Z. physiol. Chem.* **237** 40 (1935).
804. C. Weibull, *Acta chem. scand.* **11** 881 (1957).
805. H. E. Stokinger, H. Ackerman & C. M. Carpentier, *J. Bact.* **47** 129 (1944).
806. A. Fiertel & H. P. Klein, *J. Bact.* **78** 738 (1959).
807. G. A. Garton & A. E. Oxford, *J. Sci. Food Agric.* **6** 142 (1955).
808. R. H. Sifferd & R. J. Anderson, *Z. physiol. Chem.* **239** 269 (1936).
809. S. Dauchy & F. Kayser, *Bull. Soc. Chim. biol.* **40** 1533 (1958).
809*a*. K. Schubert, G. Rose, R. Tümmler & N. Ikekawa, *Z. physiol. Chem.* **339** 293 (1965).
809*b*. S. Aaronson, *J. gen. Microbiol.* **37** 225 (1964).
809*c*. S. L. Jensen, *Kgl. Norske Videnskabeis Selskabs Skrifter*, nr. 8 (1962).
810. R. E. Hartman & C. E. Holmlund, *J. Bact.* **84** 1254 (1962).
811. G. Rebel, A. M. Bader, M. Sensenbrenner & P. Mandel, *C. r. hebd. Séanc. Acad. Sci., Paris* **250** 3516 (1960).
812. J. Krembel, A. Deluzarche & R. Minck, *C. r. hebd. Séanc. Acad. Sci., Paris* **253** 2005 (1961).
813. G. Rebel & P. Mandel, *C. r. hebd. Séanc. Acad. Sci., Paris* **255** 2684 (1962).
814. G. H. Rothblat & P. F. Smith, *J. Bact.* **82** 479 (1961).
815. M. E. Tourtellotte, R. G. Jensen, G. W. Gander & H. J. Morowitz, *J. Bact.* **86** 372 (1963).
816. H. Demarteau-Ginsburg & A.-M. Miquel, *Bull. Soc. Chim. biol.* **44** 679 (1962).
817. H. E. Carter, P. Johnson, D. W. Teets & R. K. Yu, *Biochem biophys. Res. Commun.* **13** 156 (1963).
818. S. Čmelik, *Experientia* **10** 372 (1954).
819. J. Sternberg & V. Portelance, *Rev. Can. Biol.* **15** 209 (1956).
820. K. Bloch, *Z. physiol. Chem.* **244** 1 (1936).
821. K. Bloch, *Biochem. Z.* **285** 372 (1936).
822. M. Macheboeuf & M. Faure, *C. r. hebd. Séanc. Acad. Sci., Paris* **209** 700 (1939).
823. K. Saito & S. Akashi, *J. Biochem. Japan* **44** 511 (1957).
823*a*. C. K. Huston, P. W. Albro & G. B. Grindey, *J. Bacteriol.* **89** 768 (1965).
823*b*. P. MacLeod & J. P. Brown, *J. Bacteriol.* **87** 1531 (1964).
824. C. H. Lea, *J. Sci. Food Agric.* **8** 1 (1957).
825. T. Kaneshiro & A. G. Marr, *J. lipid Res.* **3** 184 (1962).
826. S. F. Velick, *J. biol. Chem.* **152** 533 (1944).
827. B. Urbaschek, O. W. Thiele & W. Wober, *Bull. Soc. Chim. biol.* **46** 224 (1964); *Biochim. biophys. Acta* **84** 376 (1964).
828. C. Lacave & Y. Le Garrec, *Bull. Acad. Vét. Fr.* **37** 107 (1964).
828*a*. G. M. Gray, *Biochem J.* **70** 425 (1958).
829. J. A. Crowder & R. J. Anderson, *J. biol. Chem.* **104** 487 (1934).
829*a*. P. F. Smith & C. V. Henrickson, *J. lipid Res.* **6** 106 (1965).
830. A. G. Marr & T. Kaneshiro, Bact. Proc., Abstr. 60th ann. Meeting, p. 63, Philadelphia (1960).
831. H. Goldfine, *Biochim. biophys. Acta* **59** 504 (1962).
832. M. Kates, S. N. Sehgal & N. E. Gibbons, *Can. J. Microbiol.* **7** 427 (1961).
833. A. V. Few, *Biochim. biophys. Acta* **16** 137 (1955).
834. S. Čmelik, *Z. physiol. Chem.* **299** 227 (1955).
835. J. Blass, *Bull. Soc. Chim. biol.* **38** 1305 (1956).
836. M. Kurokawa, K. Hotta, Y. Yoshimura, M. Makita & I. Hara, *Bull. chem. Soc., Japan* **32** 28 (1959).
837. D. Subrahmanyam, A. N. Nandedkar & R. Viswanathan, *Biochim. biophys. Acta* **63** 542 (1962).
838. G. Michel & E. Lederer, *C. r. hebd. Séanc. Acad. Sci., Paris* **240** 2454 (1955).
839. J. N. Kanfer & E. P. Kennedy, *J. biol. Chem.* **237** PC 270 (1962).
840. J. Y. Homma, N. Hamamura, N. Naio & F. Egami, *Bull. Soc. Chim. biol.* **40** 647 (1958).

840*a*. M. Kates & G. A. Adams, 8th Inter. Congr. Microbiol., abstr. A7.10 Montreal (1962); *Can. J. Biochem.*, **42** 461 (1964).

841. M. G. MacFarlane, *Biochem. J.* **80** 45P (1961).

841*a*. G. E. Jones & A. A. Benson, *J. Bacteriol.* **89** 260 (1965).

841*b*. F. A. Ibbott & A. Abrams, *Biochemistry* **3** 2008 (1964).

842. M. Faure & J. Marechal, *C. r. hebd. Séanc. Acad. Sci., Paris* **254** 4518 (1962).

842*a*. D. Subrahmanyam, *Can. J. Biochem.* **42** 1195 (1964).

842*b*. J. Lecocq & C. E. Ballou, *Biochemistry* **3** 976 (1964).

843. F. Haverkate, U. M. T. Houtsmuller & L. L. M. van Deenen, *Biochim. biophys. Acta* **63** 547 (1962).

844. S. N. Sehgal, M. Kates & N. E. Gibbons, *Can. J. Biochem. Physiol.* **40** 69 (1962).

845. M. Faure, J. Marechal & J. Troestler, *C. r. hebd. Séanc. Acad. Sci., Paris* **257** 2187 (1963).

846. M. Kates, P. S. Sastry & L. S. Yengoyan, *Biochim. biophys. Acta* **70** 705 (1963); **98** 252 (1965).

846*a*. M. Kates, B. Palameta & L. S. Yengoyan, *Biochemistry* **4** 1595 (1965).

847. P. Böhm, *Z. physiol. Chem.* **291** 155 (1952).

847*a*. N. A. Baumann, P.-O. Hagen & H. Goldfine, *J. biol. Chem.* **240** 1559 (1965).

848. R. J. Anderson, *J. Amer. chem. Soc.* **52** 1607 (1930).

849. R. J. Anderson & A. G. Renfrew, *J. Amer. Chem. Soc.* **52** 1252 (1930).

850. R. J. Anderson & E. G. Roberts, *J. biol. Chem.* **89** 611 (1930).

851. R. J. Anderson & E. G. Roberts, *J. Amer. chem. Soc.* **52** 5023 (1930).

852. H. du Mont & R. J. Anderson, *Z. physiol. Chem.* **211** 97 (1932).

853. R. J. Anderson, R. L. Peck & M. M. Creighton, *J. biol. Chem.* **136** 211 (1940).

854. G. I. de Sütö-Nagy & R. J. Anderson, *J. biol. Chem.* **171** 749 (1947).

855. G. I. de Sütö-Nagy & R. J. Anderson, *J. biol. Chem.* **171** 761 (1947).

856. E. Vilkas, *C. r. hebd. Séanc. Acad. Sci., Paris* **245** 588 (1957).

857. E. Vilkas, Thesis Dr. Sci., Univ. Paris (1960).

858. E. Vilkas, *Bull. Soc. Chim. biol.* **42** 1005 (1960).

859. E. Vilkas & E. Lederer, *Bull. Soc. Chim. biol.* **42** 1013 (1960).

860. C. E. Ballou, E. Vilkas & E. Lederer, *J. biol. Chem.* **238** 69 (1963).

861. S. J. Angyal & B. Shelton, *Proc. chem. Soc.* **1963** 57.

861*a*. Y. C. Lee & C. E. Ballou, *J. biol. Chem.* **239** 1316 (1964).

861*b*. C. E. Ballou & Y. C. Lee, *Biochemistry* **3** 682 (1964).

861*c*. Y. C. Lee & C. E. Ballou, *Biochemistry* **4** 1395 (1965).

862. M. C. Pangborn, *N. Y. State Dept. Health, Ann. Rep. Div. Lab. Res.* **1957** 8.

863. J. Asselineau, *Biochim. biophys. Acta* **54** 359 (1961).

864. W. I. Schaeffer & W. W. Umbreit, *J. Bact.* **85** 492 (1963).

865. M. Ikawa, *J. Bact.* **85** 772 (1963).

866. M. Barbier & E. Lederer, *Biochim. biophys. Acta* **8** 591 (1952).

867. T. Gendre & E. Lederer, *Annls Acad. Sci. fennicae* ser. A II **60** 313 (1955).

868. J. Westley, J. J. Wren & H. K. Mitchell, *J. biol. Chem.* **229** 131 (1957).

869. C. H. Lea & D. N. Rhodes, *Biochem. J.* **54** 467 (1953).

870. M. A. Wells & J. C. Dittmer, *Biochemistry* **2** 1259 (1963).

871. M. G. MacFarlane, *Nature, Lond.* **196** 136 (1962).

872. U. M. T. Houtsmuller & L. L. M. van Deenen, *Biochim. biophys. Acta* **70** 211 (1963); **84** 96 (1964).

873. G. D. Hunter & A. T. James, *Nature, Lond.* **198** 789 (1963).

873*a*. D. B. Shina & W. L. Gaby, *J. biol. Chem.* **239** 3668 (1964).

874. H. Goldfine & M. E. Ellis, *J. Bact.* **87** 8 (1964).

875. M.-A. Laneelle, G. Laneelle & J. Asselineau, *Biochim. biophys. Acta* **70** 99 (1963).

875*a*. A. Gorschein, *Biochim. biophys. Acta* **84** 356 (1964).

875*b*. C. J. Brady, *Biochem. J.*, **91** 105 (1964).

876. L. O. Pilgeram & D. M. Greenberg, *J. biol. Chem.* **216** 465 (1955).
877. W. L. Gaby, R. N. Naughten & C. Logan, *Archs Biochem. Biophys.* **82** 34 (1959).
878. T. Fukui & B. Axelrod, *J. biol. Chem.* **236** 811 (1961).
879. P. B. Hill, *Biochim. biophys. Acta* **57** 386 (1962).
880. O. Westphal & O. Lüderitz, *Angew. Chem.* **66** 407 (1954).
881. I. Fromme, O. Lüderitz, A. Nowotny & O. Westphal, *Pharm. Acta helv.* **33** 391 (1958).
882. A. Nowotny, *J. Amer. chem. Soc.* **83** 501 (1961).
882a. N. Kasai & A. Yamano, *Japan J. exptl. Med.* **34** 329 (1964).
883. S. Bergström, H. Theorell & H. Davide, *Ark. Kemi Miner. Geol.* **23A** no. 13 (1947).
884. G. Hauser & M. L. Karnovsky, *J. biol. Chem.* **224** 91 (1957).
885. G. Hauser & M. L. Karnovsky, *J. biol. Chem.* **233** 287 (1958).
886. M. M. Burger, L. Glaser & R. M. Burton, *J. biol. Chem.* **238** 2595 (1963).
887. D. W. Smith, H. M. Randall, A. P. MacLennan & E. Lederer, *Nature, Lond.* **187** 887 (1960).
888. A. P. MacLennan, D. W. Smith & H. M. Randall, *Biochem. J.* **74** 3P (1960); *ibid.*, **80** 309 (1961).
889. D. E. Minnikin & N. Polgar, *Chem. comm.*, **1965** 495.
890. G. B. Fregnan, D. W. Smith & H. M. Randall, *J. Bact.* **82** 517 (1961).
891. H. Demarteau-Ginsburg & E. Lederer, *Biochim. biophys. Acta* **70** 442 (1963).
892. G. G. Maher, *Adv. Carbohyd. Chem.* **10** 257 (1955).
893. D. W. Smith, H. M. Randall, S. V. Rao & G. B. Fregnan, *Amer. Rev. Resp. Dis.* **84** 117 (1961).
893a. R. G. Navalkar, E. Wiegeshaus, E. Kondo, H. K. Kim & D. W. Smith, *J. Bacteriol.*, **90** 262 (1965).
894. E. M. Gubarev, E. K. Lubenets & Yu. V. Galaev, *Biokhimiya* **18** 37 (1953).
895. E. K. Alimova, *Biokhimiya* **20** 516 (1955).
896. R. J. Anderson & M. S. Newman, *J. biol. Chem.* **101** 499 (1933).
897. J. A. Crowder, F. H. Stodola, M. C. Pangborn & R. J. Anderson, *J. Amer. chem. Soc.* **58** 636 (1936).
898. C. O. Edens, M. M. Creighton & R. J. Anderson, *J. biol. Chem.* **154** 587 (1944).
899. H. Willstaedt & M. Borggard, *Bull. Soc. Chim. biol.* **28** 733 (1946).
900. G. Middlebrook, R. J. Dubos & C. Pierce, *J. exp. Med.* **86** 175 (1947).
901. H. Bloch, *J. exp. Med.* **91** 197 (1950).
902. H. Bloch, E. Sorkin & H. Erlenmeyer, *Amer. Rev. Tuberc. pulm. Dis.* **67** 629 (1953).
903. H. Noll & H. Bloch, *Amer. Rev. Tuberc. pulm. Dis.* **67** 828 (1953).
904. J. Asselineau, H. Bloch & E. Lederer, *Amer. Rev. Tuberc. pulm. Dis.* **67** 853 (1953).
905. J. Asselineau & E. Lederer, *Biochim. biophys. Acta* **17** 161 (1955).
906. H. Noll, H. Bloch, J. Asselineau & E. Lederer, *Biochim. biophys. Acta* **20** 299 (1956).
907. S. Nojima, *J. biochem.*, *Japan* **46** 499 (1959).
908. G. Michel, *Bull. Soc. Chim. biol.* **41** 1649 (1959).
909. I. Azuma, T. Nagasuga & Y. Yamamura, *J. Biochem.*, *Japan* **52** 92 (1962).
910. I. Azuma & Y. Yamamura, *J. Biochem.*, *Japan* **52** 82 (1962).
911. J. K. Spitznagel & R. J. Dubos, *J. exp. Med.* **101** 291 (1955).
912. I. Azuma & Y. Yamamura, *J. Biochem.*, *Japan* **52** 142 (1962).
912a. I. Azuma, Y. Yamamura & Y. Fujiwara, *J. Biochem.*, *Japan* **55** 344 (1964).
913. T. Ioneda, M. Lenz & J. Pudles, *Biochem. biophys. Res. Commun.* **13** 110 (1963).
914. J. Asselineau, H. Bloch & E. Lederer, *Biochim. biophys. Acta* **15** 136 (1954).
915. T. Mashima, Y. Okada, T. Terai, K. Ogura & Y. Yamamura, *J. Biochem.*, *Japan* **48** 392 (1960).
916. H. Noll, *Adv. Tuberc. Res.* **7** 149 (1956).
917. E. Lederer, Festschrift A. Stoll, p. 384, Birkhäuser, Basle (1957).
918. E. Lederer, *Adv. Carbohyd. Chem.* **16** 207 (1961).
918a. W. J. Lennarz, *J. biol. Chem.* **239** PC 3110 (1964).
919. J. Polonovski, R. Wald & M. Paysant-Diament, *Annls Inst. Pasteur, Paris* **103** 32 (1962).
919a. J. Polonovski, R. Wald & F. Petek, *Bull. Soc. Chim. biol.* **47** 409 (1965).

919b. D. E. Brundish, N. Shaw & J. Baddiley, *Biochem. J.* **95** 21 C (1965).

920. R. A. Ferrari & A. A. Benson, *Arch. Biochem. Biophys.* **93** 185 (1961).

920a. D. E. Brundish, N. Shaw & J. Baddiley, *Biochem. biophys. Res. Commun.* **18** 308 (1965); *Biochem. J.* **97** 158 (1965).

920b. B. Kaufman, D. Kundig, J. Distler & S. Roseman, *Biochem, biophys. Res. Commun.* **18** 312 (1965).

920c. R. E. Reeves, N. G. Latour & R. J. Lousteau, *Biochemistry* **3** 1248 (1964).

921. N. Choucroun, *Amer. Rev. Tuberc. pulm. Dis.* **56** 203 (1947).

922. J. Asselineau, N. Choucroun & E. Lederer, *Biochim. biophys. Acta* **5** 197 (1950).

923. R. J. Anderson, *J. biol. Chem.* **85** 327 (1929-1930).

924. E. G. Roberts & R. J. Anderson, *J. biol. Chem.* **90** 33 (1931).

925. W. N. Haworth, P. W. Kent & M. Stacey, *J. chem. Soc.* **1948** 1220.

925a. I. Azuma, H. Kimura & Y. Yamamura, *J. Biochem., Japan* **57** 571 (1965).

926. J. Asselineau & E. Lederer, *C. r. hebd. Séanc. Acad. Sci., Paris* **230** 142 (1950).

927. E. Work, *Biochem. J.* **49** 17 (1951).

928. M. Ikawa, E. E. Snell & E. Lederer, *Nature, Lond.* **188** 558 (1960).

929. P. Jolles, H. Nguyen-Cros & E. Lederer, *Biochim. biophys. Acta* **43** 559.

930. P. Jolles, D. Samour & E. Lederer, *Archs Biochem. biophys.*, suppl. 1, 283 (1962).

931. A. Tanaka, *Biochem. biophys. Acta* **70** 483 (1963).

931a. A. Tanaka & M. Kitagawa, *Biochim. biophys. Acta* **98** 182 (1965).

932. J. Kara & B. Keil *Colln Trav. chim. Tchecosl.* **23** 1392 (1958).

933. C. S. Cummins & H. Harris, *J. gen. Microbiol.* **18** 173 (1958).

934. T. Kitaura, *Nara Igaku Zasshi* **9** 184 (1958).

935. J. Földes, *Naturwiss* **46** 432 (1959).

936. K. Takeya, K. Hisatsune & Y. Inoue, *J. Bact.* **85** 24 (1963).

937. M. Ikawa & E. E. Snell, *Biochim. biophys. Acta* **19** 576 (1955).

938. R. E. Strange & C. B. Thorne, *Biochim. biophys. Acta* **24** 199 (1957).

939. M. N. Camien, A. Yuwiler & M. S. Dunn, *Proc. Soc. exp. Biol. Med.* **94** 137 (1957).

939a. D. E. S. Stewart-Tull & R. G. White, *J. gen. Microbiol.* **34** 43 (1964).

940. P. Jolles, D. Samour & E. Lederer, *Biochim. biophys. Acta* **78** 342 (1963).

941. R. J. Anderson, R. E. Reeves & F. H. Stodola, *J. biol. Chem.* **121** 649 (1937).

942. R. J. Anderson & M. M. Creighton, *J. biol. Chem.* **131** 549 (1939).

942a. S. Kotani, S. Hashimoto, T. Matsubara, K. Kato, K. Harada, J. Kogami, T. Kitaura & A. Tanaka, *Biken's J.* **6** 181 (1963).

943. I. Azuma & Y. Yamamura, *J. Biochem., Japan* **52** 200 (1962).

943a. I. Azuma & Y. Yamamura, *J. Biochem., Japan* **53** 275 (1963).

944. N. J. Cartwright, *Biochem. J.* **60** 238 (1955).

945. H. H. Wasserman, J. J. Keggi & J. E. McKeon, *J. Amer. chem. Soc.* **83** 4107 (1961).

946. M. M. Shemyakin, Yu. A. Ovchinnikov, V. K. Antonov, A. A. Kiryushkin, V. T. Ivanov, V. I. Shchelokov & A. M. Shkrob, *Tetrahedron Let.* **1964** 47.

947. T. Ito & H. Ogawa, *Bull. agric. chem. Soc. Japan* **23** 536 (1959).

948. M. Guinand, G. Michel & E. Lederer, *C. r. hebd. Séanc. Acad. Sci., Paris* **246** 848 (1958).

949. M. Guinand & G. Michel, *C. r. hebd. Séanc. Acad. Sci., Paris* **256** 1621 (1963).

949a. M. Barber, W. A. Wolstenholme, M. Guinand, G. Michel & E. Lederer, *Tetrahedron Letters* **1965** 1331.

950. M. Ikawa & E. E Snell, *Biochim. biophys. Acta* **60** 186 (1962).

951. G. Laneelle & J. Asselineau, *Biochim. biophys. Acta* **59** 731 (1962).

951a. G. Lanéelle, J. Asselineau, W. A. Wolstenholme & E. Lederer, *Bull. Soc. Chim. Fr.* **1965** 2133.

952. D. W. Smith, H. M. Randall, A.-P. MacLennan, R. K. Putney & S. V. Rao, *J. Bact.* **79** 217 (1960).

953. A. P. MacLennan, *Biochem. J.* **84** 394 (1962).

954. P. Jolles, F. Bigler, T. Gendre & E. Lederer, *Bull. Soc. Chim. biol.* **43** 177 (1961).

955. M. Chaput, G. Michel & E. Lederer, *Biochim. biophys. Acta* **78** 329 (1963).
956. M. Chaput, G. Michel & E. Lederer, *Experientia* **17** 107 (1961).
957. Z. Dische & L. B. Shettles, *J. biol. Chem.* **175** 595 (1948).
958. A. Boivin, I. Mesrobeanu & L. Mesrobeanu, *C. r. Séanc. Soc. Biol.* **114** 307 (1933).
959. A. Boivin, "Les toxines bactériennes", *Exposés de Biochim. méd.* **1942** p. 113.
960. H. Raistrick & W. W. C. Topley, *Br. J. exp. Path.* **15** 113 (1934).
961. W. T. J. Morgan, *Biochem. J.* **31** 2003 (1937).
962. W. T. J. Morgan & S. M. Partridge, *Biochem. J.* **34** 169 (1940).
963. A. A. Miles & N. W. Pirie, *Br. J. exp. Path.* **20** 83 (1939).
964. J. Walker, *Biochem. J.* **34** 325 (1940).
965. R. S. Roberts, *J. comp. Path. Therap.* **59** 284 (1949).
965a. E. Ribi, K. C. Milner & T. D. Perrine, *J. Immun.* **82** 75 (1959).
965b. E. Ribi, W. T. Haskins, M. Landy & K. C. Milner, *J. exp. Med.* **114** 647 (1961).
965c. K. Fukushi, R. L. Anacker, W. T. Haskins, M. Landy, K. C. Milner & E. Ribi, *J. Bact.* **87** 391 (1964).
966. A. M. Nowotny, S. Thomas, O. S. Duron & A. Nowotny, *J. Bact.* **85** 418 (1963).
967. J. L. Hartwell, M. J. Shear & J. R. Adams, *J. nat. Cancer Inst.* **4** 107 (1943).
968. D. A. L. Davies, W. T. J. Morgan & B. R. Record, *Biochem. J.* **60** 290 (1955).
969. R. A. Ormsbee & C. L. Larson, *J. Immun.* **74** 359 (1955).
969a. M. S. Redfearn, *Science* **146** 648 (1964).
970. A. A. Miles & N. W. Pirie, *Br. J. exp. Path.* **20** 278 (1939).
971. A. P. MacLennan, *Biochem. J.* **74** 398 (1960).
972. D. A. L. Davies, M. J. Crumpton, I. A. Macpherson & A. M. Hutchison, *Immunology* **2** 157 (1958).
973. O. Westphal, O. Lüderitz, E. Eichenberger & W. Keiderling, *Z. Naturforsch.* **7b** 536 (1952).
974. H. Tauber & W. Garson, *J. biol. Chem.* **234** 1391 (1959).
975. H. Tauber & H. Russel, *J. biol. Chem.* **235** 961 (1960).
976. M. E. Webster, J. F. Sagin, M. Landy & A. G. Johnson, *J. Immun.* **74** 455 (1955).
977. P. Rathgeb & B. Sylven, *J. nat. Cancer Inst.* **14** 1099, 1109 (1954).
978. C. Tal & W. F. Goebel, *J. exp. Med.* **92** 25 (1950).
979. F. Binkley, W. F. Goebel & E. Perlman, *J. exp. Med.* **81** 331 (1945).
980. M. A. Jesaitis & W. F. Goebel, *J. exp. Med.* **96** 409 (1952); *ibid.*, **102** 733 (1955).
981. R. B. Johnson, *J. Immun.* **74** 286 (1955).
982. M. Naoi, F. Egami, N. Hamamura & J. Y. Homma, *Biochem. Z.* **330** 421 (1958).
983. Y. Takeda, N. Kasai, M. Araki & T. Odara, *Z. physiol. Chem.* **307** 49 (1957).
984. S. M. Dennis, *Nature, Lond.* **183** 186 (1959).
985. A. Nowotny, *J. Bact.* **85** 427 (1963).
986. C. Fouquey, E. Lederer, O. Lüderitz, J. Polonsky, A. M. Staub, S. Stirm, R. Tinelli & O. Westphal, *C. r. hebd. Séanc. Acad. Sci., Paris* **246** 2417 (1958).
987. O. Lüderitz, A. M. Staub, S. Stirm & O. Westphal, *Biochem. Z.* **330** 193 (1958).
988. I. Fromme, O. Lüderitz, H. Stierlin & O. Westphal, *Biochem. Z.* **330** 53 (1958).
989. C. Fouquey, J. Polonsky & E. Lederer, *Bull. Soc. chim. Fr.* **1959** 803.
990. D. A. L. Davies, *Nature, Lond.* **191** (1961).
991. C. L. Stevens, P. Blumbergs, F. A. Daniher, R. W. Wheat, A. Kujomoto & E. L. Rollins, *J. Amer. chem. Soc.* **85** 3061 (1963).
991a. M. J. Osborn, S. M. Rosen, L. Rothfield, L. D. Zeleznick & B. L. Horecker, *Science* **145** 783 (1964).
992. O. Westphal, O. Lüderitz, E. Eichenberger,& E. Neter, Chemistry and biology of mucopolysaccharides, a Ciba Foundation Colloquium, p. 187, London (1958).
992a. O. Westphal & O. Lüderitz, *Naturwiss.* **50** 413 (1963).
992b. M. Landy & W. Braun, Bacterial endotoxins, Rutgers University, 1964, 691 pp.

993. C. Ionesco-Mihaiesti, A. Damboviceanu & C. Leonida-Ioan, *C. r. Séanc. Soc. Biol.* **124** 973 (1937).
994. M. Stacey, P. W. Kent & E. Nassau, *Biochim. biophys. Acta* **7** 146 (1951).
995. T. Tsumita, T. Aoyagi, R. Matsumoto, E. Kondo, D. Mizuno & H. Takahashi, *Japan. J. med. Sci. Biol.* **13** 121 (1960).
996. T. Tsumita, R. Matsumoto & D. Mizuno, *Japan. J. med. Sci. Biol.* **13** 131 (1960).
997. R. Matsumoto, *Japan. J. med. Sci. Biol.* **13** 139 (1960).
998. P. W. Kent, *J. chem. Soc.* **1951** 364.
999. E. Sorkin, S. V. Boyden & J. M. Rhodes, *Helv. chim. Acta* **39** 1684 (1956).
1000. M. R. J. Salton, *Biochim. biophys. Acta* **10** 512 (1953).
1001. M. R. J. Salton, *in* "Bacterial Anatomy", p. 81, Cambridge Univ. Press, London (1956).
1002. M. R. J. Salton, "Microbial cell walls"', Wiley & Sons, New York (1960).
1003. C. S. Cummins & H. Harris, *J. gen. Microbiol.* **14** 583 (1956).
1004. C. S. Cummins, *Inter. Rev. Cytol.* **5** 25 (1956).
1005. E. Work, *Nature, Lond.* **179** 841 (1957).
1005a. H. J. Rogers, *Biochem. Soc. Symp.* no. **22**, p. 55 (1963).
1006. E. K. Alimova, *Biokhimiya* **23** 205 (1958).
1007. T. Kitaura, T. Hirano, S. Inui, S. Kotani, M. Igashigawa & T. Tsuchitani, *Nara Igaku Zasshi* **10** 45 (1959).
1008. W. R. Smithies, N. E. Gibbons & S. T. Bayley, *Can. J. Microbiol.* **1** 605 (1955).
1008a. K. Y. Cho & M. R. J. Salton, *Biochim. biophys. Acta* **84** 773 (1964).
1009. P. Mitchell & J. Moyle, *J. gen. Microbiol.* **5** 981 (1951).
1010. M. R. J. Salton & F. Shafa, *Nature, Lond.* **181** 1321 (1958).
1010a. A. T. Astvatsatur'yan, *Biokhimiya,* **29** 8 (1964).
1011. D. J. Mason & D. Powelson, *Biochim. biophys. Acta* **29** 1 (1958).
1012. B. A. Newton, *Bact. Rev.* **20** 14 (1956).
1013. W. Weidel & J. Primosigh, *Z. Naturforsch.* **12b** 421 (1958).
1014. L. Colobert, *C. r. hebd. Séanc. Acad. Sci.,* Paris **245** 1674 (1957).
1015. O. Creach & L. Colobert, *Path. Biol., Semaine des Hôpitaux* **10** 1227 (1962).
1016. M. J. Hill, A. M. James & W. R. Maxted, *Biochim. biophys. Acta* **75** 414 (1963).
1017. G. Knaysi, J. Hillier & C. Fabricant, *J. Bact.* **60** 423 (1950).
1018. E. Ribi, C. L. Larson, R. List & W. Wicht, *Proc. Soc. exp. Biol. Med.* **98** 263 (1958); *Amer. Rev. resp. Dis.* **83** 184 (1961).
1019. K. C. Milner, R. L. Anacker, K. Fukushi, W. T. Haskins, M. Landy, B. Malmgren & E. Ribi. *Bact. Rev.* **27** 352 (1963).
1020. M. D. Yudkin, *Biochem. J.* **82** 40P (1962).
1020a. L. L. M. van Deenen, *Progr. Chem. Fats Lipids* **8** part 1 (1965).
1021. K. MacQuillen, *J. gen. Microbiol.* **18** 498 (1958).
1022. A. R. Gilby, A. V. Few & K. MacQuillen, *Biochim. biophys. Acta* **29** 21 (1958).
1023. A. R. Gilby & A. V. Few, *Nature, Lond.* **182** 55 (1958).
1024. M. G. MacFarlane, *Biochem. J.* **79** 4P (1961).
1025. P. Mitchell & J. Moyle, *J. gen. Microbiol.* **9** 257 (1953).
1026. G. D. Shockman, J. J. Kolb, B. Bakay, M. J. Conover & G. Toennies, *J. Bact.* **85** 168 (1963).
1026a. M. L. Vorbeck & G. V. Marinetti, *Biochemistry* **4** 296 (1965).
1027. Y. Yamamura, M. Kusunose, S. Nagai, E. Kusunose, Y. Yamamura, J. Tani, T. Terai & T. Nagasuga, *Med. J. Osaka Union* **6** 489 (1955); *Chem. Abstr.* **50** 10180 (1956).
1028. C. E. Georgi, W. E. Militzer & T. S. Decker, *J. Bact.* **70** 716 (1955).
1029. A. R. Hands & W. Barthley, *Biochem. J.* **84** 238 (1953).
1030. C. Weibull, *J. Bact.* **66** 696 (1953).
1031. A. Widra, *J. Bact.* **71** 689 (1956).
1032. R. E. Kallio & A. A. Harrington, *J. Bact.* **80** 321 (1960).

1033. M. Nicolle & E. Alilaire, *Annls. Inst. Pasteur, Paris* **23** 547 (1909).

1034. R. T. O'Connor, E. R. MacCall & E. F. Dupré, *J. Bact.* **73** 303 (1953).

1034a. J. Lascelles & J. F. Szilágyi, *J. gen. Microbiol.* **38** 55 (1965).

1035. A. C. Hayward, W. G. C. Forsyth & J. B. Roberts, *J. gen. Microbiol.* **20** (1959).

1036. H. B. Levine & H. Wolochow, *J. Bact.* **79** 305 (1960).

1037. M. Doudoroff & R. Y. Stanier, *Nature, Lond.* **183** 1440 (1959).

1038. D. H. Nutgeren & W. Berends, *Rec. Trav. chim.* **76** 13 (1957).

1038a. T. Kaneshiro & J. H. Law, *J. biol. Chem.* **239** 1705 (1964).

1039. I. M. Lewis, *J. Bact.* **40** 271 (1940).

1040. C. Stapp, *Z. physiol. Chem.* **88** 445 (1918).

1041. A. H. Romano & J. P. Peloquin, *J. Bact.* **86** 252 (1963).

1042. E. W. Hopkins & W. H. Peterson, *J. Bact.* **19** 9 (1930).

1043. A. C. Braun, *Ann. N. Y. Acad. Sci.* **54** 1153 (1952).

1044. A. Boivin, M. Marbe, L. Mesrobeanu & P. Juster, *C. r. hebd. Séanc. Acad. Sci., Paris* **201** 984 (1935).

1045. E. Chargaff & M. Levine, *Proc. Soc. exp. Biol. Med.* **34** 675 (1936).

1046. E. Chargaff & M. Levine, *J. biol. Chem.* **124** 195 (1938).

1047. S. F. Velick & R. J. Anderson, *J. biol. Chem.* **152** 523 (1944).

1048. S. Akashi, H. Yokoi & H. Goto, *J. Biochem., Japan*, **45** 959 (1958).

1048a. A. J. Croom, J. J. McNeill & S. B. Tove, *J. Bacteriol.* **88** 389 (1964).

1048b. J. J. Gavin & W. W. Umbreit, *J. Bacteriol.*, **89** 437 (1965).

1049. K. Saito, *J. Biochem., Japan*, **47** 699 (1960).

1050. T. E. Surdy & S. E. Hartsell, *J. Bact.* **85** 1174 (1963).

1051. H. C. Eckstein & M. H. Soule, *J. biol. Chem.* **91** 395 (1931).

1052. A. R. Taylor, *J. biol. Chem.* **165** 271 (1946).

1053. L. Vaczi & P. Incze, *Acta microbiol. hung.* **5** 197 (1958).

1054. A. S. Jones, S. B. Rizvi & M. Stacey, *J. gen. Microbiol.* **18** 597 (1958).

1055. J. Kanfer & E. P. Kennedy, *J. biol. Chem.* **238** 2919 (1963).

1055a. J. Kanfer & E. P. Kennedy, *J. biol. Chem.* **239** 1720 (1964)

1055b. R. A. Pieringer & R. S. Kunnes, *J. biol. Chem.* **240** 2833 (1965).

1056. A. R. Tarlov & E. P. Kennedy, *J. biol. Chem.* **240** 49 (1965).

1057. E. E. Woodside & W. Kocholaty, *U. S. Army Med. Res. Lab.*, Rept. no. 360, 12 pp (1958); *Chem. Abstr.* **53** 11511 (1959).

1057a. D. G. Bishop & E. Work, *Biochem. J.* **96** 567 (1965).

1058. W. Sellers, R. B. Mitchell & H. M. Hughes, *U. S. Dept. Com., Office Techn. Serv.*, P. B. Rept. 146, 5 pp (1960); *Chem. Abstr.* **57** 2656 (1962).

1059. T. Sneed & H. O. Halvorson, *Appl. microbiol.* **2** 285 (1954).

1060. A. J. Castro, A. H. Corwin, F. J. Waxham & A. L. Beilby, *J. Org. Chem.* **24** 455 (1959).

1061. M. J. Shear & F. C. Turner, *J. nat. Cancer Inst.* **4** 81 (1943).

1062. H. C. Srivastava, E. Breuninger, H. J. Creech & G. A. Adams, *Can. J. biochem. Physiol.* **40** 905 (1962).

1063. R. Vendrely & R. Tulasne, *Nature, Lond.* **171** 262 (1953).

1064. G. Rebel, A.-M. Bader, M. Sensenbrenner & P. Mandel, *C. r. hebd. Séanc. Acad. Sci., Paris* **250** 3516 (1960).

1065. M. Berst, M. Brini, P.-T. Jossang, J. Krembel & R. Minck, *Annls. Inst. Pasteur, Paris* **106** 249 (1964).

1065a. G. Rebel, M. Sensenbrenner, F. Klein & P. Mandel, *Bull. Soc. Chim. biol.* **46** 987 (1964).

1066. A. Bendich & E. Chargaff, *J. biol. Chem.* **166** 283 (1946).

1066a. J. A. Nesbitt & W. J. Lennarz, *J. Bacteriol.* **89** 1020 (1965).

1067. M. Digeon, Thesis Dr. Sci, Paris (1955).

1068. S. Akasi, *J. Biochem, Japan* **29** 13 (1939).
1069. E. W. Dennis, *Amer. J. Hyg.* **32 B** 1 (1940).
1070. V. Krajciova, J. Cizmar & V. Krcmery, *Biológia, Bratisl.* **17** 148 (1962); *Chem. Abstr.* **57** 17169 (1962).
1071. Y. Takeda & K. Kurizuka, *Japan.. J. exp. Med.* **22** 57 (1952); *Chem. Abstr.* **47** 6490 (1953).
1072. T. R. Neblett, *Univ. Microfilms Inc.*, no. 58-7128 (1957).
1073. A. T. Astvatsatur'yan, *Ukr. Biokhim. Zh.* **34** 741 (1962); *Chem. Abstr.* **58** 3696 (1963).
1074. D. A. L. Davies, *Biochem. J.* **63** 105 (1956).
1075. D. A. L. Davies, *J. gen. Microbiol.* **18** 118 (1958).
1076. W. H. Stahl, *Michigan agr. exp. Sta., Techn. Bull.* **177** p. 29 (1941).
1077. R. C. Huston, I. F. Huddleston & A. D. Hershey, *Michigan agr. exp. Sta., Techn. Bull.* **137** (1934).
1078. W. H. Stahl, R. B. Pennell & I. F. Huddleston, *Michigan agr. exp. Sta., Techn. Bull.* **168** (1939).
1079. E. M. Gubarev, E. K. Alimova & G. D. Bolgova, *Biokhimiya* **21** 647 (1956).
1080. E. K. Alimova, G. D. Bolgova, E. M. Gubarev, V. G. Saprykin, *Ukr. Biokhim. Zh.* **30** 506 (1958); *Chem. Abstr.* **53** 1462 (1959).
1081. E. M. Gubarev, G. D. Bolgova & E. K. Alimova, *Trudy Otch. Nauk Konf. Rostovna-Donu med. Inst.* 557 (1956); *Chem. Abstr.* **53** 8284 (1959).
1082. E. M. Gubarev, G. D. Bolgova & E. K. Alimova, *Biokhimiya* **24** 200 (1959).
1083. G. D. Bolgova, E. K. Alimova & N. D. Moiseenko, *Ukr. Biokhim. Zh.* **32** 87 (1960); *Chem. Abstr.* **54** 21315 (1960).
1084. I. I. Dubrovskaya, N. N. Ostrovskaya & A. I. Glubokina, *Biokhimiya* **23** 523 (1958).
1085. R. B. Pennell & I. F. Huddleston, *Michigan agr. exp. Stat., Techn. Bull.* **156** (1937).
1086. A. Damboviceanu, C. Barber, A. Pop & I. Marinov, *C. r. Séanc. Soc. Biol.* **127** 736 (1938).
1087. A. A. Miles & N. W. Pirie, *Biochem. J.* **33** 1709 (1939).
1088. J. S. Paterson, N. W. Pirie & A. W. Stableforth, *Br. J. exp. Path.* **28** 223 (1947).
1089. B. Urbaschek, *Z. Immunitätsforsch* **120** 279 (1960).
1090. J. Roux, *Rev. Immun.* **25** 32 (1960).
1090*a*. I. I. Dubrovskaya, *Biokhimiya* **29** 846 (1964).
1091. S. Akashi, *The Lecture Coll. chem. Res. Inst. Kyoto Univ.* **12** 195 (1940).
1092. M. Ida & T. Otani, *Acta Sch. med. Univ. Kioto* **28** 25 (1950).
1093. I. W. Sutherland, *Immunology* **6** 246 (1963).
1094. K. Onoue & Y. Yamamura, *Nisshin Igaku* **49** 518 (1962); *Chem. Abstr.* **58** 6003 (1963).
1095. P. F. Smith & G. H. Rothblat, *J. Bact.* **83** 500 (1962).
1095*a*. T. Suzuki, *Japan J. Bact.* **8** 897 (1953).
1096. L. Colobert & G. Rocquet, *Annls. Inst. Pasteur, Paris* **93** 663 (1957).
1096*a*. J. P. Brown & B. J. Cosenza, *Nature, Lond.* **204** 802 (1964).
1097. L. Vaczi & L. Farkas, *Acta microbiol. hung.* **8** 205 (1961).
1097*a*. U. M. T. Houstmuller & L. L. M. van Deenen, *Biochim. biophys. Acta* **84** 96 (1964).
1097*b*. A. K. Bergh, S. J. Webb & C. S. McArthur, *Can. J. Biochem.* **42** 1141 (1964).
1098. E. Costin-Podhorsky, *Acad. Rep. pop. Romine, Inst. Biochim.* **2** 157 (1959).
1099. H. A. Reimann & C. M. Ecklund, *J. Bact.* **42** 435 (1941).
1100. T. Ohta, *J. pharm. Soc., Japan* **71** 1319 (1951).
1101. T. Ohta, T. Miyazaki & T. Ninomiya, *Chem. pharm. Bull., Tokyo* **7** 254 (1959); *Chem. Abstr.*, **54**, 22830 (1960).
1102. W. Steuer, *Zent. Bl. Bakt. Parasitenk. Infektionskr. Hyg.* **167** 210 (1956).
1103. G. Allegra, R. Niutta & G. Giuffrida, *Riv. Ist. Sieroterap. Ital.* **29** 263 (1954); *Chem. Abstr.* **49** 8371 (1955).
1104. B. Sobin & G. L. Stahly, *J. Bact.* **44** 265 (1942).
1104*a*. C. K. Huston & P. W. Albro, *J. Bact.* **88** 425 (1964).

1105. G. Litwack & A. F. Carlucci, *Nature, Lond.* **181** 904 (1958).
1106. E. Chargaff & J. Dieryck, *Naturwiss.* **20** 972 (1932).
1107. E. Chargaff, *C. r. hebd. Séanc. Acad. Sci., Paris* **197** 946 (1932).
1108. T. Nakamura, *Bull. chem. Soc., Japan* **11** 176 (1936).
1109. E. Lederer, *Bull. Soc. Chim. biol.* **20** 611 (1938).
1110. Y. Takeda & T. Ohta, *Z. physiol. Chem.* **268** 1 (1941).
1110a. G. H. Rothblat, D. S. Ellis & D. Kritchevsky, *Biochim. biophys. Acta* **84** 340 (1964).
1110b. T. Yamakawa & N. Ueta, *Japan. J. exper. Med.* **34** 361 (1964).
1111. A. K. Boor & C. P. Miller, *J. inf. Dis.* **75** 47 (1944).
1112. H. C. Ellinghausen & M. J. Pelczar, *J. Bact.* **70** 448 (1955).
1113. L. R. Christensen, *J. gen. Physiol.* **28** 363 (1945).
1114. P. Macleod, R. G. Jensen, G. W. Gander & J. Sampugna, *J. Bact.* **83** 806 (1962).
1115. F. Patocka, J. V. Kostir & J. Kroulikova, *Czech. farm.* **1** 348 (1952).
1116. G. Obiger, *Milchwiss.* **12** 422 (1957); *Chem. Abstr.* **53** 15196 (1959).
1116a. W. M. O'Leary, *Biochemistry* **4** 1621 (1965).
1116b. K. J. I. Thorne, *Biochim. biophys. Acta* **84** 350 (1964).
1116c. K. J. I. Thorne, B. J. Constable & K. C. Day, *Nature, Lond.* **206** 1156 (1965).
1117. M. N. Camien, A. V. Fowler & M. S. Dunn, *Archs. Biochem. Biophys.* **83** 408 (1959).
1118. E. Chargaff, *Z. physiol. Chem.* **201** 191 (1931).
1119. M. A. Machebœuf & H. Cassagne, *C. r. hebd. Séanc. Acad. Sci., Paris* **200** 1988 (1935).
1120. J. Pudles, Thesis Dr Univ. Paris (1954).
1121. M. Asano & H. Takahashi, *J. pharm. Soc., Japan* **68** 186 (1948).
1122. O. K. Orlova, *Trudy Otch. Nauk Konf., Rostovna-Donu med. Inst.* 561 (1957); *Chem. Abstr.* **52** 18645 (1958).
1123. E. M. Gubarev & E. K. Lubenets, *Dokl. Akad. Nauk SSSR* **60** 413 (1948); *Chem. Abstr.* **42** 7826 (1948).
1124. E. M. Gubarev, A. B. Gabrilovich & F. I. Shtul'baum, *Biokhimiya* **17** 303 (1952).
1125. E. K. Lubenets, *Biokhimiya* **19** 11 (1954).
1126. A. A. Kanchukh, *Ukr. Biokhim. Zh.* **28** 508 (1956); *Chem. Abstr.* **51** 7491 (1957).
1127. E. K. Alimova, *Ukr. Biokhim. Zh.* **30** 52 (1958); *Chem. Abstr.* **52**
1128. E. K. Alimova, *Vopr. med. Khim.* **5** 217 (1959); *Biokhimiya* **24** 657 (1959).
1129. E. K. Alimova, *Biochemistry N. Y.* **24** 722 (1959).
1130. L. Hoyle, *J. Hyg., Cambridge* **42** 416 (1942).
1131. G. R. Learned & T. G. Metcalf, *Trans. Kansas Acad. Sci.* **55** 431 (1952).
1132. J. Kwapinski, *Acta microbiol. sol.* **6** 133 (1957).
1133. F. M. Stone & C. B. Coulter, *J. gen. Physiol.* **15** 629 (1932).
1133a. P. B. Scholes & H. K. King, *Biochem. J.* **91** 9P (1964).
1134. H. R. Carne, N. Wickham & J. C. Kater, *Nature, Lond.* **178** 701 (1956).
1135. A. H. Etemadi, *Bull. Soc. Chim. biol.* **45** 1423 (1963).
1136. A. J. Crowle, *Antonie van Leeuwenhoek* **28** 183 (1962).
1137. C. A. Baumann, M. A. Ingraham, H. Steenbock & E. B. Fred, *J. biol. Chem.* **103** 339 (1933).
1138. M. P. Starr & S. Saperstein, *Archs. Biochem. Biophys.* **43** 157 (1953).
1139. S. Saperstein & M. P. Starr, *Biochem. J.* **57** 273 (1954).
1140. N. F. Stanley, *Aust. J. exp. Biol. med. Sci.* **27** 123 (1949).
1141. K. F. Girard & E. G. D. Murray, *Can. J. Biochem. Biophys.* **32** 1 (1954).
1142. H. Tubylewicz, *Bull. Acad. pol. Sci. Cl. II Sér. Sci. biol.* **9** 355 (1961); *Chem. Abstr.* **56** 7871 (1962).
1143. U. M. T. Houtsmuller & L. L. M. van Deenen, *Biochem. J.* **88** 43P (1963).
1144. L. C. Verna, *An. Farm. Bioquim., B. Aires* **6** 90 (1935); *Chem. Abstr.* **30** 5250 (1936).
1145. D. L. Dyer, Thesis M. S., Univ. Nebraska (1953).
1146. S. K. Long & O. B. Williams, *J. Bact.* **79** 629 (1960).

1147. J. R. Matches, H. W. Walker & J. C. Ayres, *J. Bact.* **87** 16 (1964).
1147*a*. H. Goldfine, *J. biol. Chem.* **239** 2130 (1964).
1147*b*. A. E. Chung & H. Goldfine, *Nature, Lond.* **206** 1253 (1965).
1148. W. Steenken & L. U. Gardner, *Amer. Rev. Tuberc. pulm. Dis.* **54** 62 (1946).
1149. W. Steenken & L. U. Gardner, *Amer. Rev. Tuberc. pulm. Dis.* **54** 51 (1946).
1150. J. Desbordes, E. Fournier & D. Alix, *Annls. Inst. Pasteur, Paris* **87** 223 (1954).
1151. Y. Takeda & T. Ohta, *J. pharm. Soc., Japan* **64** 67 (1944); *Chem. Abstr.* **45** 1198 (1951).
1152. I. Kasuya, *J. Biochem., Japan* **27** 283 (1938).
1153. A. Goris & S. Sabetay, *C. r. hebd. Séanc. Acad. Sci., Paris* **233** 933 (1946).
1154. N. Stendal, *C. r. hebd. Séanc. Acad. Sci., Paris* **198** 400 (1934).
1155. A. H. Etemadi, *Bull. Soc. Chim. biol.* **45** 631 (1963).
1156. P. H. Hodson & J. W. Foster, *J. Bact.* **82** 791 (1961).
1157. C. F. Allen & J. Cason, *J. biol. Chem.* **220** 407 (1956).
1158. C. L. Agre & J. Cason, *J. Biol. Chem.* **234** 2555 (1959).
1159. A. Goris, *Annls Inst. Pasteur, Paris* **34** 497 (1920).
1160. J. Cason & P. Tavs, *J. biol. Chem.* **234** 1401 (1959).
1161. R. J. Anderson & E. Chargaff, *Z. physiol. Chem.* **191** 166 (1930).
1162. J. Cason, G. L. Lange, W. T. Miller & A. Weiss, *Tetrahedron* **20** 91 (1964).
1163. A. Boquet, *Rev. Tuberc., Paris* **9** 1011 (1939).
1164. A. Calmette, "L'infection bacillaire et la tuberculose", 4th ed. revised by A. Boquet & L. Negre Masson, Paris (1936).
1165. A. Frappier & M. Panisset, *Can. med. Ass. J.* **78** 103 (1958).
1166. R. J. Anderson & E. G. Roberts, *J. biol. Chem.* **85** 529 (1929-1930).
1167. E. Chargaff, *Z. physiol. Chem.* **217** 115 (1933).
1168. M. L. Burt & R. J. Anderson, *J. biol. Chem.* **94** 451 (1932).
1169. R. J. Anderson & E. G. Roberts, *J. biol. Chem.* **89** 599 (1930).
1170. T. Tsumita, *Japan. J. med. Sci. Biol.* **9** 217 (1956).
1171. E. Kondo, *Japan. J. med. Sci. Biol.* **13** 113 (1960).
1172. T. Aoyagi, S. Nojima, E. Kondo & D. Mizuno, *Japan. J. med. Sci. Biol.* **13** 101 (1960).
1173. R. Matsumoto, *Japan. J. med. Sci. Biol.* **13** 139 (1960).
1174. T. Tsumita, T. Aoyagi, R. Matsumoto, E. Kondo, D. Mizuno & H. Takahashi, *Japan. J. med. Sci. Biol.* **13** 121 (1960).
1175. T. Tsumita, R. Matsumoto & D. Mizuno, *Japan. J. med. Sci. Biol.* **13** 131 (1960).
1176. Y. Yamamura, K. Matsui & H. Maeda, *J. Biochem., Japan* **43** 409 (1956).
1177. R. J. Anderson & E. G. Roberts, *J. biol. Chem.* **85** 519 (1929-1930).
1178. Y. Tanaka, *J. Biochem., Japan* **46** 1 (1960).
1179. R. J. Anderson & E. G. Roberts, *J. biol. Chem.* **85** 509 (1929-1930).
1180. F. Paul & E. Vilkas, *C. r. hebd. Séanc. Acad. Sci., Paris* **254** 3915 (1962).
1181. A. B. Larsen & R. S. Merkal, *Amer. Rev. Tuberc. pulm. Dis.* **77** 712 (1958).
1182. P. Hauduroy, "Inventaire et description des Bacilles paratuberculeux", Masson, Paris (1946).
1183. G. Penso, "Les Bacilles paratuberculeux" *in* "Bacilles tuberculeux et paratuberculeux" p. 99, Masson, Paris (1950).
1184. E. Chargaff, M. C. Pangborn & R. J. Anderson, *J. biol. Chem.* **90** 45 (1931).
1185. M. C. Pangborn, E. Chargaff & R. J. Anderson, *J. biol. Chem.* **98** 43 (1932).
1186. M. C. Pangborn & R. J. Anderson, *J. biol. Chem.* **94** 465 (1932).
1187. M. C. Pangborn & R. J. Anderson, *J. biol. Chem.* **101** 105 (1933).
1188. J. Francis, H. M. MacTurk, J. Madinaveitia & G. A. Snow, *Biochem J.* **55** 596 (1953).
1189. E. Vilkas & E. Lederer, *C. r. hebd. Séanc. Acad. Sci., Paris* **240** 1156 (1955).
1190. M. A. Ingraham & H. Steenbock, *Biochem. J.* **29** 2553 (1935).
1191. C. Grundmann & Y. Takeda, *Naturwiss* **25** 27 (1937).
1192. Y. Takeda & T. Ohta, *Z. physiol. Chem.* **258** 6 (1939).

1193. Y. Takeda & T. Ohta, *Z. physiol. Chem.* **262** 168 (1939).
1194. Y. Takeda & T. Ohta, *J. Biochem., Japan* **36** 535 (1944).
1195. G. Turian, *Helv. Chim. Acta* **33** 13, 1303, 1988 (1950); *ibid.* **34** 1060 (1951).
1196. G. Turian & F. Haxo, *J. Bact.* **63** 690 (1952).
1197. T. W. Goodwin & M. Jamikorn, *Biochem. J.* **62** 269 (1956).
1198. F. L. Rose & G. A. Snow, A Ciba Foundation colloquium on experimental tuberculosis, p. 41, London (1955).
1199. N. Uyei & R. J. Anderson, *J. biol. Chem.* **94** 653 (1932).
1200. R. J. Anderson, R. E. Reeves & J. A. Crowder, *J. biol. Chem.* **121** 669 (1937).
1201. Sœur Marie-Suzanne, R. Noel & R. Sohier, *Annls. Inst. Pasteur, Paris* **81** 238 (1951).
1202. G. Penso & Sœur Marie-Suzanne, *Rend. Ist. Superiore di Sanità, Roma* **17** 962 (1954).
1203. Sœur Marie-Suzanne, V. Portelance & M. Panisset, *Can. J. Microbiol.* **2** 685 (1956).
1204. R. J. Anderson & N. Uyei, *J. biol. Chem.* **97** 617 (1932).
1205. R. Bruynoghe & M. Adant, *C. r. Séanc. Soc. Biol.* **111** 1051 (1932).
1206. H. F. Haas, L. D. Bushnell & W. J. Peterson, *Science* **95** 631 (1942).
1207. H. F. Haas & L. D. Bushnell, *J. Bact.* **48** 219 (1944).
1208. E. Chargaff & E. Lederer, *Annls Inst. Pasteur, Paris* **54** 383 (1935).
1209. A. Gaudiano, *Atti Accad. naz. Lincei* **21** 308 (1956).
1210. A. Gaudiano, *Rend. Ist. Superiore di Sanità, Roma* **22** 769 (1959).
1211. T. Ohta, *J. pharm. Soc., Japan* **71** 462 (1951); *Chem. Abstr.* **49** 3308 (1955).
1211a. S. L. Jensen & B. C. L. Weedon, *Naturwiss.* **51** 482 (1964); S. L. Jensen, *Acta chem. Scand.* **18** 1562 (1964).
1212. M. Gastambide-Odier & D. W. Smith, Symposium on atypical mycobacteria, Kansas City (1957); abstr. p. 32.
1213. E. H. Runyon, *Amer. Rev. Tuberc. pulm. Dis.* **72** 866 (1955); *Adv. Tuberc. Res.* **14** 235 (1965).
1214. M. Gastambide-Odier, D. W. Smith, H. M. Randall & A. O. Kœvoet, *Amer. Rev. Tuberc. pulm. Dis.* **75** 843 (1957).
1215. G. P. Youmans, *A. Rev. Microbiol.* **17** 473 (1963).
1216. E. Vilkas & A. Rojas, *Bull. Soc. Chim. biol.* **46** 689 (1964).
1217. M.-A. Laneelle, G. Laneelle, P. Bennet & J. Asselineau, *Bull. Soc. Chim. biol.* **47** 2047 (1965).
1218. J. H. Hanks, *Ann. N. Y. Acad. Sci.* **54** 12 (1951).
1218a. R. G. Navalkar, E. H. Wiegeshaus & D. W. Smith, *J. Bact.* **88** 255 (1964).
1219. I. Dharmendra, *Indian J. med. Res.* **30** 1 (1942).
1220. K. R. Chatterjee, N. Mukerjee & R. Bose, *Bull. Calcutta Sch. trop. Med.Hyg.* **4** 164 (1956); *Chem. Abstr.* **51** 5165 (1957).
1221. M. Nakamura, *Kurume med. J.* **3** 133 (1956); *Chem. Abstr.* **51** 16703 (1957).
1222. R. J. Anderson, *Physiol. Rev.* **12** 166 (1932).
1223. N. Fethke & R. J. Anderson, *Amer. Rev. Tuberc. pulm. Dis.* **57** 294 (1948).
1224. J. Asselineau & E. Lederer, *Bull. Soc. Chim. biol.* **31** 492 (1949).
1225. J. W. Berg, *Proc. Soc. exp. Biol. Med.* **84** 196 (1953).
1226. J. W. Berg, *Yale J. Biol. Med.* **26** 215 (1953).
1227. H. Sherman, *J. inf. Dis.* **12** 249 (1913).
1228. H. S. Willis, *Amer. Rev. Tuberc. pulm. Dis.* **25** 224 (1932).
1229. R. Laporte & J. Loiseleur, *Annls Inst. Pasteur, Paris* **71** 375 (1945).
1230. C. H. Boissevain, *Amer. Rev. Tuberc. pulm. Dis.* **16** 758 (1927).
1231. A. Sordelli & A. Arena, *C. r. Séanc. Soc. Biol.* **117** 63 (1934).
1232. D. Yegian & R. J. Vanderlinde, *J. Bact.* **54** 777 (1947).
1233. E. R. Long, *Amer. Rev. Tuberc. pulm. Dis.* **6** 642 (1922).
1234. P. Hauduroy, "L'acido-résistance des Bacilles tuberculeux et paratuberculeux", *in* "Bacilles tuberculeux et paratuberculeux, p. 31, Masson, Paris (1950).
1235. N. Choucroun, *C. r. hebd. Séanc. Acad. Sci., Paris* **226** 1477 (1948).

1236. J. Paraf, J. Desbordes & R. Fournier, *C. r. Séanc. Soc. Biol.* **145** 514 (1951).
1237. M. Yoneda & M. Kondo, *Biken's J.* **2** 247 (1959).
1238. G. M. Haas, *Archs Pathol.* **27** 15 (1939).
1239. G. Middlebrook, *Bull. N. Y. Acad. Med.* **26** 498 (1950).
1240. G. J. Martin, *J. Amer. chem. Soc.* **60** 768 (1938).
1241. F. B. Seibert, E. R. Long & N. Morley, *J. inf. Dis.* **53** 175 (1933).
1242. J. Asselineau, *Progr. Explor. Tuberc.* **5** 1 (1952).
1243. R. J. Dubos, *in* "Mechanisms of microbial pathogenicity", ed. by J. W. Howie & A. J. O'Hea, p. 103, Cambridge Univ. Press (1955).
1244. L. Negre & J. Bretey, "Les Bacilles de Koch incomplètement évolués dans l'infection tuberculeuse", Masson, Paris (1955).
1245. H. Bloch, *Adv. Tuberc. Res.* **6** 49 (1955).
1246. Y. Yamamura, J. Tani, T. Terai, & Y. Yamamura, *Amer. Rev. Tuberc. pulm. Dis.* **79** 738 (1959).
1247. R. J. Dubos & G. Middlebrook, *Amer. Rev. Tuberc. pulm. Dis.* **58** 698 (1948).
1248. P. Hauduroy, "Derniers aspects du monde des Mycobactéries", Masson, Paris (1955).
1249. J. Viallier, J. C. Kalb & J. Tigaud, *C. r. Séanc. Soc. Biol.* **144** 1513 (1950).
1250. F. Ito, C. M. Coleman & G. Middlebrook, *Kekkaku* **36** 764 (1961).
1251. L. Mankiewicx, *Can. J. med. Sci.* **30** 106 (1952).
1252. H. Bloch, *Amer. Rev. Tuberc. pulm. Dis.* **61** 270 (1950).
1253. F. J. Wilson, C. Kalish & C. H. Fish, *Amer. Rev. Tuberc. pulm. Dis.* **65** 187 (1952).
1254. R. J. Dubos, "Biochemical determinants of microbial diseases", Harvard Univ. Press, Cambridge, Mass. (1954).
1255. J. Desbordes, *Annls Soc. belge Méd. trop.* **4** 503 (1962).
1256. C. Bordet & G. Michel, *Biochim. biophys. Acta* **70** 613 (1963).
1256a. C. Bordet & G. Michel, *Bull. Soc. Chim. biol.* **46** 1101 (1964).
1256b. M.-A. Lanéelle, J. Asselineau & G. Castelnuovo, *Annls Inst. Pasteur, Paris* **108** 69 (1965).
1257. J. B. Clark & C. Aldridge, *J. Bact.* **79** 756 (1960).
1258. J. N. Adams & N. M. McClung, *J. gen. Microbiol.* **28** 231 (1962).
1259. E. A. Johnson & K. L. Burdon, *J. Bact.* **54** 281 (1947).
1260. W. D. Celmer & I. A. Solomons, *J. Amer. chem. Soc.* **75** 1372 (1953).
1261. J. B. Kwapinski, *Path. Microbiol.* **23** 158 (1960).
1262. A. P. MacLennan, *Biochim. biophys. Acta* **48** 600 (1961).
1263. A. Saito, *J. Ferment. Technol., Japan* **29** 310 (1951); *Chem. Abstr.* **47** 12507 (1953).
1264. S. A. Waksman & H. A. Lechevalier, "Actinomycetes and their antibiotics", The Williams & Wilkins Co., Baltimore (1953).
1265. J. Kwapinski & M. Merkel, *Bull. Acad. pol. Sci. Cl. II, Ser. Sci. biol.* **5** 335 (1957).
1265a. W. K. Hausmann, A. H. Struck, J. H. Martin & N. Bohonos, *Antimicrobial agents Chemotherapy* **1963** 352.
1266. R. Brown & C. Kelley, *N. Y. State Dept. Health, Ann. Rep. Div. Lab. Res.* 10 (1957); *Chem. Abstr.* **53** 2347 (1959).
1267. Y. Hirata & K. Nakanishi, *Bull. chem. Soc., Japan* **22** 121 (1949).
1268. M. Inoue, H. Hitomi, K. Mizuno, M. Fujino, A Miyake, K. Nakazawa, M. Shibata & T. Kanzaki, *Bull. chem. Soc., Japan* **33** 1014 (1960).
1269. C. Djerassi & J. A. Zderic, *J. Amer. chem. Soc.* **78** 2907 (1956).
1270. F. A. Hochstein, H. Els, W. D. Celmer, B. L. Shapiro & R. B. Woodward, *J. Amer. chem. Soc.* **82** 3225 (1960).
1271. P. F. Wiley, K. Gerzon, E. H. Flynn, M. V. Sigal, O. Weaver, U. C. Quarck, R. R. Chauvette & R. Monahan, *J. Amer. chem. Soc.* **79** 6062 (1957).
1272. G. A. Garton & A. E. Oxford, *J. Sci. Food Agr.* **6** 142 (1955).
1273. M. Keeney, I. Katz & M. J. Allison, *J. Amer. oil Chem. Soc.* **39** 198 (1962).
1274. A. K. Sijpesteijn. *J. gen. Microbiol.* **5** 869 (1951).

1274a. I. Katz & M. Keeney, *Biochim. biophys. Acta* **84** 128 (1964).
1275. S. R. Elsden & D. Lewis, *Biochem. J.* **55** 183 (1953).
1276. H. G. Sammons, D. J. Vaughan & A. C. Frazer, *Nature, Lond.* **177** 237 (1956).
1277. E. Klieneberger-Nobel, *in* "The Bacteria", vol. I, 361, ed. by I. C. Gunsalus & R. Y. Stanier, Academic Press, New York (1960).
1278. R. J. Lynn & P. F. Smith, *Ann. N. Y. Acad. Sci.* **79** 493 (1960).
1279. P. F. Smith & G. H. Rothblat, *J. Bact.* **83** 500 (1962).
1280. M. E. Tourtelotte, R. G. Jensen, G. W. Gander & H. J. Morowitz, *J. Bact.* **86** 370 (1963).
1280a. P. F. Smith, *Bact. Rev.* **28** 97 (1964).
1281. W. M. O'Leary, *Biochem. biophys. Res. Commun.* **8** 87 (1962).
1282. S. S. Cohen & E. Chargaff, *J. biol. Chem.* **154** 691 (1944).
1282a. J. W. Moulder, "The psittacosis group as bacteria", Wiley, New York (1964).
1282b. E. M. Neptune, E. Weiss, J. A. Davies & E. C. Suitor, *J. inf. Diseases* **14** 39 (1964).
1283. B. Rybak, F. Gros & F. Grumbach, *Annls Inst. Pasteur, Paris* **77** 148 (1949).
1284. M. Beljanski & F. Grumbach, *C. r. hebd. Séanc. Acad. Sci., Paris* **236** 2111 (1953).
1285. S. Chandrasekhar, A. J. H. de Monte & T. A. V. Subramanian, *Indian J. med. Res.* **46** 643 (1958).
1286. M. Motomiya, *Sci. Rep. Res. Tohoku Univ.* **9** 265 (1960).
1287. J. Yamaguchi, K. Fukushi, M. Motomiya, K. Munakata & C. Shinohara, *Japan. J. Tuberc.* **9** 1 (1960).
1288. H. P. Russe & W. R. Barclay, *Amer. Rev. Tuberc. pulm. Dis.* **72** 713 (1955).
1289. F. G. Winder & J. M. Denneny, *J. Gen. Microbiol.* **15** 1 (1956).
1290. T. Nagasuga, T. Terai & Y. Yamamura, *Amer. Rev. Resp. Dis.* **83** 248 (1961).
1291. J .Youatt, *Aust. J. exp. Biol. med. Sci.* **39** 93 (1961).
1292. T. Ebina, K. Munakata & M. Motomiya, *C. r. Séanc. Soc. Biol.* **155** 1190 (1961).
1293. L. Vaczi, J. Szita & V. Cieleszky, *Acta microbiol. hung.* **4** 437 (1957).
1294. P. D. Cooper, *J. gen. Microbiol.* **12** 100 (1955).
1295. F. R. Sabin, *Amer. Rev. Tuberc. pulm. Dis.* **44** 415 (1941).
1296. F. Roulet & M. Brenner, *Zent. Bl. ges. Tuberk. Forsch.* **56** 193 (1943).
1297. C. Cattaneo, *Lotta Tuberc.* **16** 195 (1946).
1298. L. Negre, "Les lipoides dans le bacille tuberculeux et la tuberculose", Masson, Paris (1950).
1299. S. Raffel, *Experientia* **6** 410 (1950).
1300. L. Popp, *Pharmazie* **5** 193 (1950).
1301. E. Rich, "The pathogenesis of tuberculosis", Thomas, Springfield (1944).
1302. G. Canetti, "Le Bacille de Koch dans la lésion tuberculeuse", Flammarion, Paris (1946).
1303. W. F. Drea & A. Andrejew, "Metabolism of the tubercle bacillus", Thomas, Springfield (1953).
1304. L. Negre, "Prévention et traitements spécifiques de la tuberculose par le B. C. G. et par l'antigène méthylique, Masson, Paris (1956).
1305. E. R. Long, The chemistry and chemotherapy of tuberculosis, Baillière, Tindall & Cox, London (1958).
1306. E. Lederer, *Internal Colloquium, Centre national de la Recherche scientifique*, no. 115, 189 (1963).
1307. F. R. Sabin, C. A. Doan & C. E. Forkner, *J. exp. Med.* **52** suppl. 3 (1930).
1308. F. R. Sabin & K. C. Smithburn, *Physiol. Rev.* **12** 141 (1932).
1309. F. Roulet & K. Bloch, *Virchows' Arch.* **298** 311 (1936).
1310. A. J. Birch & R. Robinson, *J. chem. Soc.* **1942** 488.
1311. S. David, N. Polgar & R. Robinson, *J. chem. Soc.* **1949** 1541.
1312. N. Polgar, R. Robinson & E. Seijo, *J. chem. Soc.* **1949** 1545.
1313. B. Gerstl & R. Tennant, *Yale J. Biol. Med.* **15** 347 (1943).
1314. Ng. Buu-Hoi & A. R. Ratsimamanga, *C. r. Séanc. Soc. Biol.* **137** 189 (1943).
1315. Ng. Buu-Hoi & P. Cagniant, *Z. physiol. Chem.* **279** 76 (1943).
1316. J. Ungar, C. E. Coulthard & L. Dickinson, *Br. J. exp. Path.* **29** 322 (1948).

1317. H. Husseini & S. Elberg, *Am. Rev. Tuberc. pulm. Dis.* **65** 655 (1952).

1318. J. Ungar, A. Ciba Foundation Colloquium on experimental tuberculosis, p. 69, London (1955).

1319. J. Cason & D. J. McLeod, *J. org. Chem.* **23** 1497 (1958).

1320. W. Catel & W. Schmidt, *Dt. med. Wschr.* **75** 1140 (1950).

1321. R. M. Thomas & F. I. Dessau, *Yale J. Biol. Med.* **12** 283 (1940).

1322. F. R. Sabin, K. C. Smithburn & R. M. Thomas, *J. exp. Med.* **62** 751 (1935).

1323. B. Gerstl, R. Tennant & O. Pelzman, *Amer. L. Path.* **21** 1007 (1945).

1323a. J. Kracht & W. Gusek, *Verhandl. Deut. Gesell. Pathol.* **48** 300 (1964); *Beitr. Klin. Tuberk.* **129** 67 (1964).

1324. A. Delaunay, J. Asselineau & E. Lederer, *C. r. Séanc. Soc. Biol.* **145** 650 (1951).

1325. J. Frederic & J. Racadot, *Arch. Anat. Path. Morph. exp.* **44** 56 (1955).

1326. R. G. White, A Ciba Foundation colloquium on experimental tuberculosis, p. 83, London (1955).

1327. Y. Takeda & K. Ogata, *Japan. J. Tuberc.* **2** 314 (1954).

1328. F. Kradolfer, A Ciba Foundation colloquium on experimental tuberculosis, p. 83, London (1955).

1329. M. Yamaguchi, Y. Ogawa, K. Endo, H. Takeuchi, S. Nakamura, S. Yasaka & Y. Yamamura, *Kekkaku* **33** 12 (1958); *Chem. Abstr.* **52** 16567 (1958).

1330. Y. Yamamura, *Adv. Tuberc. Res.* **9** 13 (1958).

1331. K. Endo, *Igaku Kenkyu* **28** 1517 (1958); *Chem. Abstr.* **52** 18780 (1958).

1332. L. W. Ray & J. S. Shipman, *Amer. Rev. Tuberc. pulm. Dis.* **7** 88 (1923).

1333. K. C. Smithburn & F. R. Sabin, *J. exp. Med.* **68** 641 (1938).

1334. N. F. Stanley, *Aust. J. exp. Biol. med. Sci.* **28** 99 (1950).

1335. I. Motida, T. Nakagawa & M. Umezu, *Rep. Inst. Sci. Res. Manchoukuo* **4** 287 (1940).

1336. M. Levine & E. Chargaff, *Amer. J. Bot.* **24** 461 (1937).

1337. A. E. Dimond, *Progr. Chem. org. nat. Prod.* **17** 304 (1959).

1338. J. W. Jobling & W. Petersen, *J. exp. Med.* **19** 251 (1914).

1339. J. W. Jobling & W. Petersen, *J. exp. Med.* **19** 383 (1914).

1340. B. Gerstl & R. Tennant, *Amer. Rev. Tuberc. pulm. Dis.* **46** 600 (1942).

1341. R. L. Peck, *J. Amer. chem. Soc.* **64** 487 (1942).

1342. B. Gerstl & R. Tennant, *Yale J. Biol. Med.* **16** 1 (1943).

1343. C. Weiss & N. Halliday, *Proc. Soc. exp. Biol. Med.* **57** 299 (1944).

1344. M. Kato, *Igaku Kenkyu* **28** 1028 (1958); *Chem. Abstr.* **52** 18779 (1958).

1345. M. Kato, K. Miki, K. Matsunaga & Y. Yamamura, *Amer. Rev. Tuberc. pulm. Dis.* **77** 482 (1958).

1346. M. Kato, M. Kusunose, K. Miki, K. Matsunaga & Y. Yamamura, *Amer. Rev. resp. Dis.* **80** 240 (1959).

1347. S. P. Martin, S. N. Chaudhuri, C. D. Cooper & R. Green, A Ciba Foundation colloquium on experimental tuberculosis, p. 102, London (1955).

1347a. M. Artman, A. Bekierkunst & I. Goldenberg, *Archs. Biochem. Biophys.* **105** 80 (1964).

1348. Y. Yamamura, A. Tanaka & M. Kato, *J. Biochem., Japan* **47** 505 (1960).

1349. M. Nasta, E. Paunesco, P. Georgesco, *Annls Inst. Pasteur, Paris* **95** 272 (1958).

1350. W. B. Wartman, E. S. Ingraham, *Archs. Path.* **29** 773 (1940).

1351. M. Allgower & H. Bloch, *Amer. Rev. Tuberc. pulm. Dis.* **59** 562 (1949).

1352. S. P. Martin, C. H. Pierce, G. Middlebrook & R. J. Dubos, *J. exp. Med.* **91** 381 (1950).

1353. K. Oiwa, *Nippon Saikingaku Zasshi* **11** 787 (1956); *Chem. Abstr.* **51** 16688 (1957).

1354. N. Choucroun, A. Delaunay, S. Bazin & R. Robineaux, *Annls Inst. Pasteur, Paris* **80** 619 (1951).

1355. R. Meier & B. Schär, *Experientia,* **10** 376 (1954).

1356. E. Suter & R. A. White, *Am. Rev. Tuberc. pulm. Dis.* **70** 793 (1954).

1357. E. Suter, A Ciba Foundation colloquium on experimental tuberculosis, p. 198, London (1955).

1357a. G. Biozzi, C. Stiffel & D. Mouton, *Rev. franc. Études clin. & biol.* **8** 341 (1963).

1358. G. Schmidt, E. Eichenberger & O. Westphal, *Experientia* **14** 289 (1958).

1359. H. Bloch & H. Noll, *Br. J. exp. Path.* **36** 8 (1955).

1360. H. Bloch, A Ciba Foundation colloquium on experimental tuberculosis, p. 131, London (1955).

1361. T. Ohara, Y. Shimmyo, I. Sekikawa, K. Morikawa & E. Sumikawa, *Japan. J. Tuberc.* **5** 128 (1957).

1362. Y. Yamamura, Y. Yamamura, M. Kato, K. Miki, & K. Matsunaga, *Japan. Symp. Tuberc.*, p. 181 (1959).

1363. M. Pinner & M. Voldrich, *Amer. Rev. Tuberc. pulm. Dis.* **24** 73 (1931).

1364. C. A. Williams, unpublished results quoted in ref. 1440.

1365. K. Oiwa, *Nippon Saikingaku Zasshi* **11** 901 (1956); *Chem. Abstr.* **51** 16689 (1957).

1366. E. K. Alimova, *Zh. Mikrobiol. Epidemiol. Immunobiol.* **31** 88 (1960); *Chem. Abstr.* **58** 8247 (1963).

1367. O. Westphal, A. Nowotny, O. Lüderitz, H. Hurni, E. Eichenberger & G. Schönholzer, *Pharm. Acta Helv.* **33** 401 (1958).

1368. N. Kasai, *Nippon Saikingaku Zasshi* **11** 369 (1956); *Chem. Abstr.* **51** 12173 (1957).

1368a. L. M. Corwin & W. E. Farrar, *J. Bact.* **87** 832 (1964).

1369. J. G. Howard, D. Rowley & A. C. Wardlaw, *Nature, Lond.* **179** 314 (1957).

1370. E. Suter, G. E. Ulman & R. G. Hoffman, *Proc. Soc. exp. Biol. Med.* **99** 167 (1958).

1371. H. B. Levine, O. G. Leim & R. L. Maurer, *J. Immun.* **83** 468 (1959).

1372. S. Raffel, Immunity, hypersensitivity, and serology, Appleton-Century-Crofts, New York (1953).

1373. N. Choucroun, *C. r. hebd. Séanc. Acad. Sci., Paris* **208** 1757 (1939).

1374. N. Choucroun, *Tuberculol.* **11** 25 (1949).

1375. G. Bendixen, "Undersøgelser af hypersensibilitetsproblemet", Dissertation, Copenhagen (1962).

1376. N. Choucroun, Commun. Congr. Feder. Soc., New York, April 1952.

1377. S. Raffel, *Amer. Rev. Tuberc. pulm. Dis.* **54** 564 (1946).

1378. S. Raffel, *J. inf. Dis.* **82** 267 (1948).

1379. S. Raffel & J. E. Forney, *J. exp. Med.* **88** 485 (1948).

1380. S. Raffel, L. E. Arnaud, C. D. Dukes & J. S. Huang, *J. exp. Med.* **90** 53 (1949).

1381. K. Kanai, *Nippon Saikingaku Zasshi* **10** 1003 (1955); *Chem. Abstr.* **51** 12301 (1957).

1382. Q. Myrvik & R. S. Weiser, *J. Immun.* **68** 413 (1952).

1383. S. Raffel, E. Lederer & J. Asselineau, *Feder. Proc.* **13** 509 (1954).

1384. S. Raffel, J. Asselineau & E. Lederer, A Ciba Foundation colloquium on experimental tuberculosis, p. 174, London (1955).

1385. S. Raffel, *Progr. Allergy* **4** 173 (1954).

1386. J. E. Forney, *Amer. Rev. Tuberc. pulm. Dis.* **69** 241 (1954).

1387. A. W. Pound, *J. Path. Bact.* **70** 119 (1955).

1388. Y. Yamamura, S. Morizawa, A. Tanaka & K. Shojima, *Proc. Japan. Acad.* **35** 295 (1959).

1389. S. Akabori, Y. Yamamura & T. Saskawa, *Proc. Japan. Acad.* **26** 37 (1950).

1390. J. Desbordes, E. Fournier & C. Guyotjeanin, *Rev. Immun.* **20** 164 (1956).

1391. N. Choucroun, P. Gresland & R. Kourilsky, *C. r. hebd. Séanc. Acad. Sci., Paris* **247** 1055 (1958).

1392. S. V. Boyden & E. Sorkin, *Adv. Tuberc. Res.* **7** 17 (1956).

1393. L. Negre & A. Boquet, *Annls Inst. Pasteur Paris* **37** 787 (1923).

1394. M. A. Macheboeuf, G. Levy & M. Faure, *Bull. Soc. Chim. biol.* **17** 1210 (1935).

1395. E. Chargaff & W. Schaefer, *Annls. Inst. Pasteur, Paris* **54** 708 (1935).

1396. Y. Takahashi & K. Ono, *Science* **127** 1053 (1958).

1397. Y. Takahashi, S. Fujita & A. Sasaki, *J. exp. Med.* **113** 1141 (1961).

1398. M. C. Pangborn, *Tuberculol.* **16** 134 (1956).

1399. J. Kwapinsky, *Archwm. Immun. Terap. doświad.* **6** 29 (1958); *Chem. Abstr.* **54** 25015 (1960).

1400. Y. Takeda, T. Ota & Y. Sen, *Igaku to Seibutsugaku* **4** 88 (1943).
1401. Y. Takeda, Y Aoki, N. Wakita, T. Watanabe & N. Kasai, *Japan. J. Tuberc.* **2** 216 (1954).
1402. Y. Takeda, Y. Aoki, N. Wakita, T. Watanabe, N. Kasai & H. Suzuki, *Japan. J. Tuberc.* **2** 361 (1954).
1403. P. Burtin, *Annls. Inst. Pasteur, Paris* **97** 325 (1959).
1404. N. Choucroun, *C. r. hebd. Séanc. Acad. Sci., Paris* **229** 145 (1949).
1405. W. Catel & S. Weidmann, *Mschr. Kinderheilk.* **101** 217 (1953); *Chem. Abstr.* **47** 8230 (1953).
1406. T. Ohara, Y. Shimmyo, I. Sekikawa, K. Morikawa & E. Sumikawa, *Japan. J. Tuberc.* **5** 128 (1957).
1407. I. Hara, *Nippon Kagaku Zasshi* **76** 910 (1955); *Chem. Abstr.* **51** 18041 (1957).
1408. T. Suzuki, *Japan. J. Bact.* **8** 897 (1953); *Chem. Abstr.* **49** 10425 (1955).
1409. B. Urbaschek, H. Bauerle & O. W. Thiele, *Naturwiss,* **48** 697 (1961).
1410. W. Wober, O. W. Thiele & B. Urbaschek, *Österr. chem. Ztg.* **63** 302 (1962).
1411. B. Urbaschek, O. W. Thiele & W. Wober, *Inter. Archs Allergy* **22** 124 (1963).
1411a. A. Nowotny, *Nature, Lond.* **197** 721 (1963).
1412. E. Coulaud, *C. r. Séanc. Soc. Biol.* **119** 368 (1935).
1413. A. Saenz, *C. r. Séanc. Soc. Biol.* **120** 1050 (1935).
1414. J. Freund, J. Casals & E. P. Hosmer, *Proc. Soc. exp. Biol. Med.* **37** 509 (1937).
1415. J. Freund, *Adv. Tuberc. Res.* **7** 130 (1956).
1416. J. Freund & K. McDermott, *Proc. Soc. exp. Biol. Med.* **49** 548 (1942).
1417. R. G. White, A. H. Coons & J. M. Connolly, *J. exp. Med.* **102** 83 (1955).
1418. R. G. White, L. Bernstock, R. G. S. Johns & E. Lederer, *Immunology* **1** 54 (1958).
1419. R. G. White, P. Jolles, D. Samour & E. Lederer, *Immunology* **7** 158 (1964).
1419a. P. Jolles, D. Samour-Migliore, H. De Wijs & E. Lederer, *Biochim, biophys. Acta* **83** 361 (1964).
1419b. S. Kotani, T. Kitaura, S. Hashimoto, M. Chimori & H. Kishida, *Biken J.* **6** 321 (1963).
1420. J. Freund, K. J. Thomson, H. B. Hough, H. E. Sommer & T. M. Pisani, *J. Immun.* **60** 383 (1948).
1421. A. W. Pound, *J. Path. Bact.* **75** 55 (1958).
1422. B. H. Waksman & R. D. Adams, *J. inf. Dis.* **93** 21 (1953).
1423. J. Colover, *Nature, Lond.* **182** 105 (1958); *Proc. R. Soc. Med.* **51** 745 (1958).
1424. R. G. White & A. H. E. Marshall, *Immunology* **1** 111 (1958).
1425. J. Freund & S. H. Stone, *J. Immun.* **82** 560 (1959).
1425a. S. Kotani, T. Matsubara, T. Kitaura, Y. Mori, M. Chimori & H. Kishida, *Biken J.* **6** 211 (1963).
1426. C. M. Pearson, *in* "Mechanism of hypersensitivity", p. 647, Little-Brown, Boston (1959).
1426a. T. Neveu, A. Branellec & G. Biozzi, *Annls Inst. Pasteur, Paris* **106** 771 (1964).
1427. N. Padmanabhan & H. Selye, *Ann. Allergy* **20** 320 (1962); *Chem. Abstr.* **57** 10459 (1962).
1428. J. R. Farthing, *Br. J. exp. Path.* **42** 614 (1961).
1429. A. G. Johnson, S. Gaines & M. Landy, *J. exp. Med.* **103** 225 (1956).
1430. J. Munoz, *J. Immun.* **90** 132 (1963).
1431. R. J. Dubos, W. B. Schaefer & C. H. Pierce, *J. exp. Med.* **97** 221 (1953).
1432. H. Bloch & W. Segal, *Amer. Rev. Tuberc. pulm. Dis.* **71** 228 (1955).
1433. A. J. Crowle, *Bact. Rev.* **22** 183 (1958).
1434. L. Negre & A. Boquet, Antigénothérapie de la tuberculose par les extraits méthyliques de bacilles de Koch", Masson, Paris (1927).
1435. L. Negre, *Bull. Acad. natn. Méd.* **1950** 445.
1436. D. W. Weiss & R. J. Dubos, *J. exp. Med.* **101** 313 (1955).
1437. R. J. Dubos, D. W. Weiss & R. W. Schaedler, *Amer. Rev. Tuberc. pulm. Dis.* **75** 781 (1956).
1438. D. W. Weiss & R. J. Dubos, *J. exp. Med.* **103** 73 (1956).
1439. R. J. Dubos & R. W. Schaedler, *J. exp. Med.* **104** 53 (1956).
1440. C. A. Williams & R. J. Dubos, *J. exp. Med.* **110** 981 (1959).
1440a. M. Pigretti, E. Vilkas, E. Lederer & H. Bloch, *Bull. Soc. Chim. biol.* **47** 2039 (1965).

1441. A. Hoyt, R. L. Dennerline & C. R. Smith, *Amer. Rev. pulm. Dis.* **76** 752 (1957).
1442. A. Hoyt & M. A. Thompson, *Amer. Rev. resp. Dis.* **80** 216 (1959).
1443. A. Hoyt, M. A. Thompson, F. J. Moore & C. R. Smith. *Amer. Rev. resp. Dis.* **80** 216 (1959).
1443a. D. W. Smith, G. B. Fregnan, L. Delaquerriere-Richardson & E. Valdivia, *J. Bact.* **88** 87 (1964).
1444. J. M. Robson & J. T. Smith, *Amer. Rev. resp. Dis.* **84** 100 (1961).
1445. A. J. Crowle, *Proc. Soc. exp. Biol. Med.* **109** 969 (1962).
1446. M. Landy, *Ann. N. Y. Acad. Sci.* **66** 292 (1956).
1447. D. Rowley, *Ann. N. Y. Acad. Sci.* **66** 304 (1956).
1448. J. G. Howard, D. Rowley & A. C. Wardlaw, *Immunology* **1** 181 (1958).
1449. K. Bernhauer & G. Posselt, *Biochem. Z.* **294** 215 (1937).
1450. F. M. Strong & W. H. Peterson, *J. Amer. chem. Soc.* **56** 952 (1934).
1451. E. H. Kroeker, F. M. Strong & W. H. Peterson, *J. Amer. chem. Soc.* **57** 354 (1935).
1452. R. L. Peck & C. R. Hauser, *J. Amer. chem. Soc.* **60** 2599 (1938).
1453. R. L. Peck & C. R. Hauser, *J. Amer. chem. Soc.* **61** 289 (1939).
1454. E. A. Edelberg, P. F. Roslandsky, J. W. Myers & C. A. Coughlin, *J. Bact.* **69** 733 (1955).
1455. J. W. Beard, *J. Immun.* **58** 48 (1948).
1456. L. H. Frommhagen, C. A. Knight & N. K. Freeman, *Virology* **8** 176 (1959).
1457. M. Kates, A. C. Allison, D. A. J. Tyrell & A. T. James, *Cold Spring Harb. Symp. quant. Biol.* **27** 293 (1962).
1458. M. Prostenik & N. Z. Stanacev, *Chem. Ber.* **91** 961 (1958).
1459. F. Reindel, A. Weickmann, S. Picard, K. Luber & P. Turula, *Liebigs Annln* **544** 116 (1940).
1460. B. N. Bohonos & W. H. Peterson, *J. biol. Chem.* **149** 295 (1943).
1461. T. Oda, *J. pharm. Soc., Japan* **72** 136, 139, 142 (1952).
1462. H. Wittcoff, "The phosphatides", Reinhold Publ. Corp., New York (1951).
1463. J. R. Nunn, *J. chem. Soc.* **1952** 313.
1464. F. S. Shenstone & S. R. Vickery, *Nature, Lond.* **177** 94 (1956); J. J. MacFarland, F. S. Shenstone & J. R. Vickery. *Nature, Lond.* **179** 830 (1957).